MEN OF THE OLD STONE AGE

THEIR ENVIRONMENT, LIFE AND ART

HITCHCOCK LECTURES OF THE UNIVERSITY OF CALIFORNIA, 1914

BY THE SAME AUTHOR

Biological Series

Uniformly bound. Vols. I–IV. 12mo.

I. FROM THE GREEKS TO DARWIN. The development of the evolution idea through twenty-four centuries. $2.50. 3d thousand. New Edition.

II. IMPRESSIONS OF GREAT NATURALISTS. Darwin, Wallace, Huxley, Leidy, Cope, Balfour, Roosevelt, and others. With portraits. $2.50. 4th thousand. New Edition.

III. EVOLUTION AND RELIGION IN EDUCATION. The Fundamentalist controversy of 1922-25. $2.00. 12th thousand.

IV. CREATIVE EDUCATION in School, College, University, and Museum. With portraits. $2.50. 2d thousand.

Life-History of Earth and Man Series

Uniformly bound. Vols. I-V. 8vo.

I. THE ORIGIN AND EVOLUTION OF LIFE. On the theory of action, reaction, and interaction of energy. Profusely illustrated. $4.00. 12th thousand.

II. THE AGE OF MAMMALS in Europe, Asia, and North America. Profusely illustrated. $6.00. New edition.

III. EVOLUTION OF MAMMALIAN MOLAR TEETH to and from the Triangular Type. Profusely illustrated. $2.75.

IV. MEN OF THE OLD STONE AGE, their environment, life, and art. Profusely illustrated. $5.00. 22d thousand.

V. MAN RISES TO PARNASSUS. Sequel to "Men of the Old Stone Age." From the Eolithic to the Bronze Age. Illustrated. $3.00. 3d thousand.

Uniformly bound in brochure form. 16mo.

HUXLEY AND EDUCATION. Address at the opening of the college year, Columbia University, 1910. 50 cents.

THE NEW ORDER OF SAINTHOOD. A tribute to Pasteur. 50 cents.

EVOLUTION AND RELIGION. Opening of the controversy with Bryan. 75 cents.

FIFTY YEARS OF PRINCETON '77. A half-century record.

PRINCETON UNIVERSITY PRESS

CHARLES SCRIBNER'S SONS

NEW YORK • LONDON

Pl. I. Neanderthal man at the station of Le Moustier, overlooking the valley of the Vézère, Dordogne. Drawing by Charles R. Knight, under the direction of the author.

MEN OF THE OLD STONE AGE

THEIR ENVIRONMENT, LIFE AND ART

BY

HENRY FAIRFIELD OSBORN

A.B., SC.D., PRINCETON; LL.D., TRINITY, PRINCETON, COLUMBIA; HON. SC.D., CAMBRIDGE
HON. D.SC., YALE, OXFORD, NEW YORK; HON. PH.D., CHRISTIANIA (OSLÔ)
FOR. MEMB. ROYAL SOCIETY
RESEARCH PROFESSOR OF ZOÖLOGY, COLUMBIA UNIVERSITY
SENIOR GEOLOGIST, U. S. GEOL. SURVEY
PRESIDENT, AMERICAN MUSEUM OF NATURAL HISTORY

ILLUSTRATIONS BY
UPPER PALÆOLITHIC ARTISTS
AND
CHARLES R. KNIGHT, ERWIN S. CHRISTMAN
AND OTHERS

THIRD EDITION
With new notes and illustrations on the archæology of Spain and North Africa

NEW YORK
CHARLES SCRIBNER'S SONS
1930

Published November, 1915
Second edition, January, 1916
Reprinted March, May, June, 1916
Third edition, September, 1918
Reprinted April, 1919; April, 1921; October, 1922; June, 1923; August, 1924; November, 1925; January, 1928; February, 1930.

Printed in the United States of America

Published in England by
G. BELL AND SONS, LTD.

DEDICATED

TO

MY DISTINGUISHED GUIDES THROUGH THE UPPER

PALÆOLITHIC CAVERNS OF

THE PYRENEES, DORDOGNE, AND THE CANTABRIAN MOUNTAINS OF SPAIN

EMILE CARTAILHAC

HENRI BREUIL

HUGO OBERMAIER

PREFACE

THIS volume is the outcome of an ever memorable tour through the country of the men of the Old Stone Age, guided by three of the distinguished archæologists of France, to whom the work is gratefully dedicated. This Palæolithic tour* of three weeks, accompanied as it was by a constant flow of conversation and discussion, made a very profound impression, namely, of the very early evolution of the spirit of man, of the close relation between early human environment and industry and the development of mind, of the remote antiquity of the human powers of observation, of discovery, and of invention. It appears that men with faculties and powers like our own, but in the infancy of education and tradition, were living in this region of Europe at least 25,000 years ago. Back of these intelligent races were others, also of eastern origin but in earlier stages of mental development, all pointing to the very remote ancestry of man from earlier mental and physical stages.

Another great impression from this region is that it is the oldest centre of human habitation of which we have a complete, unbroken record of continuous residence from a period as remote as 100,000 years corresponding with the dawn of human culture, to the hamlets of the modern peasant of France of A. D. 1915. In contrast, Egyptian, Ægean, and Mesopotamian civilizations appear as of yesterday.

The history of this region and its people has been developed chiefly through the genius of French archæologists, beginning with Boucher de Perthes. The more recent discoveries, which have come in rapid and almost bewildering succession since the foundation of the *Institut de Paléontologie humaine*, have been treated in a number of works recently published by some of the

* The folding map at the end of the volume exhibits the entire extent of the author's tour.

experienced archæologists of England, France, and Germany. I refer especially to the *Prehistoric Times* of Lord Avebury, to the *Ancient Hunters* of Professor Sollas, to *Der Mensch der Vorzeit* of Professor Obermaier, and to *Die diluviale Vorzeit Deutschlands* of Doctor R. R. Schmidt. Thus, on receiving the invitation from President Wheeler to lecture upon this subject before the University of California, I hesitated from the feeling that it would be difficult to say anything which had not been already as well or better said. On further reflection, however, I accepted the invitation with the purpose of attempting to give this great subject a more strictly historical or chronological treatment than it had previously received within the limits of a popular work in our own language, also to connect the environment, the animal and human life, and the art.

This element of the *time* in which the various events occurred can only be drawn from a great variety of sources, from the simultaneous consideration of the geography, climate, plants and animals, the mental and bodily development of the various races, and the industries and arts which reflect the relations between the mind and the environment. In more technical terms, I have undertaken in these lectures to make a synthesis of the results of geology, palæontology, anthropology, and archæology, a correlation of environmental and of human events in the European Ice Age. Such a synthesis was begun many years ago in the preparation of my *Age of Mammals*, but could not be completed until I had gone over the territory myself.

The attempt to place this long chapter of prehistory on a historical basis has many dangers, of which I am fully aware. After weighing the evidence presented by the eminent authorities in these various branches of science, I have presented my conclusions in very definite and positive form rather than in vague or general terms, believing that a positive statement has at least the merit of being positively supported or rebutted by fresh evidence. For example, I have placed the famous Piltdown man, *Eoanthropus*, in a comparatively recent stage of geologic time, an entirely opposite conclusion to that reached by Doctor A. Smith Woodward, who has taken a leading part in the discovery of this famous race and has concurred with other British geologists in placing it in early Pleistocene times. The difference between early and late Pleistocene times is not a matter of thousands but of hundreds of thousands of years; if so advanced a stage as the Piltdown man should definitely occur in the early Pleistocene, we may well expect to discover man in the Pliocene; on the contrary, in my opinion even in late Pliocene times man had only reached a stage similar to the *Pithecanthropus*, or prehuman Trinil race of Java; in other words, according to my view, man as such chiefly evolved during the half million years of the Pleistocene Epoch and not during the Pliocene.

This question is closely related to that of the antiquity of the oldest implements shaped by the human hand. Here again I have adopted an opinion opposed by some of the highest authorities, but supported by others, namely, that the earliest of these undoubted handiworks occur relatively late in the Pleistocene, namely, about 125,000 years ago. Since the Piltdown man was found in association with such implements, it is at once seen that the two questions hang together.

This work represents the co-operation of many specialists on a single, very complex problem. I am not in any sense an archæologist, and in this important and highly technical field I have relied chiefly upon the work of Hugo Obermaier and of Déchelette in the Lower Palæolithic, and of Henri Breuil in the Upper Palæolithic. Through the courtesy of Doctor Obermaier I had the privilege of watching the exploration of the wonderful grotto of Castillo, in northern Spain, which affords a unique and almost complete sequence of the industries of the entire Old Stone Age. This visit and that to the cavern of Altamira, with its wonderful frescoed ceiling, were in themselves a liberal education in the prehistory of man. With the Abbé Breuil I visited all the old camping stations of Upper Palæolithic times in Dordogne and noted with wonder and admiration his detection of all the fine gradations of invention which separate the flint-makers of that period. With Professor Cartailhac I enjoyed a broad survey of the Lower and Upper Palæolithic stations and caverns of the Pyrenees region and took note of his learned and spirited comments. Here also we had the privilege of being with the party who entered for the first time the cavern of Tuc d'Audoubert, with the Comte de Bégouen and his sons.

In the American Museum I have been greatly aided by Mr. Nels C. Nelson, who has reviewed all the archæological notes and greatly assisted me in the classification of the flint and bone implements which is adopted in this volume.

In the study of the divisions, duration, and fluctuations of climate during the Old Stone Age I have been assisted chiefly by Doctor Chester A. Reeds, a geologist of the American Museum, who devoted two months to bringing together in a comprehensive and intelligible form the results of the great researches of Albrecht Penck and Eduard Brückner embraced in the three-volume work, *Die Alpen im Eiszeitalter*. The temperatures and snow-levels of the Glacial Epoch, which is contemporaneous with the Old Stone Age, together with the successive phases of mammalian life which they conditioned, afford the firm basis of our chronology; that is, we must reckon the grand divisions of past time in terms of Glacial and Interglacial Stages; the subdivisions are recorded in terms of the human invention and progress of the flint industry. I have also had frequent recourse to *The Great Ice Age* and the more recent *Antiquity of Man in Europe* of James Geikie, the founder of the modern theory of the multiple Ice Age in Europe.

It is a unique pleasure to express my indebtedness to the Upper Palæolithic artists of the now extinct Crô-Magnon race, from whose work I have sought to portray so far as possible the mammalian and human life of the Old Stone Age. While we owe the discovery and early interpretation of this art to a generation of archæologists, it has remained for the Abbé Breuil not only to reproduce the art with remarkable fidelity but to firmly establish a chronology of the stages of art development. These results are brilliantly set forth in a superb series of volumes published by the *Institut de Paléontologie humaine* on the foundation of the Prince of Monaco; in fact, the memoirs on the art and industry of *Grimaldi*, *Font-de-Gaume*, *Altamira*, *La Pasiega*, and the Cantabrian caves of Spain (*Les Cavernes de la Région Cantabrique*), representing the combined labors of Capitan, Cartailhac, Verneau, Boule, Obermaier, and Breuil, mark a new epoch in the prehistory of man in Europe. There never has been a more fortunate union of genius, opportunity, and princely support.

In the collection of materials and illustrations from the vast number of original papers and memoirs consulted in the preparation of this volume, as well as in the verification of the text and proofs, I have been constantly aided by one of my research assistants, Miss Christina D. Matthew, who has greatly facilitated the work. I am indebted also to Miss Mabel R. Percy for the preparation and final revision of the manuscript. From the bibliography prepared by Miss Jannette M. Lucas, the reader may find the original authority for every statement which does not rest on my own observation or reflection.

Interest in human evolution centres chiefly in the skull and in the brain. The slope of the forehead and the other angles, which are so important in forming an estimate of the brain capacity, may be directly compared throughout this volume, because the profile or side view of every skull figured is placed in exactly the same relative position, namely, on the lines established by the anatomists of the Frankfort Convention to conform to the natural pose of the head on the living body.

In anatomy I have especially profited by the co-operation of my former student and present university colleague Professor J. Howard McGregor, of Columbia, who has shown great anatomical as well as artistic skill in the restoration of the heads of the four races of *Trinil*, *Piltdown*, *Neanderthal*, and *Crô-Magnon*. The new reconstruction of the Piltdown head is with the aid of casts sent to me by my friend Doctor A. Smith Woodward, of the British Museum of Natural History. The problem of reconstruction of the Piltdown skull has, through the differences of interpretation by Smith Woodward, Elliot Smith, and Arthur Keith, become one of the *causes célèbres* of anthropology. On the placing of the fragments of the skull and jaws, which have few points of contact, depends the all-important question of the size of the brain and the character of the profile of the face and jaws. In Professor McGregor's reconstruction different methods have been used from those employed by the British anatomists, and advantage has been taken of an observation of Mr. A. E. Anderson that the single canine tooth belongs in the upper and not in the lower jaw. In these models, and in all the restorations of men by Charles R. Knight under my direction, the controlling principle has been to make the restoration as *human* as the anatomical evidence will admit. This principle is based upon the theory for which I believe very strong grounds may be adduced, that all these races represent stages of advancing and progressive development; it has seemed to me, therefore, that in our restorations we should indicate as much alertness, intelligence, and upward tendency as possible. Such progressive expression may, in fact, be observed in the faces of the higher anthropoid apes, such as the chimpanzees and orangs, when in process of education. No doubt, our ancestors of the early Stone Age were brutal in many respects, but the representations which have been made chiefly by French and German artists of men with strong gorilla or chimpanzee characteristics are, I believe, unwarranted by the anatomical remains and are contrary to the conception which we must form of beings in the scale of rapidly ascending intelligence.

HENRY FAIRFIELD OSBORN.

AMERICAN MUSEUM OF NATURAL HISTORY
June 21, 1915.

In sending forth the second edition I have been able to add the results of recent research on the jaw of the Piltdown man, and on the presence of anthropoid apes in Europe during the Old Stone Age.

H. F. O.

December 20, 1915.

PREFACE TO THE THIRD EDITION

THE call for a third edition of this volume has afforded me an opportunity not only to correct a number of minor errors in the illustrations and text, to which friendly reviewers and critics have called attention, but also to add an account of the Palæolithic history of Spain and of the western region of northern Africa.

The relations of the ancient life of the Iberian Peninsula with that of Tunis, Algiers, and Morocco were at times very close indeed. In fact, the very characteristic industry known as the *Capsian*, which developed in North Africa during Upper Palæolithic times, extended throughout southeastern Spain, the two regions constituting a single archæologic province. The art of Alpera and Cogul, which in the earlier editions of this work was attributed to Neolithic times, belongs rather to the close of the Palæolithic and was probably contemporary with the Capsian and Tardenoisian flint industry of these stations. It embraces hunting scenes with numerous human figures in silhouette, wholly distinct from the possibly contemporaneous Magdalenian art of the north.

Before perusing Chapter VI, which covers the close of the Upper Palæolithic in France, the reader will therefore do well to turn to the new and extensive note in the Appendix describing this African life and industry. A clear understanding of the sources of the flint industry of Aurignacian times and also of the Tardenoisian flint industry and so-called Azilio-Tardenoisian culture described in Chapter VI will thus be gained.

Although the recent researches in Spain have greatly extended our knowledge, it is still to France that we turn for the most significant developments in the prehistory of Europe. Since the first publication of this work French archæology has suffered by the tragic death of Déchelette in the war; and also by a suspension of the wonderful course of discovery and research that marked the decade preceding the fateful year of 1914. Many problems—especially those discussed in the earlier chapters of this work—which might have been cleared up by further French research have remained untouched. For the same reason it would be premature to reconsider the chronologic succession of human types and geologic events which was provisionally proposed in the first edition of this work in 1915. We hope that brighter days are coming when science and art may be able to resume their peaceful paths, and that materials may then be gathered for a fourth edition of this work in which some, at least, of the many unanswered questions may be reconsidered in the light of further researches in the archæology of France.

The anatomy of Palæolithic man has been debated in a long discussion about the Piltdown Race, and even at this writing it is not finally agreed that the Piltdown jaw belongs with the Piltdown skull, because the new evidence brought forward by Dr. Smith Woodward, although strong, is not deemed entirely conclusive. This uncertainty is an instance not of the failure of scientific inquiry, but of the general desire of scientists to accept only that which has been conclusively demonstrated and to keep on seeking for conclusive evidence. Similar uncertainty exists regarding the anatomy of the Brünn Race, to which no new contributions have been made. It is interesting to record the fact that Professor J. H. McGregor, whose models and restorations of Palæolithic man included in the illustrations of this book have been so widely appreciated, is now making a special and intensive study of Palæolithic man which will no doubt be attended by important results. Similarly, another colleague of the author, Professor William K. Gregory, is studying anew the evolution of the anthropoid apes and other Primates, so that further light on the anatomy and evolution of primitive man may shortly be expected.

HENRY FAIRFIELD OSBORN.

May 1st, 1918.

CONTENTS

INTRODUCTION

CHAPTER I

CHAPTER II

CHAPTER III

CHAPTER IV

CHAPTER V

CHAPTER VI

APPENDIX

ILLUSTRATIONS

MEN OF THE OLD STONE AGE

MEN OF THE OLD STONE AGE

INTRODUCTION

GREEK CONCEPTIONS OF MAN'S ORIGIN — RISE OF ANTHROPOLOGY, OF ARCHÆOLOGY, OF THE GEOLOGIC HISTORY OF MAN — TIME DIVISIONS OF THE GLACIAL EPOCH — GEOGRAPHIC, CLIMATIC, AND LIFE PERIODS OF THE OLD STONE AGE

THE anticipation of nature by Lucretius* in his philosophical poem, *De Rerum Natura*, accords in a broad and remarkable way with our present knowledge of the prehistory of man:

> "Things throughout proceed
> In firm, undevious order, and maintain,
> To nature true, their fixt generic stamp.
> Yet man's first sons, as o'er the fields they trod.
> Reared from the hardy earth, were hardier far;
> Strong built with ampler bones, with muscles nerved
> Broad and substantial; to the power of heat,
> Of cold, of varying viands, and disease,
> Each hour superior; the wild lives of beasts
> Leading, while many a lustre o'er them rolled.
> Nor crooked plough-share knew they, nor to drive,
> Deep through the soil, the rich-returning spade;
> Nor how the tender seedling to re-plant,
> Nor from the fruit-tree prune the withered branch.
>
> . . . .
>
> "Nor knew they yet the crackling blaze t'excite,
> Or clothe their limbs with furs, or savage hides.
> But groves concealed them, woods, and hollow hills;
> And, when rude rains, or bitter blasts o'erpowered,
> Low bushy shrubs their squalid members wrapped.
>
> . . . .

* Lucretius was born 95 B. C. His poem was completed before 53 B. C. In the opening lines of Book III he attributes all his philosophy and science to the Greek See Appendix, Note I.

"And in their keen rapidity of hand
And foot confiding, oft the savage train
With missile stones they hunted, or the force
Of clubs enormous; many a tribe they felled,
Yet some in caves shunned, cautious; where, at night,
Thronged they, like bristly swine; their naked limbs
With herbs and leaves entwining. Nought of fear
Urged them to quit the darkness, and recall,
With clamorous cries, the sunshine and the day:
But sound they sunk in deep, oblivious sleep,
Till o'er the mountains blushed the roseate dawn.

. . . .

"This ne'er distressed them, but the fear alone
Some ruthless monster might their dreams molest,
The foamy boar, or lion, from their caves
Drive them aghast beneath the midnight shade,
And seize their leaf-wrought couches for themselves.

. . . .

"Yet then scarce more of mortal race than now
Left the sweet lustre of the liquid day.
Some doubtless, oft the prowling monsters gaunt
Grasped in their jaws, abrupt; whence, through the groves,
The woods, the mountains, they vociferous groaned,
Destined thus living to a living tomb.

. . . .

"Yet when, at length, rude huts they first devised,
And fires, and garments; and, in union sweet,
Man wedded woman, the pure joys indulged
Of chaste connubial love, and children rose,
The rough barbarians softened. The warm hearth
Their frames so melted they no more could bear,
As erst, th' uncovered skies; the nuptial bed
Broke their wild vigor, and the fond caress
Of prattling children from the bosom chased
Their stern ferocious manners." *

This is a picture of many phases in the life of primitive man: his powerful frame, his ignorance of agriculture, his dependence on the fruits and animal products of the earth, his discovery of fire and of clothing, his chase of wild beasts with clubs and missile stones, his repair to caverns, his contests with the lion

* Lucretius, *On the Nature of Things*, metrical version by J. M. Good. Bohn's Classical Library, London, 1800.

and the boar, his invention of rude huts and dwellings, the softening of his nature through the sweet influence of family life and of children, all these are veritable stages in our prehistoric development. The influence of Greek thought is also reflected in the Satires of Horace,* and the Greek conception of the natural history of man, voiced by Æschylus† as early as the fifth century B. C., prevailed widely before the Christian era, when it gradually gave way to the Mosaic conception of special creation, which spread all over western Europe.

Rise of Modern Anthropology

As the idea of the natural history of man again arose, during the sixteenth and seventeenth centuries, it came not so much from previous sources as from the dawning science of comparative anatomy. From the year 1597, when a Portuguese sailor's account of an animal resembling the chimpanzee was embodied in Filippo Pigafetta's *Description of the Kingdom of the Congo*, the many points of likeness between the anthropoid apes and man were treated both in satire and caricature and in serious anatomical comparison as evidence of kinship.

The first French evolutionist, Buffon,‡ observed in 1749: "The first truth that makes itself apparent on serious study of nature is one that man may perhaps find humiliating; it is this—that he, too, must take his place in the ranks of animals, being, as he is, an animal in every material point." Buffon's convictions were held in check by clerical and official influences, yet from his study of the orang in 1766 we can entertain no doubt of his belief that men and apes are descended from common ancestors.

The second French evolutionist, Lamarck,‖ in 1809 boldly

*Horace was born 65 B. C., and his Satires are attributed to the years 35–29 B. C. See Appendix, Note II.

† Æschylus was born 525 B. C. See Appendix, Note III.

‡ Georges Louis Leclerc Buffon (b. 1707, d. 1788). For reviews of Buffon's opinions and theories see Osborn, 1894.1, pp. 130–9; also Butler, 1911.1, pp. 74–172.

‖ Jean Baptiste Pierre Antoine de Monet, known as the Chevalier de Lamarck (b. 1744, d. 1829). For a summary of the views of Lamarck see Osborn, 1894.1, pp. 152–181; also Butler, 1911.1, pp. 235–314, an excellent presentation of Lamarck's opinions.

proclaimed the descent of man from the anthropoid apes, pointing out their close anatomical resemblances combined with inferiority both in bodily and mental capacity. In the evolution of man Lamarck perceived the great importance of the erect position, which is only occasionally assumed by the apes; also that children pass gradually from the quadrumanous to the upright position, and thus repeat the history of their ancestors. Man's origin is traced as follows: A race of quadrumanous apes gradually acquires the upright position in walking, with a corresponding modification of the limbs, and of the relation of the head and face to the back-bone. Such a race, having mastered all the other animals, spreads out over the world. It checks the increase of the races nearest itself and, spreading in all directions, begins to lead a social life, develops the power of speech and the communication of ideas. It develops also new requirements, one after another, which lead to industrial pursuits and to the gradual perfection of its powers. Eventually this pre-eminent race, having acquired absolute supremacy, comes to be widely different from even the most perfect of the lower animals.

The period following the latest publication of Lamarck's[1]* remarkable speculations in the year 1822, was distinguished by the earliest discoveries of the industry of the caveman in southern France in 1828, and in Belgium, near Liége, in 1833; discoveries which afforded the first scientific proof of the geologic antiquity of man and laid the foundations of the science of archæology.

The earliest recognition of an entirely extinct race of men was that which was called the 'Neanderthal,' found, in 1856, near Düsseldorf, and immediately recognized by Schaaffhausen[2] as a primitive race of low cerebral development and of uncommon bodily strength.

Darwin in the *Origin of Species*,[3] which appeared in 1858, did not discuss the question of human descent, but indicated

* References are indicated by numbers only throughout the text. At the close of each chapter is a list giving the author, date, and reference number for every citation. A full list of all the works cited, including those from which illustrations have been taken, together with complete references, will be found in the bibliography at the end of the book.

the belief that light would be thrown by his theory on the origin of man and his history.

It appears that Lamarck's doctrine in the *Philosophie Zoologique* (1809)[4] made a profound impression on the mind of Lyell, who was the first to treat the descent of man in a broad way from the standpoint of comparative anatomy and of geologic age. In his great work of 1863, *The Geological Evidences of the Antiquity of Man*, Lyell cited Huxley's estimate of the Neanderthal skull as more primitive than that of the Australian but of surprisingly large cranial capacity. He concludes with the notable statement: "The direct bearing of the ape-like character of the Neanderthal skull on Lamarck's doctrine of progressive development and transmutation . . . consists in this, that the newly observed deviation from a normal standard of human structure is not in a casual or random direction, but just what might have been anticipated if the laws of variation were such as the transmutationists require. For if we conceive the cranium to be very ancient, it exemplifies a less advanced stage of progressive development and improvement."[5]

Lyell followed this by an exhaustive review of all the then existing evidence in favor of the great geological age of man, considering the 'river-drift,' the 'loess,' and the loam deposits, and the relations of man to the divisions of the Glacial Epoch. Referring to what is now known as the Lower Palæolithic of St. Acheul and the Upper Palæolithic of Aurignac, he says that they were doubtless separated by a vast interval of time, when we consider that the flint implements of St. Acheul belong either to the Post-Pliocene or early Pleistocene time, or the 'older drift.'

It is singular that in the *Descent of Man*, published in 1871,[6] eight years after the appearance of Lyell's great work, Charles Darwin made only passing mention of the Neanderthal race, as follows: "Nevertheless, it must be admitted that some skulls of very high antiquity, such as the famous one at Neanderthal, are well-developed and capacious." It was the relatively large brain capacity which turned Darwin's attention away from a type which has furnished most powerful support to his theory of human descent. In the two hundred pages which Darwin devotes to the descent of man, he treats especially the evidences presented in comparative anatomy and comparative psychology, as well as the evidence afforded by the comparison of the lower and higher races of man. As regards the "birthplace and antiquity of man,"[7] he observes:

". . . In each great region of the world the living mammals are closely related to the extinct species of the same region. It is therefore probable that Africa was formerly inhabited by extinct apes closely allied to the gorilla and chimpanzee; and as these two species are now man's nearest allies, it is somewhat more probable that our early progenitors lived on the African continent than elsewhere. But it is useless to speculate on this subject; for two or three anthropomorphous apes, one the *Dryopithecus* of Lartet, nearly as large as a man, and closely allied to *Hylobates*, existed in Europe during the Miocene Age; and since so remote a period the earth has certainly undergone many great revolutions, and there has been ample time for migration on the largest scale.

"At the period and place, whenever and wherever it was, when man first lost his hairy covering, he probably inhabited a hot country; a circumstance favorable for the frugivorous diet on which, judging from analogy, he subsisted. We are far from knowing how long ago it was when man first diverged from the catarrhine stock; but it may have occurred at an epoch as remote as the Eocene Period; for that the higher apes had diverged from the lower apes as early as the Upper Miocene Period is shown by the existence of the *Dryopithecus*."

With this speculation of Darwin the reader should compare the state of our knowledge to-day regarding the descent of man, as presented in the first and last chapters of this volume.

The most telling argument against the Lamarck-Lyell-Darwin theory was the absence of those missing links which, theoretically, should be found connecting man with the anthropoid apes, for at that time the Neanderthal race was not recognized as such. Between 1848 and 1914 successive discoveries have been made of a series of human fossils belonging to intermediate races: some of these are now recognized as missing links between the existing human species, *Homo sapiens*, and the anthropoid apes; and others as the earliest known forms of *Homo sapiens*:

Year	Locality	Character of Remains	Race
1848	Gibraltar.	Well-preserved skull.	Neanderthal.
1856	Neanderthal, near Düsseldorf.	Skullcap, etc.	Type of Neanderthal race.
1866	La Naulette, Belgium.	Fragment of lower jaw.	Neanderthal race.
1867	Furfooz, Belgium.	Two skulls.	Type of Furfooz race.
1868	Crô-Magnon, Dordogne.	Three skeletons and fragments of two others.	Type of Crô-Magnon race.
1887	Spy, Belgium.	Two crania and skeletons.	Spy type of Neanderthal race.
1891	Trinil River, Java.	Skullcap and femur.	Type of Pithecanthropus race.
1899	Krapina, Austria-Hungary.	Fragments of at least ten individuals.	Krapina type of Neanderthal race.
1901	Grimaldi grotto, Mentone.	Two skeletons.	Type of Grimaldi race.
1907	Heidelberg.	Lower jaw with teeth.	Type of *Homo heidelbergensis*.
1908	La Chapelle, Corrèze.	Skeleton.	Mousterian type of Neanderthal race.
1908	Le Moustier, Dordogne.	Almost complete skeleton, greater part of which was in bad state of preservation.	Neanderthal.
1909	La Ferrassie I, Dordogne.	Fragments of skeleton.	Neanderthal.
1910	La Ferrassie II, Dordogne.	Fragments of skeleton, female.	Neanderthal.
1911	La Quina II, Charente.	Fragments of skeleton, supposed female.	Neanderthal.
1911	Piltdown, Sussex.	Portions of skull and jaw.	Type of *Eoanthropus*, the 'dawn man.'
1914	Obercassel, near Bonn, Germany.	Two skeletons, male and female.	Crô-Magnon.

In his classic lecture of 1844, *On the Form of the Head in Different Peoples*, Anders Retzius laid the foundation of the modern study of the skull.[8] Referring to his original publication, he says: "In the system of classification which I devised, I have distinguished just two forms, namely, the *short* (round or four-cornered) which I named *brachycephalic*, and the *long*, oval, or *dolichocephalic*. In the former there is little or no difference between the length and breadth of the skull; in the latter there is a notable difference." The expression of this primary distinction between races is called the *cephalic index,* and it is determined as follows:

Breadth of skull × 100 ÷ length of skull.

In this sense the primitive men of the Old Stone Age were mostly 'dolichocephalic,' that is, the breadth of the skull was in general less than 75 per cent of the length, as in the existing Australians, Kaffirs, Zulus, Eskimos, and Fijians. But some of the Palæolithic races were 'mesaticephalic'; that is, the breadth was between 75 per cent and 80 per cent of the length, as in the existing Chinese and Polynesians. The third or 'brachycephalic' type is the exception among Palæolithic skulls, in which the breadth is over 80 per cent of the length, as in the Malays, Burmese, American Indians, and Andamanese.

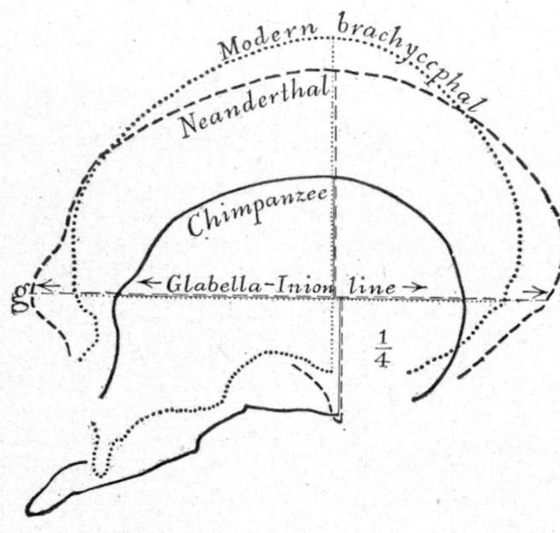

FIG. 1. Outline of a modern brachycephalic skull (fine dots), superposed upon a dolichocephalic skull (dashes), superposed upon a chimpanzee skull (line).

g. glabella or median prominence between the eyebrows.

i. inion—external occipital protuberance.

g–i. glabella-inion line.

Vertical line from *g–i* to top of skull indicates the height of the brain-case. Modified after Schwalbe.

The cephalic index, however, tells us little of the position of the skull as a *brain-case* in the ascending or descending scale, and following the elaborate systems of skull measurements which were built up by Retzius[9] and Broca,[10] and based chiefly on the *outside* characters of the skull, came the modern system of Schwalbe, which has been devised especially to measure the skull with reference to the all-important criterion of the size of the different portions of the brain, and of approximately estimating the cubic capacity of the brain from the more or less complete measurements of the skull.

Among these measurements are the slope of the forehead, the height of the median portion of the skullcap, and the ratio between the upper portion of the cranial chamber and the lower portion. In brief, the seven principal measures which Schwalbe now employs are chiefly expressions of diameters which correspond with the number of cubic centimetres occupied by the brain as a whole.

In this manner Schwalbe[11] confirms Boule's estimates of the variations in the cubic capacity of the brain in different members of the Neanderthal race as follows:

Neanderthal race	—La Chapelle	1620	c.cm.
"	" —Neanderthal	1408	"
"	" —La Quina	1367	"
"	" —Gibraltar	1296	"

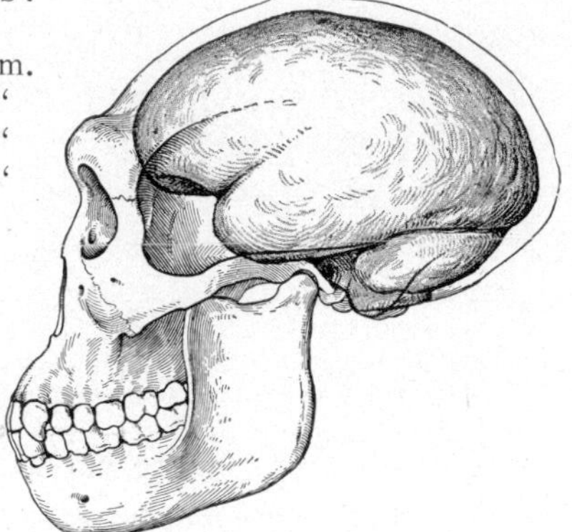

FIG. 2. The skull and brain-case, showing the low, retreating forehead, prominent supraorbital ridges, and small brain capacity, of *Pithecanthropus*, the Java ape-man, as restored by J. H. McGregor.

Thus the variations between the largest known brain in one member of the Neanderthal race, the male skull of La Chapelle, and the smallest brain of the same race, the supposed female skull of Gibraltar, is 324 c.cm., a range similar to that which we find in the existing species of man (*Homo sapiens*).

As another test for the classification of primitive skulls, we may select the well-known *frontal angle* of Broca, as modified by Schwalbe, for measuring the retreating forehead. The angle is measured by drawing a line along the forehead upward from the bony ridge between the eyebrows, with a horizontal line carried from the *glabella* to the *inion* at the back of the skull. The various primitive races are arranged as follows:

		PER CENT
Homo sapiens, with an average forehead	frontal angle	90
Homo sapiens, with extreme retreating forehead	" "	72.3
Homo neanderthalensis, with the least retreating forehead	" "	70
Homo neanderthalensis, with the most retreating forehead	" "	57.5
Pithecanthropus erectus (Trinil race)	" "	52.5
Highest anthropoid apes	" "	56

For instance, this illustrates the fact that in the Trinil race the forehead is actually lower than in some of the highest anthropoid apes; that in the Neanderthal race the forehead is more retreating than in any of the existing human races of *Homo sapiens*.

ARCHÆOLOGY OF THE OLD STONE AGE *

The proofs of the prehistory of man arose afresh, and from an entirely new source, in the beginning of the eighteenth century through discoveries in Germany, by which the Greek anticipations of a stone age were verified. For a century and a half the great animal life of the diluvial world had aroused the wonder and speculation of the early naturalists. In 1750 Eccardus[17] of Braunschweig advanced the first steps toward prehistoric chronology, in expressing the opinion that the human race first lived in a period in which stone served as the only weapon and tool, and that this was followed by a bronze and then by an iron period of human culture. As early as 1700 a human skull was discovered at Cannstatt and was believed to be of a period as ancient as the mammoth and the cave-bear.†

France, favored beyond all other countries by the men of the Old Stone Age, was destined to become the classic centre of prehistoric archæology. As early as 1740 Mahudel[18] published a treatise upon stone implements and laid the foundations both of Neolithic and Palæolithic research. By the beginning of the nineteenth century the problem of fossil man had awakened wide-spread interest and research. In Buckland's[19] *Reliquiæ diluvianæ*, published in 1824, the great mammals of the Old Stone Age are treated as relics of the flood. In 1825 MacEnery explored the cavern of Kent's Hole, near Torquay, finding human bones and flint flakes associated with the remains of the

* The best reference works on the history of French and German Palæolithic Archæology are: Cartailhac,[12] *La France Préhistorique;* Déchelette,[13] *Manuel d'Archéologie*, T. I; Reinach,[14] *Catalogue du Musée de St.-Germain: Alluvions et Cavernes;* Schmidt,[15] *Die diluviale Vorzeit Deutschlands;* Avebury,[16] *Prehistoric Times*.

† The Cannstatt skull and Cannstatt race are now regarded as Neolithic, and therefore not contemporary with the mammoth or the cave-bear.

cave-bear and cave-hyæna, but the notes of this discovery were not published until 1840, when Godwin-Austen[20] gave the first description of Kent's Hole. In 1828 Tournal and Christol[21] announced the first discoveries in France (Languedoc) of the association of human bones with the remains of extinct animals. In 1833–4 Schmerling[22] described his explorations in the cav-

FIG. 3. Three great types of flint implements.
A. An eolith of accidental shape.
B. A palæolith of Chellean type, partly fashioned.
C. A Neolithic axe head, partly polished.
After MacCurdy.

erns near Liége, in Belgium, in which he found human bones and rude flint implements intermingled with the remains of the mammoth, the woolly rhinoceros, the cave-hyæna, and the cave-bear. This is the first published evidence of the life of the Cave Period of Europe, and was soon followed by the recognition of similar cavern deposits along the south coast of Great Britain, in France, Belgium and Italy.

The work of the caveman, gradually revealed between 1828 and 1840, is now known to belong to the closing period of the Old Stone Age, and it is very remarkable that the next discovery related to the very dawn of the Old Stone Age, namely, to the life of the 'river-drift' man of the Lower Palæolithic.

This discovery of what is now known as Chellean and Acheulean industry came through the explorations of Boucher de Perthes, between 1839 and 1846, in the valley of the River Somme, which flows through Amiens and Abbeville and empties into the English Channel half-way between Dieppe and Boulogne. In 1841 this founder of modern archæology unearthed near Abbeville a single flint, rudely fashioned into a cutting instrument, buried in river sand and associated with mammalian remains. This was followed by the collection of many other ancient weapons and implements, and in the year 1846 Boucher de Perthes published his first work, entitled *De l'Industrie primitive, ou des Arts à leur Origine,*[23] in which he announced that he had found human implements in beds unmistakably belonging to the age of the 'river-drift.' This work and the succeeding (1857), *Antiquités celtiques et antédiluviennes,*[24] were received with great scepticism until confirmed in 1853 by Rigollot's[25] discovery of the now famous 'river-drift' beds of St. Acheul, near Amiens. In the succeeding years the epoch-making work of Boucher de Perthes was welcomed and confirmed by leading British geologists and archæologists, Falconer, Prestwich, Evans, and others who visited the Somme. Lubbock's[26] article of 1862, on the *Evidence of the Antiquity of Man Afforded by the Physical Structure of the Somme Valley*, pointing out the great geologic age of the river sands and gravels and of the mammals which they contained, was followed by the discovery of similar flints in the 'river-drifts' of Suffolk and Kent, England, in the valley of the Thames near Dartford. Thus came the first positive proofs that certain types of stone implements were widespread geographically, and thus was afforded the means of comparing the age of one deposit with another.

This led Sir John Lubbock[27] to divide the prehistoric period into four great epochs, in descending order as follows:

The *Iron Age*, in which iron had superseded bronze for arms, axes, knives, etc., while bronze remained in common use for ornaments.

The *Bronze Age*, in which bronze was used for arms and cutting instruments of all kinds.

The later or polished Stone Age, termed by Lubbock the *Neolithic Period*, characterized by weapons and instruments made of flint and other kinds of stone, with no knowledge of any metal excepting gold.

Age of the Drift, termed by Lubbock the *Palæolithic Period*, characterized by chipped or flaked implements of flint and other kinds of stone, and by the presence of the mammoth, the cave-bear, the woolly rhinoceros, and other extinct animals.

Edouard Lartet, in 1860, began exploring the caverns of the Pyrenees and of Périgord, first examining the remarkable cavern of Aurignac with its burial vault, its hearths, its reindeer and mammoth fauna, its spear points of bone and engravings on bone mingled with a new and distinctive flint culture. This discovery, published in 1861,[28] led to the full revelation of the hitherto unknown Reindeer and Art Period of the Old Stone Age, now known as the Upper Palæolithic. As a palæontologist, it was natural for Lartet to propose a fourfold classification of the 'Reindeer Period,' based upon the supposed succession of the dominant forms of mammalian life, namely:

(*d*) Age of the Aurochs or Bison.

(*c*) Age of the Woolly Mammoth and Rhinoceros.

(*b*) Age of the Reindeer.

(*a*) Age of the Cave-Bear.

Lartet, in association with the British archæologist, Christy, explored the now famous rock shelters and caverns of Dordogne —Laugerie, La Madeleine, Les Eyzies, and Le Moustier—which one by one yielded a variety of flint and bone implements, engravings and sculpture on bone and ivory, and a rich extinct fauna, in which the reindeer and mammoth predominated. The results of this decade of exploration are recorded in their classic work, *Reliquiæ Aquitanicæ*.[29] Lartet, observes Breuil,[30] clearly perceived the level of Aurignac, where the fauna of the great cave-bear and of the mammoth appears to yield to that of the reindeer. Above he perceived the stone culture of the Solutrean type in Laugerie Haute, and of the Magdalenian type in Laugerie Basse. Lartet also distinguished between the archæological period of St. Acheul (= Lower Palæolithic) and that of Aurignac (= Upper Palæolithic).

It remained, however, for Gabriel de Mortillet, the first French archæologist to survey and systematize the development of the flint industry throughout the entire Palæolithic Period, to recognize that the Magdalenian followed the Solutrean, and that during the latter stage industry in stone reached its height, while during the Magdalenian the industry in bone and in wood developed in a marvelous manner. Mortillet failed to recognize the position of the Aurignacian and omitted it from his archæological chronology, which was first published in 1869, *Essai de classification des cavernes et des stations sous abri, fondée sur les produits de l'industrie humaine:*[31]

(5) *Magdalénien,** characterized by a number and variety of bone implements;

(4) *Solutréen,* leaf-like lance-heads beautifully worked;

(3) *Moustérien,* flints worked mostly on one side only;

(2) *Acheuléen,* the 'langues de chat' hand-axes of St. Acheul;

(1) *Chelléen,* bold, primitive, partly worked hand-axes.

Shortly after the Franco-Prussian War, Edouard Piette (b. 1827, d. 1906), who had held the office of magistrate in various towns in the departments of Ardennes and Aisne, France, and who was already distinguished for his general scientific attainments, began to devote himself especially to the evolution of art in Upper Palæolithic times, and assembled the great collections which are described and illustrated in his classic work, *L'Art pendant l'Age du Renne* (1907).[32] He first established several phases of artistic evolution in the Magdalenian stage, and only recognized in his later years the station of Brassempouy, not

* Note that lists and tables of races, cultural stages, faunæ, etc., in this volume are given not in chronological but in *stratigraphic* order, beginning with the *most recent* at the top and ending with the *oldest* at the bottom.

comprehending that the Aurignacian art which he found there underlay the Solutrean culture and was separated by a long interval of time from the most ancient Magdalenian. His distinct contribution to Palæolithic history is his discovery of the

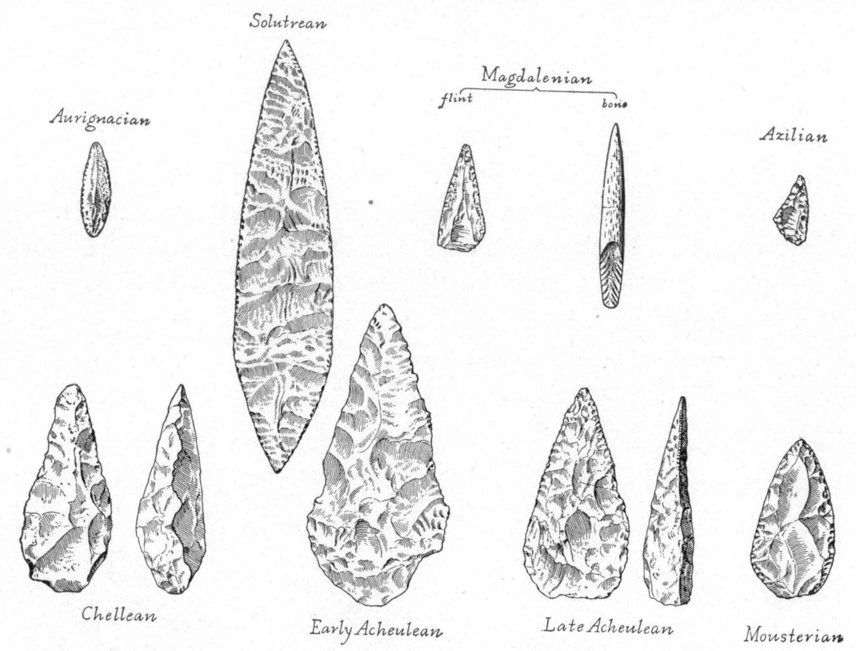

FIG. 4. Evolution of the lance-point, spear, or dart head. Note the increasing symmetry and skill in the flaking and retouch as the types pass in ascending order through the Chellean, Acheulean, Mousterian, and Aurignacian, into the perfected, symmetrical, double-pointed 'laurel-leaf' of the Solutrean; and into the subsequent decline in the flint industry of the Magdalenian and Azilian stages. After de Mortillet, Obermaier, and Hoernes.

Étage azilien overlying the Magdalenian in the cavern of Mas d'Azil.

Henri Breuil, a pupil of Piette and of Cartailhac, exploring during the decade, 1902–12, chiefly under the influence of Cartailhac, formed a clear conception of the whole Upper Palæolithic and its subdivisions, and placed the Aurignacian definitely at the base of the series.

Thus step by step the culture stages of archæological evolution have been established and may be summarized with the type stations as follows:

ÉTAGE	STATION
Tardenoisien,	Fère-en-Tardenois, Aisne.
Azilien,	Mas d'Azil, Ariège.
Magdalenien,	La Madeleine, près Tursac, Dordogne.
Solutréen,	Solutré près Mâcon, Saône-et-Loire.
Aurignacien,	Aurignac, Haute-Garonne.
Moustérien,	Le Moustier, commune de Peyzac, Dordogne.
Acheuléen,	St. Acheul, près Amiens, Somme.
Chelléen,	Chelles-sur-Marne, Seine-et-Marne.
Pre-Chelléen (= Mesvinien, Rutot),	Mesvin, Mons, Belgique.

These stages, at first regarded as single, have each been subdivided into three or more substages, as a result of the more refined appreciation of the subtle advances in Palæolithic invention and technique.

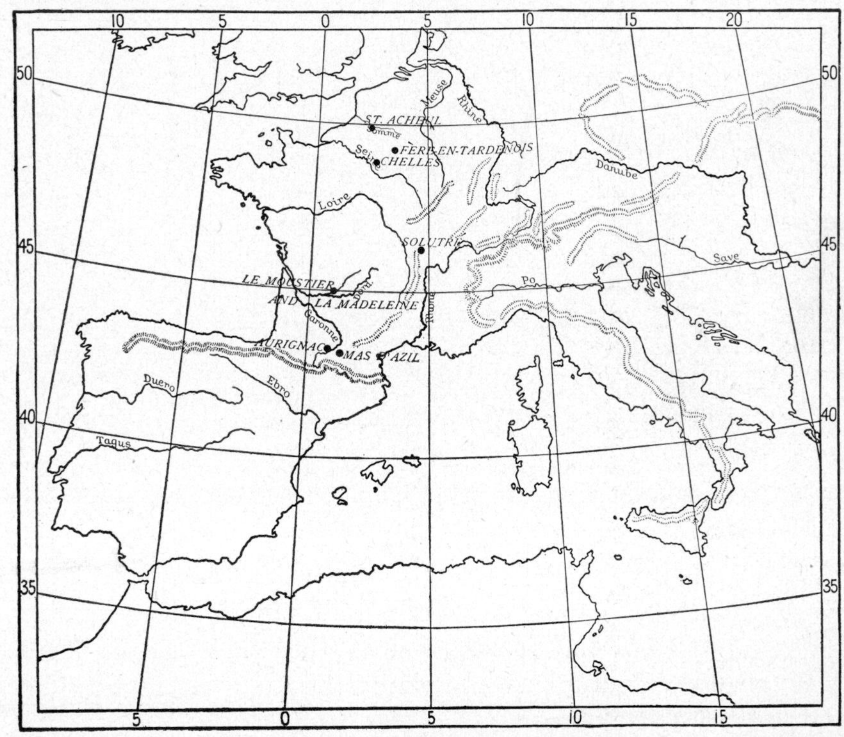

FIG. 5. The type stations of the successive stages of Palæolithic culture from the Chellean to the Azilian-Tardenoisian.

A new impulse to the study of Palæolithic culture was given in 1895, when E. Rivière discovered examples of Palæolithic mural art in the cavern of La Mouthe,[33] thus confirming the original discovery, in 1880, by Marcelino de Sautuola of the wonderful ceiling frescoes of the cave of Altamira, northern Spain.[34] This created the opportunity for the establishment by the Prince of Monaco of the *Institut de Paléontologie humaine* in 1910, supporting the combined researches of the Upper Palæolithic culture and art of France and Spain, by Cartailhac, Capitan, Rivière, Boule, Breuil, and Obermaier, and marking a new epoch in the brilliant history of the archæology of France.

It remained for the prehistory of the borders of the Danube, Rhine, and Neckar to be brought into harmony with that of France, and this has been accomplished with extraordinary precision and fulness through the labors of R. R. Schmidt, begun in 1906, and brought together in his invaluable work, *Die diluviale Vorzeit Deutschlands*.[35]

To an earlier and longer epoch belongs the Prepalæolithic or Eolithic stage. Beginning in 1867 with the supposed discovery by l'Abbé Bourgeois[36] of a primordial or Prepalæolithic stone culture, much observation and speculation has been devoted to the Eolithic[37] era and the Eolithic industry, culminating in the complete chronological system of Rutot, as follows:

LOWER QUATERNARY, OR PLEISTOCENE

Strépyan (=Pre-Chellean, in part).
Mesvinian, culture of Mesvin, near Mons, Belgium (= Pre-Chellean).
Mafflean, culture of Maffle, near Ath, Hennegau.
Reutelian, culture of Reutel, Ypres, West Flanders.

TERTIARY

Prestian, culture of St. Prest, Eure-et-Loire, Upper Pliocene.
Kentian, culture of the plateau of Kent, Middle Pliocene.
Cantalian, culture of Aurillac, Cantal, Upper Miocene or Lower Pliocene.
Fagnian, culture of Boncelles, Ardennes, Middle Oligocene.

Only the Mesvinian stage is generally accepted by archæologists, and this embraces the prototypes of the Lower Palæolithic culture, which among most French authors are termed Pre-Chellean or Proto-Chellean. The Eolithic problem has aroused the most animated controversy, in which opinion is divided. A critical consideration of this era, however, falls without the province of the present work.

SUCCESSION OF HUMAN INDUSTRIES AND CULTURES *

V. *LATER IRON AGE* (La Tène Culture)		Europe	500 B. C. to Roman Times.
IV. *EARLIER IRON AGE*		Europe	1000–500 B. C.
(Hallstatt Culture)		Orient	1800–1000
III. *BRONZE AGE*		Europe	about 2000–1000
		Orient	" 4000–1800
II. *NEW STONE AGE, NEOLITHIC*			
3. *LATE NEOLITHIC* and *COPPER AGE* (Transition Period)		Europe	" 3000–2000.
2. *TYPICAL NEOLITHIC AGE* (Robenhausian, Swiss Lake-Dwellers)		Europe	" 7000.
1. *EARLY NEOLITHIC STAGES* (Campignian Culture)		Europe	
I. *OLD STONE AGE, PALÆOLITHIC*			
UPPER PALÆOLITHIC		Europe	
8. Azilian–Tardenoisian.	Reindeer, Shelter, and Cave Period.		" 12,000.
7. Magdalenian. (Close of Post-glacial time.)			" 16,000.
6. Solutrean.			
5. Aurignacian. (Beginning of Post-glacial time.)			
LOWER PALÆOLITHIC			
4. Mousterian. (Fourth Glacial time.)			" 40,000.
3. Acheulean. (Transition to shelters.)	River-Drift and Terrace Period.		
2. Chellean.			" 100,000.
1. Pre-Chellean (Mesvinian.)			
EOLITHIC.			

* This table is a modification of that of Obermaier in his *Mensch der Vorzeit.*[38] To each period of the chronologic reckoning should be added the 1900 years of our era.

Geologic History of Man

Man emerges from the vast geologic history of the earth in the period known as the Pleistocene, or Glacial, and Postglacial, the 'Diluvium' of the older geologists. The men of the Old Stone Age in western Europe are now known through the latter

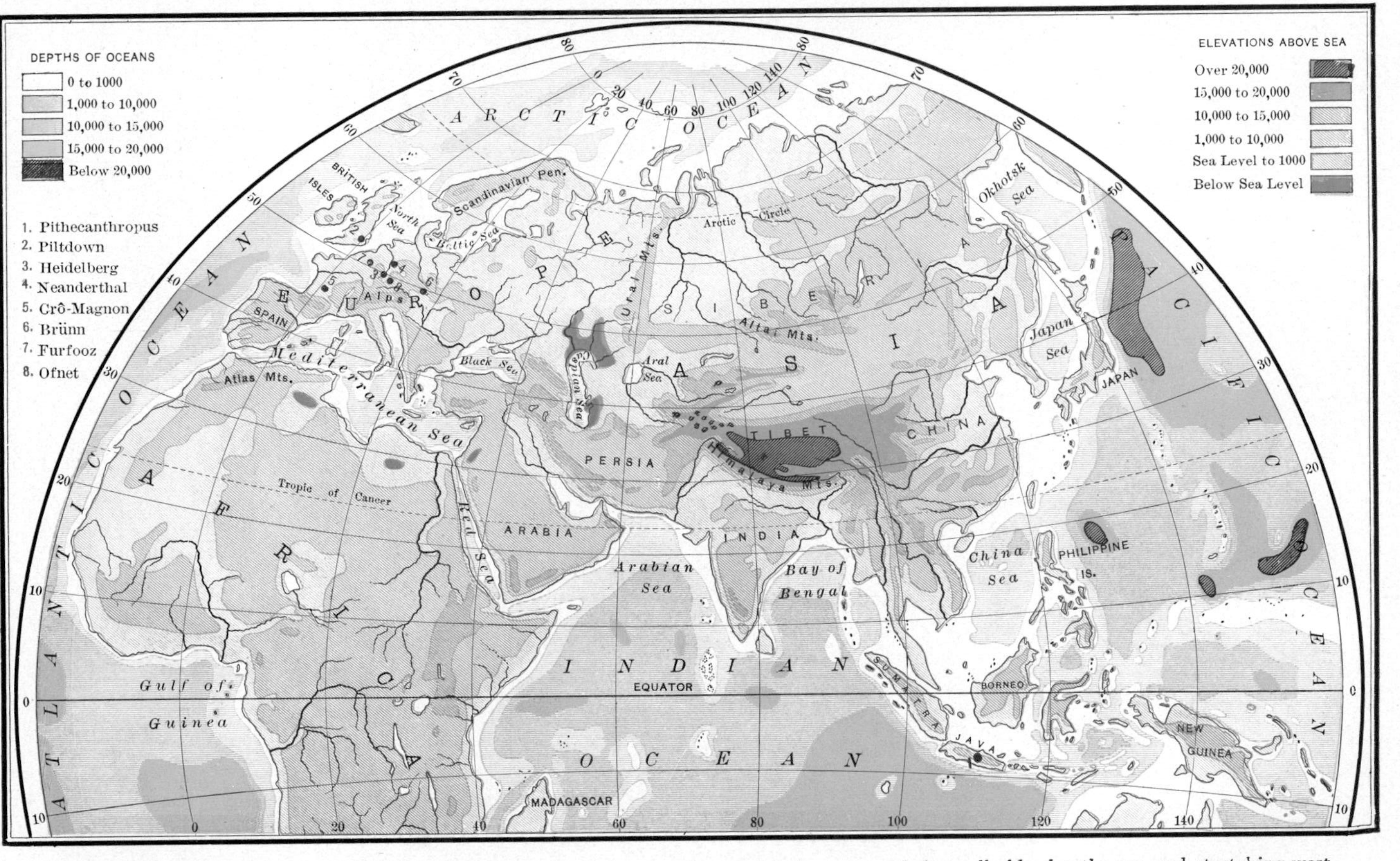

PL. II. "Throughout this long epoch western Europe is to be viewed as a peninsula, surrounded on all sides by the sea and stretching westward from the great land mass of eastern Europe and of Asia, which was the chief theatre of evolution both of animal and human life." 1–8. Discovery sites of the type specimens of human and prehuman races.

half of Glacial times to the very end of Postglacial times, when the Old Stone Age, with its wonderful environment of mammalian and human life, comes to a gradual close, and the New Stone Age begins with the climate and natural beauties of the forests, meadows, and Alps of Europe as they were before the destroying hand of economic civilization fell upon them.

It is our difficult but fascinating task to project in our imagination the extraordinary series of prehistoric natural events which were witnessed by the successive races of Palæolithic men in Europe; such a combination and sequence never occurred before in the world's history and will never occur again. They centred around three distinct and yet closely related groups of causes. First, the formation of the two great ice-fields centring over the Scandinavian peninsula and over the Alps; second, the arrival or assemblage in western Europe of mammals from five entirely different life-zones or natural habitats; third, the arrival in Europe of seven or eight successive races of men by migration, chiefly from the great Eurasiatic continent of the East.

Throughout this long epoch western Europe is to be viewed as a peninsula, surrounded on all sides by the sea and stretching westward from the great land mass of eastern Europe and of Asia, which was the chief theatre of evolution both of animal and human life. It was the 'far west' of all migrations of animals and men. Nor may we disregard the vast African land mass, the northern coasts of which afforded a great southern migration route from Asia, and may have supplied Europe with certain of its human races such as the 'Grimaldi.'

These three principal phenomena of the ice-fields, the mammals, and the human life and industry, together establish the chronology of the Age of Man. In other words, there are four ways of keeping *prehistoric time:* that of geology, that of palæontology, that of anatomy, and that of human industry. Geologic events mark the grander divisions of time; palæontologic and anatomic events mark the lesser divisions; while the successive phases of human industry mark the least divisions. The geologic chronology deals with such immense periods of time that its ratio to the animal and to the human chronology is like that of years to hours and to minutes of our own solar time.

The Glacial Epoch when first revealed by Charpentier[39] and Agassiz,[40] between 1837 and 1840, was supposed to correspond to a single great advance and retreat of the ice-fields from various centres. The vague problem of the antiquity of Pliocene man and Diluvial man soon merged into the far more definite chronology of *glacial* and *interglacial man.* As early as 1854, Morlot discovered near Dürnten, on the borders of the lake of Zürich, a bed of fossil plants indicating a period of south temperate climate intervening between two great deposits of glacial origin. This led to the new conception of cold glacial stages and warm interglacial stages, and Morlot[41] himself advanced the theory that there had been three glacial stages separated by two interglacial stages. Other discoveries followed both of fossil plants and mammals adapted to warmer periods intervening between the colder periods. Moreover, successive glacial moraines and 'drifts,' and successive river 'terraces' were found to confirm the theory of multiple glacial stages. The British geologist, James Geikie (1871–94) marshalled all the evidence for the extreme hypothesis of a succession of six glacial and five interglacial stages, each with its corresponding cold and warm climates. Strong confirmation of a theory of four great glaciations came through the American geologists, Chamberlin,[42] Salisbury,[43] and others, in the discovery of evidence of four chief glacial and three interglacial stages in northern portions of our own continent. Finally, a firm foundation of the quadruple glacial theory in Europe was laid by the classic researches of Penck and Brückner[44] in the Alps, which were published in 1909. Thus the exhaustive research of Geikie, of Chamberlin and Salisbury, of Penck and Brückner, and finally of Leverett[45] has firmly established eight subdivisions or stages of Pleistocene time, namely, four glacial, three interglacial, and one postglacial. These not only mark the great eras of European time but also make possible the synchrony of America with Europe.

Since most of the skeletal and cultural remains of man can now be definitely attributed to certain glacial, interglacial, or

Major Divisions	Periods and Epochs		Advances in Life	Dominant Life
QUATERNARY.	*HOLOCENE.*	Recent alluvial.	Rise of world civilization.	AGE OF MAN.
	....	....	Industry in iron, copper, and polished stone.	IRON, BRONZE, AND NEW STONE AGES.
	PLEISTOCENE, or ICE AGE.	**Postglacial stage.**	**Extinction of great mammals.**	**Men of the Old Stone Age.**
		Glacial stages.	**Dawn of mind, art, and industry.**	
TERTIARY.	*PLIOCENE.*	Late Tertiary.	Transformation of man-ape into man.	AGE OF MAMMALS AND MODERN PLANT LIFE.
	MIOCENE.		Culmination of mammals.	
	OLIGOCENE.	Early Tertiary.	Beginnings of anthropoid ape life.	
	EOCENE.		Appearance of higher types of mammals, and vanishing of archaic forms.	
	PALÆOCENE.		Rise of archaic mammals.	
LATE MESOZOIC.	Cretaceous.		Extinction of great reptiles.	AGE OF REPTILES.
			Extreme specialization of reptiles.	
	Comanchian.		Rise of flowering plants.	
EARLY MESOZOIC.	Jurassic.		Rise of birds and flying reptiles.	
	Triassic.		Rise of dinosaurs.	

PLACE OF THE OLD STONE AGE IN THE EARTH'S HISTORY
(Indicated in **heavy-face letter.**)
Compare Schuchert's Table, 1914.

postglacial stages, vast interest attaches to the very difficult problem of the duration of the whole Ice Age and the relative duration of its various glacial and interglacial stages. The following figures set forth the wide variations in opinion on this subject and the two opposite tendencies of speculation which lead to greatly expanded or greatly abbreviated estimates of Pleistocene time:

DURATION OF THE ICE AGE

1863.	Charles Lyell,[46] *Principles of Geology*	800,000 years.
1874.	James D. Dana,[47] *Manual of Geology*	720,000 "
1893.	Charles D. Walcott,[48] *Geologic Time as Indicated by the Sedimentary Rocks of North America*	400,000 "
1893.	W. Upham,[49] *Estimates of Geologic Times, Amer. Jour. Sci.*, vol. XLV	100,000 "
1894.	A. Heim,[50] *Ueber das absolute Alter der Eiszeit*	100,000 "
1900.	W. J. Sollas,[51] *Evolutional Geology*	400,000 "
1909.	Albrecht Penck,[52] *Die Alpen im Eiszeitalter*	520,000–840,000
1914.	James Geikie,[53] *The Antiquity of Man in Europe*	620,000 (min.)

We may adopt for the present work the more conservative estimate of Penck, that since the first great ice-fields developed in Scandinavia, in the Alps, and in North America west of Hudson Bay a period of time of not less than 520,000 years has elapsed. The relative duration of the subdivisions of the Glacial Epoch is also studied by Penck in his *Chronologie des Eiszeitalters in den Alpen.*[52] These stages are not in any degree rhythmic, or of equal length either in western Europe or in North America.

The unit of glacial measurement chosen by Penck is the time which has elapsed since the close of the fourth and last great glaciation; this is known as the *Würm* in the Alpine region and as the *Wisconsin* in America. While more limited than the ice-caps of the second glaciation, those of the fourth glaciation were still of vast extent in Europe and in this country, so that an estimate of 20,000 to 34,000 years for the unit of the entire *Postglacial* stage is not extreme. Estimating this unit at 25,000 years and accepting Reeds's[54] estimate of the relative length of time occupied by each of the preceding glacial and interglacial stages, we reach the following results (compare Fig. 14, p, 41):

		Relative Duration	Grand Totals	Descent of Alpine Snow-Line
POSTGLACIAL TIME.	Units	Years	Years	Meters
(Period of Upper Palæolithic culture, Crô-Magnon and Brünn races)	1	25,000	25,000	
IV. GLACIAL STAGE (=Würm, Wisconsin). (Close of Lower Palæolithic culture, Neanderthal race)	1	25,000	50,000	1,200
3d. *Interglacial Stage.* (Opening period of Lower Palæolithic culture, Piltdown and pre-Neanderthaloid races)	4	100,000	150,000	
III. GLACIAL STAGE (=Riss, Illinoian)	1	25,000	175,000	1,250
2d. *Interglacial Stage* (=Mindel-Riss, Yarmouth). (Period of Heidelberg race.)	8	200,000	375,000	
II. GLACIAL STAGE (=Mindel, Kansan)	1	25,000	400,000	1,300
1st. *Interglacial Stage* (=Günz-Mindel, Aftonian). (Period of *Pithecanthropus* or Trinil race.)	3	75,000	475,000	
I. GLACIAL STAGE (=Günz, Nebraskan)	1	25,000	500,000	1,200

The Postglacial time divisions are dated by three successive advances of the ice-caps, which broadly correspond with Geikie's fifth and sixth glaciations; they are known in the Alpine region as the *Bühl*, *Gschnitz*, and *Daun*. These three waves of cold and humid climate, each accompanied by glacial advances, finally terminated with the retreat of the snow and ice in the Alpine region, the same conditions prevailing as with the present climate. The minimum time estimates of these Postglacial stages and the corresponding periods of human culture, as calculated by Heim,[50] Nüesch,[55] Penck,[52] and many others, are summarized in the Upper Palæolithic (p. 281).

GEOLOGIC AND HUMAN CHRONOLOGY

There are four ways in which the lesser divisions and sequence of human chronology may be dated through geologic or earth-forming events. First, through the age of the culture stations or human remains, as indicated by the 'river-drifts' and 'river terraces' in or upon which they occur; second, through the age of the open 'loess' stations which are found both on the 'older terraces' and on the plateaus between the river valleys; third, through the age of the shelters and caverns in which skeletal and cultural remains occur; fourth, through the age of the 'loam' deposits, which have drifted down on the 'terraces' from the surrounding meadows and hills. The men of the Old Stone Age were attracted to these natural camps and dwelling-places both by the abundance of the raw flint materials from which the palæoliths were fashioned and by the presence of game.

In more than ninety years of exploration only three skeletal relics of man have been found in the ancient 'river-drifts'; these are the 'Trinil,' the 'Heidelberg,' and the 'Piltdown'; in each instance the human remains were buried accidentally with those of extinct animals, after drifting for some distance in the river or stream beds. It is only in late Acheulean times that human burial rites or interments begin and that skeletal remains are found. Owing to the less perishable nature of flint, relics of the quarries and stations are infinitely more common; they are found both in the river sands and gravels, in the 'river terraces,' and in the 'loess' stations of the plateaus and uplands. Thus prehistoric chronology is based on observations of the geologist, who in turn is greatly aided by the archæologist, because the evolution stages of each type of implement are practically the same all over western Europe, with the exception of unimportant local inventions and variations. In brief, the large divisions of time are determined by the amount of work done by geologic agencies; the comparative age of the various camp sites is determined by their geologic succession, by the mammals and plants which occur in them, and finally by the cultural type of any industrial remains that may be found.

Times of the 'High' and 'Low' River 'Terraces'

The so-called 'terrace' chronology is to be used by the prehistorian with caution, for it is obvious that the 'terraces' in the different river-valleys of western Europe were not all formed at the same time; thus the testimony of the 'terraces' is always to be checked off by other evidence.

As to the origin of the sands and gravels which compose the 'terraces' we know that the glacial stages were periods of the wearing away of vast materials from the summits and sides of the mountains, which were transported by the rivers to the valleys and plains. These vast deposits of glacial times spread out over the very broad surfaces of the pristine river-bottoms, which in many valleys it is important to note were from 100 to 150 feet above the present levels. The diminished and contracted

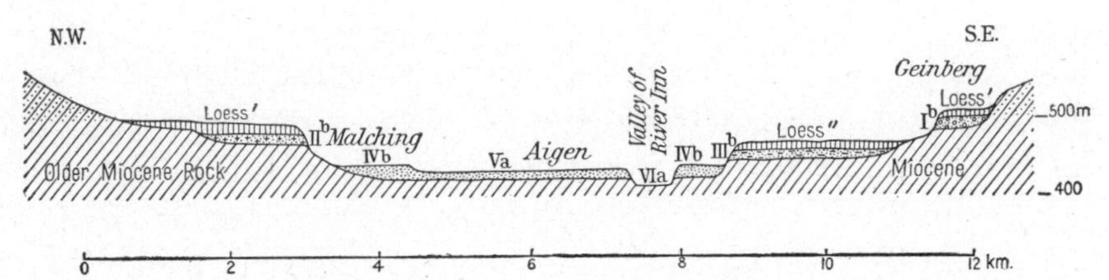

Fig. 6. Terraces on either side of the valley of the River Inn, Scharding, Austria, formed by sand and gravel deposits partly covered with loess. After Brückner.

Ib. Very broad river deposits of First Glaciation, on the first erosion level, covered with the 'Upper Loess' of the Second Interglacial Stage.

IIb. Somewhat narrower river deposits of Second Glaciation on the second erosion level.

IIIb. Still narrower river terraces of the Third Glaciation on the third erosion level, covered with the 'Lower Loess' of the Third Interglacial Stage.

IVb. Fourth or lowest terrace of the Fourth Glaciation on the fourth erosion level.

Va. Erosion terraces, Achen.

VIa. Post-Bühl erosion.

Loess', 'Upper Loess' of Second Interglacial. *Loess"*, 'Lower Loess' of Third Interglacial.

streams of interglacial times cut into these ancient river beds, forming narrower channels into which they transported their own materials. Thus, as the successive 'river terraces' were formed, a descending series of steps was created along the sides of the valleys. In many valleys there are four of these 'terraces,' which may correspond with several glacial stages; in other valleys there are only three; in others, again, like the valley of the River Inn which flows past Innsbruck in the Tyrol (Fig. 6), there are five 'terraces,' while in the valley of the Rhine above Basle there are six, corresponding, it is believed, with the materials brought down by the four great glaciations and with the river levels of Postglacial times. In general, therefore, the 'high terraces' are the oldest ones, that is, they are composed of materials brought down during the pluvial periods of the First, Second, and Third Glacial Stages, while the 'lower terraces' and the 'lowest terraces' in the alpine regions are composed of materials borne by the great rivers of the Fourth Glacial and Postglacial Stages. In the region around the Alps the 'higher terraces' are products chiefly of the third glaciation; in the

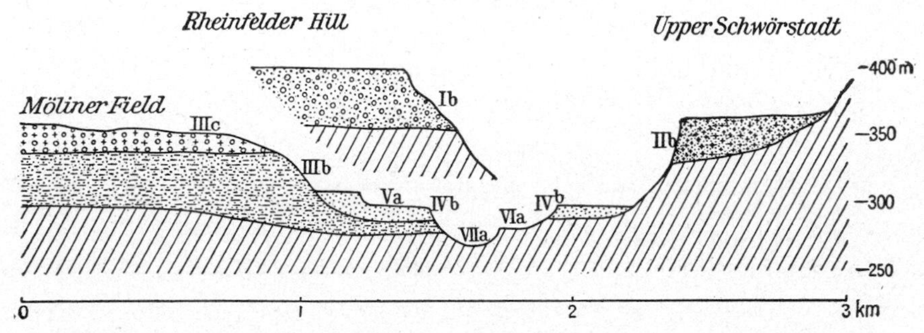

FIG. 7. Cross-section through the terraced Pleistocene formations of the Rhine valley above Basle, Switzerland. After Penck.

Ib. Outwash of the First Glaciation—Günz—Deposits on the first erosion level.
IIb. Outwash of the Second Glaciation—Mindel—Deposits on the second erosion level.
IIIb. Outwash of the Third Glaciation—Riss—Deposits on the third erosion level.
IVb. Outwash of the Fourth Glaciation—Würm—Deposits on the fourth erosion level.
Va. Erosion terrace, Achen oscillation—fifth erosion level.
VIa. } Post-Bühl erosion—sixth and seventh erosion levels.
VIIa. }
IIIc. Moraine of the Third Glaciation—Riss.

The section of the Rheinfelder Hill lies 3 km. west from the Möliner Field.

valley of the Rhine they are visible near Basle. On the upper Rhine the 'low terraces' are products of the fourth glaciation; they cover vast surfaces and contain remains of the woolly mammoth (*E. primigenius*), an animal distinctive of Fourth Glacial and Postglacial times.

More remote from the glacial regions, but equally subject to the inundations of glacial times are the 'high terraces' along the River Seine, which are ninety feet above the present level of the river and contain the remains of mammals characteristic of the First Interglacial Stage, such as the southern elephant (*E. meridionalis*), while the 'low terraces' along the Seine are only fifteen feet above the present level of the river and contain mammals belonging to the Third Interglacial Stage. Similarly, the 'high terraces' of the River Eure contain mammals of First Interglacial times, such as the southern elephant (*E. meridionalis*) and Steno's horse (*E. stenonis*); these fossils occur in coarse river sands and gravels which were deposited by a broad stream that flowed at least ninety feet above the present waters of the Eure.

The human interest which attaches to these dry facts of geology appears especially in the valleys of the Somme and the Marne in northern France; here again we find 'high terraces,' 'middle terraces,' and 'low terraces'; the latter are still subject to flooding. In the deep gravels upon each of these terraces we find the first proofs of human residence, for here occur the earliest Pre-Chellean and Chellean implements associated with the remains of the hippopotamus, of Merck's rhinoceros, and of the straight-tusked elephant (*E. antiquus*), together with mammals which are characteristic both of Second and Third Interglacial times.

This raises a very important distinction, which is often misunderstood; namely, between the materials *composing* the original terraces and those subsequently *deposited upon* the terraces. It appears to be in the latter that human artifacts are chiefly, if not exclusively, found.

Times of the Loam Stations

The 'loam' which washes down over the original sand and gravel 'terraces' from the surrounding hills and meadows is of much later date than the 'terraces' themselves, and the archæologist in the valley of the Somme as well as in that of the Thames may well be deceived unless he clearly distinguishes between the newer deposits of gravels and of loams and the far older gravels and river sands which compose the original 'terraces.' This is well illustrated by the observations of Commont on the section of St. Acheul.[56] The loams and brick-earth are of much more recent age than the original gravels and sands of the 'terraces' which they overlap and conceal; the lowest and oldest 'loam' (*limon fendillé*) contains Acheulean flints, while the overlying 'loam' contains Mousterian flints. Although occurring on the 'higher terraces,' these flints are of somewhat later date than the primitive Chellean flints which occur in the coarse gravels and sands that have collected upon the very *lowest levels* (Fig. 59).

A similar prehistoric inversion doubtless occurs in the 'terraces' of the Thames, for materials on the 'highest terrace' (Fig. 8) contain Acheulean flints, while materials on the 'lowest terrace' belong to a much more recent age.

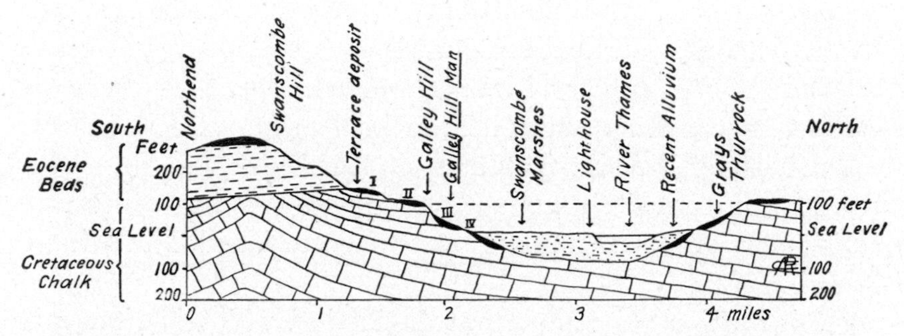

Fig. 8. Section—Four terraces indicated in the valley of the Thames at Galley Hill, near London. Site of the discovery of the 'Galley Hill Man' in deposits overlying one of the high terraces. Site also of Gray's Thurrock, a deposit of Third Interglacial times containing mammals and flints of Chellean age. A typical camping station of 'river-drift man.' Drawn by Dr. C. A. Reeds.

We have no record of a single Palæolithic station found in the true original sands and gravels of the 'higher terraces' in any part of Europe; only eoliths are found on the 'high terrace' levels, as at St. Prest.

The earliest palæoliths occur in the gravels on both the 'middle' and 'upper terraces' of the Somme and the Marne, proving that the gravels were deposited long subsequent to the cutting of the original terraces. Geikie,[57] moreover, is of the opinion that the valley of the Somme has remained as it is since early Pleistocene times, and that even the 'lowest terrace' here was completed at that period; this is contrary to the view of Commont, who considers that this 'lowest terrace' belongs to Third Interglacial times; a restudy of the stations along the Thames may throw light upon this very important difference of opinion.

Times of the 'Loess' Stations

The glacial stages were generally times of relatively great humidity, of heavy rain and snow fall, of full rivers charged with gravels and sands, and with loam the finest product of the ero-

Fig. 9. Magdalenian loess station of Aggsbach, in Lower Austria. A quarry camping station of the open-plains type. This typical Postglacial loess deposit contains flints of early Magdalenian age. After Obermaier.

sive action of ice upon the rocks. This loam on the barren wastes left bare by the glaciers or on the river borders and overflow basins was retransported by the winds and laid down afresh in layers of varying thickness known as 'loess.' There was no 'loess' formation either in Europe or America during the humid climate of First Interglacial times, but during the latter part of the Second Interglacial Stage, again toward the close of the Third Interglacial Stage, and finally during Postglacial times there were periods of arid climate when the 'loess' was lifted and transported by the prevailing winds over the 'terraces' and plateaus and even to great heights among the mountain valleys. As observed by Huntington[58] in his interesting book *The Pulse of Asia*, even at the present time there are districts where we find 'loess' dust filling the entire atmosphere either during the heated months of summer or during the cold months of winter.

In Pleistocene Europe there were at least three warm or cold arid periods, accompanied in some phases by prevailing westerly winds,[59] in which 'loess' was widely distributed over northern Germany, covering the 'river terraces,' plateaus, and uplands bordering the Rhine and the Neckar. These 'loess' periods can be dated by the fossil remains of mammals which they contain, also by the stations of the flint quarries in different culture stages. Thus we find late Acheulean implements in drifts of 'loess' at Villejuif, south of Paris. Among the most famous stations of late Acheulean times is that of Achenheim, west of Strasburg, and not far distant is the 'loess' station of Mommenheim, of Mousterian times; both belong to the period of the fourth glaciation. An Aurignacian 'loess' station is that of Willendorf, Austria.

Times of the Limestone Shelters and Caverns

Beginning in the late or cold Acheulean period, the Palæolithic hunters commenced to seek the warm or sheltered side of deepened river-valleys, also the shelter afforded by overhanging cliffs and the entrances of caverns. It is quite probable that during the warm season of the year they still repaired to their open flint quarries along the rivers and on the uplands; in fact, the river Somme was a favorite resort through Acheulean into Mousterian times.

In general, however, the open rivers and plateaus were abandoned, and all the regions of limestone rock favorable to the formation of shelter cliffs, grottos, and caverns were sought out by the early Palæolithic men from Mousterian times on; and thus from the beginning of the Mousterian to the close of the Upper Palæolithic their lines of migration and of residence followed the exposures of the limestones which had been laid down by the sea in bygone geologic ages from Carboniferous to Cretaceous times. The upper valleys of the Rhine and Danube traversed the white Jurassic limestones which are again exposed in a broad band along the foot-hills of the Pyrenees, extending far west to the Cantabrian Alps of modern Spain. In Dordogne the great horizontal plateau of Cretaceous limestone had been dissected by branching rivers, such as the Vézère, to a depth of two hun-

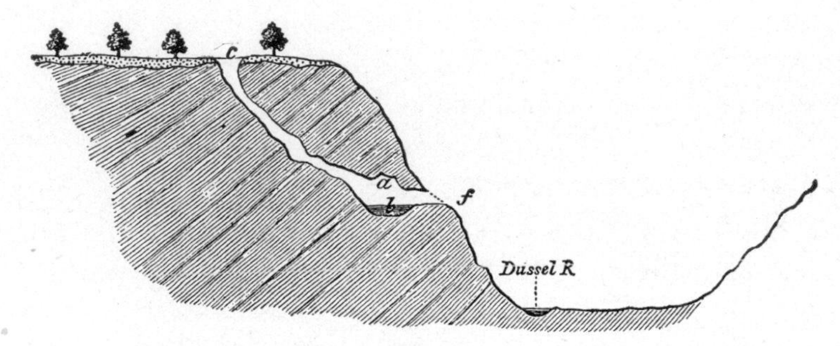

Fig. 10. Ideal section of the bluff overlying the Düssel River, near Düsseldorf, showing the mode of formation of the famous Neanderthal Cave, where the original type of the Neanderthal race was discovered in 1856. A typical resort of the 'cave man.' After Lyell.

c. Entrance of percolating waters from above.
f. Exit from the grotto.
a–b. Interior of the cavern.

dred feet. Under overhanging cliffs long rock shelters were formed, such as that of the Magdalenian station at La Madeleine.

Many caverns were formed, some of them in early Pleistocene times, by water percolating from above and (Fig. 11) resulting in subterranean streams which issued at the entrance; this formed the expanded grotto, sometimes a chamber of vast dimensions, such as the *Grotte de Gargas*. Outside of this, again, may be an *abri* or shelter of overhanging rock. In other cases the rock shelter is found quite independent of any cave.

Where the glaciers or ice-caps passed over the summits of the hills the subglacial streams penetrated the limestone of the mountain and formed vast caverns, such as that of Niaux, near the river Ariège. Here a nearly horizontal cavern was formed, extending half a mile into the heart of the mountain. The material with which the floors of the caverns are covered is either a fine cave loam or the insoluble remainder of the limestone forming a brown or gray clayey substance. The Magdalenian artists produced drawings on these soft clays and, in rare instances, used them for modelling purposes, as in the Tuc d'Audoubert. The sands and gravels were also swept in from the streams above and carried by strong currents along the wall surfaces, smoothing and polishing the limestone in preparation for the higher forms of Upper Palæolithic draughtsmanship and painting.

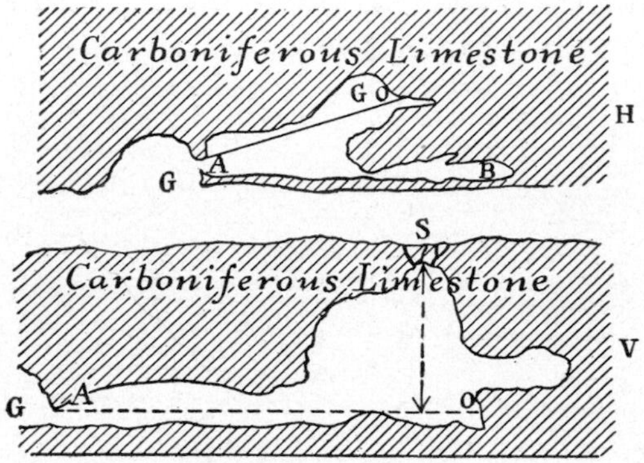

FIG. 11. Formation of the typical limestone cavern. After Gaudry.

V. Vertical section of limestone cliff showing (*S*) waters percolating from above; (*A*–*O*) interior of the cavern; and (*G*) grotto entrance, original exit of the cavern waters. *H*. Horizontal section of the same cavern showing the (*G*) grotto entrance and (*A*, *G*, *O*, *B*) the ramifications of the cavern.

It would appear that the majority of the caverns were formed in pluvial periods of early glacial times; the formation had been completed, the subterranean streams had ceased to flow, and the interiors were relatively dry and free from moisture in Fourth Glacial and Postglacial times, when man first entered them. There is no evidence, however, that the cavern depths were generally inhabited, for the obvious reason that there was no exit for the smoke; the old hearths are invariably found close to or outside of the entrance, the only exception being in the entrance to the great cavern of Gargas, where there is a natural chimney for the exit of smoke. There was no cave life, strictly speaking—it was grotto life; the deep caves and caverns were probably penetrated only by artists and possibly also by magicians or priests. It is in the *abris* or shelters in front of the grottos and in the floors of the caverns that remarkable prehistoric records are found from late Acheulean times to the very close of the Palæolithic, as in the wonderful grotto in front of the cave at Castillo, near Santander. Thus, as Obermaier[60] observes: "In Chellean times primitive man was a care-free hunter wandering as he chose in the mild and pleasant weather, and even the colder climate of the arid 'loess' period of the late Acheulean was not sufficient to overcome his love of the open; he still made his camp on the plains at the edge of the forest, or in the shelter of some overhanging cliff." Only in rare instances, as at Castillo, were the Acheulean hearths brought within the entrance line of the grotto.

Geologic Time	Penck, 1910 Geikie, 1914	Wiegers, 1913	Boule, Breuil, Obermaier, 1912 Schmidt, 1912
Postglacial.	Magdalenian.	Bronze. Neolithic. Azilian.	Magdalenian. Solutrean. Aurignacian.
IV. GLACIAL.	Solutrean.	Magdalenian. Solutrean. Aurignacian. Mousterian.	Mousterian.
Third Interglacial.	Mousterian.	Mousterian.	Early Mousterian. Cold Acheulean. Warm " Chellean. Pre-Chellean.
III. GLACIAL.	Mousterian.	Cold Acheulean.	
Second Interglacial.	Acheulean. Chellean.	Warm Acheulean. Chellean.	
II. GLACIAL.		Pre-Chellean	
First Interglacial.			

DIFFERENCES OF OPINION AS TO THE GEOLOGIC AGE OF THE PALÆOLITHIC CULTURE STAGES

The right-hand column represents the theory adopted in this volume.

Interpretation of these four kinds of evidence as to the antiquity of human culture in western Europe still leads to widely diverse opinions. On the one hand, we have the high authority of Penck[61] and Geikie[62] that the Chellean and Acheulean cultures are as ancient as the second long warm interglacial period.

An extreme exponent of the same theory is Wiegers,[63] who would carry the Pre-Chellean back even into First Interglacial times. On the other side, Boule,[64] Schuchardt,[65] Obermaier,[66] Schmidt,[67] and the majority of the French archæologists place the beginning of the Pre-Chellean culture in Third Interglacial times.

In favor of the latter theory is the strikingly close succession of the Lower Palæolithic cultures in the valley of the Somme, followed by an equally close succession from Acheulean to Magdalenian times, as, for example, in the station of Castillo. It does not appear possible that a vast interval of time, such as that of the third glaciation, separated the Chellean from the Mousterian culture.

On the other hand, in favor of the greater antiquity of the Pre-Chellean and Chellean cultures may be urged their alleged association in several localities with very primitive mammals of early Pleistocene type, namely, the Etruscan rhinoceros, Steno's horse, and the saber-tooth tiger, as witnessed in Spain and in the deposits of the Champs de Mars, at Abbeville.

It is true, moreover, that at points distant from the great ice-fields, like the valley of the Somme and that of the Marne, we have no other means of separating glacial from interglacial times than that afforded by the deposition and erosion of the 'terraces'; in fact, the interpretation of the age of the cultures may be similar to that applied to the age of the mammalian fauna. There are no proofs of periods of severe cold in western Europe in any country remote from the glaciers until the very cold steppe-tundra climate immediately preceding the fourth glaciation swept the entire land and drove out the last of the African-Asiatic mammals.

Geographic Changes

The migrations of mammals and of races of men into western Europe from the Eurasiatic continent on the east and from Africa on the south were favored or interrupted by the periods of elevation or of subsidence of the coastal borders of the Ægean, Mediterranean, and North Seas, and also of the Iberian and

British coast-lines. The maximum period of elevation of the coastal borders, as represented in the accompanying map (Fig. 12), never occurred in all portions of the continent of Europe at the same time, because there were oscillations both on the north-

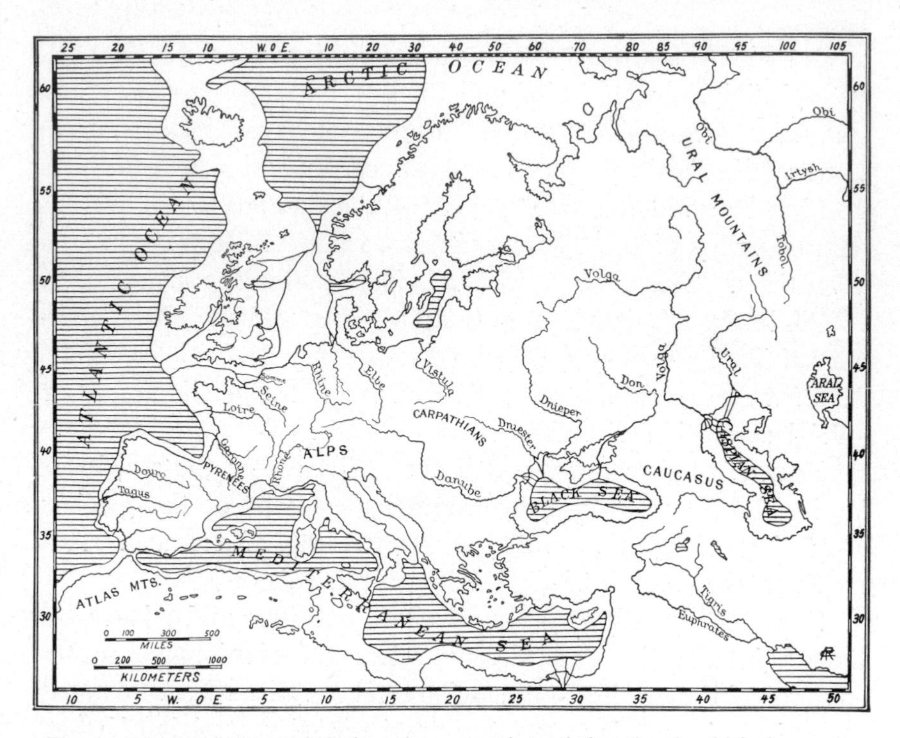

FIG. 12. Europe in the period of maximum continental elevation, in which the coast-lines are widely extended, connecting Africa and Europe—including Great Britain and Ireland—in a single vast peninsula, and affording free migration routes for animal and human races north and south, as well as east and west. The ocean boundaries are more remote and the interior seas are greatly reduced in area. After Obermaier.

ern and southern coasts of Europe and Africa. The early Pleistocene, especially the period of the First Interglacial Stage, was one of elevation remarkable for the broad land bridges which brought the animal life of Europe, Africa, and Asia together. The Mediterranean coast rose 300 feet. Land bridges from Africa were formed at Gibraltar and over to the island of Sicily, so that for the time there was a free migration of mammalian life north and south. It is to this that western Europe owes the majestic mammals of Asiatic and African life which dominated the native fauna.

In general, the *elevation* of the continent took place during interglacial, the *subsidence* during glacial times, but Great Britain appears to have been almost continuously elevated and a part of the continent, and was certainly so during the Third Interglacial, Fourth Glacial, and Postglacial Stages, because there was a free migration of animal life and of human culture. The Lower Palæolithic peoples of Pre-Chellean and Chellean times wandered at will from the valley of the Somme to the not far distant valley of the Thames, interchanging their weapons and inventions. The close proximity of these stations is well illustrated in the admirable map (Fig. 56) prepared under the direction of Lord Avebury (Sir John Lubbock). The relation which *elevation* and *subsidence* respectively bear to the glacial and interglacial stages is believed to be as follows:

Elevation, emergence of the coast-lines from the sea, broad land connections facilitating migration, retreat of the glaciers, deepening of the river-valleys, and cutting of terraces. Arid continental climate and deposition of 'loess.'

Subsidence, submergence of the coast-lines and advance of the sea, interruption of land connections and of migration routes, advance of the glaciers, filling of the river-valleys with the products of glacial erosion, the sand and gravel materials of which the 'terraces' are composed, and subglacial erosion of the loam, from which in arid periods the 'loess' is derived.

Subsidence was the great feature of closing glacial times both in Europe and America. During the Fourth Glacial and Postglacial Stages the Black and Caspian Seas and the eastern portion of the Mediterranean were deeply depressed, while the British Isles were still connected with France, but by a narrower isthmus than that of early interglacial times. The scattered stations of Upper Palæolithic culture found in the British Isles include one Aurignacian, one Solutrean, two Magdalenian, and two Azilian; this shows that travel communication with the continent continued throughout that period, in all probability by means of a land connection. In late Neolithic times the English Channel was formed, Great Britain became isolated from Europe, and Ireland lost its land connection first with Wales and then with Scotland.

Changes of Climate

Penck[68] estimates the intensity of the cold and of the humidity which prevailed during the glacial stages by the *descent* of the snow-line in the Alps, which in the two periods of greatest

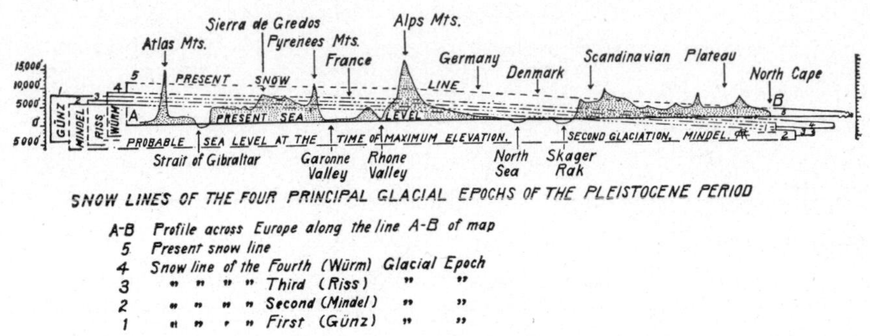

FIG. 13. An ideal earth section from the North Cape across the Scandinavian plateau, through the North Sea, Swiss Alps, Pyrenees, and Straits of Gibraltar, to the Atlas Mountains in northern Africa, along the line indicated on the map (Fig. 25, p. 65), illustrating the sea-level at the time of the greatest elevation of the continent during the Second Glacial Stage, as compared with the present sea-level; also the successive lines of descent of the region of perpetual snow during the four great glacial advances, as compared with the present snow-line. From studies by Dr. C. A. Reeds.

glaciation reached from 1,200 m. (3,937 ft.) to 1,500 m. (4, 921 ft.) below the present snow-level, with the consequent formation of vast ice-caps hung with glaciers which flowed great distances down the valleys of the Rhône and of the Rhine and left their moraines at very distant points. The moraines and drifts of the lesser glaciations, such as the first and fourth, stand considerably within the boundaries of these outer moraines and drift fields. On the contrary, the warmer climates of interglacial times are indicated by the sun-loving plants found at Hötting, along the valley of the Inn, in the Tyrol, which are proofs of a temperature higher than the present and of the *ascent* of the snow-line 300 m. (984 ft.) above the existing snow-level of the Alps.

The alternation of the cold climates of the glacial stages with the warm temperate climates of the interglacial stages formed great oscillations of temperature (Figs. 13, 14). The fossil plant life indicates that during the periods of the First, Second, and Third Interglacial Stages the climate of western Europe was cooler than it had been during the preceding Pliocene Epoch and somewhat warmer than it is at the present time in the same localities. During the First, Second, and Third Glacial Stages there was certainly a marked lowering of temperature in the regions bordering the great glacial fields. This is indicated by the arrival in the northern glacial border regions of animals and plants adapted to arctic and subarctic climates.

It has been generally believed that the whole of western Europe was extremely cold during these glacial stages, and that the heat-loving animals, the southern elephants, rhinoceroses, and hippopotami, were driven to the south, to return only with the renewed warmth of the next interglacial stage.

There is, however, no proof of the departure of these supposedly less hardy mammals nor of the spread over Europe of the more hardy arctic and steppe types until the advent of the Fourth Glacial Stage. Then, for the first time, all western Europe north of the Pyrenees experienced a general fall of temperature, and conditions of climate prevailed such as are now found in the arctic tundra regions of the north and in the high steppes of central Asia, which are swept by dry and cold winter winds. Fluctuations of temperature, of moisture, and of aridity in Pleistocene time, are evidenced not only by the rise and fall of the snow-line and the advance and retreat of the ice-caps but also by the appearance of plant and animal life in the periods of the 'loess' deposition, indicating the following cycles of climatic change as witnessed from beginning to end of the Third Interglacial Stage:

IV. Glacial maximum, cold and moist climate, arctic and cold steppe fauna and flora.

Cool and dry steppe climate, wide-spread deposition of 'loess.'

Interglacial maximum, a long period of warm temperate forest and meadow conditions.

Glacial retreat, cool and moist climate bordering the glacial regions.

III. Glacial maximum, cold and humid climate bordering the glaciers, favorable to arctic and subarctic plant and animal life.

That great fields of ice and advancing glaciers alone do not constitute proof of very low temperatures is shown at the present time in southeastern Alaska, where very heavy snowfall or precipitation causes the accumulation of vast glaciers, although the mean annual temperature is only 10° Fahr. (5.56° C.) lower than that of southern Germany. Neumayr[69] estimated that during the Ice Age there was a general lowering of temperature in Europe of not more than 6° C. (10.8° Fahr.), and held that even during the glacial advances a comparatively mild climate prevailed in Great Britain. Martins[70] estimated that a lowering of the temperature to the extent of 4° C. (7.2° Fahr.) would bring the glaciers of Chamonix down to the level of the plain of Geneva. Penck estimates that, all the atmospheric conditions remaining the same as at present, a fall of temperature to the extent of 4° to 5° C. would be sufficient to bring back the Glacial Epoch in Europe. These moderate estimates entirely agree with our theory that animals of African and Asiatic habit flourished in western Europe to the very close of the Third Interglacial Stage, and that then for the first time the warm fauna, or *faune chaude*, gradually disappeared.

Similarly the hypothesis of extremely warm or subtropical conditions prevailing in interglacial times as far north as Britain, which originated with the discovery of the northerly distribution of the hippopotami and rhinoceroses, animals which we now associate with the torrid climate of Africa, is not supported by the study either of the plant life of interglacial stages or by the history of the animals themselves. It is quite probable that both the hippopotami and the rhinoceroses of the 'warm fauna' were protected by hairy covering, although not by the thick undercoating of wool which protected the woolly rhinoceros and woolly mammoth, animals favoring the borders of glaciers and flourishing during the last very cold glacial and Postglacial periods.

The combined evidence from all these great events in western Europe leads us to conclusions somewhat different from those reached by Penck as to the chronology of human culture. In the chart (Fig. 14) on the opposite page, prepared by Dr. C. A. Reeds in collaboration with the author, a new correlation of geologic, climatic, human, industrial, and faunal events is presented. The great waves of glacial advance and retreat (oblique shading) are based upon Penck's estimates of the rise and fall of the snow-line (vertical dotted lines) in the Swiss Alps. (Compare Fig. 13.) The length of these waves corresponds with the relative duration of the glacial and interglacial stages as estimated by the varying amounts of erosion and deposition of materials. The entire Palæolithic or Old Stone Age is thus seen to occupy not more than 125,000 years, or only the last quarter of the Glacial Epoch, which is estimated as extending over a period of 525,000 years. The present opinion of the leading archæologists of France and Germany, which is shared by the author, is that the Pre-Chellean industry is not older than the Third Interglacial Stage. As the Piltdown man was found in deposits containing Pre-Chellean implements, he probably lived in the last quarter of the Glacial Epoch, and not in early Pleistocene times as estimated by some British geologists. This causes us to regard the Piltdown remains as more recent than the jaw of Heidelberg, which all authorities agree is probably of Second Interglacial Age. According to our estimates the Heidelberg man is nearly twice as ancient as the Piltdown man, while *Pithecanthropus* (Trinil Race) is four times as ancient. Yet the Piltdown man must still be regarded as of very great antiquity, for he is four times as ancient as the final type of Neanderthal man belonging to the Mousterian industrial stage. The various archæologic and palæontologic evidences for this

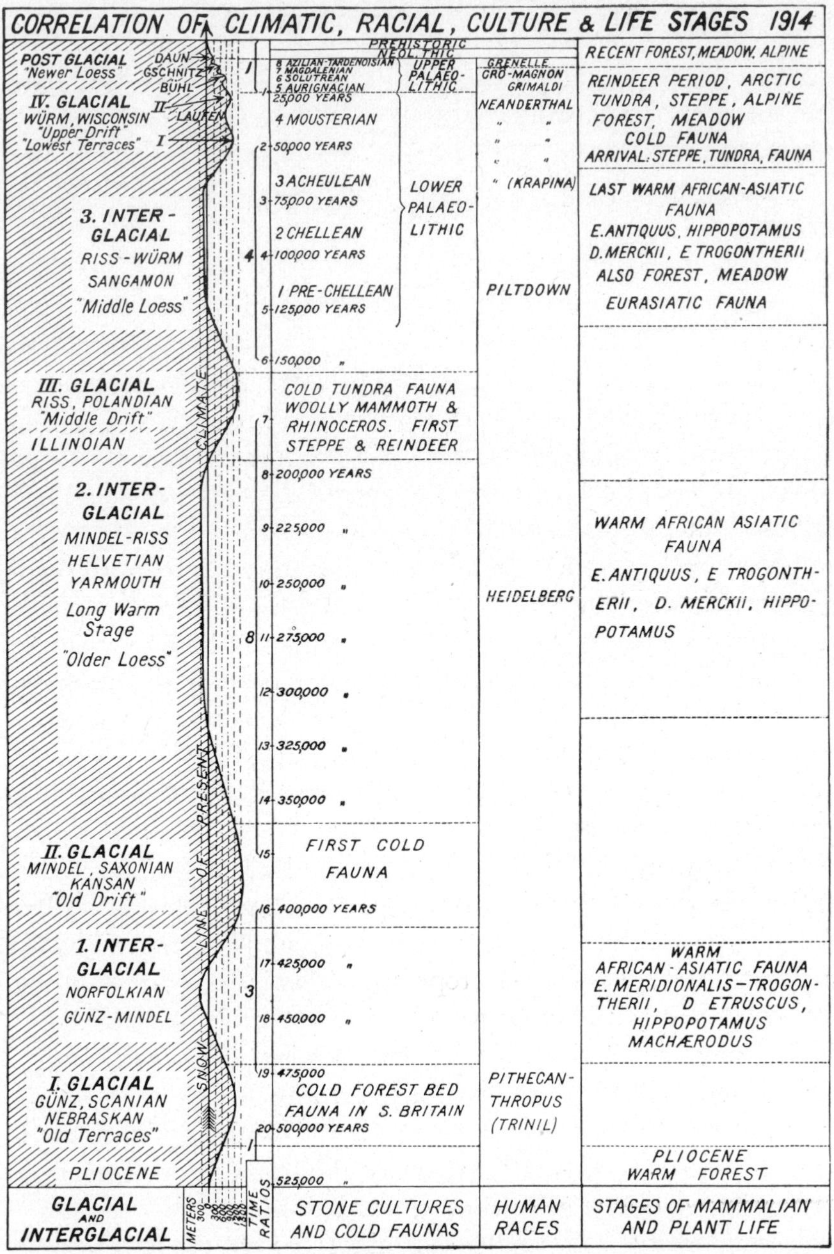

CORRELATION OF CLIMATIC, RACIAL, CULTURE & LIFE STAGES 1914

POST GLACIAL
"Newer Loess"
DAUN
GSCHNITZ
BÜHL
IV. GLACIAL
WÜRM, WISCONSIN
"Upper Drift"
"Lowest Terraces"
II
LAUFEN
I
3. INTER-GLACIAL
RISS-WÜRM
SANGAMON
"Middle Loess"
III. GLACIAL
RISS, POLANDIAN
"Middle Drift"
ILLINOIAN
2. INTER-GLACIAL
MINDEL-RISS
HELVETIAN
YARMOUTH
Long Warm Stage
"Older Loess"
II. GLACIAL
MINDEL, SAXONIAN
KANSAN
"Old Drift"
1. INTER-GLACIAL
NORFOLKIAN
GÜNZ-MINDEL
I. GLACIAL
GÜNZ, SCANIAN
NEBRASKAN
"Old Terraces"
PLIOCENE

LINE OF PRESENT CLIMATE
SNOW

1 4 8 3 1

PREHISTORIC
NEOLITHIC
8 AZILIAN-TARDENOISIAN
7 MAGDALENIAN
6 SOLUTREAN
5 AURIGNACIAN
UPPER PALAEOLITHIC
1 25,000 YEARS
4 MOUSTERIAN
2 50,000 YEARS
3 ACHEULEAN
3 75,000 YEARS
2 CHELLEAN
LOWER PALAEOLITHIC
4 100,000 YEARS
1 PRE-CHELLEAN
5 125,000 YEARS
6 150,000 "
COLD TUNDRA FAUNA WOOLLY MAMMOTH & RHINOCEROS. FIRST STEPPE & REINDEER
7
8 200,000 YEARS
9 225,000 "
10 250,000 "
11 275,000 "
12 300,000 "
13 325,000 "
14 350,000 "
15 FIRST COLD FAUNA
16 400,000 YEARS
17 425,000 "
18 450,000 "
19 475,000
COLD FOREST BED FAUNA IN S. BRITAIN
20 500,000 YEARS
525,000 "

GRENELLE
CRO-MAGNON
GRIMALDI
NEANDERTHAL
" "
" "
" "
" (KRAPINA)
PILTDOWN
HEIDELBERG
PITHECANTHROPUS (TRINIL)

RECENT FOREST, MEADOW, ALPINE
REINDEER PERIOD, ARCTIC TUNDRA, STEPPE, ALPINE FOREST, MEADOW
COLD FAUNA
ARRIVAL: STEPPE, TUNDRA, FAUNA
LAST WARM AFRICAN-ASIATIC FAUNA
E. ANTIQUUS, HIPPOPOTAMUS
D. MERCKII, E TROGONTHERII
ALSO FOREST, MEADOW
EURASIATIC FAUNA
WARM AFRICAN ASIATIC FAUNA
E. ANTIQUUS, E TROGONTHERII, D. MERCKII, HIPPOPOTAMUS
WARM
AFRICAN-ASIATIC FAUNA
E. MERIDIONALIS—TROGONTHERII, D ETRUSCUS,
HIPPOPOTAMUS
MACHÆRODUS
PLIOCENE
WARM FOREST

GLACIAL AND INTERGLACIAL | METERS 300 0 300 600 900 1200 1500 | TIME RATIOS | STONE CULTURES AND COLD FAUNAS | HUMAN RACES | STAGES OF MAMMALIAN AND PLANT LIFE

FIG. 14. Great events of the Glacial Epoch. To the left the relation of glacial and interglacial stages in Europe and North America, with the author's theory regarding the divisions of time, the beginning of the Old Stone Age, and the successive appearance in Europe of different branches of the human race. To the right the prolonged warm temperate period in Europe in the non-glaciated regions, followed by the relatively brief cold period during the past 70,000 years. Prepared by Dr. C. A. Reeds, in co-operation with the author

general correlation theory of the Glacial Epoch are fully discussed in the succeeding chapters of this volume.

Mammals of Five Distinct Geographic Regions

(Compare Color Map, Pl. II, and Fig. 15)

As we have already observed, during the whole history of mammalian life in various parts of the world never did there prevail conditions so unusual and so complex as those which surrounded the men of the Old Stone Age in Europe. The successive races of Palæolithic men in Europe were all flesh eaters, depending upon the chase. The mammals, first pursued only for food, utensils, and clothing, finally became subjects of artistic appreciation and endeavor which resulted in a remarkable æsthetic development.

From the beginning to the end of Palæolithic times the various races of man witnessed the assemblage in Europe of animals indigenous to every continent on the globe except South America and Australia and adapted to every climatic life-zone, from the warm and dry plains of southern Asia and northern Africa to the temperate forests and meadows of Eurasia; from the heights of the Alps, Himalayas, Pyrenees, and Altai Mountains to the high, arid, dry steppes of central Asia with their alternating heat of summer and cold of winter; from the tundras or barren grounds of Scandinavia, northern Europe, and Siberia to the mild forests and plains of southern Europe.[71] Members of all these highly varied groups of animals had been evolving in various parts of the northern hemisphere from the Eocene Epoch onward. In Pliocene times they had become thoroughly adapted to their various habitats. Throughout early Pleistocene times, with the increasing cold extending southward from the arctic circle, such mammals as the elephant, rhinoceros, musk-ox, and reindeer had become thoroughly adapted to the climate of the extreme north. There is every reason to believe that when these tundra quadrupeds first arrived in Europe, during early midglacial stages, they had already acquired the heavy coat of hair

Stage	Regions near the Ice-fields	More Sheltered Regions	Period
RECENT PREHISTORIC.	Return of the Alpine Mammals to the Mountains. Wide dispersal of Forest and Meadow Mammals over the Northern Hemisphere.		PERIOD OF RECENT ANIMALS.
POSTGLACIAL. Severe climate.	Retreat of the Tundra and Steppe Mammals to the North and East. Mingling in the lowlands of France and Germany of the Reindeer-Mammoth fauna, the Alpine fauna, the Steppe Mammals, and the hardy Eurasiatic Forest and Meadow Mammals.		REINDEER PERIOD IN WESTERN EUROPE.
IV. GLACIAL. Cold Steppe climate.	Arrival of the Tundra Mammals from the North. Arrival of the Steppe Mammals from Western Asia.		
3d INTERGLACIAL. Warm climate.	Southward migration and extinction of all the African-Asiatic Mammals except the lions and hyænas. Mingled African-Asiatic and Eurasiatic Mammals in different parts of the non-glaciated regions, the hippopotamus, southern mammoth, straight-	tusked elephant, Merck's broad-nosed rhinoceros, lion, hyæna, jackal, sabre-tooth tiger.	PERIOD OF THE HIPPOPOTAMUS, RHINOCEROS, AND ELEPHANT. ALSO OF THE STAG AND BISON IN WESTERN EUROPE.
III. GLACIAL.	Reindeer and Woolly Mammoth in North Germany and the Alps.		
2d INTERGLACIAL.		Also the stag, giant deer, bison, wild cattle, forest horse, boar, wolf, fox, lynx, wildcat, several species of bear.	
II. GLACIAL.	Reindeer and Woolly Mammoth in Northern Germany.		
1st INTERGLACIAL.		Survival of many Pliocene African-Asiatic Mammals, mingled with Pliocene and recent Eurasiatic Forest and Meadow Mammals.	
I. GLACIAL.	Musk-ox in Sussex, England.		
GEOLOGIC AND CLIMATIC STAGES.	Early Migrations of Scandinavian and North Siberian Mammals near the Ice-fields.	'Warm' African-Asiatic Mammals. Temperate and sheltered parts of Western Europe. More hardy Eurasiatic Mammals. Cool temperate forests and meadows.	THREE CHIEF LIFE PERIODS.
	REGIONS NEAR THE ICE-FIELDS AND GLACIAL BORDERS.	MORE SHELTERED NON-GLACIATED REGIONS REMOTE FROM THE GLACIAL BORDERS AND ICE-FIELDS.	

MIGRATIONS AND EXTINCTIONS OF MAMMALIAN LIFE DURING THE FOUR GLACIAL, THREE INTERGLACIAL, AND POSTGLACIAL STAGES and undercoating of wool, such as now characterizes the musk-ox, one of the living representatives of this northern fauna.

The five great sources of mammalian migration into western Europe in Pleistocene times were accordingly as follows:

1. Warm plains of northern Africa and of southern Asia. "African Asiatic" fauna—hippopotamus, rhinoceros, elephant.

2. Temperate meadows and forests of Europe and Asia. "Eurasiatic" fauna—deer, bison, horse.

3. High, cool mountain ranges—Alps, Pyrenees, Caucasus, Urals. Fauna—chamois, ibex, ptarmigan. (See Fig. 185.)

4. Steppes and deserts. Dry, elevated plateaus and steppes of eastern Europe and central Asia. Fauna—desert ass and horse, saiga antelope, jerboa. (See Fig. 186.)

5. Tundras and barren grounds within or near the arctic circle. Fauna—reindeer, musk-ox, arctic fox. (See Figs. 95 and 96.)

(Compare Figs. 14 and 15.)

In the warm plains, forests, and rivers of southern Asia and northern Africa there developed the elephants, rhinoceroses, hippopotami, lions, hyænas, and jackals, which, taken together, may be known as the *African-Asiatic* fauna. It contains altogether fourteen species of mammals. The great geographic area from the far east to the far west over which ranged similar or identical species of these pachyderms and carnivores is indicated by the oblique lines in the geographic chart (Fig. 15).

The north temperate belt of Asia and Europe, with its hardy forests and genial meadows, was the home of the even more highly varied *Eurasiatic Forest and Meadow* fauna. This includes twenty-six or more species. Of these the red deer, or stag, was most characteristic of the forests and the bison and wild cattle* of the meadows. Even at the very beginning of Pleistocene times there appear the stag, the wild boar, and the roe-deer with their natural pursuers, the wolf and the brown bear. From the northern woods came the moose and the wolverene. Most of these mammals were so similar to existing forms that the older naturalists

* Bison and wild cattle are grass eaters, and their natural habitats are the open plain and meadow regions. They also range into open forest lands where grasses can be found. The prehistoric 'urus' and 'wisent' of Europe were both found in forests, but this may not have been their natural habitat in Palæolithic times. See Appendix, Note IV.

placed them in existing species, but the tendency now is to separate them or place them in distinct subspecies. Mingled with these forest and meadow mammals were a few others which have

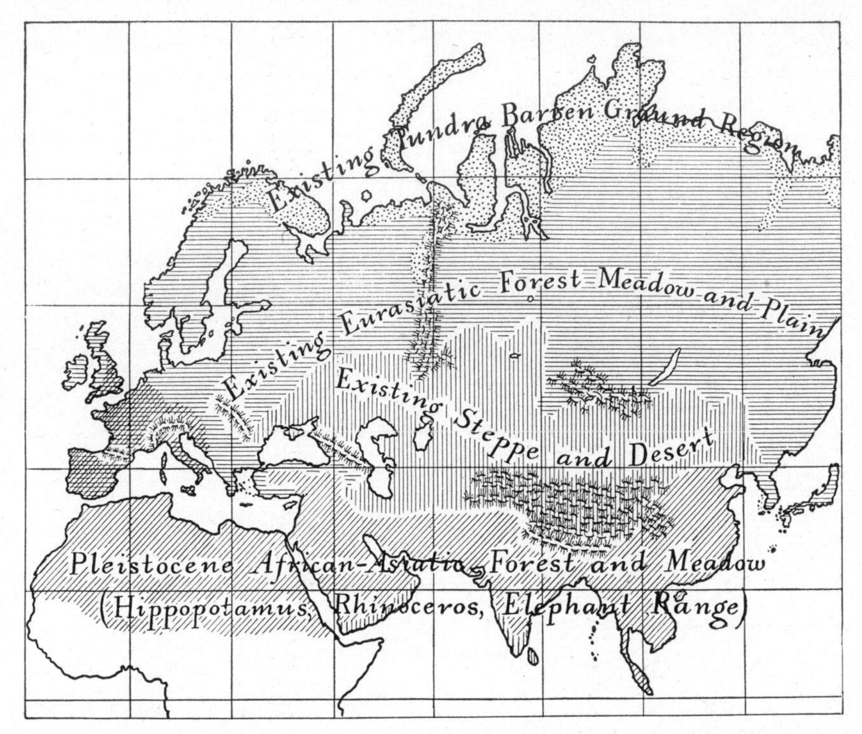

FIG. 15. Zoogeographic map. Range of the large mammals of Africa and southern Asia in Pliocene and Pleistocene times until nearly the close of the Lower Palæolithic (oblique lines). Range of the forest and meadow fauna of Europe and Asia from early Pleistocene to prehistoric times; stag and bison fauna (horizontal lines). Present range of the tundra or barren-ground mammals (dots) which wandered south during the fourth glaciation, expelling the large Asiatic mammals. Present range of mammals of the deserts and steppes of eastern Europe and southern Asia, which also invaded western Europe during the glacial and Postglacial stages (vertical lines). The alpine mammals dwelt in the high mountain regions and invaded the plains and lowlands during Fourth Glacial and Postglacial times.

since become extinct, such as the giant deer (*Megaceros*), the giant beaver (*Trogontherium*), and the primitive forest and meadow horses. From this region also there developed the cave-bear (*Ursus spelæus*). Certainly it is astonishing to find the remains of these mammals mingled with those from southern Asia and Africa, as is frequently the case. In early glacial times the bison and wild cattle mingled freely with the hippopotami and rhinoceroses, but in late glacial and Postglacial times they occurred as companions of the mammoth and the woolly rhinoceros. In prehistoric times they survived with the mammals brought from the Orient by the Neolithic agriculturists.

During a great glaciation, but especially during the severe climate of late Pleistocene times, the *Alpine* mammals were driven down from the heights into the plains and among the lower mountains and foot-hills. Thus the ibex, chamois, and argali sheep from the Altai Mountains are represented both in drawing and in sculpture by the men of the Reindeer Period.

Still more remarkable is the arrival in Europe of the *Steppe Fauna* of Russia and of western Siberia, mammals which now survive in the vast Kirghiz steppes, east of the Caspian Sea and the Ural Mountains, where the climate is one of hot, dry summers and prolonged cold winters, with sweeping dust and snow storms. These animals are very hardy, alert, and swift of foot, such as the jerboa, the saiga antelope, the wild asses, and the wild horses, including the Przewalski type, which still survives in the desert of Gobi. From this region also came the Elasmothere (*E. sibiricum*), with its single giant horn above the eyes. Very distinctive of the fauna frequenting the caverns are the small rodents, including the dwarf pikas, the steppe hamsters, and the lemmings. These animals were attracted into Europe during the 'steppe' and 'loess' periods of cold, dry climate.

The advance of the great Scandinavian glaciers from the north crowded to the south the *Tundra or Barren Ground* fauna of the arctic circle. The herald of this fauna during the First Glacial Stage was the musk-ox, which appears in Sussex, and then came the reindeer of the existing Scandinavian type. These animals are followed by the woolly mammoth (*E. primigenius*) and the woolly rhinoceros (*D. antiquitatis*) with their panoply of hair and wool which had long been developing in the north. Finally in the Fourth Glacial Stage arrived the lemming of the river Obi, also the more northern banded lemming, the arctic fox, the wolverene, and the ermine, as well as the arctic hare.

These tundra mammals for a short period mingled in places with survivors of the *African-Asiatic* fauna, such as Merck's rhinoceros and the straight-tusked elephant (*E. antiquus*). In general, they swept southward as far as the Pyrenees over country which had long been enjoyed by the African-Asiatic mammals, while the hippopotami and the southern elephants retreated still farther south and became extinct.

The only survivors of the great *African-Asiatic* fauna in Fourth Glacial and Postglacial times were the hyænas (H. *crocuta spelæa*) and the lions (*Felis leo spelæa*). The lion frequently appears in the drawings of the cavemen.

The various species belonging to these five great faunæ apparently succeed each other, and wherever their remains are mingled with the palæoliths, as along the rivers Somme, Marne, and Thames, or in the hearths of the shelters and caverns, they become of extreme interest both in their bearing on the chronology of man and on the development of human culture, art, and industry. They also tell the story of the sequence of climatic conditions both in the regions bordering the glaciers and in the more temperate regions remote from the ice-caps. Thus they guide the anthropologist over the difficult gaps where the geologic record is limited or undecipherable. The general succession of these great faunæ is illustrated in Fig. 14 and also in the above table.

(1) Lamarck, 1815.1.
(2) Schaaffhausen, 1858.1.
(3) Darwin, C., 1909.2.
(4) Lamarck, 1809.1.
(5) Lyell, 1863.1, pp. 84–89.
(6) Darwin, C., 1871.1, p. 146.
(7) Darwin, C., 1909.1, p. 158.
(8) Retzius, A., 1864.1, p. 27.
(9) *Op. cit.*, p. 166.
(10) Broca, 1875.1.
(11) Schwalbe, G., 1914.1, p. 592.
(12) Cartailhac, 1903.1.
(13) Déchelette, 1908.1, vol. I.
(14) Reinach, S., 1889.1.
(15) Schmidt, 1912.1.
(16) Avebury, 1913.1.
(17) Eccardus, 1750.1.
(18) Mahudel, 1740.1.
(19) Buckland, 1824.1.
(20) Godwin-Austen, 1840.1.
(21) Christol, 1829.1.
(22) Schmerling, 1833.1.
(23) Boucher de Perthes, 1846.1.
(24) *Op. cit.*
(25) Rigollot, 1854.1.
(26) Lubbock, 1862.1.
(27) Avebury, 1913.1, pp. 2, 3.
(28) Lartet, 1861.1.
(29) Lartet, 1875.1.
(30) Breuil, 1912.7, p. 165.
(31) de Mortillet, 1869.1.
(32) Piette, E., 1907.1.

(33) Rivière 1897.1.
(34) de Sautuola, 1880.1.
(35) Schmidt, 1912.1.
(36) Bourgeois, 1867.1.
(37) Schmidt, *op. cit.*, p. 5.
(38) Obermaier, 1912.1, pp. 170–174; 316–320; 332, 545.
(39) Charpentier, 1841.1.
(40) Agassiz, 1837.1; 1840.1; 1840.2.
(41) Morlot, 1854.1.
(42) Chamberlin, 1895.1; 1905.1, vol. III, chap. XIX, pp. 327–516.
(43) Salisbury, 1905.1.
(44) Penck, 1909.1.
(45) Leverett, 1910.1.
(46) Lyell, 1867.1, vol. I, pp. 293–301; 1877.1, vol. I, p. 287.
(47) Dana, 1875.1, p. 591.
(48) Walcott, 1893.1.
(49) Upham, 1893.1, p. 217.
(50) Heim, 1894.1.
(51) Sollas, 1900.1.
(52) Penck, 1909.1, vol. III, pp. 1153–1176.
(53) Geikie, 1914.1, p. 302.
(54) Reeds, 1915.1.
(55) Nüesch, 1902.1.
(56) Geikie, *op. cit.*, pp. 111–114.
(57) *Op. cit.*, p. 108.
(58) Huntington, 1907.1.
(59) Leverett, 1910.1.
(60) Obermaier, 1912.1, p. 132.
(61) Penck, 1908.1; 1909.1.
(62) Geikie, 1914.1, p. 312.
(63) Wiegers, 1913.1.
(64) Boule, 1888.1.
(65) Schuchardt, 1913.1, p. 144.
(66) Obermaier, 1909.2; 1912.1.
(67) Schmidt, 1912.1, p. 266.
(68) Penck, 1909.1, vol. III, p. 1168, Fig. 136.
(69) Neumayr, 1890.1, vol. II, p. 621.
(70) Martins, 1847.1, pp. 941, 942.
(71) Osborn, 1910.1, pp. 386–427.

CHAPTER I

ANCESTRY OF THE ANTHROPOID APES — PLIOCENE CLIMATE, FORESTS, AND LIFE OF WESTERN EUROPE — TRANSITION TO THE PLEISTOCENE, OR AGE OF MAN — THE FIRST GLACIATION, ITS EFFECTS ON CLIMATE, FORESTS, AND ANIMAL LIFE — THE PREHUMAN TRINIL RACE OF JAVA — THE EOLITHS OR PRIMITIVE FLINTS — THE SECOND GLACIATION — THE HEIDELBERG, EARLIEST KNOWN HUMAN RACE — THE THIRD GLACIATION

THE partly known ancestors of the anthropoid apes and the unknown ancestors of man probably originated among the forests and flood-plains of southern Asia and early began to migrate westward into northern Africa and western Europe.

As early as Oligocene times a forerunner of the great apes (*Propliopithecus*), most nearly resembling the gibbons, appears in the desert bordering the Fayum in northern Egypt. Early in Miocene times true tree-living gibbons found their way into Europe and continued throughout the Pliocene in the forms known as *Pliopithecus* and *Pliohylobates*, the latter being a true gibbon in its proportions; it ranged northward into the present region of Germany. Another ape which early reached Europe is the *Dryopithecus;* it is found in Miocene times in southern France; the grinding-teeth suggest those of the orang, the jaw is deep and in some ways resembles that of the Piltdown man. A third ape (*Neopithecus*) occurs in the Lower Pliocene near Eppelsheim, in Germany, and is known only from a single lower molar tooth, which recalls the dentition of *Dryopithecus* and more remotely that of *Homo*. In the Pliocene of the Siwalik hills of Asia is found *Palæopithecus*, a generalized form which is believed to be related to the chimpanzee, the gorilla, and the gibbon; the upper premolars resemble those of man.

None of these fossil anthropoids either of Europe or of Asia can be regarded as ancestral to man, although both *Neopithecus* and *Dryopithecus* have been placed in or near the line of human ancestry by such high authorities as Branco and Gaudry. When *Dryopithecus* was first discovered by Lartet, Gaudry[1] considered it to be by far the most manlike of all the apes, even attributing to it sufficient intelligence for the working of flints, but fuller

Fig. 16. The gibbon is primitive in its skull and dentition, but extremely specialized in the adaptation of its limbs to arboreal life. Photograph from the New York Zoological Park.

knowledge of this animal has shown that some of the living anthropoids are more manlike than *Dryopithecus*. This animal is closely related to the ancestral stock of the chimpanzee, gorilla, and orang. The jaw, it is true, resembles that of the Piltdown man (*Eoanthropus*), but the grinding-teeth are much more primitive and there is little reason to think that it is ancestral to any human type.*

* A recent article by A. Smith Woodward describes the fourth known specimen of *Dryopithecus*, lately discovered in northern Spain (see Woodward, 1914.2).

Among these fossil anthropoids, as well as among the four living forms, we discover no evidence of direct relationship to man but very strong evidence of descent from the same ancestral stock. These proofs of common ancestry, which have already been observed in the existing races of man, become far more conspicuous in the ancient Palæolithic races; in fact, we cannot interpret the anatomy of the men of the Old Stone Age without

FIG. 17. The orang has a high rounded skull and long face. Photograph from the New York Zoological Park.

a survey of the principal characters of the existing anthropoid apes, the gibbon, the orang, the chimpanzee, and the gorilla.

The gibbon is the most primitive of living apes in its skull and dentition, but the most specialized in the length of its arms and its other extreme adaptations to arboreal life. As in the other anthropoids, the face is abbreviated, the narial region is narrow, *i. e.*, catarrhine, and the brain-case is widened, but the top of the skull is smooth, and the forehead lacks the prominent ridges above the orbits; thus the profile of the skull of the gibbon (Fig. 16) is more human than that of the other anthropoid apes. When on the ground the gibbon walks erect and is thus afforded the free use of its arms and independent movements of its fingers. In the brain there is a striking development of the centres of sight, touch, and hearing. It is these characteristics of the modern gibbon which preserve with rela-

FIG. 18. The chimpanzee. This figure illustrates the walking powers of the chimpanzee, the great length of the arms, and the abbreviation of the legs. Photograph from the New York Zoological Park.

tively slight changes the type of the original ancestor of man, as noted by Elliot Smith.[2]

The limbs of the orang are less elongated and less extremely specialized for arboreal life than those of the gibbon but more so than those of the chimpanzee and the gorilla. The skull is rounded and of great vertical height, with broad, bony ridges above the orbits and a great median crest on top of the skull in old males. The lower jaw of the orang is stout and deep, and, although used as a fighting weapon, the canine tusks are much less prominent than in either the gibbon, chimpanzee, or gorilla.

In the chimpanzee we observe the very prominent bony ridges above the eyes, like those in the Trinil and Neanderthal races of men. Of all the anthropoid apes the lower jaw of the chim-

FIG. 19. The chimpanzee. This figure shows certain facial characteristics which are preserved in the Neanderthal race of men. Note also the shortening of the thumb and the enlargement of the big toe. Photograph from the New York Zoological Park.

panzee most nearly resembles that of the Piltdown man. The prognathous or protruding tooth rows and receding chin suggest those in the Heidelberg, Piltdown, and Neanderthal races. When the chimpanzee is walking (Fig. 18) the arms reach down below the level of the knees, whereas in the higher races of man they reach only half-way down the thighs.

Thus, the fore limb, although much shorter than that of the gibbon, is relatively longer than that of any human race, recent or ancient. We observe also in the walking chimpanzee (Fig. 18)

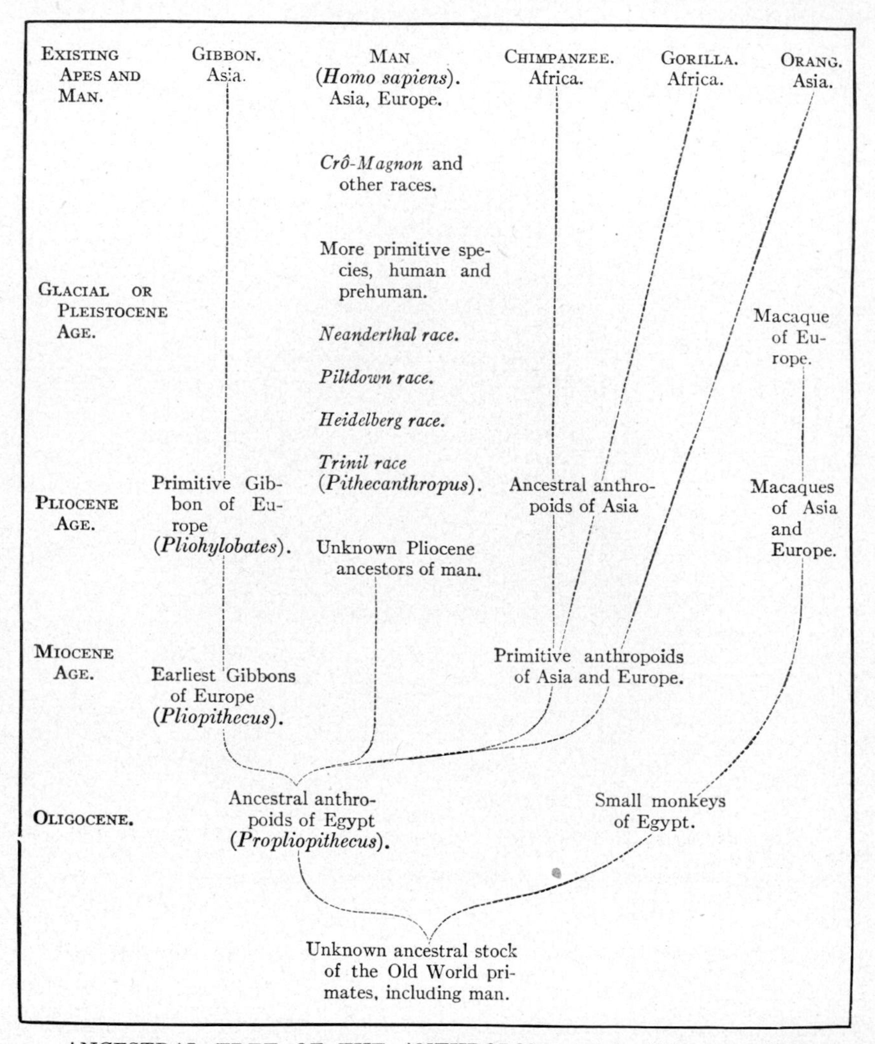

ANCESTRAL TREE OF THE ANTHROPOID APES AND OF MAN

From the unknown and ancestral stock of the anthropoid apes and man the GIBBON was the first to branch off in Oligocene times; the ORANG then branched off in a widely different direction. The stem of the CHIMPANZEE and of the GORILLA branched off at a more recent date and is more nearly allied to that of man. Five early human races have been found in Europe in Glacial or Pleistocene times, but no traces of other primates except the macaques, which are related to the lower division of the baboons, have been found in Europe in Pleistocene times. Modified after Gregory. (For latest discovery see Appendix, Note VII.)

that the upper part of the leg, the thigh-bone, or femur, is relatively long, while the lower part, the shin-bone, or tibia, is relatively short. Indeed, both in the arm and in the leg the upper bones are relatively long and the lower bones are relatively short. These proportions, which are inheritances of arboreal life, are in very marked contrast to those observed in the arms and

FIG. 20. The Gorilla. An immature female, about three years of age, showing none of the adult male characteristics. Photograph from the New York Zoological Park.

legs of the Neanderthal race of men, in which the limbs are of the terrestrial or walking type.

We observe also in the chimpanzee a contrast between the grasping power of the big toe, which is a kind of thumb, and the lack of that power in the hand, in which the thumb is nearly useless; in all apes this function is characteristic of the foot, in man of the hand alone. The *opposable thumb*, with its power of bringing the thumb against each of the fingers, is the one character which is lacking in every one of the anthropoid apes and which was early developed among the ancestors of man.

The skull of the chimpanzee is longer than that of the orang, the most prominent feature in the top view being the extreme protuberance of the orbits, which are surrounded by a supraorbital and circumorbital bony ridge, which is also strongly developed in the Neanderthal skull as well as in the *Pithecanthropus* or Trinil skull but, so far as we know, is entirely lacking in that of Piltdown. As in the orang and the gorilla, a crest develops along the middle of the top of the skull for the insertion of the powerful muscles of the jaws, a crest which is wholly wanting in the gibbon and probably wanting in all the true ancestors of man.

The gorilla illustrates in the extreme the specializations which are begun in the chimpanzee, and which are attributable to a

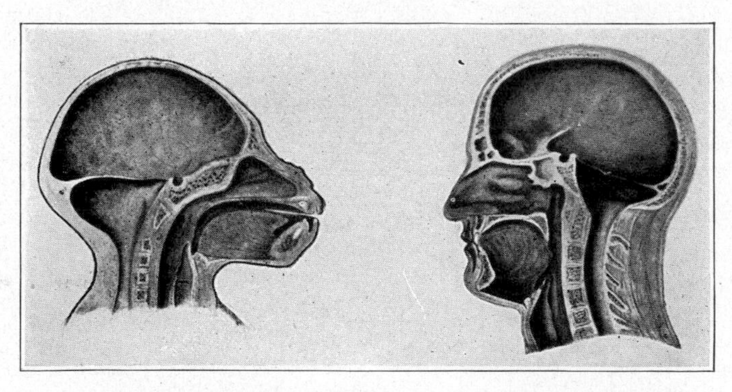

FIG. 21. Contrast of the projecting face (prognathism), retreating forehead, and small brain-case of a young gorilla, as compared with the vertical face, prominent nose, high forehead, and large brain-case of a high race of man. After Klaatsch.

life partly arboreal, partly terrestrial, with the skull and jaws used as powerful fighting organs. The head is lengthened by the forward growth of the muzzle into an extreme prognathism. The limbs and body of the gorilla show a departure from the primitive, slender-limbed, arboreal type of apes and are partly adapted to a bipedal, ground-dwelling habit.

As regards psychic evolution,[3] Elliot Smith observes that the arboreal mode of life of the early ancestors of man developed quick, alert, and agile movements which stimulated the progressive development of the posterior and lateral portions of the brain. The sense of smell had been well developed in a previous terrestrial life, but once these creatures left the earth and took to the trees, guidance by the olfactory sense was less essential, for life amidst the branches of the trees is most favorable to the high development of the senses of vision, touch, and hearing. Moreover, it demands an agility and quickness of movement that necessitate efficient motor centres in the brain to co-ordinate and control such actions as tree life calls for. The specialization of sight awakens curiosity to examine objects with greater mi-

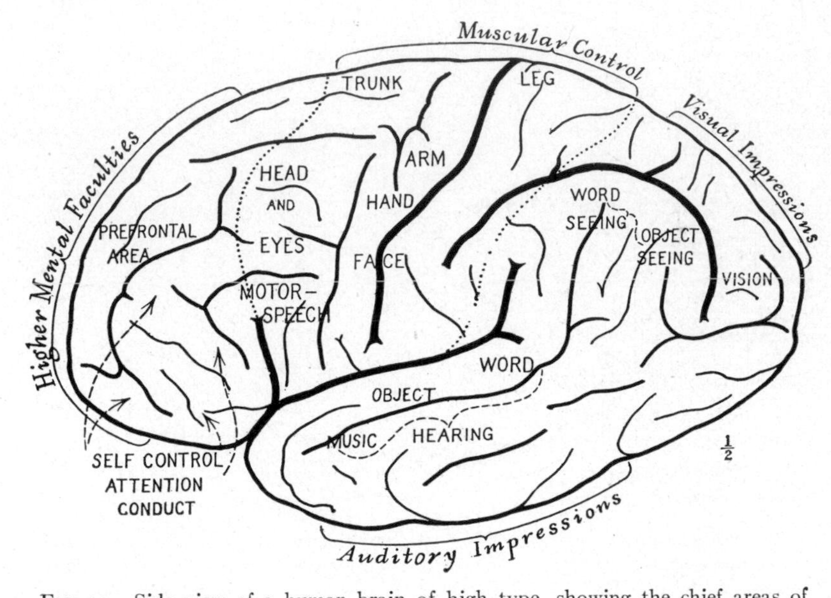

FIG. 22. Side view of a human brain of high type, showing the chief areas of muscular control and of the sensory impressions of sight and hearing, also the prefrontal area in which the higher mental faculties are centred. Modified after M. Allen Starr.

nuteness and guides the hands to more precise and skilled movements.

The anatomy of man is full of remote reminders of this original arboreal existence, which also explains the very large and early development of the posterior portions of the brain, in which the various senses of sight, touch, and hearing are located.

The first advance from arboreal to terrestrial life is marked by the power of walking more or less erect on the hind limbs and thus releasing the arms; this power is developed to a greater or less degree in all the anthropoid apes; with practice they become expert walkers. The additional freedom which the erect attitude gives to the arms and to the movements of the hands and the separate movements of the fingers is especially noticeable in the gibbon. The cultivation of the powers of the hand reacts upon the further growth and specialization of the brain; thus the brain and the erect attitude react upon each other. In

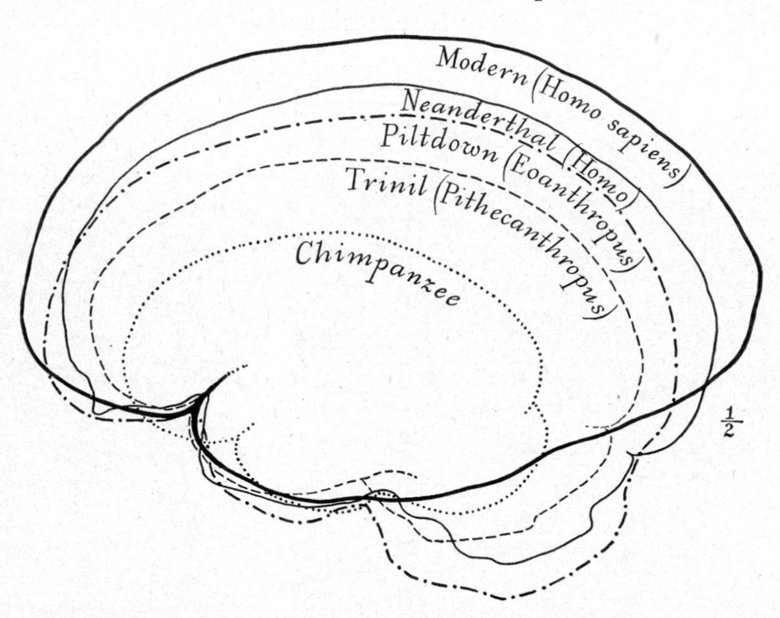

Fig. 23. The evolution of the brain. Outlines (side view) of typical human and prehuman brains, showing the early development of the posterior portions of the brain and the relatively late development of the anterior portions, the seat of the higher mental faculties.

the gibbon there is a marked increase in the size of those portions of the brain which supply the centres of touch, vision, and hearing.

Discussion as to how the ancestors of man were fashioned has chiefly dealt with the rival claims of four lines of structural evolution: first, the assumption of the *erect attitude;* second, the development of the *opposable thumb;* third, the *growth of the brain;* and fourth, the acquisition of the *power of speech.* The argument for the erect attitude suggested by Lamarck, and ably put by Munro[4] in 1893, indicates that the cultivation of skill with the hands and fingers lies at the root of man's mental supremacy. Elliot Smith's argument that the steady growth and specialization of the brain itself has been the chief factor in leading the ancestors of man step by step upward indicates that

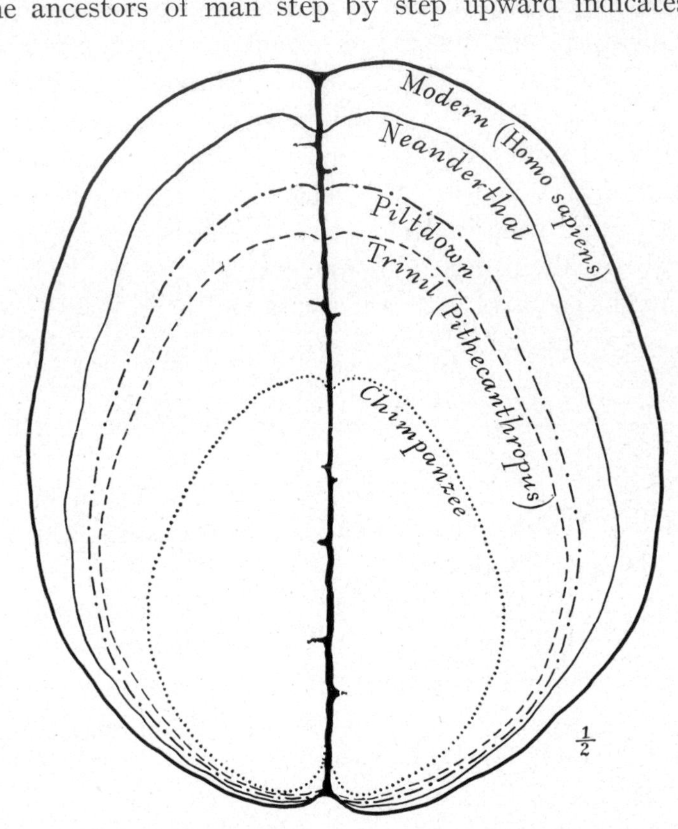

FIG. 24. The evolution of the brain. Outlines (top view) of typical human and prehuman brains, showing the narrow forebrain of the primitive type and the successive expansion of the seat of the higher mental faculties in the successive races.

such an advance as the erect attitude was brought about because the brain had made possible the skilled movements of the hands.

The true conception of prehuman evolution, which occurred during Miocene and Pliocene times, is rather that of the coincident development of these four distinctively human powers. It appears from the limb proportions in the Neanderthal race that the partly erect attitude and walking gait were assumed much earlier in geologic time than we formerly imagined. The intimate relation between the use of the opposable thumb and the development of the higher mental faculties of man is sustained to-day by the discovery that one of the best methods of developing the mind of the child is to insist upon the constant use of the hands, for the action and reaction between hand and brain is found to develop the mind. A similar action and reaction between foot and brain developed the erect gait which released the hand from its locomotive and limb-grasping function, and by the resultant perfecting of the motion of thumbs and fingers turned the hand into an organ ready for the increasing specialization demanded by the manufacture of flint implements.

This is the stage reached, we believe, in late Pliocene times in which the human ancestor emerges from the age of mammals and enters the age of man, the period when the prehistory of man properly begins. The attitude is erect, the hand has a well-developed opposable thumb, the centres of the brain relating to the higher senses and to the control of all the motions of the limbs, hands, and fingers are well developed. The power of speech may still be rudimentary. The anterior centres of the brain for the storing of experience and the development of ideas are certainly very rudimentary.

Change of Environment in Europe

Considering that the origin and development of any creature are best furthered by a struggle for existence sufficiently severe to demand the full and frequent exercise of its powers of mind and body, it is interesting to trace the sequence of natural events which prepared western Europe for the entrance of the earliest branches of the human race. The forests and plants portray even more vividly than the animals the changing conditions of the environment and temperature which marked the approach and various vicissitudes of the great Ice Age.

The forests of central France in Pliocene times, as well as those of the valley of the Arno in northern Italy, were very similar to the forests of the middle United States at the present time, comprising such trees as the sassafras, the locust, the honey-locust, the sumach, the bald cypress, and the tulip. Thus the regions which harbored the rich forest and meadow fauna of northern Italy in Upper Pliocene times abounded in trees familiar to-day in North and South Carolina, including even such distinctively American forms as the sweet gum (*Liquidambar styraciflua*), the sour gum (*Nyssa sylvatica*), and the bay, beside those above mentioned. To the south, along the Mediterranean, there also flourished trees incident to a more tropical climate, the bamboo, the sabal palm, and the dwarf fan-palm; most interesting is the presence of the sabal, which now flourishes in the subtropical rain forests of central Florida. The sequoia also was abundant. Toward the close of the Pliocene the first indications of the coming Glacial Epoch were a lowering of the temperature, and, in the higher mountainous areas perhaps, a beginning of the glacial stages.

The ancestors of the modern forests of Europe predominated in central France: the oak, the beech, the poplar, the willow, and the larch. It is these forests, which survived the vicissitudes of glacial times, that gave descent to the forests of Postglacial Europe, while all the purely American types disappeared from Europe and are now found only in the temperate regions of the United States.[5]

We have seen that few anthropoid apes have been discovered either in the Middle or Upper Pliocene of Europe; the gibbon-ape line disappears with the *Pliohylobates* of the Upper Pliocene. These animals are, however, rarely found in fossil form, owing to their retreat to the trees in times of flood and danger, so that we need not necessarily assume that the anthropoids had actually become extinct in France. The primates which are found in the Upper Pliocene belong to the lower types of the Old World monkeys, related to the living langur of India and to the macaque and baboon. The evidence, as far as it goes, indicates that the ancestors of man were at this time evolving in Asia and not in Europe. This evidence, nevertheless, would be completely offset if it could be proven that the eoliths, or primitive flints, found in various parts of Europe from Oligocene to Pleistocene times are really artifacts of human or prehuman origin.

The mammals of Europe in Pliocene times were derived by very remote migrations from North America and, more directly, from southern Asia. The Oriental element is very strong, including types of rhinoceroses now peculiar to Sumatra and southern Asia, numerous mastodons very similar to the south Asiatic types of the times, gazelles and antelopes, including types related to the existing elands, and primitive types of horses and of tapirs. Among the carnivores in Europe similar to south Asiatic species were the hyænas, the dog bears (*Hyænarctos*), the civets, and the pandas (*Ailurus*); there were also the sabre-tooth tigers and numerous other felines. In the trees were found the south Asiatic and north African monkeys; and in the forests the axis deer, now restricted to Asia. But the most distinctive African-Asiatic animal of this period was found in the rivers; namely, the hippopotamus, which arrived in Italy in the early Pliocene and ranged south by way of the Sicilian land bridge into northern Africa and east along the southern shores of the Black Sea to the Siwalik hills of India. Thus, many of the ancestors of what we have termed the African-Asiatic mammal group of Pleistocene times had already found their way into Europe early in Pliocene times. In middle and late Pliocene times there arrived three very important types of mammals which played a great rôle in the early Pleistocene. These are:

The true horses (*Equus stenonis*) of remote North American origin.

The first true cattle (*Leptobos elatus*), originating in southern Asia.

The true elephants, first *Elephas planifrons* and later *E. meridionalis*, better known as the southern mammoth, both originating in Asia.

The forests and river borders of the valley of the Arno, near Florence, contained all these African-Asiatic animals in Upper Pliocene times. Here they received their names which remind us of this region of Italy as it is to-day, such as the Etruscan rhinoceros (*Dicerorhinus etruscus*), the Florentine macaque (*Macacus florentinus*), Steno's horse (*Equus stenonis*), the Etruscan cattle (*Leptobos etruscus*), which was the earliest ox to reach Europe.

In Italy and France these African-Asiatic mammals were mingled with ancestors of the more hardy Eurasiatic forest and meadow group. Of these the most graceful were a variety of deer with very elaborate or many-branched antlers, hence known as the 'polycladine' deer. In the forests roamed the wild boars of Auvergne (*Sus arvernensis*), also the bears of Auvergne (*Ursus arvernensis*), lynxes, foxes, and wildcats. In the rivers swam the otter and the beaver, closely allied to existing forms. Among the rocks of the high hills were the pikas or tailless hares (*Lagomys*), also hamsters, moles, and shrews.

Many of the most characteristic animals of the dry modern plateaus of Africa had disappeared from Europe before the close of Pliocene times, namely, species of gazelles, antelopes, and the hipparion horses, all of which were adapted to the dry uplands or deserts of Africa. In the remaining *faune Pliocène récente* of French authors we find evidence that the Pliocene in all of western Europe closed with a moist, warm, temperate climate, with widespread forests and rivers interspersed with meadows favorable to the life of a great variety of browsing deer as well as of grazing elephants, horses and cattle. The flora of the Middle Pliocene as found at Meximieux indicates a mean annual temperature of 62° to 63° Fahr.

One of the proofs of the gradual lowering of temperature toward the close of Pliocene times in Europe is the southward retreat and disappearance of the apes and monkeys; the Upper Miocene gibbon is found as far north as Eppelsheim, near Worms, Germany; in Lower Pliocene times the monkeys and apes are found only in the forests of the south of France; in Upper

Pliocene times they are recorded only in the forests of northern Italy; the evidence, so far as it goes, indicates a gradual retreat toward the south.

Finally, at the end of the Pliocene there existed very close geographic relations eastward with the mammalian life of India by way of what was then the isthmus of the Dardanelles and southward with the mammalian life of Africa by way of the Sicilian land bridge. This would indicate that the long lines of *eastward* and *westward* migration were open and favorable to the arrival in western Europe of new migrants from the far east, including perhaps the most primitive races of man. *There is not the least evidence that Pliocene man or ancestors of man existed in Europe*, excepting such as may be afforded by the problematic eoliths, or most primitive flints.

The First Glaciation

In Upper Pliocene times cold marine currents[6] from the north began to flow along the southeastern coast of England, with indications of a gradually lowering temperature culminating at a time when the sea abounded in the arctic mollusks, which have been preserved in the 'Weybourn Crags,' a geologic formation along the coast of Norfolk. This arctic current was the herald of the First Glacial Stage.

It does not appear that a glacial cap of any considerable extent was formed in Great Britain at this stage, but about this time the first great ice-cap was formed in British North America west of Hudson Bay, which sent its ice-sheets as far south as Iowa and Nebraska. In the latter State forests of spruce and other coniferous species indicate the appearance of a cool temperate flora in advance of the glaciation. In the Swiss Alps the snow descended 1,200 meters below the present snow-line, and in Scandinavia and northern Germany the first great ice-sheets were formed from which flowed the glaciers and rivers conveying the 'Old Diluvium,' or the 'oldest drift.' Accompanying the cold wave along the eastern coast of England we note, in the famous fossil deposits known as the 'Forest Bed of Cromer,' which overlie the Weybourn Crags, the arrival from the north of the fir-tree (*Abies*). This is most significant, because it had hitherto been known only in the arctic region of Grinnell Land, and this was its first appearance in central Europe. Another

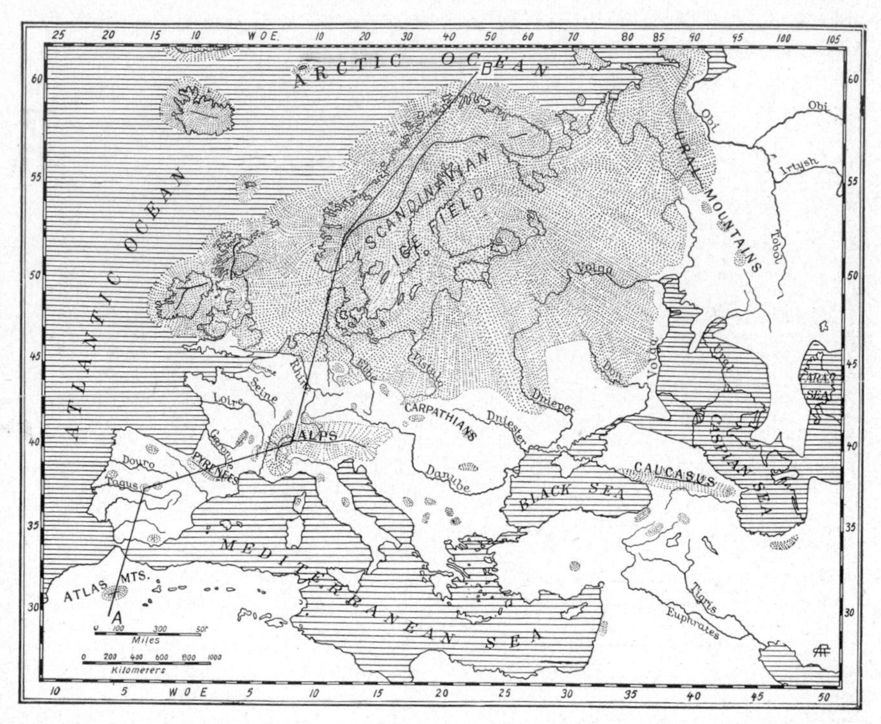

FIG. 25. The First (*Günz*) Glacial Stage was far less extensive than that in the above map, which shows Europe in the Second Glacial Stage, during the greatest extension of the ice-fields and glaciers (dots), a period of continental depression in which the Mediterranean, Black, and Caspian Seas were connected. The line from Scandinavia to the Atlas Mountains corresponds with the section shown in Fig. 13, p. 37. Drawn by C. A. Reeds, after James Geikie and Penck.

herald of northern conditions was the first occurrence of the musk-ox in England, which is attributed[7] to the 'Forest Bed' deposits.

While Great Britain was less affected at this time than other regions, there is no doubt as to the vast extent of the First Glacial Stage in British America, in Scandinavia, and in the Alps; in the latter region it has been termed 'the *Günz* stage' by Penck and Brückner. The 'drift' deposits have a general thickness of 98½ feet (30 m.), but they are largely covered and buried by those of the far more extensive Second Glacial Stage. The Scandinavian ice-sheet[8] not only occupied the basin of the Baltic but overflowed Scania—the southern part of Sweden—and extended as far south as Hamburg and Berlin. In the Alps the glaciers

FIG. 26. The musk-ox, belonging to the tundra region of the arctic circle, which is reported to have migrated as far south as the southern coast of England during the First (*Günz*) Glacial Stage.

passed down all the great mountain valleys to the low grounds of the foreland, implying a depression of the snow-line to 4,000 feet below its present level.

THE FIRST INTERGLACIAL STAGE. EOLITHS

Proofs that a prolonged cool wave passed over Britain during the first glaciation are seen in its after effects, namely, in the modernization of the forests and in the disappearance both in Britain and France of a very considerable number of animals which were abundant in Upper Pliocene times. Yet by far the greater part of the Pliocene mammal life survived, a fact which tends to show that, while very cold conditions of climate and great precipitation of moisture may have characterized the regions immediately surrounding the ice-fields, the remainder of western Europe at most passed through a prolonged cool period during the climax of the First Glacial Stage. This was followed during the First Interglacial by the return of a period somewhat warmer than the present.

This First Interglacial Stage is known as the *Norfolkian*, from the fact that it was first recognized in Europe in the deposits known as the 'Forest Bed of Cromer,' Norfolk, which contain rich records not only of the forests of the period, but of the noble forms of mammals which roamed over Great Britain and France in *Norfolkian* times. The forests of Norfolk, in latitude 52° 40′ N. mainly abounded in trees still indigenous to this region, such as the maple, elm, birch, willow, alder, oak, beech, pine, and spruce, a forest flora closely corresponding to that of the Norfolk and Suffolk coasts of England at the present time, although we find in this fossil flora several exotic species which give it a slightly different character.[9] From this tree flora Reid concludes that the climate of southeastern England was nearly the same as at present but slightly warmer.

We note especially that a very great change had taken place in the entire disappearance in these forests of the trees which in Pliocene times were common to Europe and America, as described above; in other words, the flora of Europe was greatly impoverished during the first cold wave.

In southern France, as at the present time, the interglacial climatic conditions were milder, for we find numerous species of plants, which are now represented in the Caucasus, Persia, southern Italy, Portugal, and Japan. Thus the First Interglacial Stage, which was a relatively short one, enjoyed a temperature now belonging about 4° of latitude farther south.

This First Interglacial Stage is also known as the *St.-Prestien*, because among the many localities in France and Italy which preserve the plant and mammal life of the times that of St. Prest, in the Paris basin, is the most famous. Here in 1863 Desnoyers[10] first reported the discovery of a number of mammal bones with incision lines upon them, which he considered to be the work of man. These deposits were regarded at the time as of Pliocene age, and this gave rise immediately to a wide-spread theory of the appearance of man as early as the Pliocene. The human origin of the incisions discovered by Desnoyers has long been a matter of dispute and is now regarded as very improbable. Similar lines may be of animal origin, namely, marks left by claws

FIG. 27. The giant deer (*Megaceros*), which first appears in western Europe during the First Interglacial Stage, probably as a migrant from the forested regions of Eurasia. After a painting by Charles R. Knight, in the American Museum of Natural History.

or teeth, or due to accidental pressure of sharp cutting surfaces. However, we do not pretend to express an opinion of any value as to the cause of these incisions. Supposed confirmation of the evidence of Desnoyers of the existence of Pliocene man was the alleged finding by Abbott of several worked flints, two *in situ*, in the 'Forest Bed of Cromer,' Norfolk. Many years later in similar deposits at St. Prest were discovered the supposed 'eoliths' which have been referred to the *Étage Prestien* by Rutot. The age of the St. Prest deposits is, therefore, a matter of the very highest interest and importance.

St. Prest is not Pliocene; it is rather the most ancient Pleistocene deposit in the basin of Paris,[11] and these incised mammal bones probably date from the First Interglacial Stage. The bed which has yielded the incised bones and the rich series of fossils consists of coarse river sands and gravels, forming part of a 'high terrace,' 98½ feet (30 m.) above the present level of the river Eure. This, like other 'high terraces,' contains a characteristic First Interglacial fauna, including the southern mammoth (*E. meridionalis*), and Steno's horse (*E. stenonis*). We also find here other very characteristic early Pleistocene mammals, such as the Etruscan rhinoceros (*D. etruscus*), the giant hippopotamus of early Pleistocene times (*H. major*), the giant beaver of the early Pleistocene (*Trogontherium*), three forms of the common beaver (*Castor*), and one of the bison (*Bison antiquus*). This mammalian life of St. Prest is very similar to that of Norfolk, England; to that of Malbattu in central France, Puy-de-Dôme; of Peyrolles, near the mouth of the Rhône, in southern France; of Solilhac near Puy; of Durfort, Gard; of Cajarc, Lot-et-Garonne; and finally to that of the valley of the Arno, in northern Italy.

One reason why certain authors, such as Boule and Depéret, have placed this stage in the Upper Pliocene is that the mammals include so many surviving Pliocene forms, such as the sabre-tooth tigers (*Machærodus*), the 'polycladine' deer with the elaborate antlers (*C. sedgwicki*), the Etruscan rhinoceros, and the primitive Steno's horse. But we have recently discovered that, with the exception of the 'polycladine' deer, these mammals certainly survived in Europe as late as the *Second* Interglacial Stage, and there is said to be evidence that some even persisted into the *Third* Interglacial Stage.

It is, therefore, the extinction or disappearance from Europe of many of the animals very abundant even in late Pliocene times which marks this fauna as early Pleistocene. Anthropoid apes are no longer found; indeed, there is no evidence of the survival of any of the primates, except macaques, which survive in the Pyrenees to late Pleistocene times; the tapir has entirely disappeared from the forests of Europe; but the most significant departure is that of the mastodon, which is believed to have lingered in north Africa and which certainly survived in America into very late Pleistocene times. The animal life of western Europe, like the plant life, has lost one part of its Pliocene aspect while retaining another part, both in its mammalian fauna and in its forest flora.

The living environment as a whole, moreover, takes on a novel aspect through the arrival, chiefly from the north, of the

Fig. 28. The sabre-tooth tiger (*Machærodus*), which survives from the Upper Pliocene and is widely distributed over western Europe until the Middle Pleistocene. After a painting by Charles R. Knight, in the American Museum of Natural History.

more hardy animals and plants which had been evolving for a very long period of time in the temperate forests and meadows of Eurasia to the northeast and northwest. From this Eurasiatic region came the stag, or red deer (*Cervus elaphus*), also the giant deer (*Megaceros*), and from the northerly swamps the broad-headed moose (*Alces latifrons*). The presence of members of the deer family (Cervidæ) in great numbers and representing many different lines of descent is one of the most distinctive features of First Interglacial times. Beside the new northerly forms mentioned above, there was the roe-deer (*Capreolus*), which still survives in Europe, but there is no longer any record of the beautiful axis deer (*Axis*), which has now retreated to southern Asia. The 'polycladine' deer, first observed in the valley of the Arno, is represented in First Interglacial times by Sedgwick's deer (*C. sedgwicki*), in Norfolk, and by the species *C. dicranius* of northern Italy, where there also occurs the 'deer of the Carnutes' (*C. carnutorum*).

We observe that browsing, forest-living, and river-living types predominate. Among the forest-frequenting carnivores were the wolverene, the otter, two kinds of bear, the wolf, the fox, and the marten; another forest dweller was a wild boar, related to the existing *Sus scrofa* of Europe.

Thus in the very beginning of Pleistocene times the forests of Europe were full of a wild life very similar to that of prehistoric times, mingled with which was the Oriental element, the great elephants, rhinoceroses, and hippopotami connecting Europe with the far east. Among these eastern migrants in the early Pleistocene were two new arrivals, the primitive wild cattle (*Bos primigenius*), and the first of the bison (*Bison priscus*).

The theoretical map of western Europe during First Interglacial times (Fig. 12, also Fig. 56) enables us to understand these migrations from the northeast and from the Orient. As indicated by the sunken river channels discovered on the old continental shelf, the coast-line extended far to the west to the borders of the continental plateau which is now sunk deep beneath the ocean; the British Isles were separated from France not by the sea but by a broad valley, while the Rhine, with the Thames as a western tributary flowed northward over an extensive flood-plain, which is the present floor of the North Sea basin.[12] It is not improbable that the rich mammalian life deposits in the 'Forest Bed of Cromer,' Norfolk, were washed down by tributaries of this ancient Rhine River.

In all the great rivers of this enlarged western Europe occurred the hippopotami, and along the river borders and in the forests browsed the Etruscan rhinoceros. Among the grazing and meadow-living forms of the Norfolk country of Britain were species of wild cattle (*Bos*, *Leptobos*), together with two species of horses, including a lighter form resembling Steno's horse (*E. stenonis cocchi*) of the Val d'Arno and a heavier type probably belonging to the forests. The giant elephant of this period is the southern mammoth (*E. meridionalis trogontherii*), a somewhat specialized descendant of the Pliocene southern mammoth of the valley of the Arno; this animal is best known from a superb specimen discovered at Durfort (Fig. 42) and preserved in the Paris Museum. It is said to have attained a height of over 12 feet as compared with 11 feet 3 inches, the height of the largest existing African elephants. It is probable that all these south Asiastic migrants into Europe were partially or wholly covered with hair, in adaptation to the warm, temperate climate of the summers and the cool winters. To the south, in the still milder climate of Italy, the arrival of another great species, known as the 'ancient' or 'straight-tusked elephant' (*E. antiquus*), is recorded. This animal had not yet reached France or Britain.

Preying upon the defenseless members of this heterogeneous fauna were the great machærodonts, or sabre-tooth tigers, which ranged over Europe and northern Africa and into Asia. It does not appear that the true lions (*Felis leo*) had as yet entered Europe.

An intercommunication of life over a vast area extending 6,000 miles from the Thames valley on the west to India on the southeast is indicated by the presence of six or more similar or related species of elephants and rhinoceroses. Twenty-five hundred miles southeast of the foot-hills of the Himalayas similar herds of mammals, but in an earlier stage of evolution, roamed over the island of Java, which was then a part of the Asiatic mainland.

The Trinil Race of Java

The human interest in this great life throng lies in the fact that the migration routes opened by these great races of animals may also have afforded a pathway for the earliest races of men. Thus the discovery of the Trinil race in central Java, amidst a fauna closely related to that of the foot-hills of the Himalayas and more remotely related to that of southern Europe, has a more direct bearing upon our subject than would at first appear.

On the Bengawan River in central Java, a Dutch army surgeon, Eugen Dubois, had been excavating for fossils in the hope of finding prehuman remains. In the year 1891 he found near Trinil a deposit of numerous mammal bones, including a single upper molar tooth which he regarded as that of a new species of

FIG. 29. Restoration of *Pithecanthropus*, the Java ape-man, modelled by the Belgian artist Mascré, under the direction of Professor A. Rutot, of Brussels, Belgium.

ape. On carefully clearing away the rock the top of a skull appeared at about a meter's distance from the tooth. Further excavation at the close of the rainy season brought to light a second molar tooth and a left thigh-bone about 15 meters from the spot where the skull was found, imbedded and fossilized in the same manner. These scattered parts were described by Dubois[13] in 1894 as the type of *Pithecanthropus erectus*,* a term signifying the

* There is a vast *Pithecanthropus* literature. That chiefly utilized in the present description includes Dubois,[13] Fischer,[14] Schwalbe,[15] Büchner.[16]

upright-standing ape-man. The specific term *erectus* refers to the thigh-bone, of which the author observes: "We must therefore conclude that the femur of *Pithecanthropus* was designed for the same mechanical functions as that of man. The two articulations and the mechanical axis correspond so exactly to the same parts in man that the law of perfect harmony between the form and function of a bone will necessitate the conclusion that this

FIG. 30. The Solo or Bengawan River in central Java. Scene of the discovery of the type specimen of *Pithecanthropus erectus* in 1894. After Selenka and Blanckenhorn. Compare map (Fig. 32, p. 75).

fossil creature had the same upright posture as man and likewise walked on two legs. . . . From this it necessarily follows that the creature had the free use of the upper extremities—now superfluous for walking—and that these last were no doubt already far advanced in that line of differentiation which developed them in mankind into tools and organs of touch. . . . From a study of the femur and skull it follows with certainty that this fossil cannot be classified as simian. . . . And, as with the skull, so also with the femur, the differences that separate *Pithecanthropus* from man are less than those distinguishing it from the highest anthropoid. . . . Although far advanced in the course of differentiation, this Pleistocene form had not yet attained to the human type. *Pithecanthropus erectus* is the transition form between man and the anthropoids which the laws of evolution teach us must have existed. He is the ancestor of man."

Thus the author placed *Pithecanthropus* in a new family, of the order Primates, which he named the Pithecanthropidæ.

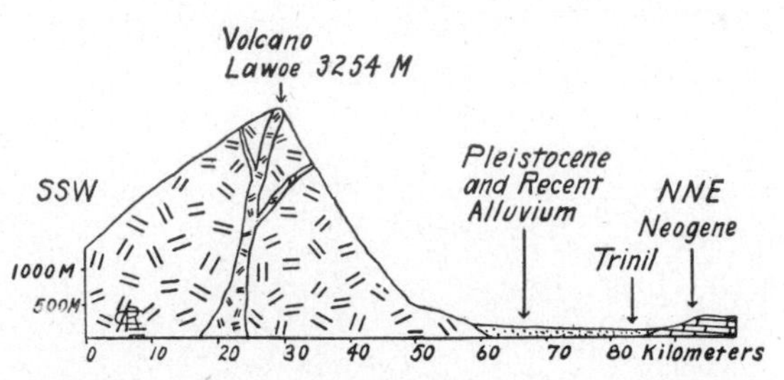

FIG. 31. Geological section of the volcano of Lawoe in the Solo River basin. Drawn by C. A. Reeds.

The geologic age of the bones referred to is a matter of first importance. The remains of *Pithecanthropus* lay in a deposit about one meter in thickness, consisting of loose, coarse, tufaceous sandstones, below this a stratum of hard, blue-gray clay, and under that marine breccia. Above the *Pithecanthropus* layer were the 'Kendeng' strata, a many-layered tufaceous sandstone, about 15 meters in thickness. This geologic series was considered by Dubois and others to be of late Tertiary or Pliocene age; *Pithecanthropus* accordingly became known as the long-awaited 'Pliocene ape-man.' Subsequent researches by expert geologists have tended to refer the age to the early Pleistocene.[17] According to Elbert[18] the Kendeng strata overlying the *Pithecanthropus* layer correspond to an early pluvial period of low temperature and, in point of time, to the

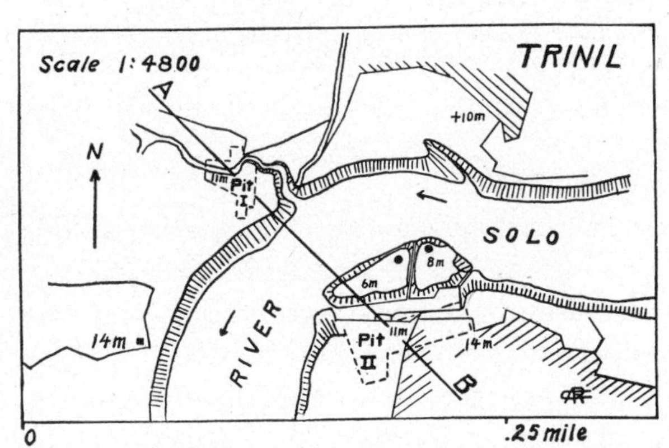

FIG. 32. Map of the Solo River, showing the *Pithecanthropus* discovery site, also two excavations (Pit No. 1, Pit No. 2) in the ancient gravel of the river-bottom, made by the Selenka-Blanckenhorn expedition of 1907. After Selenka and Blanckenhorn.

Ice Age of Europe. For even in Java one can distinguish three divisions of the Pleistocene period, including the first period of low temperature to which the *Pithecanthropus* layer is referred.

The fossil mammals contained in the *Pithecanthropus* layer have also been thoroughly studied,[19] and they tend to confirm the original reference to the uppermost Pliocene. They yield a very rich fauna similar to that of the Siwalik hills of India, including the porcupine, pangolin, several felines, the hyæna, and

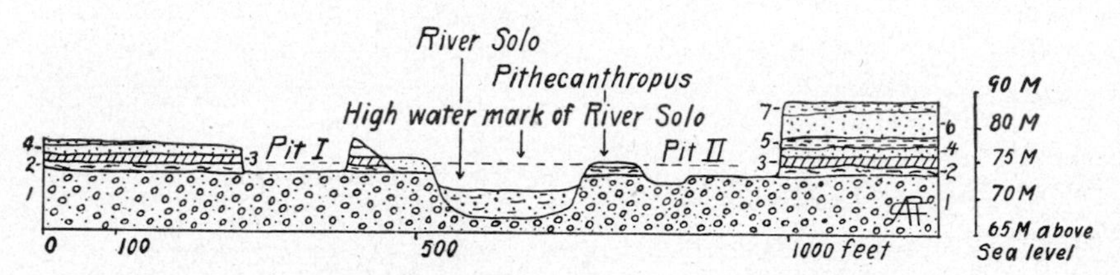

FIG. 33. Section corresponding to line *A–B* in Fig. 32, showing the river-drift gravels and sands at the point where the skull-top of *Pithecanthropus* was found. Drawn by C. A. Reeds.

Recent	7 River wash, blue-black clay.
Pleistocene	6 Light-colored sandstone, like tuff.
	5 Gray tuff with balls of clay, fresh-water shells.
	4 White streaked sandstone resembling tufa.
	3 Blue-black clay with plant remains.
	2 Bone-bearing stratum. *Pithecanthropus.*
	1 Lahar conglomerate.

the otter. Among the primates beside *Pithecanthropus* there is a macaque. Among the larger ungulates are two species of rhinoceros related to existing Indian forms, the tapir, the boar, the hippopotamus, the axis and rusa deer, the Indian buffalo, and wild cattle. It is noteworthy that three species of late Pliocene elephants, all known as *Stegodon*, and especially the species *Stegodon ganeza*, occur, as well as *Elephas hysudricus*, a species related to *E. antiquus*, or the straight-tusked elephant, which entered Europe in early Pleistocene times. Fossils of the same animals are found in the foot-hills of the Himalayas of India, about 2,500 miles distant to the northwest. The India deposits are considered of uppermost Pliocene age,[20] for this is the closing life period of the upper Siwaliks of India.

Certainly Java was then a part of the Asiatic continent, and similar herds of great mammals roamed freely over the plains from the foot-hills of the Himalaya Mountains to the borders of the ancient Trinil River, while similar apes inhabited the forests. At this time the orang may have entered the forests of Borneo, which are at present its home; it is the only ape thus far found in the uppermost Pliocene of India. We may, therefore, anticipate the discovery, at any time, in India of a race similar to *Pithecanthropus*.

The geologic age of the Trinil race is, therefore, to be considered as late Pliocene or early Pleistocene.

This great discovery of Dubois aroused wide-spread and heated discussion, in which the foremost anatomists and palæontologists of the world took part. Some regarded the skull as that of a giant gibbon, others as prehuman, and still others as a transition form. We may form our own opinion, however, from a fuller understanding of the specimens themselves, always keeping in mind that it is a question whether the femur and the skull belong to the same individual or even to the same race. First, we are struck by the marked resemblance which the top of the skull bears, both on viewing it from the side and from above, to that of the Neanderthal race. This fully justifies the opinion of the anatomist Schwalbe[21] that the skull of *Pithecanthropus* is nearer to that of Neanderthal man than to that of even the

FIG. 34. The top (1) and side (1*a*) views of the skull-top of *Pithecanthropus erectus*. After Dubois. One-third life size.

highest of the anthropoid apes. As measured by Schwalbe, the index of the height of the cranium (*Kalottenhöheindex*) may be compared with others as follows:

Lowest human race	52 per cent.
Neanderthal man	40.4 per cent.
Pithecanthropus, or Trinil race	34.2 per cent.

This accords with the estimate of the brain capacity* of 855 c.cm. (Dubois) as compared with 1,230 c.cm., the smallest brain

Fig. 35. Head of chimpanzee—front and side views—exhibiting a head of somewhat similar shape to that of *Pithecanthropus*, with prominent eyebrow ridges, but much smaller brain capacity. Photograph from the New York Zoological Park.

capacity found in a member of the Neanderthal race. Second, as seen from above, we are struck with the great length of the calvarium as compared with its breadth, the cephalic index or ratio of breadth to length being 73.4 per cent (Schwalbe) as compared with 73.9 per cent in the Neanderthal type skull; this dolichocephaly accords with the fact that all of the earliest human races thus far found are long-headed, although according to Schwalbe[22] all anthropoids are broad-headed. This is a very important distinction. The third feature is the prominence and width of the bony eyebrow ridges above the orbits, which are almost as great as in the chimpanzee and greatly exceed those

* In the Trinil skull as restored by McGregor (Fig. 36) the cranial capacity is 900 c.cm.

of the Neanderthal race and of the modern Australian. The profile of the Trinil head restored by McGregor (Fig. 38) exhibits this prominent bony ridge and the low, retreating forehead. In the latest opinion of Schwalbe[23] *Pithecanthropus* may be regarded as one of the direct ancestors of Neanderthal man and even of the highest human species, *Homo sapiens*. He also considers that when the lower jaw of the Trinil race becomes

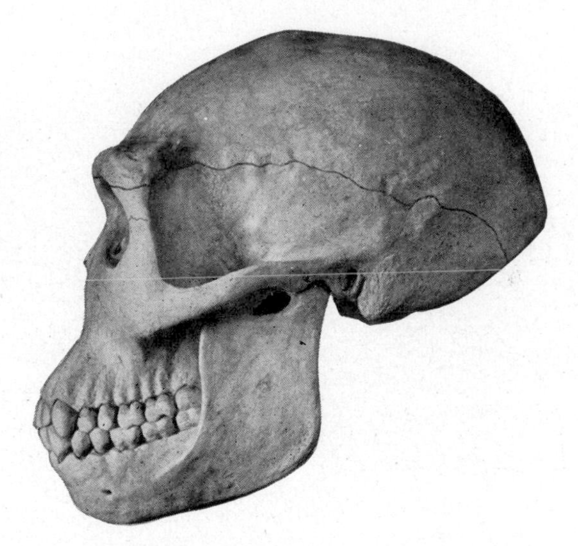

FIG. 36. Profile of the skull of *Pithecanthropus*, as restored by J. H. McGregor. 1914. One-third life size.

known, it will be found to be very similar to that of the Heidelberg man, the final conclusion being that *Pithecanthropus* and the nearly allied Heidelberg man may be regarded as the common ancestors of the Neanderthal race, on the one hand, and of the higher races on the other. There are, however, reasons for excluding *Pithecanthropus* from the direct ancestral line of the higher races of man.

This prehuman stage has, none the less, a very great significance in the developmental history of man. In our opinion it is the very stage which, theoretically, we should anticipate finding in the dawn of the Pleistocene. A similar view is taken by Büchner,[24] who presents in an admirable diagram (Fig. 117) the result of his comparison of twelve different characters in the skulls of *Pithecanthropus*, the Neanderthals, the Australians, and the Tasmanians. One of the main objects of Büchner's research was a very detailed comparison of the Trinil skull with that of the lowly and now extinct Tasmanian race, which, we observe

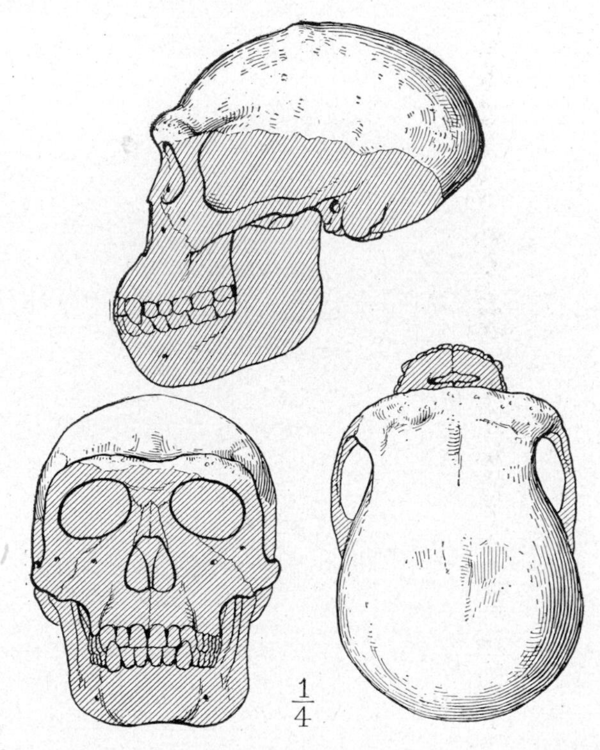

FIG. 37. Three views of the skull of *Pithecanthropus*, as restored by J. H. McGregor, showing the original (shaded) and restored (black lines) portions. About one-quarter life size.

in the diagram, occupies a position only a little higher than that of the Spy-Neanderthal race.

If the femur belongs with the skull, the Trinils were a tall race, reaching a height of 5 feet 7 inches as compared with 5 feet 3 inches in the Neanderthals. The thigh-bone (Fig. 122) has a very slight curvature as compared with that of any of the apes or lemurs, and in this respect is more human; it is remarkably elongate (455 mm.), surpassing that of the Neanderthals; the shin-bone (tibia) was probably correspondingly short. The two upper grinding-teeth preserved are much more human than those of the gibbon, but they do not resemble those of man closely enough to positively confirm the prehuman theory. Dubois observes:[25] "That the tooth belongs to some hominid form needs no

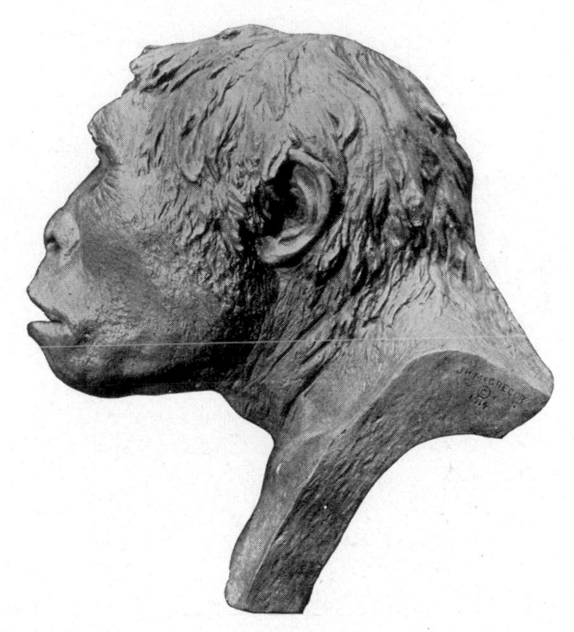

FIG. 38. Profile view of the head of *Pithecanthropus*, the Java ape-man, after a model by J. H. McGregor. One-quarter life size.

further demonstration. Aside from its size and the greater roughness of the grinding surface, it differs from the human grinder in that the less developed cusp of *Pithecanthropus* is the posterior cusp next the cheek, while in man it is generally the posterior cusp next the tongue. The simplification of the crown and the root of the Trinil grinder is quite as extensive as it usually is in man."

Various efforts have been made to supplement the scattered and scanty materials collected by Dubois. The Selenka expedition of 1907–8 brought back a human left lower molar as the only result of an express search for more *Pithecanthropus* remains.

Dubois is also said to possess the fragment of a primitive-looking lower jaw from the range known as the Kendeng Hills, at the southern base of which lies the village of Trinil.

It remains for us to consider the stage of psychic evolution attained by the Trinil race, and this naturally turns upon the

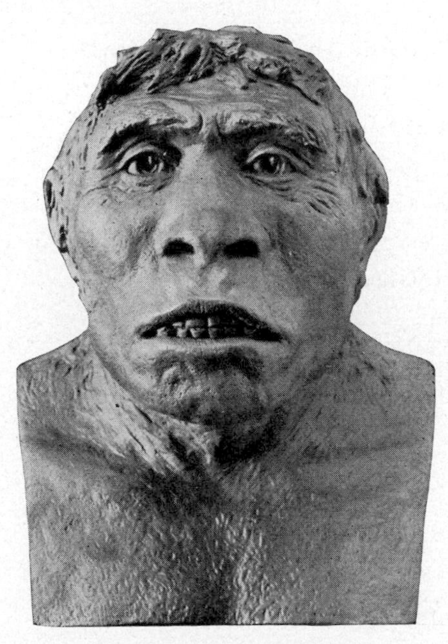

FIG. 39. Front view of the head of *Pithecanthropus*, the Java ape-man, after a model by J. H. McGregor. One-quarter life size.

erect attitude and what little is known of the size and proportions of the brain.

The assumption of the erect attitude is not merely a question of learning to balance the body on the hinder extremities.[26] It involves changes in the interior of the body, the loss of the tail, the freeing of the arms, and the establishment of the diaphragm as the chief muscle of respiration. The thigh-bone of *Pithecanthropus* is so much like that of man as to support the theory that the erect position may have been assumed by the ancestors of man as early as Oligocene times. It would appear that *Pithecanthropus* had free use of the arms and it is possible that the control of the thumb and fingers had been cultivated, perhaps in the fashioning of primitive implements of wood and stone. The discovery of the use of wood as an implement and weapon probably preceded that of the use of stone.

Elliot Smith describes this stage of development as follows:[27] ". . . The emancipation of the hands from progression threw the whole responsibility upon the legs, which became more efficient for their purpose as supports once they lost their prehensile powers and became elongated and specialized for rapid progression. Thus the erect attitude became stereotyped and fixed and the limbs specialized, and these upright simians emerged from their ancestral forests in societies, armed with sticks and stones and with the rudiments of all the powers that eventually enabled them to conquer the world. The greater exposure to danger which these more adventurous spirits encountered once they emerged in the open, and the constant struggles these first semihuman creatures must have had in encounters with definite enemies, no less than with the forces of Nature, provided the factors which rapidly weeded out those unfitted for the new conditions and by natural selection made real men of the survivors."

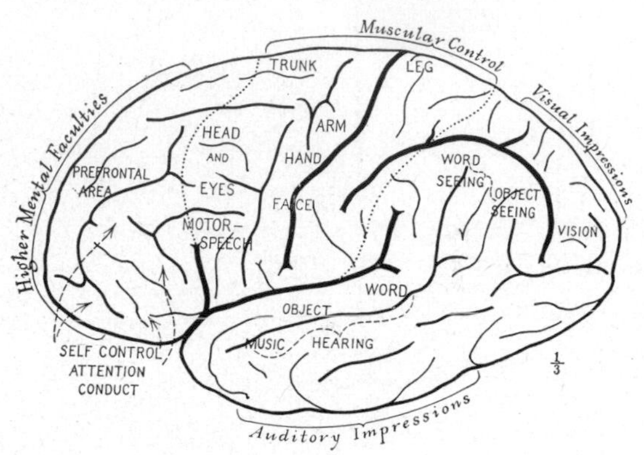

FIG. 40. Side view of brain of high type, illustrating the contrast between the motor, sensory, and ideational centres in a high type of modern brain; and Elliot Smith's characterization of the probable centres in the *Pithecanthropus* type of brain. Modified after M. Allen Starr.

The undeveloped forehead of *Pithecanthropus* and the diminutive frontal area of the brain indicate that the Trinil race had a limited faculty of profiting by experience and accumulated tradition, for in this prefrontal area of the brain are located the powers of attention and of control of the activities of all other parts of the brain. In the brain of the ape the sensory areas of touch, taste, and vision predominate, and these are well developed in *Pithecanthropus*. The central area of the brain, which is the storehouse of the memories of actions and of the feelings associated with them, is also well developed, but the prefrontal area, which is the seat of the faculty of profiting by experience or of recalling the consequences of previous responses to experience, is developed to a very limited degree.[28] Thus, while the brain of *Pithecanthropus* is estimated at 855–900 c.cm., as compared with 600 c.cm. of the largest simian brain, and 930 c.cm. of the smallest brain recorded in the lower members of the human race, it indicates a very low stage of intelligence.

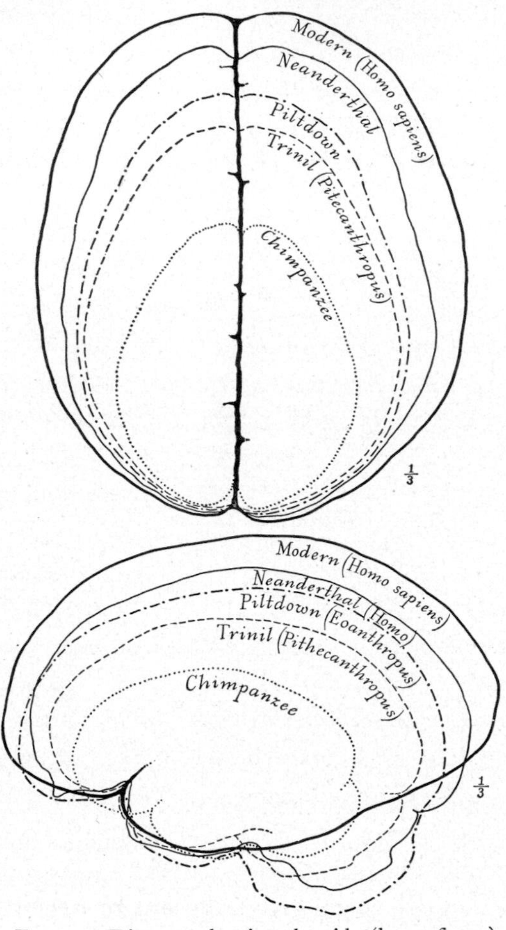

FIG. 41. Diagram showing the side (lower figure) and top (upper figure) views of the outline of the *Pithecanthropus* brain as compared with that of the chimpanzee and the higher human types of the Piltdown, Neanderthal, and modern races.

Absence of Palæoliths and Presence of Eoliths in Western Europe

Returning to First Interglacial conditions in Europe, we observe that the river courses flowed through the same valleys as at present but that in early glacial times the channels were far broader and were elevated from 100 to 150 feet above the present relatively narrow river levels. The vast floods of the succeeding glaciation filled these valleys, but some of the 'high terraces' were already formed. It is extremely important to note that Pre-Chellean flints or true palæoliths have never been found in the sands or gravels of these 'high terraces.'

Eoliths found on this 'high-terrace' level at St. Prest belong to the Prestien culture of Rutot,[29] who regards this station as of Upper Pliocene age. These, like other supposed Eolithic flints, are very rough, but, rude as they are, they generally exhibit one part shaped as if to be grasped by the hand, while the other part is edged or pointed as for cutting. It is generally admitted that these flints are mostly of accidental shapes, and there has been little or no proof of their being fashioned by human hands. On this point Boule[30] observes: "As to the eoliths, I have combated the theory not only because it seems to me improbable but because a long geological experience has shown me that it is often impossible to distinguish stones split, cut, or retouched by purely physical agents from certain products of rudimentary workmanship."

On the other side, it is interesting at this point to quote the words of MacCurdy:[31] "My opinion, based on personal experience, . . . is that the existence of a primitive industry, antedating what is commonly accepted as Palæolithic, has been established. This industry occurs as far back as the Upper Miocene and continues on through the Upper Tertiary into and including the Lower Quaternary. The distinguishing characters of the industry remain but little changed throughout the entire period, the subdivision of the period into epochs being based on stratigraphy [geologic stages] and not on industrial characters. The requirements in the way of tools being very simple and the supply of material in the way of natural flakes and fragments of flint being very plentiful, the inventive powers of the population remained dormant for ages. Hammer and knife were the original tools. Both were picked up ready-made. A sharp-edged, natural flake served for one, and a nodule or fragment served for the other. When the edge of the flake became dulled by use, the piece was either thrown away or the edge was retouched for further use. If hammer or flake did not admit of being held comfortably in the hand, the troublesome points or edges were removed or reduced by chipping. The stock of tools increased slowly with the slowly growing needs. As these multiplied and the natural supply of raw material diminished, the latter was supplemented by the manufacture of artificial flakes. When the lesson of associating definite forms of implements with definite uses was learned, special types arose, notably the amygdaloid implement and the poniard. Then came the transition from the Eolithic to the Palæolithic, a stage that has been so thoroughly investigated by Rutot."

It is not improbable that the Trinil race was in a stage of Eolithic culture; it is highly probable that the prehuman races of this very remote geologic age used more than one weapon of wood and stone.

The Great Second Glaciation

(Fig. 25, p. 65)

In early Pleistocene times a general *elevation* of southern Europe united the islands of the Mediterranean with Europe on the north and with Africa on the south, forming broad land connections between the two continents which afforded both northward and southward migration routes. At this time certain characteristically African mammals, such as the straight-tusked elephant and the lion, were probably finding their way north; Sicily at this time gained its large fauna of elephants and hippopotami, and the island of Malta was connected with the mainland, as well as the easterly islands of Cyprus and Crete. It appears probable that the connection between the Italian mainland and Malta was renewed more than once.

The approach of the second glaciation is indicated along the southeast coast of Great Britain by the *subsidence* of the land and the rise of the sea, accompanied by a fresh arctic current, bringing with it an invasion of arctic mollusks which were deposited in a layer of marine beds directly over those which contain the

Pl. III. *Pithecanthropus erectus*, the ape-man of Java. Antiquity estimated at 500,000 years. After the restoration modelled by J. H. McGregor. It is not improbable that the prehuman races of this remote geologic age used more than one natural weapon of wood or stone, the latter of the accidental 'Eolithic' type.

rich warm fauna and flora of the 'Forest Bed of Cromer,' Norfolk.[32] It also appears probable that a cold northern current swept along the western coasts of Europe, and Geikie estimates that a lowering of temperature occurred of not less than 20° Fahr., a change as great as is now experienced in passing from the south of England to the North Cape.

The second glaciation was by far the greatest both in Europe and America. In the region of the Pyrenees, which at the very much later period of the Third Interglacial Stage became a favorite country with Palæolithic man, there were glaciers of vast extent. This is realized by comparison with present conditions. The largest of the present glaciers of the Pyrenees is only 2 miles in length and terminates at a height of 7,200 feet above the sea. During the greatest glaciation the snow appears to have descended 4,265 feet below its present level. From the Pyrenees through the Gallego valley into Spain there flowed a glacier 38 miles in length, while to the north the glacier in the valley of the Garonne flowed for a distance of 45 miles to a point near Montréjeau. Even in its lower reaches this glacier was over half a mile in thickness. To the east was a glacier 38 miles in length, filling the valley of the Ariège and covering the sites of such great Palæolithic caverns as that of Niaux; it is probable that at this time the formation of this cavern began. That these glaciers were all prior to the period of the Lower Palæolithic Acheulean culture is proven by the fact that Acheulean implements are frequently met with lying on the surface of the moraines laid down by these ancient ice-floes.[33]

To the north was the vast Scandinavian ice-field, which swept over Great Britain and beyond the valleys of the Rhine, Elbe, and Vistula, reaching nearly to the Carpathians. Even the lesser mountain chains were capped with glaciers, including the Atlas Mountains in northern Africa.

In North America from the great centre west of Hudson Bay the ice-cap extended its drift southward into Missouri, Iowa, Kansas, and Nebraska, beyond the limits of earlier and subsequent glaciations.

The materials of the chief 'high terraces' of the great river-valleys of western Europe were deposited at this time.

Life of the Warm Second Interglacial Stage

The long warm period which followed the great glaciation is remarkable in presenting the first proofs of the presence of man in western Europe. It is the period of the Heidelberg race of man (*Homo heidelbergensis*), known only from a single jaw discovered by Schoetensack in the Mauer sands near Heidelberg, in 1907. No other proofs of the existence of man have been found in any of the deposits which took place during this vast interval of geologic time, unless we accept the theory of Penck and of Geikie that the Pre-Chellean and Chellean quarries of the River Somme belong in the Second Interglacial Stage.

The vast duration of this interglacial time is evidenced both in Europe and America by the deep cutting and wearing away of the 'drifts' brought down by the second glaciation. Penck believes that this 'long warm stage' represents a greater period of time than the entire interval between the third glaciation and the present time. The climate immediately following the retreat of the glaciers was cool and moist in the glaciated regions, but this was followed by such a prolonged period of heat and dryness that the glaciers on the Alps withdrew to a point far above their present limits.

In one of the old 'high terraces' of the River Inn, in the north Tyrol, is a deposit containing the prevailing forest flora of the period, from which Penck concludes that the climate of Innsbruck was 2° C. higher than it is at the present time. Corresponding with this the snow-line stood 1,000 feet above its present level, and the Alps, save for the higher peaks, were almost completely denuded of ice and snow. A characteristic plant is the Pontic alpine rose (*Rhododendron ponticum*), which flourishes now in an annual temperature of 57°–65° Fahr.,[34] indicating that the climate of Innsbruck was as genial as that of the Italian slopes of the Alps to-day. This rhododendron is now found in the Caucasus. Other southern species of the time were a buckthorn, related to a species now living in the Canary Islands, and the box. There were also more hardy plants, including the fir (*Pinus sylvestris*), spruce, maple, willow, yew, elm, beech, and mountain-ash. The forests of the same period in Provence were, for the most part, similar to those now found in that region; out of thirty-seven species twenty-nine still occur in this part of southern France. On the whole, the aspect of southern France at this time was surprisingly modern. The forests included oaks, elms, poplars, willows, lindens, maples, sumachs, dogwood, and hawthorn. Among the climbing plants were the vine and the clematis. Here also were some forms which have since retreated to the south, such as species of the sweet bay and laurel which are now confined to the Canary Islands. The great humidity of the time is indicated by the presence of certain species of conifers which require considerable moisture. As in First Interglacial times, the presence of the fig indicates mild winters.

It is difficult to imagine forests of this modern character, which farther northward included a number of still more temperate and hardy species, as the setting of the great African and Asiatic life that roamed all over western Europe at this time. It was the presence of hippopotami, elephants, and rhinoceroses which gave to Lyell, Evans, and other early observers the impression that a tropical temperature and vegetation were characteristic of this long life period. These animals were formerly regarded as proofs of an almost tropical climate, but the more trustworthy evidence of the forests, strengthened by that of the presence of very numerous hardy types of forest and meadow animals, has set aside all the early theories as to extremely warm temperatures during Second Interglacial times.

The remains of what is still conveniently known as the '*faune chaude*,' or warm fauna, are chiefly found in the sands and gravels of the ancient beds of the Neckar, Garonne, and Thames, and other rivers of the north and south, also in Essex, England. The most surprising fact is that the mammal life of western Europe remained entirely unchanged by the vast second glaciation just described; the few extinctions which occurred as well as a number of new arrivals may be attributed to new geographical connections with Africa on the south and to the steady progress of migration from the far east.

Fig. 42. The hippopotamus (*H. major*) and the southern mammoth (*E. meridionalis trogontherii*), a pair of mammals which enjoyed a similar range over western Europe from the close of the Pliocene until the middle of Third Interglacial times, when their remains are found associated with flints of Pre-Chellean, Chellean, and early Acheulean age. One-sixtieth life size. Drawn by Erwin S. Christman.

There were four very important and distinctive new arrivals from the African-Asiatic world, namely, the straight-tusked or ancient elephant (*E. antiquus*), the broad-nosed rhinoceros (*D. merckii*), the African lion (*Felis leo*), and the African hyæna (*H. striata*), which bespeak close geographical connections with northern Africa. Of these the ancient elephant and the broad-nosed rhinoceros were close companions; they enjoyed the same regions and the same temperatures, their remains are very frequently found together, and they survived to the very end of the great life stage of western Europe, which closed with the advent of the fourth glaciation. They are in contrast to the other pair

FIG. 43. The other and hardier pair of large African-Asiatic mammals, namely, the broad-nosed or Merck's rhinoceros (*R. merckii*) and the straight-tusked or ancient elephant (*E. antiquus*), which entered western Europe in Second Interglacial times and survived until Third Interglacial times, when their remains are found intermingled with flints of the Acheulean and early Mousterian cultures. These mammals were doubtless hunted by men of the early Neanderthal races. One-sixtieth life size. Drawn by Erwin S. Christman.

of great mammals which was already present in Europe in Pliocene and First Interglacial times, namely, the southern mammoth, at this stage known as *Elephas trogontherii*, which had a preference for the companionship of the hippopotamus (*H. major*); it would seem that these animals were less hardy because both disappeared from Europe a little earlier than the ancient elephant and Merck's rhinoceros.

The African lion would appear to have been a competitor of the sabre-tooth tiger, for the latter animal now becomes less abundant, although there is reason to believe that it survived until the Third Interglacial Stage. With the ancient Pliocene

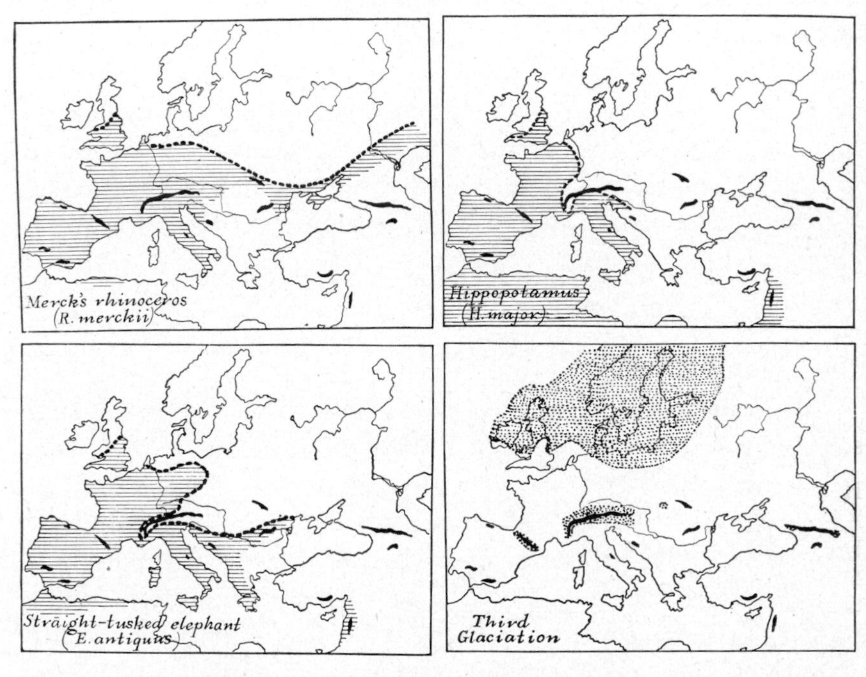

FIG. 44. Map showing the wide geographic distribution (horizontal lines) of Merck's rhinoceros and the straight-tusked elephant, which first entered western Europe during the First Interglacial Stage and survived until nearly the close of the Third Interglacial Stage. The hippopotamus, which entered Europe in Pliocene times, survived until after the middle of the Third Interglacial Stage and had a more limited distribution. After Boule.

type of the sabre-tooth were also found the Etruscan rhinoceros, the primitive bear of Auvergne (*Ursus arvernensis*), and the giant beaver (*Trogontherium cuvieri*).

The northern forests of the time were frequented by the broad-faced moose, the giant deer, and the roe-deer, as well as by noble specimens of the stag (*Cervus elaphus*). In the open forests and meadows the wild cattle (*Bos primigenius*) began to be more numerous and the bison (*Bison priscus*) also occurred. Among the meadow or forest frequenting forms were horses of larger size, such as the horses of Mosbach and of Süssenborn. In this assemblage of northern and southern types it is noteworthy that the Eurasiatic forest and meadow types of mammals greatly predominate in numbers and in variety over the African-Asiatic types; this, together with the flora, is an indication that the climate was of a temperate character; it is probable, therefore, that all the mammals were well protected with a hairy covering and adapted to a temperate climate. The fact that the fauna as a whole remained practically unchanged throughout the second glaciation is a proof not that it migrated to the south and then returned but that the non-glaciated regions of western Europe were temperate rather than cold.

The Heidelberg Race

To us by far the most interesting mammalian life is that found south of the mouth of the Neckar along the ancient stream Elsenz, where were deposited the lower 'sands of Mauer,' containing the lower jaw of the Heidelberg man and the remains of many animals of the period. The enumeration of this entire fauna is very important, as indicating the temperate climatic conditions which surrounded the first true species of man which has thus far been discovered in Europe. The discoverer, Schoetensack,[35] referred these mammals and the Heidelberg man to the First Interglacial Stage, and a similar opinion has recently been expressed by Geikie. The presence of the Etruscan rhinoceros would appear to point to such great antiquity, but the evidence afforded by this primitive animal is overborne by that of three mammals which are highly characteristic of Second Interglacial times; these are the straight-tusked or

Heidelberg man.
Ancient elephant.
Etruscan rhinoceros.
Mosbach horse.
Wild boar.
Broad-faced moose.
Red deer, or stag.
Roe-deer.
Primitive bison (wisent).
Primitive ox (Aurochs, urus).
Auvergne bear.
Deninger's bear.
Lion.
Wildcat.
Wolf.
Beaver.

ancient elephant (*E. antiquus*), the lion, and the Mosbach horse. Excepting only the Etruscan rhinoceros, all these species frequenting the ancient stream Elsenz and deposited with the 'sands of Mauer' occurred also in the forests and meadows of the region now known as Baden, where the fossil mammal deposits of Mosbach near the Neckar are found. A similar mammalian life of a somewhat more recent time occurs in the river gravels of Süssenborn, near Weimar. The horses of Mauer, of Mosbach,

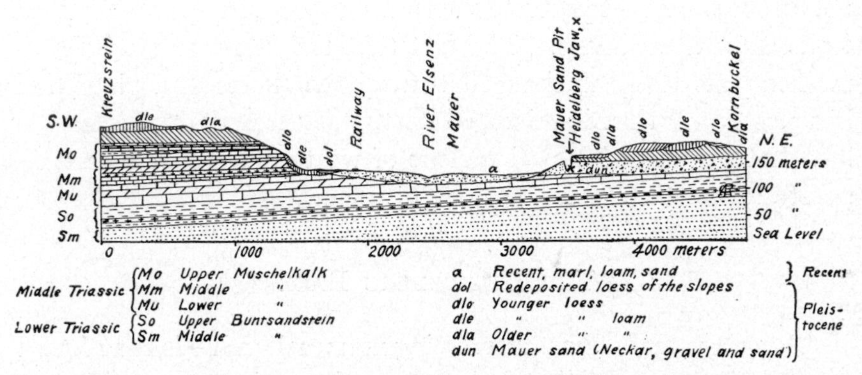

FIG. 45. Section of the valley of the stream Elsenz, near Heidelberg, showing the location of the Mauer sand-pit in which the Heidelberg jaw was discovered. An ancient layer of river-drift. Drawn by C. A. Reeds.

and of Süssenborn* were of much larger size and of more specialized character than Steno's horse of First Interglacial times.

Thus the Heidelbergs, the first human race recorded in western Europe, appear in southern Germany early in Second Interglacial times, in the midst of a most imposing mammalian fauna of northern aspect and containing many forest-living species, such as bear, deer, and moose; in the meadows and forests browsed the giant, straight-tusked elephant (*E. antiquus*), which from the simple structure of its grinding-teeth is regarded as similar in habit to the African elephant now inhabiting the forests of central Africa; the presence of this animal indicates a relatively moist climate and well-forested country. The Etrus-

* These horses are now identified respectively as *E. mauerensis*, *E. mosbachensis*, and *E. süssenbornensis*.

can rhinoceros differed from the larger Merck's form in the possession of relatively short-crowned grinding-teeth, adapted to

FIG. 46. Sand-pit at Mauer, near Heidelberg, discovery site of the jaw of Heidelberg man. After Schoetensack.

a–b. 'Newer loess,' either of Third Interglacial or of Postglacial times.
b–c. 'Older loess' (sandy loess) of the close of Second Interglacial times.
c–f. The 'sands of Mauer.'
d–e. An intermediate layer of clay.

The white cross (X) indicates the spot at the base of the 'sands of Mauer' at which the jaw of Heidelberg was discovered.

browsing habits and a forested country; on the head were borne two horns; it was a long-limbed, rapidly moving type; the herds of bison and of wild cattle (urus) which roamed over the plains were now subject to the attack of the lion.

The discovery in 1907 of a human lower jaw in the base of the 'Mauer sands' is one of the most important in the whole history of anthropology. The find was made at a depth of 79 feet (24.10 m.) from the upper surface of a high bluff (Fig. 46), in ancient river sands which had long been known to yield the very old mammalian fauna described above. For years the

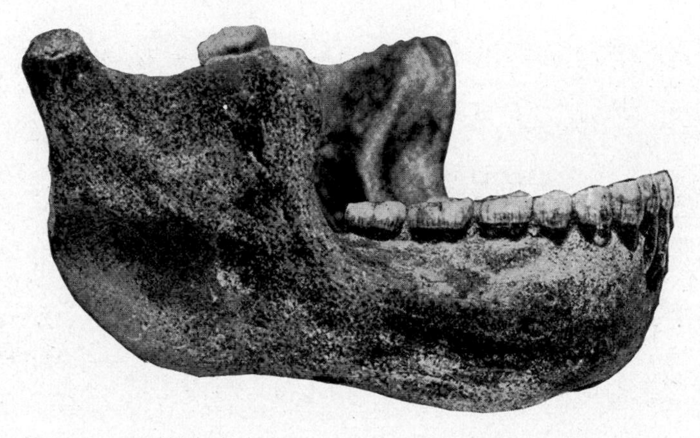

FIG. 47. The Heidelberg jaw, type of *Homo heidelbergensis*. About two-thirds life size. After Schoetensack.

workmen had been instructed to keep a sharp lookout for human remains. The jaw had evidently drifted down with the river sands and had become separated from the skull, but it remained in perfect preservation. The author's description may first be quoted.[36] The mandible shows a combination of features never before found in any fossil or recent man. The protrusion of the lower jaw just below the front teeth which gives shape to the human chin is entirely lacking. Had the teeth been absent it would have been impossible to diagnose it as human. From a fragment of the symphysis of the jaw it might well have been classed as some gorilla-like anthropoid, while the ascending ramus resembles that of some large variety of gibbon. The absolute certainty that these remains are human is based on the form of the teeth—molars, premolars, canines, and incisors are all essentially human and, although somewhat primitive in form, show no trace of being intermediate between man and the anthropoid apes but rather of being derived from some older common ancestor. The teeth, however, are somewhat small for the jaw; the size of the border would allow for the development of much larger teeth; we can only conclude that no great strain was put on the teeth, and therefore the powerful development of the bones of the jaw was not designed for their benefit. The conclusion is

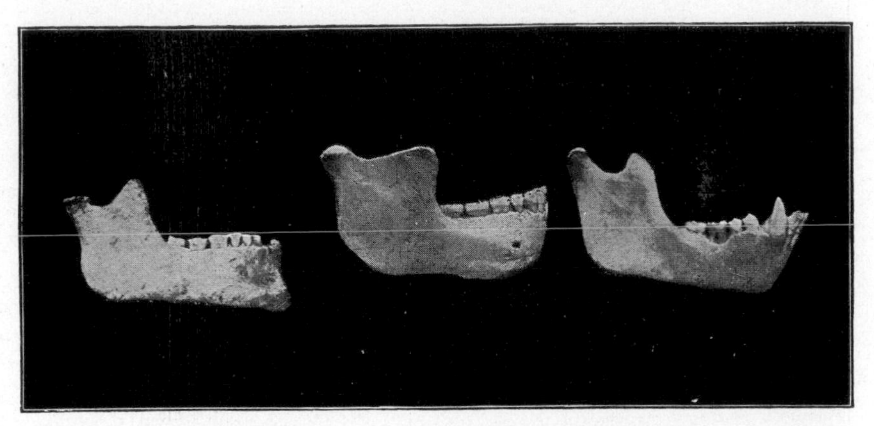

FIG. 48. Side view of Heidelberg jaw (centre) compared with that of a chimpanzee (right) and of an Eskimo (left); the latter an individual of exceptionally large proportions.

that the jaw, regarded as unquestionably human from the nature of the teeth, ranks not far from the point of separation between man and the anthropoid apes. In comparison with the jaws of Neanderthal races, as found at Spy, in Belgium, and at Krapina, in Croatia, we may consider the Heidelberg jaw as pre-Neanderthaloid; it is, in fact, a generalized type.

In a conservative spirit, Schoetensack named the type represented by this jaw *Homo heidelbergensis*. Other authors have regarded it as of distinct generic rank; thus it has been termed *Palæoanthropus heidelbergensis* by Bonarelli.[37] The jaw itself is extremely massive; the canine teeth, unlike those of the anthropoid apes and of the Piltdown race, do not project beyond the line of the other teeth and were therefore not used as weapons of offense and defense as in the anthropoids, in which these teeth are prominently developed as tusks. As noted by Schoetensack, the teeth are not very massive in proportion to the jaw itself, which is the most powerful human jaw known, even exceeding the largest Eskimo jaw and indicating a skull of very massive and primitive character. It resembles that of the ape in the recession of the chin, hence it has been termed *amentalis*. There is a large development of the coronoid process of the mandible for the attachment of the temporal muscle. This jaw may well have been used as a tool in the last stages of the preparation of hides, as is the practice of the Eskimo races. We observe that the powerful bony branches of the jaw, when regarded from above, close in upon the space left for the tongue; in fact, the bone closes in to such an extent as to interfere seriously with the free use of the tongue in articulate speech.

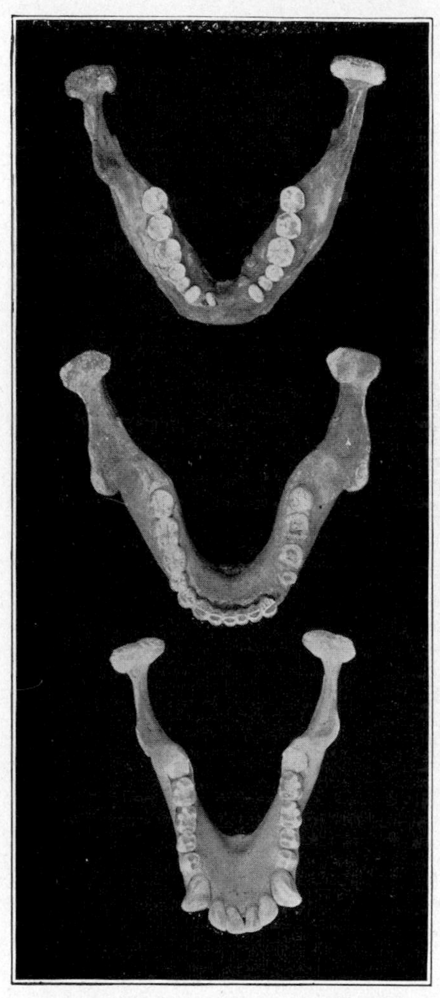

Fig. 49. The jaws shown in Fig. 48 seen from above. A massive Eskimo jaw (above), the Heidelberg jaw (centre), the jaw of a chimpanzee (below).

It would seem that in the jaw, and probably in all other characters of the skull, as they become known, the Heidelberg race will be found to be a Neanderthal in the making, that is, a primitive, more powerful, and more ape-like ancestral form. In the matter of the retreating chin, the true Neanderthals of Spy, Malarnaud, Krapina, and La Chapelle rank exactly half-way between the most inferior races of recent man and the anthropoid apes.

Not only among the Eskimos, but generally throughout the savage races of Australia and of other countries, the jaws are used as tools; among the Australians the teeth are very much worn

Fig. 50. Restoration of the Man of Heidelberg by the Belgian artist Mascré, under the direction of Professor A. Rutot, of Brussels. This restoration presents an advance upon the *Pithecanthropus* type. In our opinion the Heidelberg man was more human and less ape-like in appearance.

down but are in admirable preservation. When seen from above, we observe that the 'Heidelberg' grinding-teeth form a perfect arch, or horseshoe-shaped arrangement, whereas in all the apes the two lines of grinding-teeth are almost parallel with each other. Thus, while there may be wide differences of opinion as regards the relationships of the Heidelberg man, all agree that Schoetensack's discovery affords us one of the great missing links or types in the chain of human development.

The typical mammalian life of Second Interglacial times as found at Mosbach and Süssenborn belongs perhaps to a somewhat more recent stage of Second Interglacial times than that of the 'Mauer sands,' for in these localities the Etruscan rhinoceros is wanting and the more specialized broad-nosed rhinoceros is abundant; this animal differs from the Etruscan form in the possession of relatively long-crowned grinding-teeth, which were better adapted to grazing habits. On the head were borne two horns. A variety of the southern mammoth (*E. trogontherii*) is so highly characteristic of Second Interglacial times that Pohlig refers to this life period as the *E. trogontherii stage*. From the structure of its grinding-teeth it is regarded as similar in habit to the Asiatic elephant, which now inhabits the forests of India, but it has the peculiar concave forehead distinctive of the mammoth and quite unlike the convex forehead of the Indian elephant. The bears of this period belong to the primitive species *U. deningeri* and *U. arvernensis*, for so far there is no certain record of the presence of the true brown bear of Europe (*U. arctos*). The sabre-tooth tiger of this time is preserved in the caverns of the Pyrenees near Montmaurin, associated with the remains of the striped hyæna (*H. striata*), a species which was widely distributed over western Europe in early Pleistocene times. This species was contemporary with, and later replaced by, the spotted hyæna (*H. crocuta*), from which the very hardy cave-hyæna (*H. crocuta spelæa*) of the 'Reindeer Period,' descended. We observe that the 'polycladine' deer of Upper Pliocene and First Glacial times has disappeared from western Europe; nor are there any traces of the axis deer. The hippopotamus is still represented by the giant species, *H. major*.

Early Northern Migrations of the Reindeer

The animals that we have described belong in the warmer and more temperate regions of Europe. In the regions near the glaciers the reindeer was already to be found; in fact, this characteristically northern animal is recorded in the gravels of Süssenborn, near Weimar.

There is evidence of a succession of climatic changes in the region of Heidelberg. The Heidelberg jaw with its temperate mammalian fauna occurred at the very base of the Mauer bluff, but higher up the bluff (Fig. 46) on a corresponding level are found the remains of mammals which indicate a marked lowering of temperature and which are referred by some authorities to the period of chilling climate that characterized northern Europe toward the close of Second Interglacial times. The reindeer also occurs in the 'high terrace' gravels of the River Murr, near Steinheim; thus, at Mauer, at Süssenborn, and at Steinheim, we find proof that the reindeer had begun to spread over the colder regions of Europe, and there is some ground for belief that it found its way even as far south as the Pyrenees.

The evidence of the first cold, arid period which for the time greatly affected the climate of western Europe is also found in the layer of so-called 'ancient loess' which lies in the bluff above the 'sands of Mauer.' This loess covers the warm mammalian deposits of the 'sands of Mosbach' as well as the 'high terraces' of many of the ancient river-valleys. Both in Europe and America the climatic sequence of the Second Interglacial Stage from moist to dry appears to have been the same.

Thus, after the recession of the ice-fields of the second glaciation, the climate was at first cold and moist; then followed a long warm stage, favorable to the spread of forests; this was finally succeeded by a period of aridity in which the most ancient 'loess' deposits occurred. In Russia, also, the third glaciation was preceded by an arid and steppe-like climate with high winds favorable to the transportation of 'loess.'

No palæoliths or other proofs of human occupation have been found in this cold, dry period, for there is no evidence in any part of Europe of camping stations in this 'ancient loess' such as we find in the 'loess' which was deposited during the similar arid period toward the close of Third Interglacial and again during Postglacial times. Nor have we any record of the mammalian life in this 'ancient loess' of Europe.

The Third Glaciation *

This arid period in northern Europe and in North America was followed by the moist, cool climate of the third glaciation. It is estimated by Penck that the advance of these new ice-fields began 120,000 years ago and that the period of advance and retreat of the glaciers was not less than 20,000 years. In the Alps the snow-line descended 1,250 metres below the present level; consequently this glaciation was more severe than the first but somewhat less severe than the second. In northern Europe the Scandinavian ice-field did not cover so wide an area as during the second glaciation, although Britain and Scandinavia were again deeply buried by ice; the glacial cap and glaciers flowed in a westerly and southwesterly direction across Denmark and the southern portion of the basin of the Baltic into Holland and northern Germany. In the Alps the third glaciation sent vast ice-floes along the valley of the Rhine, into eastern France, and into the valley of the Po, where this glaciation was even more extensive than the second. But the greatest glacier of this time was that of the Isar, a southern tributary of the Danube, which rises in the Bavarian Alps.[38]

During the Third Glacial Stage certain of the 'middle terraces' along the Rhine and other rivers flowing from the Alps were formed. In Britain,[39] whereas during the second glaciation the ice-fields extended as far south as the Thames, during the third glaciation they did not extend beyond the midlands; yet an arctic climate prevailed over southern England, with tundra conditions and temperature, as indicated by the plant deposits at Hoxne[40] in Suffolk. Even before the third glaciation began in Europe a great ice-cap had formed over Labrador, on the eastern coast of North America, and the ice-sheets flowing to the south and southwest extended as far as Illinois, depositing the great Illinoian 'drifts.'

* This glaciation as it occurs in northern Europe has been termed *Polandian* by Geikie; in the Alps Penck has termed it the *Riss;* in America it is known as the *Illinoian* from the great drifts it deposited over the State of Illinois.

Along the borders of these great ice-fields in both countries a cold and moist climate prevailed, for a prime condition of glaciation is the heavy precipitation of snow. In northern Europe, between the great Alpine and Scandinavian ice-fields of the third glaciation a cold climate undoubtedly prevailed; in the region

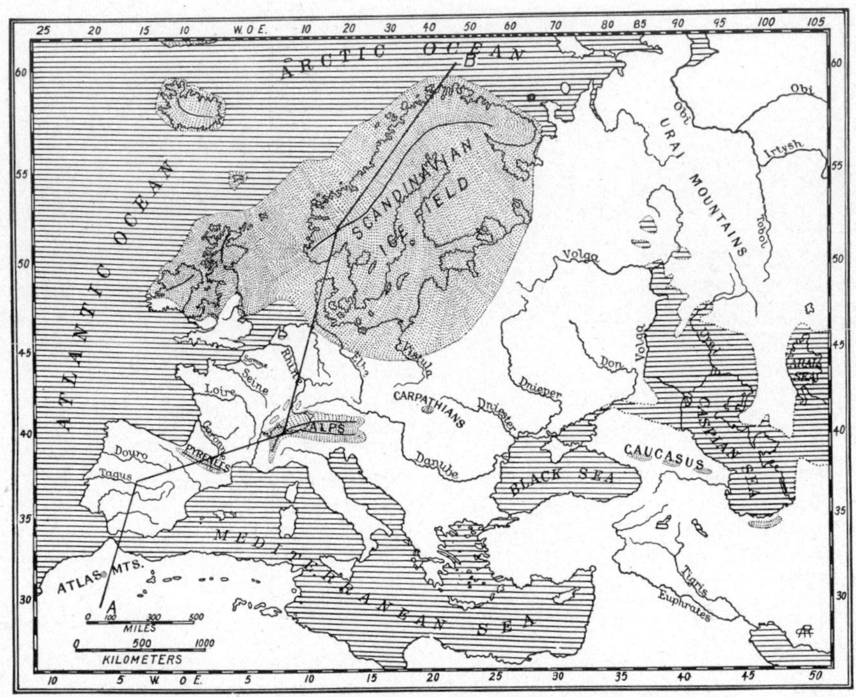

EUROPE DURING THE THIRD GLACIAL EPOCH. (RISS) (AFTER JAMES GEIKIE)
A-B Line of Profile

FIG. 51. The ice-fields and glaciers of the Third Glacial Stage are seen to be much less extensive than those of the Second Glacial Stage, shown in Fig. 25, p. 65. The continental depression and invasion of the sea is also believed to have been less extensive. At this stage there are broad areas free from ice between the Scandinavian, the Alpine, and the Pyrenean ice-caps. Drawn by C. A. Reeds, after James Geikie. (Compare Fig. 13.)

of the Neckar River, near Cannstatt, is found a deposit known as 'mammoth loam,' which Koken believed to be contemporaneous with the period of the third glaciation, although the evidence is certainly not convincing.[41] Here are found fossil remains of the Scandinavian reindeer, also of two very important new arrivals in Europe from the tundra regions of the far northeast, animals which had wandered along the southern borders of the Scandinavian ice-sheet from the tundras of northern Russia and Siberia. This is the first appearance in western Europe of the woolly mammoth (*E. primigenius*) and the woolly rhinoceros (*D. antiquitatis*). In this 'mammoth loam' there also occur two species of horse, the giant deer (*Megaceros*), the stag, the wisent, and the Aurochs. If the woolly mammoth and the woolly rhinoceros actually entered eastern Germany at this time, they certainly retreated to the north with the approach of the warm temperate climate of the Third Interglacial Stage, because no trace of these animals has been found again in Europe until the advent of the fourth glaciation.

(1) Gaudry, 1890.1.
(2) Smith, G. E., 1912.1, p. 582.
(3) *Op. cit.*
(4) Munro, 1893.1.
(5) Osborn, 1910.1, pp. 306, 307.
(6) Geikie, J., 1894.1, pp. 329–336; 1914.1, p. 227.
(7) Dawkins, 1883.1, pp. 576–579.
(8) Geikie, J., 1914.1, p. 248.
(9) Reid, C., 1908.1.
(10) Desnoyers, 1863.1.
(11) Haug, 1911.1, p. 1807.
(12) Geikie, J., 1894.1, p. 682; 1914.1, p. 250.
(13) Dubois, 1894.1.
(14) Fischer, 1913.1.
(15) Schwalbe, 1899.1; 1914.1.
(16) Büchner, 1914.1.
(17) Volz, 1907.1.
(18) Elbert, 1908.1.
(19) Selenka, 1911.1.
(20) Pilgrim, 1913.1.
(21) Schwalbe, 1899.1, pp. 227, 228.
(22) *Op. cit.*, p. 223.
(23) Schwalbe, 1914.1, pp. 601–606.
(24) Büchner, 1914.1, p. 129.
(25) Dubois, 1894,1, p. 14.
(26) Keith, 1912.1.
(27) Smith, G. E., 1912.1, p. 595.
(28) *Op. cit.*
(29) Rutot, 1907.1.
(30) Boule, 1913.1, pp. 266, 267.
(31) MacCurdy, 1905.1, pp. 468, 469.
(32) Geikie, J., 1914.1, p. 251.
(33) *Op. cit.*, p. 255.
(34) *Op. cit.*, p. 238.
(35) Schoetensack, 1908.1.
(36) *Op. cit.*, pp. 25–43.
(37) Bonarelli, 1909.1.
(38) Penck, 1909.1.
(39) Geikie, J., 1914.1, p. 258.
(40) *Op. cit.*, pp. 257–262.
(41) Schmidt, 1912.1, p. 181

CHAPTER II

ARRIVAL OF THE PRE-CHELLEAN FLINT WORKERS DURING THE THIRD INTERGLACIAL — GEOGRAPHY, CLIMATE, AND THE RIVER DRIFTS — PRE-CHELLEAN FLINT INDUSTRY — THE PILTDOWN RACE — MAMMALIAN LIFE — CHELLEAN AND ACHEULEAN INDUSTRIES — THE USE OF FIRE — THE SECOND PERIOD OF ARID CLIMATE — THE NEANDERTHAL RACE OF KRAPINA, CROATIA

The geologic epoch of the arrival of the Pre-Chellean flint workers in western Europe is by far the most important and interesting one before the prehistorian. Upon it depends the question of the duration of the Old Stone Age, the date of appearance of the Piltdown and of the Neanderthal races, and the whole sequence of climatic and geographic changes surrounding the early history of man. After weighing all the evidence very carefully, the balance of opinion seems to sustain the view that this epoch should be placed *after* the close of the third glaciation and *before* the advent of the fourth, that is, during the Third Interglacial Stage.

Penck estimated that the third warm interglacial stage* opened about 100,000 years ago and lasted between 50,000 and 60,000 years. According to the theory that we have adopted in this work, the Third Interglacial and Fourth Glacial embraced the entire period of Lower Palæolithic time, a period of from 70,000 to 100,000 years, much longer than that of Upper Palæolithic time, which is estimated at 16,000 to 25,000 years.

Geologic Antiquity of the Beginning of the Stone Age

Attention should first be called to the fact that, preceding the epoch we have now entered, the glacial and interglacial forces

* This stage is known as the *Helvetian* or *Dürntenian* of Geikie; it is the *Riss-Würm* of Penck's terminology and the *Sangamon* of the American glaciologists.

operating over the great peninsula of western Europe had left their impress chiefly on the glaciated areas and only to a minor degree on the free, non-glaciated areas. Until toward the close of Third Interglacial times no traces of northern much less of arctic forests and animals are discovered anywhere, except along the borders of the ice-fields. It would appear as if the animal and plant life of Europe were, in the main, but slightly affected

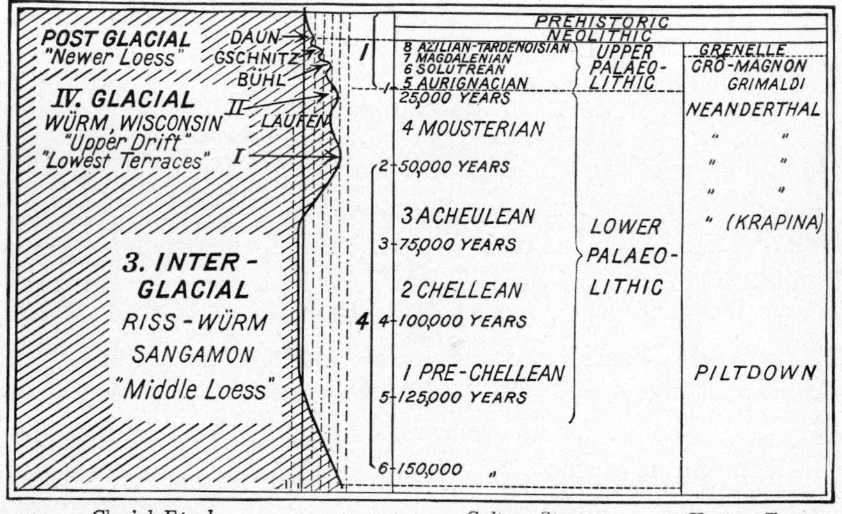

FIG. 52. Human types and culture stages of the last third of the Glacial Epoch. Theoretic estimates of the geologic and time divisions and introduction of human races during the Third Interglacial, Fourth Glacial, and Postglacial Stages (see Fig. 14, p. 41). Prepared by the author with the aid of C. A. Reeds.

by the first three glaciations. We cannot entertain for a moment the belief that in glacial times all the warm flora and fauna migrated southward and then returned, because there is not a shred of evidence for this theory. It is far more in accord with the known facts to believe that all the southern and eastern forms of life had become very hardy, for we know how readily animals now living in the warm earth belts are acclimatized to northern conditions.

If, on the other hand, we depend solely on the testimony of the life conditions, we might conclude that the Pre-Chellean flint workers reached western Europe either in Second Interglacial times, or during the third glaciation, or again during Third Interglacial times. Let us consider this evidence of the fossil mammals more closely.

In favor of the theory that the Pre-Chellean culture is as ancient as Second Interglacial times, we should consider the fact

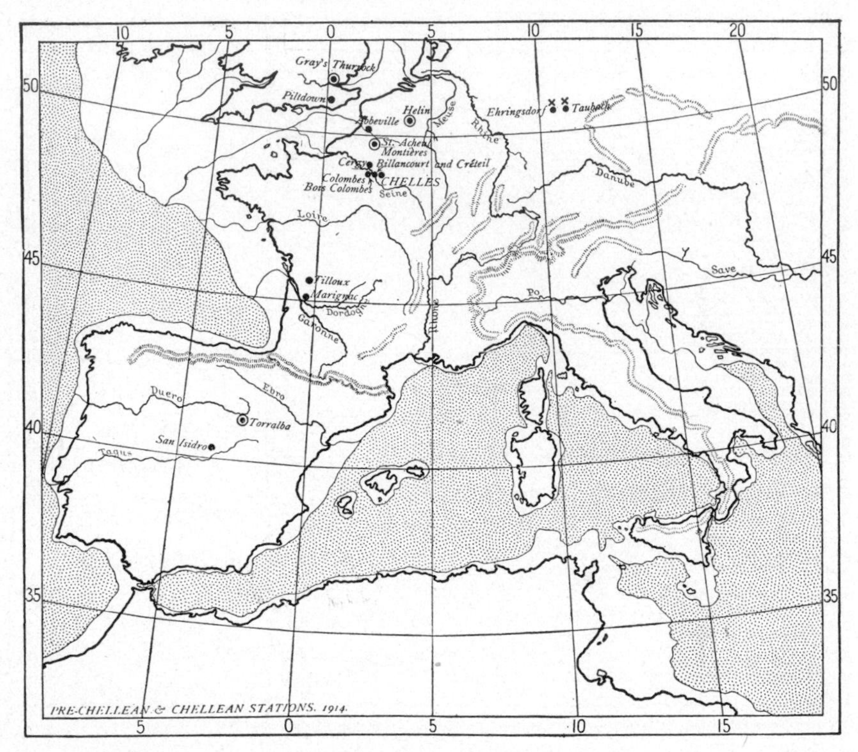

Fig. 53. Distribution of the principal Pre-Chellean and Chellean industrial stations in western Europe.

that in several localities palæoliths of Pre-Chellean if not of Chellean type have been recorded in association with the remains of a number of the more primitive mammals which we have described above as characteristic of Second Interglacial times. For example, at Torralba, Province of Soria, Spain, there has been discovered[1] an old typical Chellean camp site, containing abundant remains of the broad-nosed rhinoceros and of the southern mammoth, mingled with the remains of other mammals of very ancient type, identified as the Etruscan rhinoceros and as

Steno's horse. Again, along the River Somme, near Abbeville, in the *gisement du Champ de Mars*,[2] it is said that Pre-Chellean and Chellean implements have been found in association with the Etruscan rhinoceros, Steno's horse, and very numerous specimens of the sabre-tooth tiger and of the striped hyæna. Moreover, in

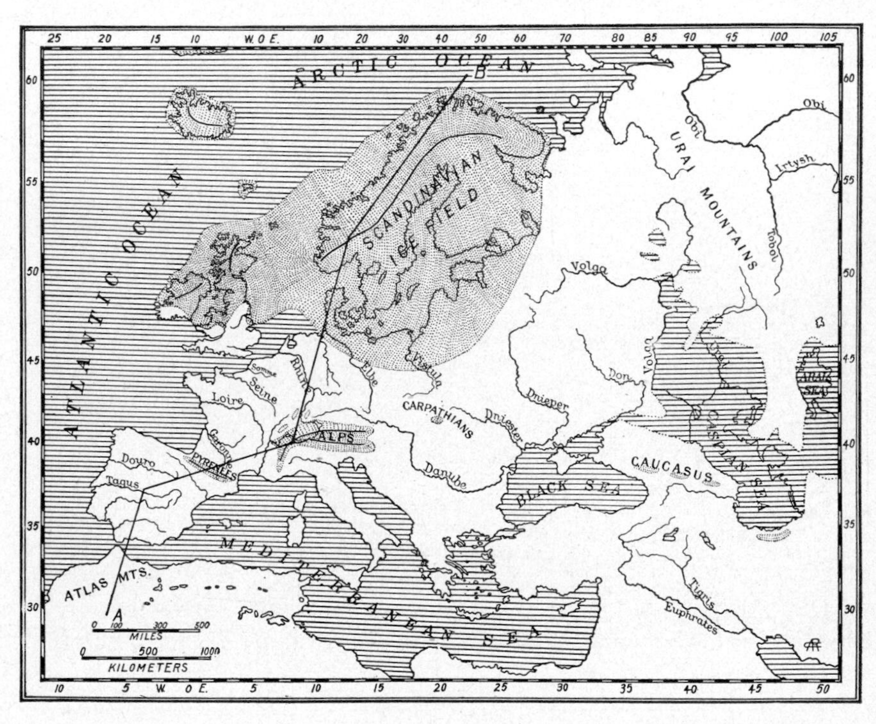

FIG. 54. Western Europe during the extension of the ice-fields and glaciers (dots) of the Third Glacial Stage—a period of continental depression believed to have been less extensive than that of the Second Glacial Stage (see Fig. 25, p. 65). The line from Scandinavia to northern Africa corresponds to the section shown in Fig. 13, p. 37. Drawn by C. A. Reeds, after Geikie and Penck. (Compare Fig. 13.)

Piltdown, Sussex, Pre-Chellean flints and the Piltdown skull are said to have occurred in a layer containing a rhinoceros which may be identified with the Etruscan. If these very ancient species of animals are rightly recognized and determined, and if they are truly found as reported in close association in the same layers with Pre-Chellean and Chellean flints, the evidence may be considered as quite strong that the beginning of Chellean culture dates from Second Interglacial times; unless, indeed, it should prove that these primitive species of mammals survived into Third Interglacial times in certain favored districts. We should also consider the possibility that these more ancient animals, the sabre-tooth tiger, Steno's horse, the Etruscan rhinoceros, and the giant beaver, did not really belong in the same layer with these

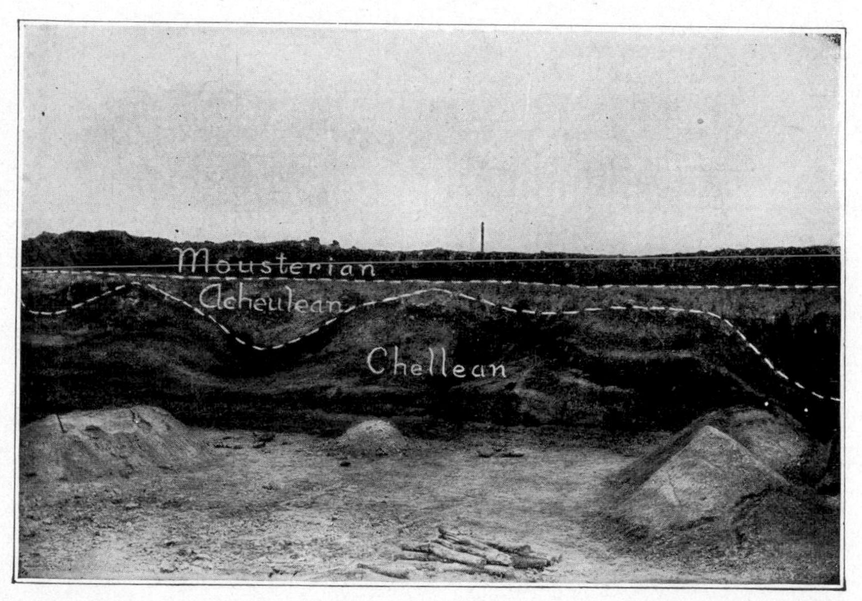

FIG. 55. Excavation at Chelles-sur-Marne, the Palæolithic station where Chellean flint implements were first discovered. We observe the very close, regular, and unbroken succession of the geological layers containing the Chellean, Acheulean, and Mousterian flints.

old palæoliths but were accidentally washed into this layer from other more ancient deposits. As a rule, it is the most recent animals which establish a prehistoric date, because we know that a palæolith cannot be older than the most recent mammal with which it occurs.

The record of the three early glaciations is not fully written in the animal and plant life, but it appears to be found in the river channels. Both in England and France these channels attest flooded conditions during the earlier glaciations, in which large quantities of gravels and sands were transported, and it is of these materials that the 'high terraces' were built up. It is chiefly the geologic evidence which establishes the Pre-Chellean date.

Geologic and climatic lines of evidence in France indicate that the Pre-Chellean culture is first witnessed during the beginning of Third Interglacial times. This is the opinion of Boule, Haug, Obermaier, Breuil, Schmidt, and many other geologists and archæologists. That the first Palæolithic flint workers found their way into western Europe during the early part of Third Interglacial times is consistent with our observations on the sequence of climate, on the formation of the 'low river terraces,' where palæoliths of the earliest type occur, as well as with the general succession of mammalian life throughout the climatic changes of this interglacial period. It would appear, in explanation of the facts cited above regarding the fossil mammals, that when the Pre-Chellean flint workers established their camps along the valley of the River Somme in northern France a very genial climate prevailed in this region, favorable even, as we shall see, to the survival of some of the Pliocene types of mammals, such as the sabre-tooth tiger and the Etruscan rhinoceros.

During the early part of the Third Interglacial Stage the climate, so far as we can judge by the unchanged aspect of the animal life, remained of the same warm temperate character. Two only of the surviving Pliocene forms, namely, the sabre-tooth tigers and the Etruscan rhinoceroses, became rare or extinct. From evidence afforded in Kent's Hole, Devonshire, Dawkins is led to believe that the sabre-tooth tiger survived in Britain until Postglacial times. All the rest of the animal world, both the African-Asiatic and the Eurasiatic mammals, continued to flourish throughout western Europe.

Not until the latter part of Acheulean times do we discover proofs of a decided change of climate; in the approach of arid conditions similar to those of the steppes of western Asia there was a renewal of the great dust-storms and depositions of 'loess,' such as had previously occurred toward the close of Second Interglacial times; this was followed by the still colder climate of the fourth glaciation, which corresponds with the closing period of Lower Palæolithic culture.

The evolution of the Pre-Chellean into the Chellean and finally into the Lower Acheulean palæoliths certainly occupied a very long period of time if we assign it merely the 50,000 or 60,000 years allotted to the Third Interglacial; but even this allotment seems far too long when we observe the relatively limited depth of the river deposits in which these flint cultures succeed each other. For we cannot fail to be impressed by the regular and very close and unbroken succession of the geologic layers containing the Chellean and Acheulean artifacts. (See Fig. 55.)

None the less it follows that a long lapse of time must be allowed for each culture period, and for the advance in technique.[3] It is this wide distribution that has enabled the de Mortillets (father and son), Capitan, Rivière, Reboux, Daleau, Peyrony, Obermaier, Commont, Schmidt, and others to establish in various parts of Europe the main stages of the industrial evolution of the Old Stone Age, or Lower Palæolithic.

Subdivisions of the Lower Palæolithic Cultures[4]*

Mousterian. Late industry of the Neanderthal races. Extensive use of the 'flake.'

Late Mousterian. La Quina scrapers, small 'coups de poing,' and bone anvils, closing with the Abri Audit culture.

Middle Mousterian. Culmination of the Mousterian 'point' finely flaked and chipped on one side, the best examples approaching the Solutrean perfection of technique.

Early Mousterian. Heart-shaped 'coups de poing' and Mousterian flake 'points' and flake scrapers.

Acheulean. Early industry of the Neanderthal races. Extensive use of the nodular core.

Late Acheulean. Miniature 'lance points' of La Micoque type, triangular 'coups de poing,' and flint flakes of Levallois type.

Middle Acheulean. Pointed oval 'coups de poing,' much lighter than the Chellean types, and small implements similar to the Chellean but much improved in workmanship.

Early Acheulean. Broad oval 'coups de poing' much more symmetrical than the Chellean but still rather heavy. Small types.

* Modified after Schmidt.

CHELLEAN.

Late Chellean. Long pointed 'coups de poing,' in most cases flaked on both sides, with little of the crust of the nodule adhering and the edges still unsymmetrical. First appearance of the oval 'coups de poing.'

Early Chellean. First appearance of 'coups de poing' of almond shape. Small implements, including scrapers, planes, and borers. All implements unsymmetrical and with uneven edges.

PRE-CHELLEAN. Probable industry of the Piltdown and of the (Pre-Neanderthaloid) Heidelberg races. Use of chance and accidental forms. Forms partly accidental; retouch limited to the few strokes necessary to give a point or edge to the tool, or to allow a firm grasp (protective retouch). Prototypes of 'coup de poing' formed of flint nodules with crust only partially removed.

If we suppose that the Pre-Chellean flint workers arrived in Europe not earlier than Third Interglacial times, we can explain all the gradations in the evolution of their implements in connection with the changes of climate and of animal life which the geologic and fossil deposits reveal, especially in the valleys of the Somme and of the Thames.

If, on the other hand, the Pre-Chellean is dated in Second Interglacial times,* it carries this culture back another hundred thousand years and involves our prehistory in great difficulties. First, there is no proof whatever that the Pre-Chellean and Chellean flint workers lived during the period of the formation of the 'high river terraces' of the third glaciation, for no Palæolithic flints have ever been found buried in the sands or gravels of the 'high terraces.' The occurrence of archaic flints on the 'high terraces' of the Somme and of the Seine is in superficial gravel beds which were deposited long after these 'terraces' had been cut by river action; this is best seen in the Somme, where archaic flints occur alike in the gravels deposited upon the 'low,' 'middle,' and 'high terraces.' Second, there is no proof that the Pre-Chellean and Chellean flint workers passed through the cold climatic period of the third glaciation; nowhere in Europe have

* The weakness of Penck's argument for placing the Chellean in the Second Interglacial was exposed by precise observations of Boule[5] and Obermaier[6] in the Alps, the Jura, and the Pyrenees.

any records been found of their camps or stations in association with the cold fauna or flora of Third Glacial times. Third, the geographical evidence is equally at variance with the theory that the Pre-Chellean flint workers entered Europe during the Second Interglacial Stage, for we know positively that in many of the great river-valleys of Europe, especially those surrounding the Alps, the rivers were at much higher levels than at present and that they were transporting the materials out of which the 'high terraces' were being formed or cutting these 'terraces' down by erosion.

In other words, the geography of Europe in First and Second Interglacial times was very different from what it is at present; most of the river-valleys were broader and less deep; some of them had been eroded to a point below their present levels and had begun to silt up in alluvial deposits. In Third Interglacial times the river geography of Europe was substantially as it is to-day, although the coast-lines were still very different.

When Pre-Chellean man appeared, we shall see that the river-valleys of the Somme and Marne, in northern France, as well as of the Thames, in southeastern England, were closely similar to what they are at present in respect to their water-levels; in other words, the inland geography of Europe in the north in Chellean times and in central and southern France in the immediately succeeding Acheulean times was very much like it is at present. The superficial characters of the valleys were different; the streams in Chellean times flowed through gravels and sands, partaking of a glacial aspect; one or more of the 'river terraces' composed of sands and gravels were still sharply defined, for the soft covering of 'loam' and alluvial soil from the surrounding uplands and hills had not yet washed down to soften the outlines of the 'terraces.' Neither were the 'terraces' covered with the newer deposits of 'loess.'

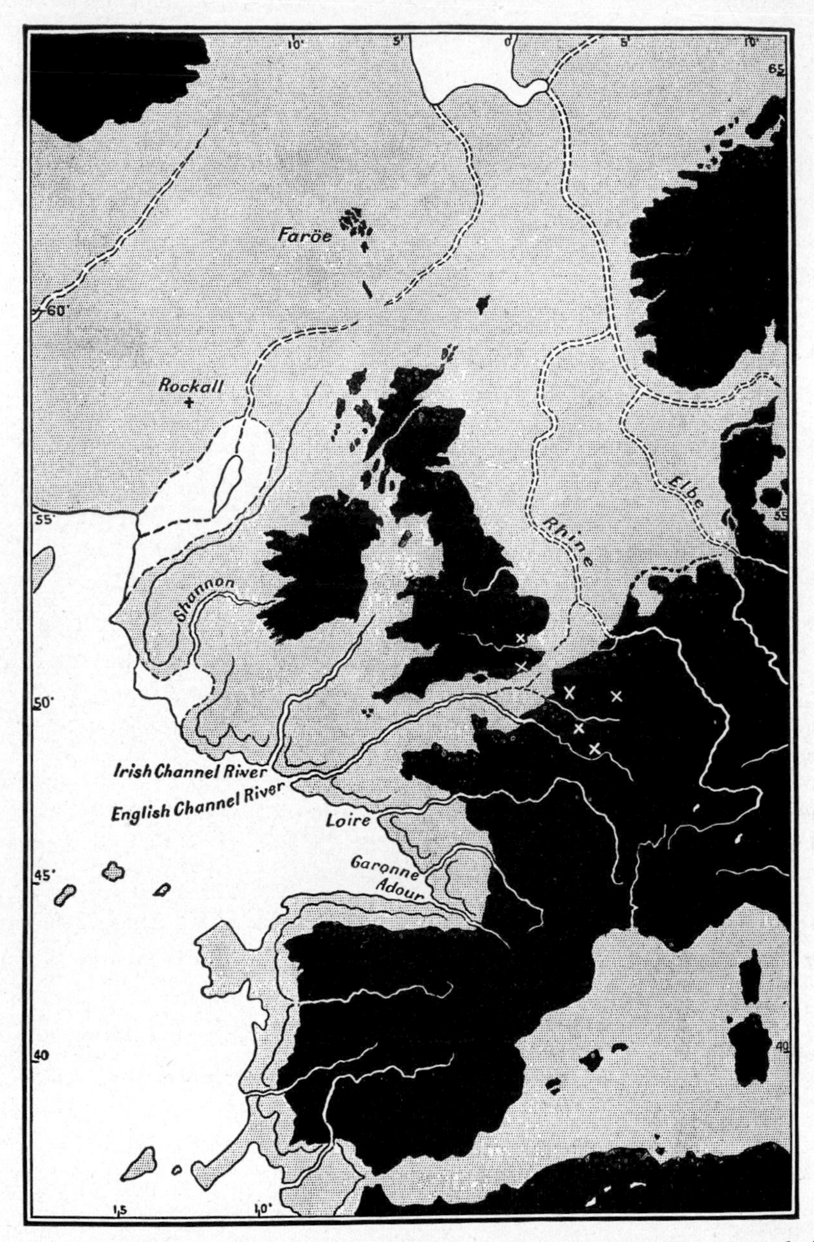

FIG. 56. Restoration of the geography of western Europe during the Third Interglacial Stage, showing the ancient land areas (dots) and the ancient river channels now submerged by the sea. Modified after Avebury's *Prehistoric Times* by permission of Henry Holt & Co. The six white crosses (X) indicate the location of the principal Pre-Chellean stations of Piltdown on the Ouse, and Gray's Thurrock on the Thames, in England; of Abbeville, on the north bank, and St. Acheul, on the south bank of the Somme, and Chelles on the Marne, in France; and of Helin in Belgium. It will be observed that the English stations are separated from the others only by the ancient broad valley corresponding with the present English Channel.

Secular Changes of Climate in Lower Palæolithic Times

We find evidences of four climatic and life phases during the long period of Lower Palæolithic evolution, as follows:

4. *Cold Moist Climate.*—Advent of the fourth glaciation. Arrival of the 'full Mousterian' culture and of the Neanderthal race in Belgium and France. Repair of men to the warmer shelters, grottos, and entrances to the caverns. Final disappearance of the hardy Merck's rhinoceros and the straight-tusked elephant. Arrival of the tundra fauna, the reindeer, the woolly mammoth, and the woolly rhinoceros. Refrigeration of western Europe as far south as northern Spain and Italy. Wide distribution of cold alpine, tundra, and steppe mammals all over Germany and France, and into northern Spain. Cold tundra flora in the Thames valley, and at Hoxne, in Suffolk. Migration of the tundra mammals, the reindeer, mammoth, and rhinoceros all over southern Britain, Belgium, France, Germany, and Austria.

3. *Arid Climate in Western Europe.*—Period of the close of the Acheulean culture; some of the flint workers seeking the shelter of cliffs and approaching the entrances to the grottos during the cold season of the year. A dry steppe climate, prevailing westerly winds, and deposits of 'loess' all over northern France and Germany. Appearance of the first Neanderthaloid men in Krapina, Croatia. Cool forest flora in the region of La Celle-sous-Moret near Paris, followed by depositions of 'loess' and increasingly cool and arid climate. Early Mousterian industry. Disappearance first of the more sensitive pair of Asiatic mammals, the hippopotamus and the southern mammoth (*E. trogontherii*); persistence of the more hardy, straight-tusked elephant (*E. antiquus*) and the broad-nosed rhinoceros (*D. merckii*).

2. *Continued Warm Temperate Period.*—Time of the Chellean culture found at Chelles, St. Acheul, Gray's Thurrock, Ilford, Essex, and southward in Torralba, Spain. Abundance of hippopotami, rhinoceroses, southern mammoths, and straight-tusked elephants in northern Germany at Taubach, Weimar, Ehringsdorf, and Achenheim. Rare appearance of sabre-tooth tigers. Temperate forest and alpine flora of Dürnten and Utznach, Switzerland. Early Acheulean culture widely distributed over all of western Europe.

1. *Early Warm Temperate Period.*—The warm climate of the Pre-Chellean culture period, as seen in the valleys of the Somme, of the Thames, and of the Seine near Paris, favorable to the southern mammoth and the hippopotamus. Apparent survival of the sabre-tooth tiger and the Etruscan rhinoceros in favored regions. A warm temperate forest flora in La Celle-

sous-Moret near Paris and in Lorraine. Arrival of the Pre-Chellean flint workers and of the Piltdown race in southern England.

It is believed that the climate of Third Interglacial times when it reached its maximum warmth was again somewhat milder than the present climate in the same region. In the Alps the glaciers and the snow-line retreated once more to their present levels. The period opened with humid continental conditions. The areas left bare by the ice were gradually reforested. A picture of the climate in this warm period is presented in the region near Paris in the so-called *tuf de La Celle-sous-Moret* (Seine-et-Marne). This tufa, which is a hot-springs deposit, overlies river-gravels of Pleistocene age.[7] The lower levels of the tufa contain the sycamore-maple (*Acer pseudoplatanus*), willows, and the Austrian pine, indicating a temperate climate. Higher up in the same deposits we find evidences of increasingly mild temperatures in the presence of the box (*Buxus*) and not infrequently of the fig-tree; the Canary laurel (*Laurus nobilis*) is somewhat rarer and both it and the fig indicate that the winters were mild, because these plants have the peculiarity of flowering during the winter season; we infer, therefore, that the climate was somewhat milder and more damp than it is in the same region at the present time. The mollusks also indicate greater equability of climate. These deposits are believed to correspond with the period of Chellean and early Acheulean industry.

The plants in the highest levels of the same tufa, however, indicate the advent of a colder climate and also connect this with the Acheulean culture stage through the presence of Acheulean flints. The deposit of tufa is covered by a sheet of 'loess' corresponding with the return of an arid period in late Acheulean times, in the very heart of northern France. Thus we have a record in the region near the present city of Paris of three climatic phases, which are also more or less completely indicated in deposits to the north along the River Somme and in the valley of the ancient Thames.

In western France we again interpret the fossil flora of Lorraine as belonging to the cooler closing period of Third Interglacial times and to the advent of the fourth glaciation, for here the most northern varieties of the larch (*Larix*) and of the mountain-pine (*Pinus lambertiana*) predominate.

The clearest view of the contemporary alpine forests is found near Zürich in the lignitic deposits of Dürnten and of Utznach, which are so characteristic of the temperate period of the Third Interglacial Stage that Geikie has proposed to call this stage the *Dürntenian.*[8] It was, we recall, at Dürnten that Morlot[9] found the first proofs of a warm or temperate interglacial flora, between the deposits of a retreating glacier and those of an advancing glacier; for Dürnten is well within the region which was covered by the vast ice-fields both of the third and fourth glaciations. The forests which flourished there in Third Interglacial times were similar to those now found in the same region, consisting of the spruce, fir, mountain-pine, larch, beech, yew, and sycamore, with undergrowth of hazel. With this hardy flora are associated the remains of the straight-tusked elephant, of Merck's rhinoceros, of wild cattle, and of the stag; another evidence for our opinion that all these Asiatic mammals had become habituated to the cool temperate climate of the north.

Life on the River Somme from Pre-Chellean to Neolithic Times

The borders of the River Somme at St. Acheul give us a vista of the whole story of the succession of geologic events; the great changes of climate, the procession of animal life, the sequence of human races and cultures. Here Commont[10] has found the key to the history of this entire country and enabled us to parallel events here with those occurring far away in Taubach, on the borders of the Thuringian forest, and at Krems in Lower Austria, as studied by Obermaier. This is because the 'older' and 'newer' loess periods, the succession of climates and of mammals, and the development of human cultures were all not local but *continental* events. The purely local events are found in the kinds of gravels and soils which washed down over the terraces.

It is very important first to clearly picture in our minds and understand the geography of the Somme at the time of the arrival of the Pre-Chellean flint workers. It appears certain that all three of the old river terraces composed of limestone had been cut long before and that the river had already reached the bottom level of the underlying chalk rock.[11] The higher terrace, then as now, was 100 feet above the Somme, the middle terrace about 70 feet, and the lowest terrace extended from a height of about 40 feet down underneath the present river level (see Fig. 59).

FIG. 57. Three ancient river terraces (I, II, III), on the west bank of the Connecticut River in Vermont, believed to be of Postglacial age. The terraces are respectively 140, 60, and 20 feet above the river, and thus show a profile similar to that of the terraces on the Somme in Pre-Chellean times previous to the accumulation of the deposits bearing Palæolithic flints. Photograph by H. H. H. Langill.

Since the most primitive Pre-Chellean flints occur in the coarse gravels which lie on the floors of these terraces immediately above the chalk, they prove that the entire excavation of the valley had been completed when the Pre-Chellean workers arrived there. Commont believes that this was the actual topography of the valley during the Third Interglacial Stage. The occurrence of Chellean flints in the white sands overlying the coarse gravels of the middle and upper terraces does not indicate that the flint workers were encamped here while these terraces were being cut out by the River Somme but rather that they sought these convenient bluffs for their quarries during the time that these sands and gravels were washing down from the sides of the valleys and from the plateaus above.

FIG. 58. Four typical forms of the Chellean *coup de poing*, or 'hand-stone,' from the ancient quarries of St. Acheul. About one-half actual size.

a. Disc-shaped—upper left.
b. Oval—upper right.
c. Poniard-shaped—lower left.
d. Almond-shaped—lower right.

In the collection of the American Museum of Natural History.

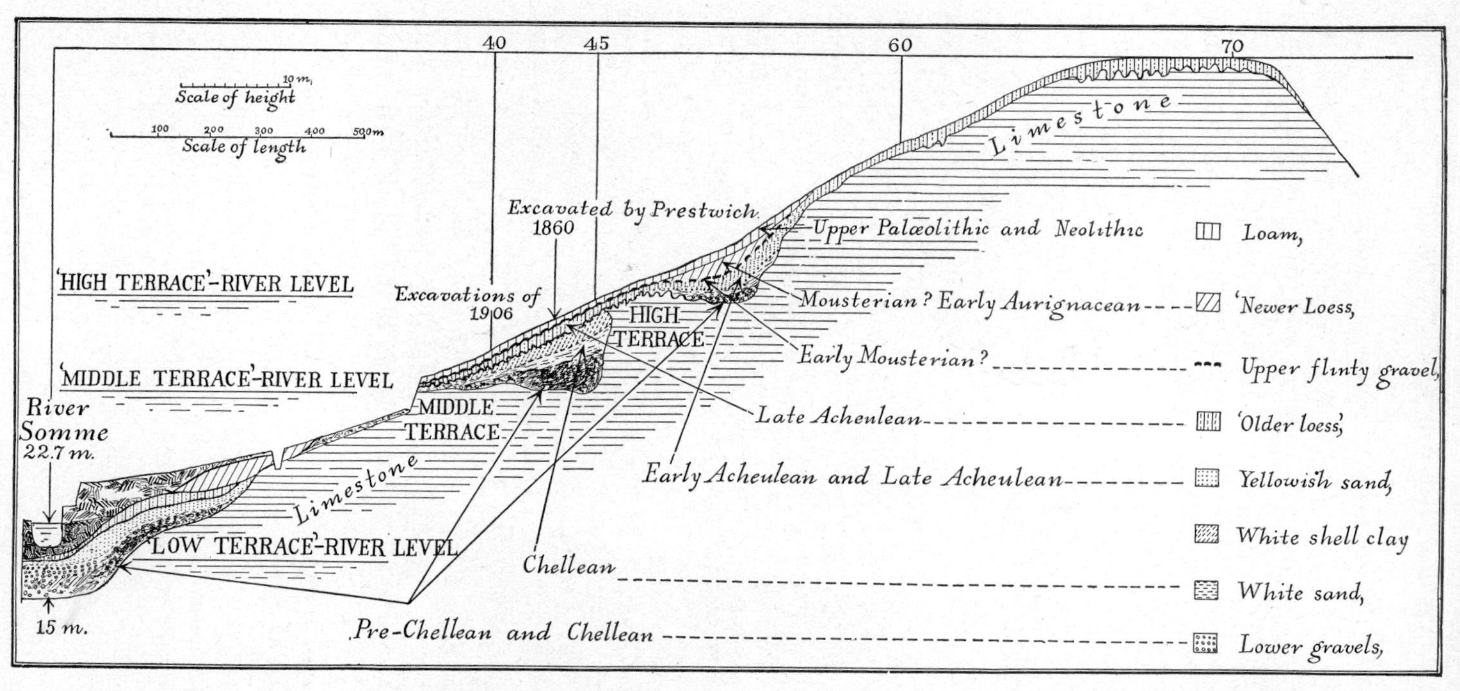

FIG. 59. Section of the ancient river terraces on the south bank of the River Somme at St. Acheul-Amiens, showing stations on the low, middle, and high terraces where flints were worked from the very beginning to the very end of the Old Stone Age. After Commont, 1908, 1909—modified and redrawn. The section shown runs northwest and southeast, in a gentle slope nearly 1½ miles in length, from the summit, 70 meters (about 230 feet) above sea-level, down to the river 47.3 meters (155 feet) below. Since Rigollot's excavations in 1851 sixteen flint-working stations have been discovered here, chiefly through building operations, most of them being on the middle and high terraces. This gives some idea of the vast extent of these ancient encampments, which cover the entire period of the Old Stone Age—perhaps 125,000 years.

The history of the climatic changes in the ancient valley of the Somme is most clearly written in these successive deposits, 15 feet in thickness, above the 'lower gravels' at St. Acheul. Along with the Pre-Chellean and Chellean flints in the 'old gravels' and 'white sands' we find records of the moist warm temperate climate which then prevailed in northern France and which undoubtedly was most favorable to the hippopotami, rhinoceroses, and elephants of those times. The river mollusks found with the late Chellean flints are another indication of the temperate forest climate which continued through early Acheulean times.

PREHISTORY OF ST. ACHEUL

NEOLITHIC.

- *Campignian*, recent earth and loam.

UPPER PALÆOLITHIC.

- *Solutrean.*
- *Upper Aurignacian*, loam.
- *Middle Aurignacian*, 'newer loess' and gravel.

LOWER PALÆOLITHIC.

- *Late Mousterian*, gravel and 'newer loess.'
- *Early Mousterian*, base of 'newer loess' (*l'ergeron*).
- *Middle Acheulean*, 'older loess' and drift.
- *Early Acheulean*, gravels below 'older loess' (*E. antiquus*).
- *Late Chellean*, fluviatile sands and mollusk fauna.
- *Early Chellean*, first coups de poing; old 'white sands' (*E. antiquus*).
- *Pre-Chellean*, prototypes of coup de poing; old 'lower gravels' (*E. antiquus*).

In the middle Acheulean are found the earliest deposits of 'older loess' which indicate a climate still temperate but arid, belonging to the middle of the Third Interglacial Stage. In Mousterian times we find heavy deposits of gravels corresponding to the moist cold climate of the Fourth Glacial Stage, followed in middle Aurignacian times by fresh layers of 'newer loess,' indicating the return of a dry climate. Finally, the layers of loam which were washed down over the sides of the valley, and in which the remains of Solutrean and Aurignacian camps are found, indicate the renewal of moist and probably forested conditions.

Thus, two dry loess periods are indicated in this valley, the first or 'older loess' belonging to Third Interglacial times, and the second or 'newer loess' to Postglacial times; and we clearly perceive that in the culture layers here there is no evidence whatever of more than one glacial stage preceded by a dry climatic period and deposits of loess. If the Pre-Chellean flint workers had arrived in this river-valley as early as Second Interglacial times, we should find proofs of three periods of arid climate and loess deposition and of two glaciations.

Beginning with middle Acheulean times the flints are found in deposits of gravels, loams, brick-earths, and 'older loess,' which all belong to a succeeding geologic stage and are of more recent date than the lower gravels and sands on the terraces which they overlap and conceal. Deposits of this kind have also been drifted down from the highest levels toward the bottom of the valley, and Commont distinguishes three different depositions or layers of 'loess loam,' the lowest or oldest of which contain Acheulean flints, while the middle loams contain Mousterian implements.

Even toward the close of the Third Interglacial Stage there were periods of warmth, perhaps during the height of the hot summer season, when animals of the warm fauna migrated from the south. Thus Commont has recently discovered in the valley of the Somme a station of Mousterian flint workers, whose industry is associated with remains of the three animals typical of the warmer climatic phase; namely, the straight-tusked elephant, the broad-nosed rhinoceros, and the hippopotamus. He has reaffirmed his belief that the greater part of this chapter of human prehistory, both as to the surface topography of the Somme valley and the evolution of the flint cultures from Pre-Chellean to Mousterian times, occurred during the Third Interglacial Stage.

The Early Warm Temperate Period of the Pre-Chellean Culture*

We have observed that from Torralba in the Province of Soria, Spain, to Abbeville, near the mouth of the Somme, in the north of France, three types of animals which entered Europe as

* The writer is indebted to M. Marcelin Boule and to M. l'Abbé Henri Breuil for their observations on this fauna and culture period.

early as Upper Pliocene times, namely, the Etruscan rhinoceros, the horse of Steno, and the sabre-tooth tiger, are said to occur in connection with early Chellean artifacts. The two former species may possibly be confused with early forms of Merck's rhinoceros and the true forest horses of Europe, but there can be no question as to the identification of the sabre-tooth tiger, numbers of which were found by M. d'Ault du Mesnil, at Abbeville, on the Somme, with early Chellean flints.

The mammalian life of the Somme at this time, as found in the *gisement du Champ de Mars* near Abbeville, is very rich. Among the larger forms there is certainly the great southern mammoth (*E. meridionalis trogontherii*), and possibly also the straight-tusked elephant (*E. antiquus*). There are unquestionably two species of rhinoceros, the smaller of which is recognized by Boule as the Etruscan, and the larger as Merck's rhinoceros. Steno's horse is said to occur here, and there are abundant remains of the great hippopotamus (*H. major*); the sabre-tooth tigers were very numerous as attested by the discovery of the lower jaws of thirty or more individuals. The short-faced hyæna (*H. brevirostris*) is also found, and there are several species of deer and wild cattle.

PRE-CHELLEAN FAUNA

Southern mammoth.
Etruscan rhinoceros.
Hippopotamus.
Primitive horse
(*Equus stenonis*)?
Sabre-tooth tiger.
Broad-nosed rhinoceros.
Straight-tusked elephant.
Giant beaver
(*Trogontherium cuvieri*).
Short-faced hyæna.
Typical Eurasiatic forest and meadow fauna, including deer, bison, and wild cattle.

This remarkably rich collection of mammals is associated with flints of primitive Chellean or, possibly, of Pre-Chellean type.[12] In Torralba, Spain, the same very ancient animals occur, and it appears possible that this was the prevailing mammalian life of Pre-Chellean times.

We may conclude, therefore, that there is considerable evidence, although not as yet quite convincing, that the early Chellean flint workers arrived in western Europe before the disappearance of the Etruscan rhinoceros and the sabre-tooth tiger.

The Pre-Chellean Stations

(See Figs. 53 and 56.)

The dawn of the Palæolithic Age is indicated in various river-drift stations by the appearance of crude flint *weapons* as well as *tools* or *implements*, in addition to the supposed tools of Eolithic times. There is an unmistakable effort to fashion the flint into a definite shape to serve a definite purpose: there can no longer be any question of human handiwork. Thus there gradually arise various *types* of flints, each of which undergoes its own evolution into a more perfect form. Naturally, the workers at some stations were more adept and inventive than at others. Nevertheless, the primitive stages of invention and of technique were carried from station to station; and thus for the first time we are enabled to establish the archæological age of various stations in western Europe.

Only a few stations have been discovered where the Palæolithic men were first fashioning their flints into prototypes of the Chellean and Acheulean forms. With relation to the theory that these primitive flint workers may have entered Europe by way of the northern coast of Africa, we observe that these stations are confined to Spain, southern and northern France, Belgium, and Great Britain. Neither Pre-Chellean nor Chellean stations of unquestioned authenticity have been found in Germany or central Europe, and, so far as present evidence goes, it would appear that the Pre-Chellean culture did not enter Europe directly from the east, or even along the northern coast of the Mediterranean, but rather along the northern coast of Africa,* where Chellean culture is recorded in association with mammalian remains belonging to the middle Pleistocene Epoch.

The southernmost stations of Chellean culture at present known in Europe are those of Torralba and San Isidro, in central Spain. In the Department of the Gironde is the Chellean station of Marignac, and it is not unlikely that other stations will be dis-

* Industry similar to the Chellean, but not necessarily of the same age, is distributed all over eastern Africa from Egypt to the Cape.

covered in the same region, because the Palæolithic races strongly favored the valleys of the Dordogne and Garonne, but thus far this is the only station known in southern France which represents this period of the dawn of human culture.

The chief Pre-Chellean and Chellean stations were clustered along the valleys of the Somme and Seine. Of those rare sites

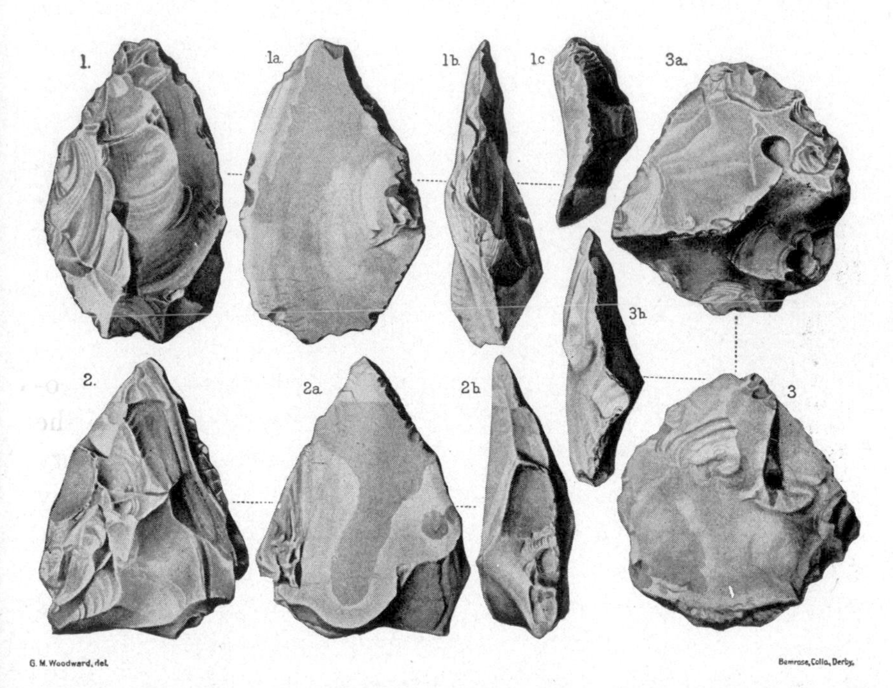

FIG. 60. Very primitive palæoliths from Piltdown, Sussex, consisting chiefly of tools and points of triangular and oval form, fashioned out of flint nodules split in two and flaked on one side only, with very coarse marginal retouch. After Dawson. Nos. 1 and 2 are nearly one-half actual size; No. 3 nearly one-quarter actual size.

presenting a typical Pre-Chellean culture, we may note the neighboring stations of St. Acheul and Montières, both in the suburbs of Amiens on the Somme, and the station of Helin, near Spiennes, in Belgium, explored by Rutot. A very primitive and possibly Pre-Chellean culture was found on the site of the Champ de Mars, at Abbeville. This culture also extended westward across the broad plain which is now the Strait of Dover to the valley of the Thames, on whose northern bank is the important station of

Gray's Thurrock, while farther to the south is the recently discovered site of Piltdown, in the valley of the Ouse, Sussex.

The flint tools (Fig. 60) found in the layer immediately overlying the Piltdown skull are excessively primitive and indicate that the Piltdown flint workers had not attained the stage of craftsmanship described by Commont as 'Pre-Chellean' at St. Acheul. "Among the flints," observes Dawson, "we found several undoubted flint implements besides numerous 'eoliths.' The workmanship of the former is similar to that of the Chellean or Pre-Chellean stage; but in the majority of the Piltdown specimens the work appears chiefly on one face of the implements."

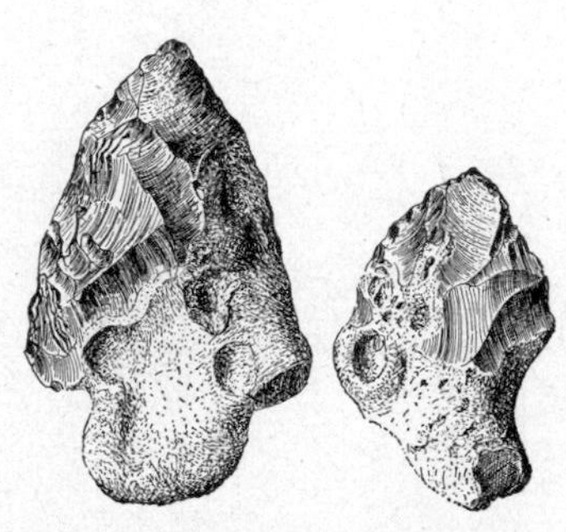

Fig. 61. Primitive *coups de poing* or 'hand-stones' of Pre-Chellean type, found in the lower gravels of the middle and high terraces at St. Acheul. After Commont. One-quarter actual size.

In the Helin quarry near Spiennes[13] occur rude prototypes of the Palæolithic coup de poing associated with numerous flakes which do not greatly differ from those in the lowest river-gravels of St. Acheul; there is a close correspondence in the workmanship of the two sites, so that we may regard the Mesvinian of Rutot* as a culture stage equivalent to the Pre-Chellean. The river-gravels and sands of Helin which contain the implements also resemble those of St. Acheul in their order of stratification. Of special interest is the fact that a primitive flint from this Helin quarry, known as the 'borer,' is strikingly similar to the 'Eolithic' borer found in the same layer with the Piltdown skull in Sussex. By such indications as this, when strengthened by further evidence of the same kind, we may be able eventually to establish the date both of this Pre-Chellean or Mesvinian culture and of the Piltdown race.

In considering the Pre-Chellean implements found at St. Acheul in 1906, we note[14] that at this dawning stage of human

* Schmidt regards the *Strépyan* implements, which are considered by Rutot and others to be transitional, between the Mesvinian and the Chellean, as closely similar to the Pre-Chellean of France and probably of the same age.

invention the flint workers were not deliberately designing the form of their implements but were dealing rather with the chance shapes of shattered blocks of flint, seeking with a few well-directed blows to produce a sharp point or a good cutting edge. This was the beginning of the art of 'retouch,' which was done by means of light blows with a second stone instead of the hammer-stone with which the rough flakes were first knocked off. The retouch served a double purpose: Its first and most important object was further to sharpen the point or edge of the

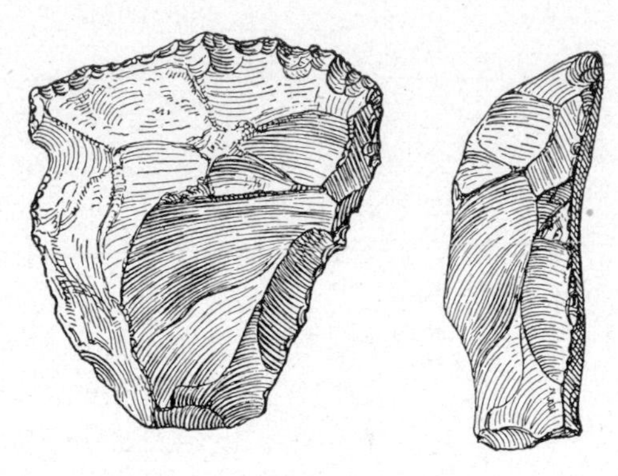

FIG. 62. Primitive *grattoir*, or planing tool (side and edge views), of Pre-Chellean type; found in the lowest gravels of the terraces at St. Acheul. After Commont. One-quarter actual size.

tool. This was done by chipping off small flakes from the upper side, so as to give the flint a saw-like edge. Its second object was to protect the hand of the user by blunting any sharp edges or points which might prevent a firm grip of the implement. Often the smooth, rounded end of the flint nodule, with crust intact, is carefully preserved for this purpose (Fig. 61). It is this grasping of the primitive tool by the hand to which the terms 'coup de poing,' 'Faustkeil,' and 'hand-axe' refer. 'Hand-stone' is, perhaps, the most fitting designation in our language, but it appears best to retain the original French designation, coup de poing.

As the shape of the flint is purely due to chance, these Pre-Chellean implements are interpreted by archæologists chiefly according to the manner of retouch they have received. Already they are adapted to quite a variety of purposes, both as weapons of the chase and for trimming and shaping wooden implements and dressing hides. Thus Obermaier observes that the concave, serrated edges characteristic of some of these implements may well have been used for scraping the bark from branches and smoothing them down into poles; that the rough coups de poing would be well adapted to dividing flesh and dressing hides; that the sharp-pointed fragments could be used as borers, and others that are clumsier and heavier as planes (see Fig. 62).

The inventory of these ancestral Pre-Chellean forms of implements, used in industrial and domestic life, in the chase, and in war, is as follows:

Grattoir,	planing tool.
Racloir,	scraper.
Perçoir,	drill, borer.
Couteau,	knife.
Percuteur,	hammer-stone.
Pierre de jet?	throwing stone?
Prototypes of coup de poing,	hand-stone.

It includes five, possibly six, chief types. The true coup de poing, a combination tool of Chellean times, is not yet developed in the Pre-Chellean, and the other implements, although similar in form, are more primitive. They are all in an experimental stage of development.

Indications that this primitive industry spread over south-eastern England as well, and that a succession of Pre-Chellean into Chellean culture may be demonstrated, occur in connection with the recent discovery of the very ancient Piltdown race.

The Piltdown Race[15]

The 'dawn man' is the most ancient human type in which the form of the head and size of the brain are known. Its anatomy, as well as its geologic antiquity, is therefore of profound interest and worthy of very full consideration. We may first review the authors' narrative of this remarkable discovery and the history of opinion concerning it.

Piltdown, Sussex, lies between two branches of the Ouse, about 35 miles south and slightly to the east of Gray's Thurrock, the Chellean station of the Thames. To the east is the plateau of Kent, in which many flints of Eolithic type have been found.

The gravel layer in which the Piltdown skull occurred is situated on a well-defined plateau of large area and lies about 80 feet above the level of the main stream of the Ouse. Remnants of the flint-bearing gravels and drifts occur upon the plateau and

Fig. 63. Discovery site of the famous Piltdown skull near Piltdown, Sussex. After Dawson. A shallow pit of dark-brown gravel, at the bottom of which were found the fragments of the skull and a single primitive implement of worked flint (see Fig. 65).

the slopes down which they trail toward the river and streams. This region was undoubtedly favorable to the flint workers of Pre-Chellean and Chellean times. Kennard[16] believes that the gravels are of the same age as those of the 'high terrace' of the lower valley of the Thames; the height above the stream level is practically the same, namely, about 80 feet. Another geologist, Clement Reid,[17] holds that the plateau, composed of Wealden chalk, through which flowed the stream bearing the Piltdown gravels, belongs to a period later than that of the maximum depression of Great Britain; that the deposits are of Pre-Glacial or early Pleistocene age; that they belong to the epoch after the cold period of the first glaciation had passed but occur at the very base of the succession of implement-bearing deposits in the south-east of England.

On the other hand, Dawson,[18] the discoverer of the Piltdown skull, in his first description states: "From these facts it appears probable that the skull and mandible cannot safely be described as being of earlier date than the first half of the Pleistocene Epoch. The individual probably lived during the warm cycle in that age."

The section of the gravel bed (Fig. 64) indicates that the remains of the Piltdown man were washed down with other fossils by a shallow stream charged with dark-brown gravel and unworked flints; some of these fossils were of Pliocene times from strata of the upper parts of the stream. In this channel were found the remains of a number of animals of the same age as the Piltdown man, a few flints resembling eoliths, and one very primitive worked flint of Pre-Chellean type, which may also have been washed down from deposits of earlier age. These precious geologic and archæologic records furnish the only means we have of determining the age of *Eoanthropus*, the 'dawn man,' one of the most important and significant discoveries in the whole history of anthropology. We are indebted to the geologist Charles Dawson and the palæontologist Arthur Smith Woodward for preserving these ancient records and describing them with great fulness and accuracy as follows (pp. 132 to 139):

Several years ago Dawson discovered a small portion of an unusually thick human parietal bone, taken from a gravel bed which was being dug for road-making purposes on a farm close to Piltdown Common. In the autumn of 1911 he picked up among the rain-washed spoil-heaps of the same gravel-pit another and larger piece of bone belonging to the forehead region of the same skull and including a portion of the ridge extending over the left eyebrow. Immediately impressed with the importance of this discovery, Dawson enlisted the co-operation of Smith Woodward, and a systematic search was made in these spoil-heaps and gravels, beginning in the spring of 1912; all the material was looked over and carefully sifted. It appears that the whole or greater part of the human skull had been scattered by the workmen, who had thrown away the pieces unnoticed. Thor-

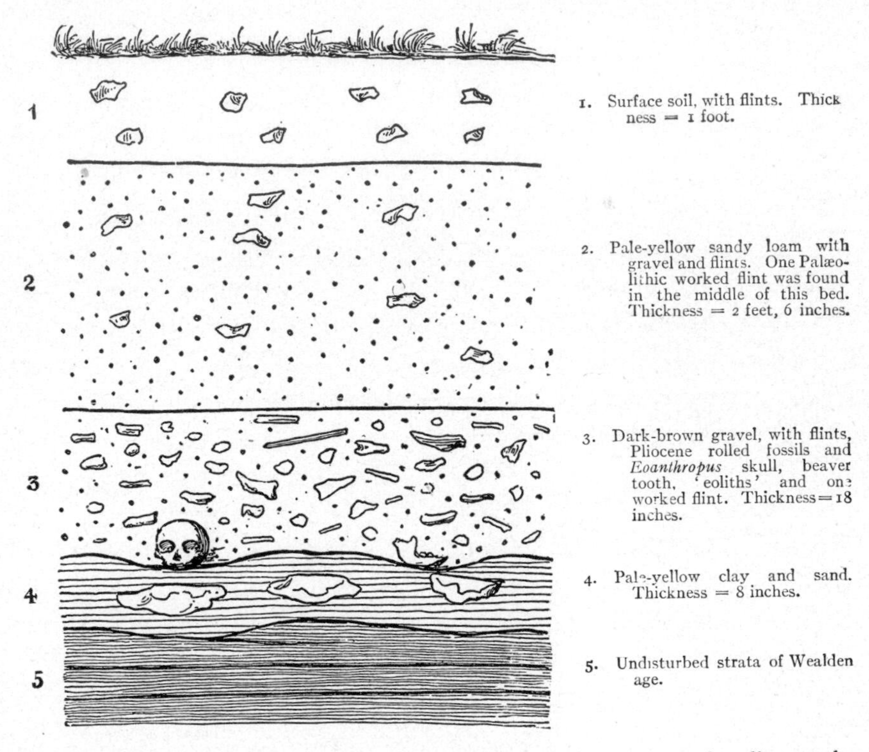

Fig. 64. Geologic section of the Piltdown gravel bed, showing in restored outlines at the bottom of layer 3 the position in which the fragments of the skull and jaw were found. After Dawson.

ough search in the bottom of the gravel bed itself revealed the right half of a jaw, which was found in a depression of undisturbed, finely stratified gravel, so far as could be judged on the spot identical with that from which the first portions of the cranium were exhumed. A yard from the jaw an important piece of the occipital bone of the skull was found. Search was renewed in 1913 by Father P. Teilhard, of Chardin, a French anthropologist, who fortunately recovered a single canine tooth, and later a pair of nasal bones were found, all of which fragments are of very great significance in the restoration of the skull.

The jaw appears to have been broken at the symphysis, and somewhat abraded, perhaps after being caught in the gravel before it was completely covered with sand. The fragments of the cranium show little or no signs of stream rolling or other abrasion save an incision caused by the workman's pick.

Analysis of the bones showed that the skull was in a condition of fossilization, no gelatine or organic matter remained, and

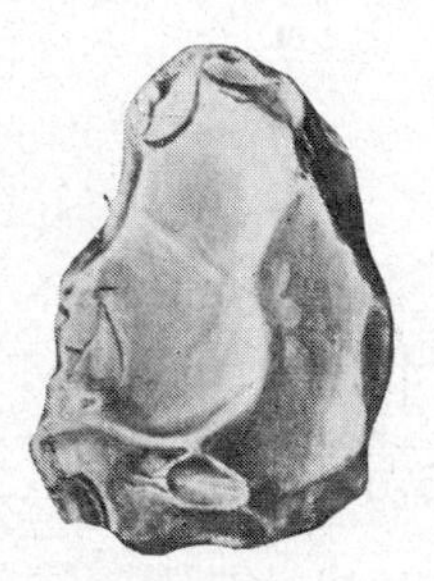

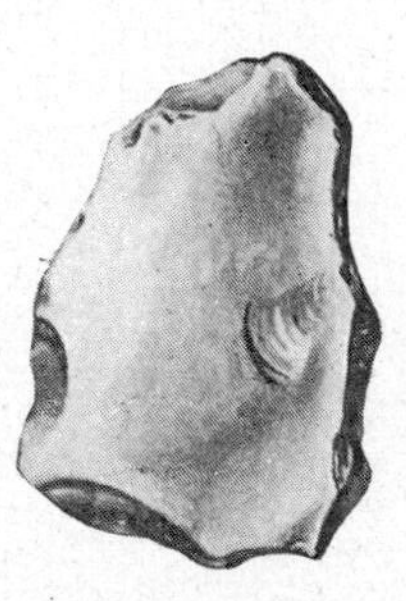

FIG. 65. The single worked flint of very primitive type found in the same layer (3) with the fragments of the Piltdown skull. After Dawson. One-half actual size.

mingled with a large proportion of the phosphates, originally present, was a considerable proportion of iron.*

The dark gravel bed (Fig. 64, layer 3), 18 inches in thickness, at the bottom of which the skull and jaw were found, contained a number of fossils which manifestly were not of the same age as the skull but were certainly from Pliocene deposits up-stream; these included the water-vole and remains of the mastodon, the southern mammoth, the hippopotamus, and a fragment of the grinding-tooth of a primitive elephant, resembling *Stegodon*. In the spoil-heaps, from which it is believed the skull of the Piltdown man was taken, were found an upper tooth of a rhinoceros, either of the Etruscan or of Merck's type; the tooth of a beaver and of a hippopotamus, and the leg-bone of a deer, which may have been cut or incised by man. Much more distinctive was a

* The original paper describing this remarkable discovery was read before the Geological Society of London, December, 1912, and published as a separate pamphlet in March, 1913. A discussion as to the geologic age by Kennard, Clement Reid, and others was held at the time of the reading of the original paper.

single flint (Fig. 65), worked only on one side, of the very primitive or Pre-Chellean type. Implements of this stage, as the author observes, are difficult to classify with certainty, owing to the rudeness of their workmanship; they resemble certain rude implements occasionally found on the surface of the chalk downs near Piltdown. The majority of the flints found in the gravel were worked only on one face; their form is thick, and the flaking is broad and sparing; the original surface of the flint is left in a smooth, natural condition at the point grasped by the hand; the whole implement thus has a very rude and massive form. These flints appear to be of even more primitive form than those at St. Acheul described as Pre-Chellean by Commont.

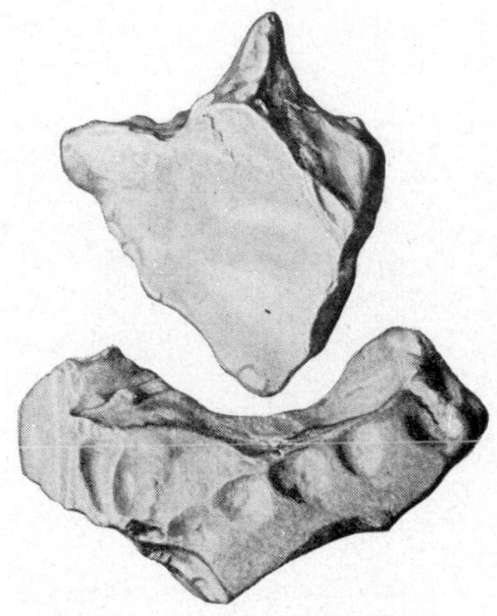

Fig. 66. Eoliths found in or near the Piltdown gravel-pit. After Dawson. One-half actual size.
a. Borer (above).
b. Curved scraper (below).

The eoliths found in the gravel-pit and in the adjacent fields are of the 'borer' and 'hollow-scraper' forms; also, some are of the 'crescent-shaped-scraper' type, mostly rolled and water-worn, as if transported from a distance. This is a stream or river bed, not a Palæolithic quarry.

There can be little doubt, however, that the Piltdown man belonged to a period when the flint industry was in a very primitive stage, antecedent to the true Chellean. It has subsequently been observed that the gravel strata (3) containing the Piltdown man were deeper than the higher stratum containing flints nearer the Chellean type.

The discovery of this skull aroused interest as great as or even greater than that attending the discovery of the two other 'river-drift' races, the Trinil and the Heidelberg. In this discussion the most distinguished anatomists of Great Britain, Arthur Smith Woodward, Elliot Smith, and Arthur Keith, took part, and finally the original pieces were re-examined by three anatomists of this country.*

It is important to present in full the original opinions of Smith Woodward, who devoted most careful study to the first reconstruction of the skull (Fig. 67), a model which was subsequently modified by the actual discovery of one of the canine teeth. In his original description it is observed that the pieces of the skull preserved are noteworthy for the great thickness of the bone, it being 11 to 12 mm. as compared with 5 to 6 mm., the average thickness in the modern European skull, or 6 to 8 mm., the thickness in the skull of the Neanderthal races and in that of the modern Australian; the cephalic index is estimated at 78 or 79, that is, the skull is believed to have been proportionately low and wide, almost brachycephalic; there was apparently no prominent or thickened ridge above the orbits, a feature which immediately distinguishes this skull from that of the Neanderthal races; the several bones of the brain-case are typically human and not in the least like those of the anthropoid apes; the brain capacity was originally estimated at 1070 c.cm., not equalling that of some of the lowest brain types in the existing Australian races and de-

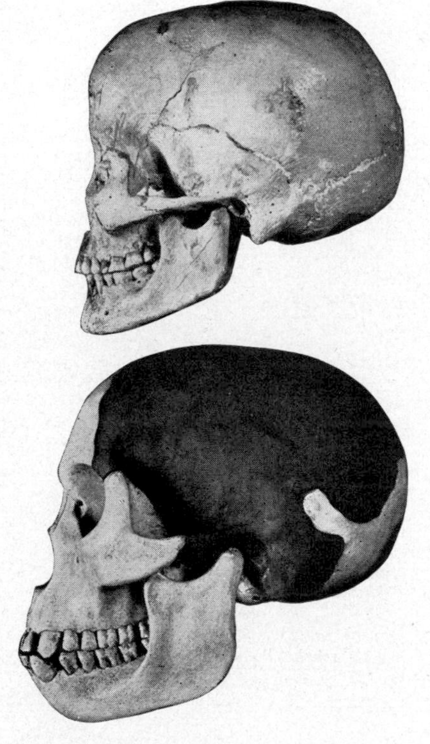

Fig. 67. Skull of South African Bushman (upper) exhibiting the contrast in the structure of the jaw and forehead. One-quarter life size. Original restoration of the Piltdown skull (lower) made by Smith Woodward in 1913. One-quarter life size.

* By the author of this work, and also by Professor J. Howard McGregor of Columbia University and Doctor William K. Gregory of Columbia University and of the American Museum of Natural History.

cidedly below that of the Neanderthal man of Spy and La Chapelle-aux-Saints; the nasal bones are typically human but relatively small and broad, so that the nose was flattened, resembling that in some of the existing Malay and African races.

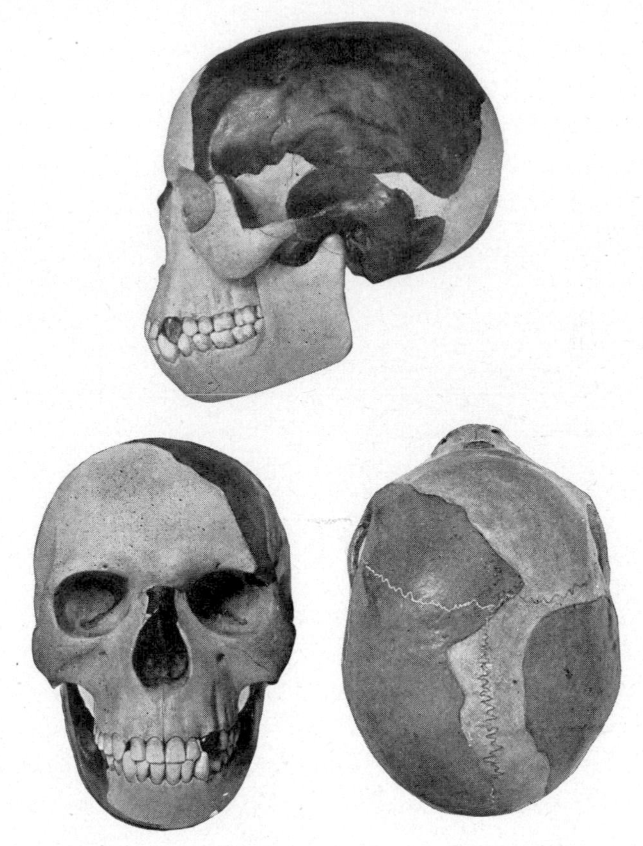

Fig. 68. Three views of the Piltdown skull as reconstructed by J. H. McGregor, 1914. This restoration includes the nasal bones and canine tooth, which were not known at the time of Smith Woodward's reconstruction of 1913. One-quarter life size.

The jaw presents profoundly different characters; the whole of the bone preserved closely resembles that of a young chimpanzee; thus the slope of the bony chin as restored is between that of an adult ape and that of the Heidelberg man, with an extremely receding chin; the ascending portion of the jaw for the attachment of the temporal muscles is broad and thickened anteriorly. Associated with the jaw were two elongated molar teeth, worn down by use to such an extent that the individual could not have been less than thirty years of age and was probably older. These teeth are relatively longer and narrower than those in the modern human jaw. The canine tooth, identified by Smith Woodward as belonging in the lower jaw, strengthened by the evidence afforded by the jaw itself, proves that the face was elongate or prognathous and that the canine teeth were very prominent like those of the anthropoid apes; it affords definite proof that the front teeth of the Piltdown man resembled those of the ape.

The author's conclusion is that while the skull is essentially human, it approaches the lower races of man in certain characters of the brain, in the attachment of the muscles of the neck, in the large extent of the temporal muscles attached to the jaw, and in the probably large size of the face. The mandible, on the other hand, appears precisely like that of the ape, with nothing human except the molar teeth, and even these approach the dentition of the apes in their elongate shape and well-developed fifth or posterior intermediate cusp. This type of man, distinguished by the smooth forehead and supraorbital borders and ape-like jaw, represents a new genus called *Eoanthropus*, or 'dawn man,' while the species has been named *dawsoni* in honor of the discoverer, Charles Dawson. This very ancient type of man is defined by the ape-like chin and junction of the two halves of the jaw, by a series of parallel grinding-teeth, with narrow lower molar teeth, which do not diminish in size backward, and by the steep forehead and slight development of the brow ridges. The jaw manifestly differs from that of the Heidelberg man in its comparative slenderness and relative deepening toward the symphysis.

The discussion of this very important paper by Smith Woodward and Dawson centred about two points. First, whether the ape-like jaw really belonged with the human skull rather than with that of some anthropoid ape which happened to be drifted down in the same stratum; and second, whether the extremely low original estimate of the brain capacity of 1070 c.cm., was not due to incorrect adjustment or reconstruction of the separate pieces of the skull.

Keith,[19] the leader in the criticism of Woodward's reconstruction, maintained that when the two sides of the skull were properly restored and made approximately symmetrical, the brain capacity would be found to equal 1500 c.cm.; the brain cast of the skull even as originally reconstructed was found to be close to 1200 c.cm. This author agreed that skull, jaw, and canine tooth belonged to *Eoanthropus* but that they could not well belong to the same individual.

In defense of Woodward's reconstruction came the powerful support of Elliot Smith.[20] He maintained that the evidence afforded by the re-examination of the bones corroborated in the main Smith Woodward's identification of the median plane of the skull; further, that the original reconstruction of the prognathous face was confirmed by the discovery of the canine tooth, also that there remained no doubt that the association of the skull, the jaw, and the canine tooth was a correct one. The back portion of the skull is decidedly asymmetrical, a condition found both in the lower and higher races of man. A slight rearrangement and widening of the bones along the median upper line of the skull raise the estimate of the brain capacity to 1100 c.cm. as the probable maximum.

Elliot Smith continued that he considered the brain to be of a more primitive kind than any human brain that he had ever seen, yet that it could be called human and that it already showed a considerable development of those parts which in modern man we associate with the power of speech; thus, there was no doubt of the unique importance of this skull as representing an entirely new type of "man in the making." As regards the form of the lower jaw, it was observed that in the dawn of human existence teeth suitable for weapons of offense and defense were retained long after the brain had attained its human status. Thus the ape-like form of the chin does not signify inability to speak, for speech must have come when the jaws were still ape-like in character, and the bony changes that produced the recession of the tooth line and the form of the chin were mainly due to sexual selection, to the reduction in the size of the grinding-teeth, and, in a minor degree, to the growth and specialization of the muscles of the jaw and tongue employed in speech.

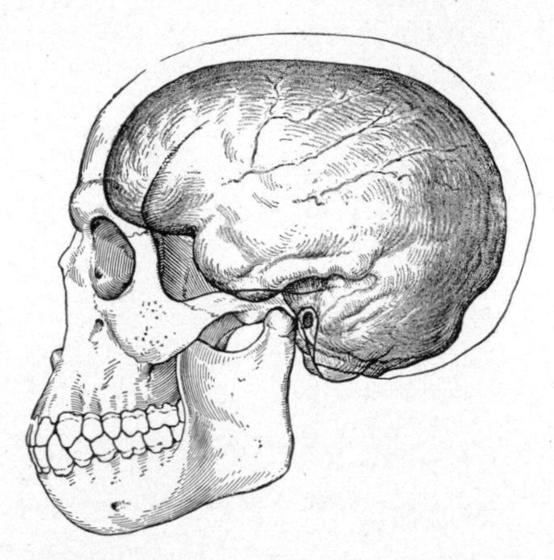

FIG. 69. The Piltdown skull with the right half removed to display the extreme thickness of the bones and the shape of the brain. As restored by J. H. McGregor. One-quarter life size.

At first sight the brain-case resembles that of the Neanderthal skull found at Gibraltar, which is supposed to be that of a woman; it is relatively long, narrow, and especially flat, but it is smaller and presents more primitive features than those of any known human brain. Taking all these features into consideration, we must regard this as being the most primitive and most ape-like human brain so far

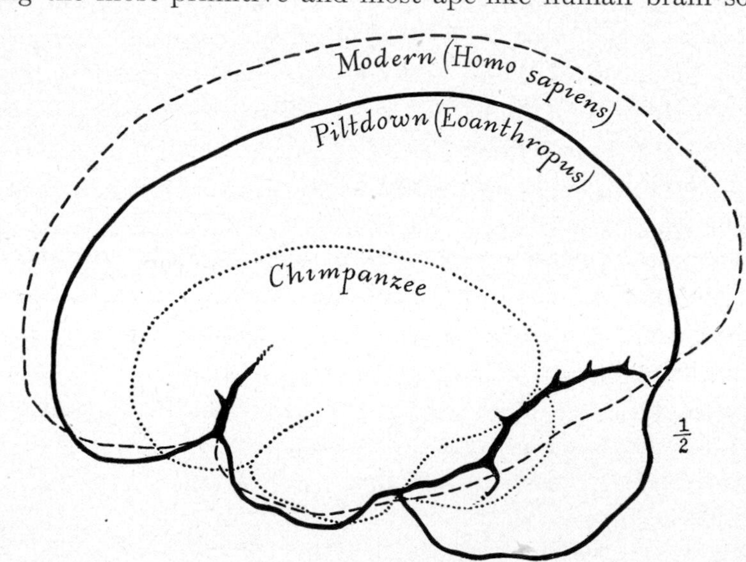

FIG. 70. Outline of the left side of the Piltdown brain, compared with similar brain outlines of a chimpanzee and of a high type of modern man. One-half life size.

recorded; one such as might reasonably be associated with a jaw which presented such distinctive ape characters. The brain, however, is far more human than the jaw, from which we may infer that the evolution of the brain preceded that of the mandible, as well as the development of beauty of the face and the human development of the bodily characters in general.

The latest opinion of Smith Woodward* is that the brain, while the most primitive which has been discovered, had a bulk of nearly 1300 c.cm., equalling that of the smaller human brains of to-day and surpassing that of the Australians, which rarely exceeds 1250 c.cm.

The original views of Smith Woodward and of Elliot Smith regarding the relation of the Piltdown race to the Heidelberg and Neanderthal races are also of very great interest and may be cited. First, the fact that the Piltdown and Heidelberg races are almost of the same geologic age proves that at the end of the Pliocene Epoch the representatives of man in western Europe had already branched into widely divergent groups: the one (Heidelberg-Neanderthal) characterized by a very low projecting forehead, with a subhuman head of Neanderthaloid contour; the other with a flattened forehead and with an ape-like jaw of the Piltdown contour. We should not forget that in the Piltdown skull the absence of prominent ridges above the eyes may possibly be due in some degree to the fact that the type skull may belong to a female, as suggested by certain characters of the jaw; but among all existing apes the skull in early life has the rounded shape of the Piltdown skull, with a high forehead and scarcely any brow ridges. It seems reasonable, therefore, to interpret the Piltdown skull as exhibiting a closer resemblance to the skulls of our human ancestors in mid-Tertiary times than any fossil skull hitherto found. If this view be accepted, we may suppose that the Piltdown type became gradually modified into the Neanderthal type by a series of changes similar to those passed through by the early apes as they evolved into typical modern apes, with their low brows and prominent ridges above the eyes. This

* *Guide to the Fossil Remains of Man*, 1915.1.

would tend to support the theory that the Neanderthal men were degenerate offshoots of the Tertiary race, of which the Piltdown skull provides the first discovered evidence—a race with a simple, flattened forehead and developed eye ridges.

Elliot Smith concluded that members of the Piltdown race might well have been the direct ancestors of the existing species

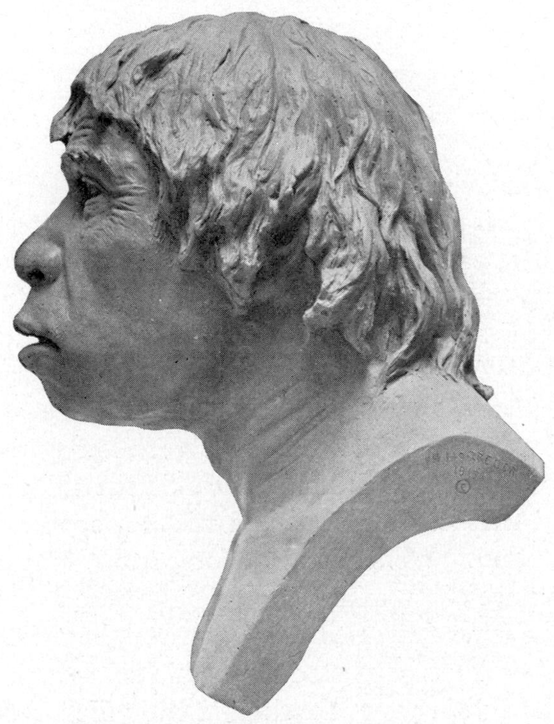

FIG. 71. Restoration of the head of Piltdown man, in profile, based upon the reconstruction shown in Fig. 68, p. 137. After model by J. H. McGregor. One-quarter life size.

of man (*Homo sapiens*), thus affording a direct link with undiscovered Tertiary apes; whereas, the more recent fossil men of the Neanderthal type, with prominent brow ridges resembling those of the existing apes, may have belonged to a degenerate race which later became extinct. According to this view, *Eoanthropus* represents a persistent and very slightly modified descendant of the type of Tertiary man which was the common ancestor of a branch giving rise to *Homo sapiens*, on the one hand, and of another branch giving rise to *Homo neanderthalensis*, on the other.

Another theory as to the relationships of *Eoanthropus* is that of Marcelin Boule,[21] who is inclined to regard the jaws of the Piltdown and Heidelberg races as of similar geologic age, but of

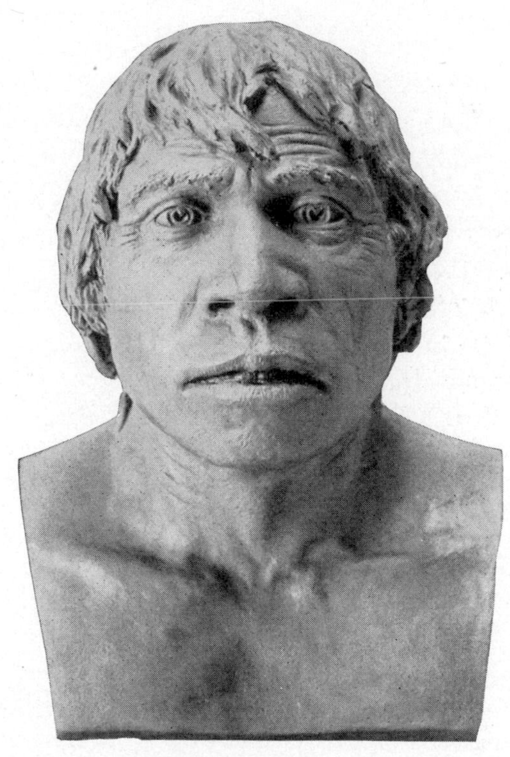

FIG. 72. Restoration of the head of Piltdown man, full front, after model by J. H. McGregor. One-quarter life size. (Compare Figs. 68 and 71.)

dissimilar racial type. He continues: "If the skull and jaw of Piltdown belong to the same individual, and if the mandibles of the Heidelberg and Piltdown men are of the same type, this discovery is most valuable in establishing the cranial structure of the Heidelberg race. But it appears rather that we have here two types of man which lived in Chellean times, both distinguished by very low cranial characters. Of these the Piltdown race seems to us the probable ancestor in the direct line of the recent species of man, *Homo sapiens;* while the Heidelberg race may be considered, until we have further knowledge, as a possible precursor of *Homo neanderthalensis.*"

The latest opinion of the German anatomist Schwalbe[22] is that the proper restoration of the region of the chin in the Piltdown man might make it possible to refer this jaw to *Homo sapiens*, but this would merely prove that *Homo sapiens* already existed in early Pleistocene times. The skull of the Piltdown man, continues Schwalbe, corresponds with that of a well-developed, good-sized skull of *Homo sapiens;* the only unusual feature is the remarkable thickness of the bone.*

Finally, our own opinion is that the Piltdown race is not ancestral to either the Heidelbergs or the Neanderthals. Very recently† the jaw of the Piltdown man has been restudied and referred by more than one expert to a fully adult chimpanzee. This leaves us still in doubt as to the exact geologic age and relationships of the Piltdown man (see Appendix, Note IX), whom we are still inclined to regard as a side branch of the human family as shown in the family tree on p. 491.

Mammalian Life of Chellean and Acheulean Times[23]

The mammalian life which we find with the more advanced implements of Chellean times apparently does not include the old Pliocene mammals, such as the Etruscan rhinoceros and the sabre-tooth tiger. With this exception it is so similar to that of Second Interglacial times that it may serve to prove again that the third glaciation was a local episode and not a wide-spread climatic influence. This life is everywhere the same, from the

* The reconstruction (Fig. 68) of the Piltdown skull made by Professor J. H. McGregor has a cranial capacity of about 1300 c.cm. The brain (Fig. 70) is seen to be very narrow and low in the prefrontal area, the seat of the higher mental faculties. In the reconstruction the cranial region is in the main very like the second restoration by Doctor Smith Woodward, but the jaws differ in some respects. The tooth hitherto regarded as a right lower canine is now placed as the left upper canine, in accord with the conclusions of the author of this work and of Doctors Matthew and Gregory of the American Museum of Natural History.

† See Appendix, Note IX, p. 512.

Pl. IV. The Piltdown man of Sussex, England. Antiquity variously estimated at 100,000 to 300,000 years. The ape-like structure of the jaw does not prevent the expression of a considerable degree of intelligence in the face. After the restoration modelled by J. H. McGregor.

valley of the Thames, as witnessed in the low river-gravels of Gray's Thurrock and Ilford, to the region of the present Thuringian forests near Weimar, where it is found in the deposits of Taubach, Ehringsdorf, and Achenheim, in which the mammals belong to the more recent date of early Acheulean culture. The life of this great region during Chellean and early Acheulean times was a mingling of the characteristic forest and meadow fauna of western Europe with the descendants of the African-Asiatic invaders of late Pliocene and early Pleistocene times.

Southern mammoth.
Hippopotamus.
Straight-tusked elephant.
Broad-nosed rhinoceros.
Spotted hyæna.
Lion.
Bison and wild ox.
Red deer.
Roe-deer.
Giant deer.
Brown bear.
Wolf.
Badger.
Marten.
Otter.
Beaver.
Hamster.
Water-vole.

The forests were full of the red deer (*Cervus elaphus*), of the roe-deer (*C. capreolus*), and of the giant deer (*Megaceros*), also of a primitive species of wild boar (*Sus scrofa ferus*) and of wild horses probably representing more than one variety. The brown bear (*Ursus arctos*) of Europe is now for the first time identified; there was also a primitive species of wolf (*Canis suessi*).

The small carnivora of the forests and of the streams are all considered as closely related to existing species, namely, the badger (*Meles taxus*), the marten (*Mustela martes*), the otter (*Lutra vulgaris*), and the water-vole (*Arvicola amphibius*). The prehistoric beaver of Europe (*Castor fiber*) now replaces the giant beaver (*Trogontherium*) of Second Interglacial times.

Among the large carnivora, the lion (*Felis leo antiqua*) and the spotted hyæna (*H. crocuta*) have replaced the sabre-tooth tiger and the striped hyæna of early Pleistocene times. Four great Asiatic mammals, including two species of elephants, one species of rhinoceros, and the hippopotamus, roamed through the forests and meadows of this warm temperate region. The horse of this period is considered[24] to belong to the Forest or Nordic type, from which our modern draught-horses have descended. The lions and hyænas which abounded in Chellean and early Acheulean times are in part ancestors of the cave types which appear in the succeeding Reindeer or Cavern Period. In general, this mammalian life of Chellean and early Acheulean times in Europe frequented the river shores and the neighboring forests and meadows favored by a warm temperate climate with mild winters, such as is indicated by the presence of the fig-tree and of the Canary laurel in the region of north central France near Paris.

Undoubtedly the Chellean and Acheulean hunters had begun the chase both of the bison, or wisent (*B. priscus*), and of the wild cattle, or aurochs.*

This warm temperate mammalian life spread very widely over northern Europe, as shown especially in the distribution (Fig. 44) of the hippopotamus, the straight-tusked elephant, and Merck's rhinoceros. The latter pair were constant companions and are seen to have a closely similar and somewhat more northerly range than the hippopotamus, which is rather the climatic companion of the southern mammoth and ranges farther south. These animals in the gravel and sand layers along the river slopes and 'terraces' mingled their remains with the artifacts of the flint workers. For example, in the gravel 'terraces' of the Somme we find the bones of the straight-tusked elephant and Merck's rhinoceros in the same sand layers with the Chellean flints. Thus the men of Chellean times may well have pursued this giant elephant (*E. antiquus*) and rhinoceros (*D. merckii*) as their tribal successors in the same valley hunted the woolly mammoth and woolly rhinoceros.

Distribution of the Chellean Implements

All over the world may be found traces of a Stone Age, ancient or modern, primitive implements of stone and flint analogous to

* The early Teutonic designation of these animals was as follows: bison, 'wisent,' wild ox, 'auerochs,' 'urochs' (the 'urus' of Cæsar). The urus survived in Germany as late as the seventeenth century, while a few of the bison or 'wisent' survive to the present time. The bison was distinctively a short-headed animal, while its contemporary, the urus, was long-headed and less agile. At Dürnten, near Zürich, remains of the urus are found associated with those of the hardy, straight-tusked elephant and of Merck's rhinoceros. (See Appendix, Note IV.)

those of the true Chellean period of western Europe but not really identical when very closely compared. These represent the early attempts of the human hand, directed by the primitive mind, to fashion hard materials into forms adapted to the purposes of war, the chase, and domestic life. The result is a series

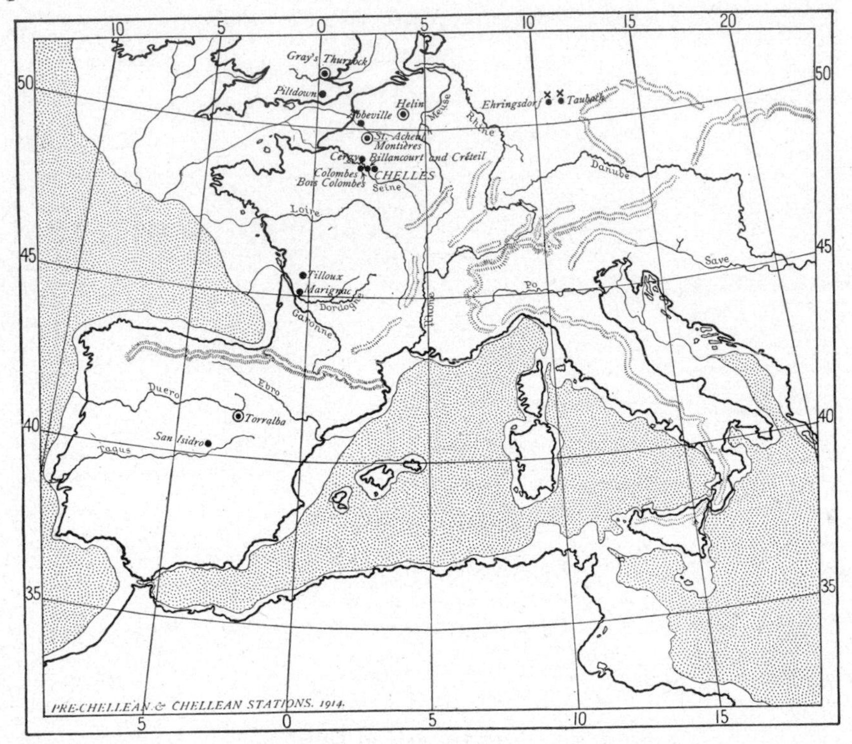

Fig. 73. Distribution of the principal Pre-Chellean and Chellean industrial stations in western Europe.

of parallels in form which come under the evolution principle of convergence. Thus, in all the continents except Australia—in Europe, in Asia, and even in North and South America—primitive races have passed through an industrial stage similar to the typical Chellean of western Europe. This we should rather attribute to a similarity in human invention and in human needs than to the theory that the Chellean industry originated at some particular centre and travelled in a slowly enlarging wave over the entire world.

In western Europe the Chellean culture certainly had a development all its own, adapted to a race of bold hunters who lived in the open and whose entire industry developed around the products of the chase. For them flint and quartzite took the place of bronze, iron, or steel. This culture marked a distinct and probably a very long epoch of time in which inventions and multiplications of form were gradually spread from tribe to tribe,

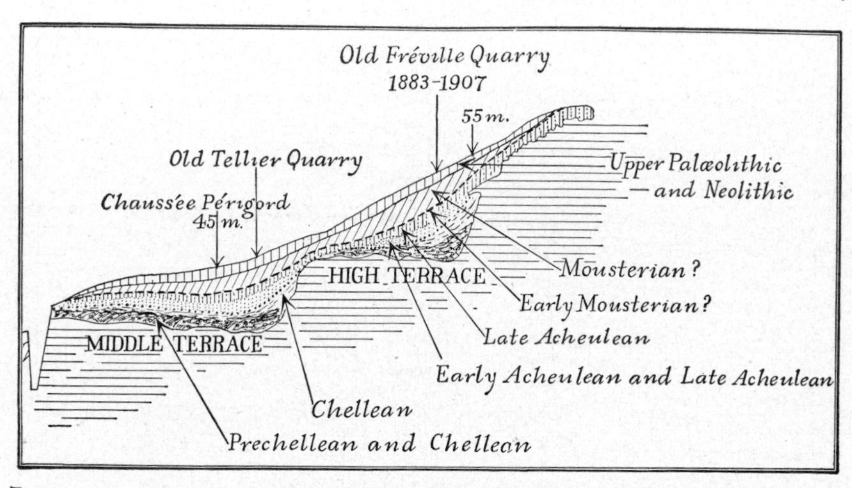

FIG. 74. Section of the middle and high terraces at St. Acheul, from southwest to northeast. After Commont, 1908, 1909, modified and redrawn. The Pre-Chellean workers first established themselves here at the time when the Somme was visited by the straight-tusked elephant and other primitive mammals of the warm African-Asiatic fauna. (Compare Fig. 59, p. 122.)

exactly as modern inventions, usually originating at a single point and often in the mind of one ingenious individual, gradually spread over the world.

The clearest examples of the evolution of the seven or eight implements of the Chellean culture from the five or six rudimentary types of the Pre-Chellean have been found at St. Acheul by Commont. The abundance and variety of flint at this great station on the Somme made it a centre of industry from the dawn of the Old Stone Age to its very close. It was probably a region favorable to all kinds of large and small game. The researches of Commont show that with the exception of Castillo in northern Spain no other station in all Europe was so continuously occupied.

From Pre-Chellean to Neolithic times the men of every culture stage except the Magdalenian and Azilian-Tardenoisian found their way here, and thus the site of St. Acheul presents an epitome of the entire prehistoric industry. Even during the colder periods of climate this region continued to be visited—possibly during the warm weather of the summer seasons. At Montières, along the Somme, we find deposits of Mousterian culture which

FIG. 75. Excavation on the 'high terrace' at St. Acheul, known as the *ancienne carrière Dupont* and more recently as the *carrière Bultel*, showing eight geologic layers from the Upper Palæolithic deposits of brick-earth at the top (9) down to the sub-Chellean yellow gravels (2) overlying the chalk terrace at the bottom.

is generally characteristic of the cold climatic period but is here associated with a temperate fauna, including the hippopotamus, Merck's rhinoceros, and the straight-tusked elephant. Great geographic and climatic changes took place in the valley of the Somme during this long period of human evolution. The Pre-Chellean workers first established their industry on the middle and high 'terraces' at the time when the Somme was visited by the straight-tusked elephant and other much more primitive mammals of the warm Asiatic fauna. The early Acheulean camps on the same terraces were pitched in the gravels below layers of 'loess' which betoken an entire climatic change. The fourth glaciation passed by, and the Upper Palæolithic flint workers again returned and left the débris of their industry in the layers of loam which swept down the slopes of the valley from the surrounding hills. This succession will be studied more in detail in connection with the industry.

As contrasted with the four or more Pre-Chellean stations already known, namely, St. Acheul, Montières, Helin, Gray's Thurrock, and possibly Abbeville and Piltdown, there are at least sixteen stations in western Europe which are characteristically Chellean. In addition to the sites named above, all of which show deposits of typical Chellean implements above the Pre-Chellean, we may note the important Chellean stations of San Isidro and Torralba in central Spain; Tilloux and Marignac in southwestern France; Créteil, Colombes, Bois Colombes, and Billancourt on the Seine, in the immediate vicinity of Paris; Cergy on the Oise; the type station of Chelles on the Marne; Abbeville on the northern bank of the Somme; and the famous station of Kent's Hole, Devon, on the southwestern coast of England. Thus far no typical Chellean station has been discovered in Portugal, Italy, Germany, or Austria, nor, indeed, in any part of central Europe. This leaves the original habitat of the tribes that brought the Chellean culture to western Europe still a mystery; but, as already observed, the location of the stations favors the theory of a migration through northern Africa rather than through eastern Europe.

Compared with the Pre-Chellean flint workers the Chellean artisans advanced both by the improvement of the older types of implements and by the invention of new ones.[25] As observed by Obermaier, the flint worker is still dependent on the chance shape of the shattered fragments of flint which he has not yet learned to shape symmetrically. In the experimental search after the most useful form of flint which could be grasped by the hand, the very characteristic Chellean coup de poing was evolved out of its Pre-Chellean prototype. This implement was made of an elongate nodule, either of quartzite or, preferably, of flint, and flaked by the hammer on both sides to a more or less almond shape; as a rule, the point and its adjacent edges are sharpened; the

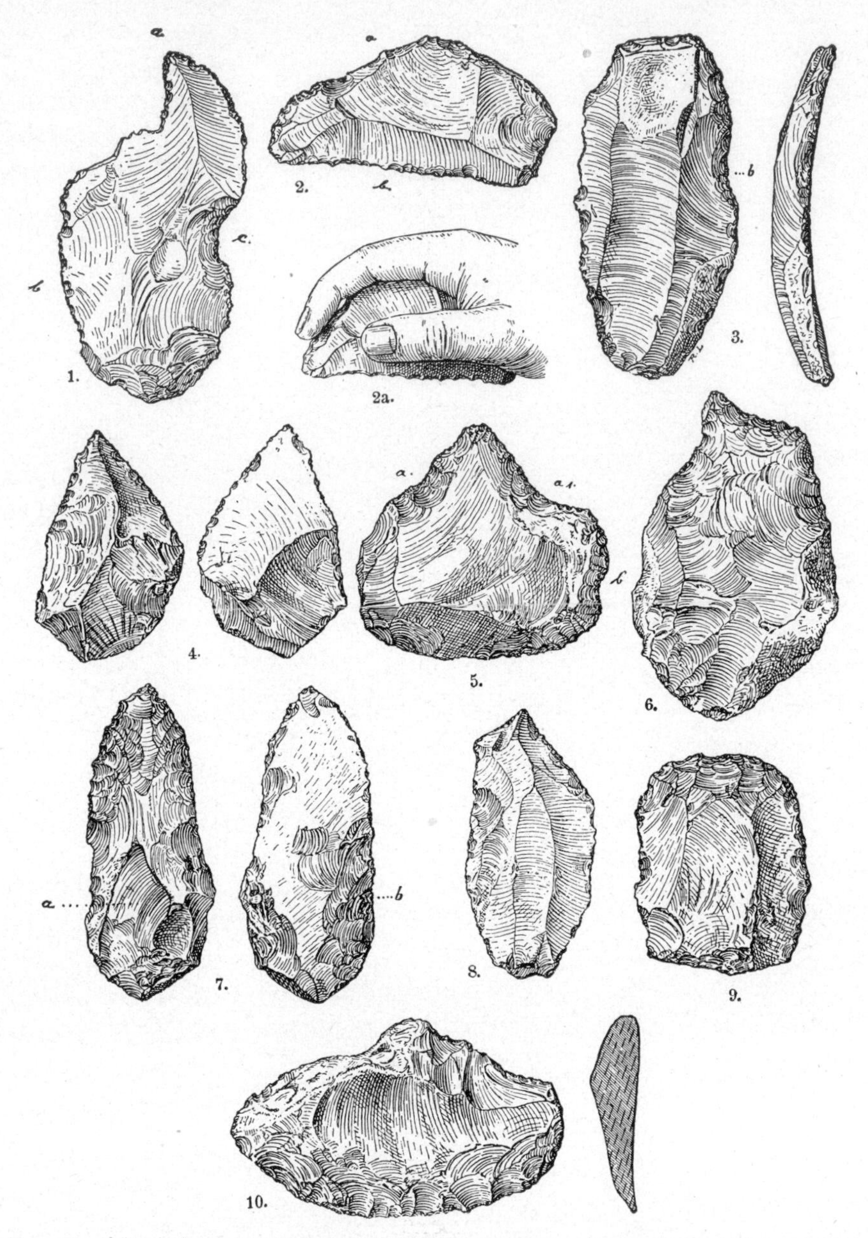

FIG. 76. Principal forms of small, late Chellean scraping, planing, and boring tools of flint, after Commont and Obermaier. One-half actual size. 1. Combination tool—small flake with a sharp point (*a*), cutting edge (*b*), and curved-in scraper (*c*). 2. Cutting tool with protective retouch for the index finger on the upper edge (*a*), and a sharp cutting edge (*b*). 3. Primitive knife. 4. 'Point.' 5. Combination tool—small flake with scraper edge (*b*), and two curved-in scraper edges (*a* and *a*1). 6. Borer. 7. Pointed scraper. 8. Knife with coarse boring point at one end. 9. Thick scraper or planing tool. 10. Curved scraper.

other end being rounded and blunted. Like most, if not all, of the Chellean implements, it was designed to be grasped by the bare hand and not furnished with a wooden haft or handle. It is not impossible that some of the pointed forms may have been wedged into a wooden handle, but there is no proof of it. In size the coup de poing varies from 4 to 8 inches in length, and examples have been found as large as 9½ inches. That it served a variety of purposes is indicated by the existence of four well-defined, different forms: first, a primitive, almond-shaped form; second, an ovaloid form; third, a disk form; and fourth, a pointed form resembling a lance-head. De Mortillet[26] speaks of it as the only tool of the Chellean tribes, but in its various forms it served all the purposes of axe, saw, chisel, and awl, and was in truth a combination tool. Capitan[27] also holds that the coup de poing is not a single tool but is designed to meet many various needs. The primitive almond and ovaloid forms were designed for use along the edges, either for heavy hacking or for sawing; the disk forms may have been used as axes or as sling-stones; the more rounded forms would serve as knives and scrapers; while the pointed, lance-shaped forms might be used as daggers, both in war and in the chase.

The Chellean flint workers also developed especially a number of small, pointed forms from the accidentally shaped fragments of flint, showing both short and long points carefully flaked and chipped. Thus, out of the small types of the Pre-Chellean there evolved a great variety of tools adapted to domestic purposes, to war, and to the chase.

Chellean Geography in England and France

The type station of the Chellean culture is somewhat east of the present town of Chelles. Here in Chellean times the broad floods of the ancient River Marne were transporting great quantities of sand and débris, products of the early pluvial periods of Third Interglacial times; and here, on the right bank, embedded in sands and gravels 24 feet thick, are found the typical Chellean implements mingled with remains of the hippopotamus, straight-tusked elephant, Merck's rhinoceros, giant beaver, hyæna, and many members of the Asiatic forest and meadow fauna.

The flint-working stations at St. Acheul were on bluffs from 40 to 80 feet above the present level of the Somme. The Chellean and the following Acheulean industry was carried on here on a very extensive scale. In one year Rigollot collected as many as 800 coups de poing from the ancient quarries; near by are other quarries equally rich in material, and we may imagine that the products of the flint industry in this favorable locality were carried far and wide into other parts of the country.

In the vicinity of Paris, and again at Arcy, in the valley of the Bièvre, the workers of Chellean, Acheulean, and Mousterian flints sought in succession the old river-gravels belonging to the lower levels; these 'low terraces' are only 15 feet above the present height of the river and are still occasionally flooded by the high waters of the Seine, indicating that the Seine borders have not altered their levels. The animal life here was identical with that of the Somme and of the Thames and included the hippopotamus, Merck's rhinoceros, and the straight-tusked elephant.

Thus it would appear that, in regard to the river courses and the hills through which they flowed, the topography and landscape of northern France and of southern Britain were everywhere the same as at the present time. The forests which clothed the hills were not greatly different from the present, except for the presence of a few trees of a warmer clime, nor was there anything strange or unfamiliar in the majority of the animals that roamed through forest and meadow. The three chief archaic elements consisted in the presence of two very ancient races of men and their rude stage of culture, in the great forms of Asiatic and African life which mingled with the more familiar native types, and in the broad, continuous land surfaces which swept off unbroken to the west and southwest.

For in those days Europe, though even then little more than a great peninsula, extended far beyond its present limits. England and Ireland were still part of the mainland, and great rivers flowed through the broad valleys that are now the Irish Sea, the North Sea, and the English Channel—rivers that counted the Seine, the Thames, the Garonne, and even the Rhine, as mere tributaries. The Strait of Gibraltar was then the Isthmus of Gibraltar—a narrow land bridge connecting Europe with Africa. The Mediterranean was then an inland lake, or rather two inland lakes, for Italy and Sicily stretched out in a broad, irregular mass to join the northern coast of Africa, while Corsica and Sardinia formed a long peninsula extending from the Italian mainland and almost, if not quite, reaching to the African coast.

The Thames Valley in Chellean Times

The interpretation of the features of stratification in the valley of the Somme is especially interesting because it gives us a key to the understanding of a similar sequence of prehistoric events in the valley of the Thames.

The station of Gray's Thurrock in this valley is barely 120 miles distant from the Chellean station of Abbeville, in the valley of the Somme, and it is apparent that the old flint workers were freely passing across the broad intervening country and interchanging their ideas and inventions. Thus it happened that Chellean implements identical with, or closely related to, the types of the Somme valley were being fashioned all over southern Britain from the Thames to the Ouse. The ancient River Thames (Lyell,[28] Geikie[29]) was then flowing over a bed of boulder-clays which had been deposited during the preceding glaciations. Its broad, swift stream was bringing down great deposits of ochreous gravels and of sands interstratified with loams and clays. It is these old true river-gravels which display their greatest thickness on the lowest levels of the Thames and which are largely made up of well-bedded and distinctly water-worn materials. On these low levels the flint workers sought their materials, and here they left behind them the archaic Chellean implements which are now found embedded in these older river-gravels, just as they occur in the gravels washed down over the three terraces of the Somme and the Marne. In the Thames this old gravel wash seems to have been down-stream, whereas on the middle and upper terraces of the Somme the gravel wash came directly down the sides of the valley, except, perhaps, in very high floods. These deep beds of gravel, sand, and loam lie for the most part above the present overflow plain of the Thames, although in some places they descend below it; which proves that the main landscape of the Thames also, except for the changes of the flora and of animal life, was the same in Pre-Chellean and Chellean times as it is at present. Thus the Somme, the Thames, and the Seine had all worn their channels to the present or even to lower levels when the Pre-Chellean hunters appeared. Since Chellean times all three rivers have silted up their channels.

The changes along the Thames which have since occurred are in the superficial layers brought down from the sides of the valley which have softened the contours of the old terraces and have also entombed the later phases of the valley's prehistory.

Sections on the south bank at Ilford, Kent, and on the north bank at Gray's Thurrock, Essex, confirm this view. At the latter station, in low-lying strata of brick-earth, loam, and gravel, such as would be formed by the silting up of the bottom of an old river channel, are found the remains of the straight-tusked elephant, broad-nosed rhinoceros, and hippopotamus. All the discoveries of recent years lead to the conclusion that the old fluviatile gravels which contain these ancient mammals and flints are restricted to the lower levels of the Thames valley, while the high level gravels and loams are of later date. Old Chellean flints also occur occasionally on the higher levels, but here it would seem that they have been washed down from the old land surfaces above, because they are found mingled with flints of the late Acheulean and early Mousterian industry.

England in Early Palæolithic Times

It is on the higher levels of the Thames, as of the Somme, and in the superficial deposits covering the sides of the valley that we read the story of the subsequent Palæolithic cultures and of an early warm temperate climate being followed by a cold climate with frozen subsoil belonging to the fourth glaciation and the contemporary Mousterian flint industry. The Palæolithic history of the Thames[30] has not yet been fully interpreted, but it would appear that the relics of the old stations of Kent and Norfolk will yield all the forms of Chellean and Acheulean implements, and probably also those of the Mousterian which have been discovered in the valley of the Somme, thus proving that the Lower Palæolithic races of this region pursued the same culture development as the neighboring tribes of France and Belgium, as well as those of Spain, up to the close of middle Acheulean times.

A similar sequence of events appears to be indicated at Hoxne, Suffolk, where archaic palæoliths were discovered as far back as 1797. This discovery was neglected for upward of sixty years, until in 1859 these flints were re-examined by Prestwich and Evans after their visit to the stations of the Somme (Geikie,[31] Avebury[32]). This site was in the hollow of a surface of boulder-clay, overlain by the deposit of a fresh-water stream; in the bed of its narrow channel, besides flint implements of early Acheulean type, abundant plant remains were found which give us an interesting vision of the flora of the time.

These plants are decidedly characteristic of a temperate climate, including such trees as the oak, yew, and fir, and mostly of species which are still found in the forests of the same region. This life gave place, as indicated in plant deposits of a higher level, to an arctic flora, probably corresponding with the tundra climate of Mousterian times, the period of the fourth glaciation. Above these are found again layers of plants and of mollusks which point to the return of a temperate climate.

Spread of the Acheulean Industry

It is noteworthy that not a single 'river-drift,' Pre-Chellean or Chellean, station has been found in Germany or Switzerland, or, in fact, in all central Europe in the region lying between the Alpine and Scandinavian glaciers. Either this region was unfavorable to human habitation or the remains of the stations have been buried or washed away.

It is significant that the earliest proof of human migration into this region, whether from the east or from the west we do not certainly know, is coincident with the dry climate of Acheulean times. The 'loess' conditions of climate seem to be coincident with the earliest Acheulean stations in Germany, such as Sablon. 'Loess' deposition is by no means a proof of a cold climate but rather of an arid one, especially in regions where areas of finely eroded soil were liable to be raised by the wind; such areas were found over the whole recently glaciated country north of the Alps and south of the Scandinavian peninsula.

The Palæolithic discovery sites of Germany are principally grouped in three regions[33] as follows:

To the south, along the *headwaters of the Rhine and the Danube*, among the limestones of Swabia and the Jura were formed the caverns sought by early Mousterian man. To the west of these were many older stations in the 'loess' deposits of the upper Rhine, between the mountain ridges of the Vosges and the Black Forest, and still nearer the sources of the Rhine, extending over the border into Switzerland, are a number of famous cave sites in the valleys cut by the Rhine and its tributaries through the white Jurassic limestone. To the west is the group of the *middle Rhine and of Westphalia*, which includes the open Acheulean camps in the 'loess' deposits above the river and a number of cavern stations. To the north is the scattered group of stations, both of Acheulean and Mousterian times, of *north Germany*. Here the sites are few and far between. The open-country camps were established chiefly in the valley of the Ilm and near the caves of the Harz Mountains, in the neighborhood of Gera. No discoveries of certain date or unquestioned authenticity are reported from *eastern Germany*.

Along the upper Rhine the flint workers of Acheulean times established their ancient camps mostly in the open on the broad sheets of the 'lower loess,' which, constantly drifted by the wind, covered and preserved the stations. These stations are

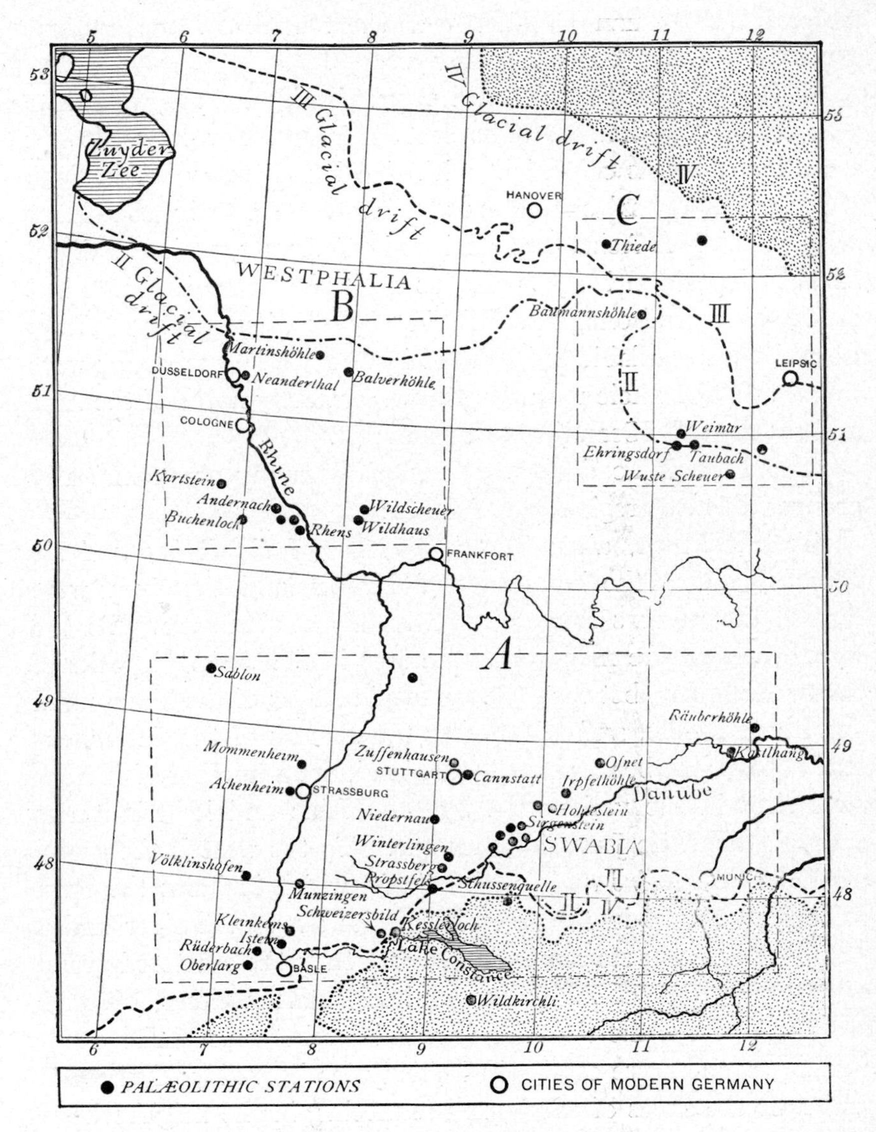

FIG. 77. Flint working stations of the Men of the Old Stone Age along the waters of the Ilm, the Rhine, and the Danube, from Acheulean to Azilian times. After R. R. Schmidt, modified and redrawn. These Palæolithic sites of Germany lie between the terminal moraines of the successive glacial advances of the Second, Third, and Fourth (II, III, IV) Glacial Stages, extending from the borders of the Scandinavian ice-fields on the north to those of the Alpine ice-fields on the south. The dotted surface represents the area covered by the drift of the Fourth Glacial Stage.

widely scattered, but they were frequented from earliest Acheulean times, and the region was revisited to the very close of the Upper Palæolithic.

Early in Acheulean times the important 'loess' station of Achenheim was established. This is a most famous locality and is of especial importance because it is the only station in Germany which was continuously frequented from late Acheulean times throughout the Lower Palæolithic and into the beginning of the Upper Palæolithic; here the 'older loess' of the Third Interglacial Stage yields a typical Acheulean industry.

Thus far the region of the middle Rhine and of Westphalia has not shown any evidence of Acheulean culture. The north German stations, however, were entered in Acheulean times, and the principal open stations of this region lie along the valley of the Ilm. Here, at Taubach, Ehringsdorf, and Weimar, we find implements of typical Acheulean form belonging to the early warm temperate Acheulean period. The stations of the Ilm valley southwest of Leipsic are also of great importance because of the rich record which they contain of the warm temperate animal life of early Acheulean times; the flint culture is typically Acheulean, and the climatic conditions are read both in the travertines and in the subsequent deposits of the 'lower loess,' which belong to the cold dry period of late Acheulean times. Here lingered the straight-tusked elephant and Merck's rhinoceros, contemporary with the workers of the Acheulean flints.

It will be observed that in Germany the early Acheulean was a warm period which in certain regions was also arid and subject to great dust-storms. At this time the camps were for the most part in the open country. In the late period, also arid and subject to high winds but with a cooler climate, the flint workers continued to frequent the open Acheulean stations in the 'loess.' If there were shelter and cavern stations in this region, they have not as yet been discovered. This would appear to indicate that the climate had not yet become severe.

Similar testimony is found in the great scarcity of cavern and shelter stations in Acheulean times in every part of western Europe; yet occasionally the tribes repaired to the vicinity of sheltering cliffs, as along the Vézère. In some scattered localities they sought the caverns, as at Krapina, in Croatia, at Spy, on the Meuse in Belgium, and at Castillo, in northern Spain. These rare exceptions to the open camps would tend to prove that the caverns were sought rather for protection from enemies and as rain shelters than as retreats from a bitter-cold climate.

In the valley of the Beune, a small tributary of the Vézère, in Dordogne, we find a true Acheulean station quite close to the river shore. This proves that in Acheulean times this valley was already deepened to the same degree as it is to-day. In the valley of the Somme the Acheulean culture stretches from the 'highest terrace' down below the present level of the river, which has made for itself a new high channel. The fact that two Acheulean stations are found on the upper Garonne, high above the present water-level, is of little significance, as at that time the water-level was also high.

In general the Acheulean flint workers preferred the open stations throughout all Acheulean times, and their camps are found on the open plateaus between the rivers or on the various 'terrace' levels, as on the higher, middle, and lower 'terraces' of the Somme at St. Acheul, or again close along the borders of the rivers and streams, as in the Dordogne region.

Even during the early Acheulean stage a dry climate had begun to prevail in certain parts of Germany. Near Metz is the 'older loess' station of Sablon, which was occupied in early Acheulean times, indicating a warm period of arid climate favorable to the transportation of the wind-blown 'loess'; doubtless, this fine dust at times filled the entire atmosphere and obscured the sun, as is the case to-day on the high steppes and deserts of eastern Asia.

An exception to the open-country life preferred by the Acheulean flint workers is found in the great grotto* of Castillo, near Puente Viesgo, in the Province of Santander, northern Spain.

* The author was guided through this station by Doctor Hugo Obermaier in the summer of 1912.

The deposits which filled this grotto to a thickness of 45 feet from the floor to the roof were explored by Obermaier, who found them divided into thirteen layers, covering eleven periods of industry and presenting the most wonderful epitome of the pre-

FIG. 78. Entrance (white cross) to the great grotto of Castillo in northern Spain. This grotto was frequented by the Men of the Old Stone Age from Acheulean to Azilian times, an archæologic sequence surpassed only by that of the open camps along the terraces of the Somme. Photograph from Obermaier.

history of western Europe from Acheulean times to the Age of Bronze, in Spain (Fig. 79).

As early as 1908, Breuil[34] discovered in the interior of the cave back of the grotto some quartzites worked into Acheulean types, proving that the cavern was entered in Acheulean times. Obermaier,[35] in the course of three years' work, has found that the floor of the grotto was possibly used as a flint-making station in Acheulean and, possibly, in Chellean times. The culture section which he has revealed here under the direction of the *Institut de Paléontologie humaine* can be compared only with that which Commont has found on the 'terraces' of the Somme at St. Acheul. The difference is that in the shelter of the Castillo

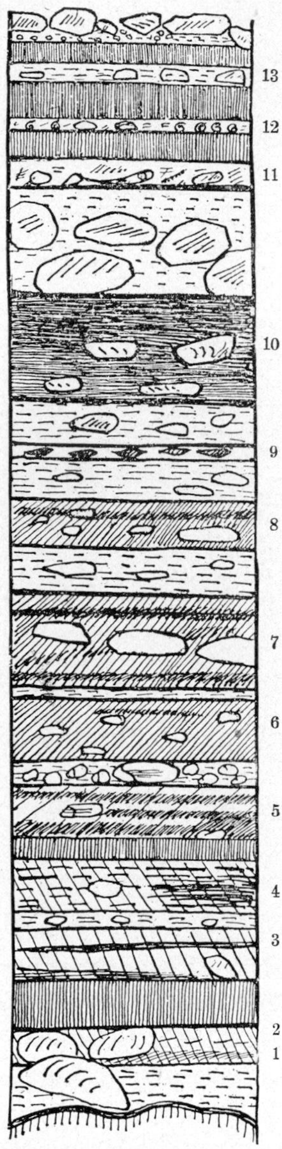

FIG. 79. Stratigraphic section showing the archæologic layers of the great grotto of Castillo. After Obermaier.

grotto the climate is recorded only through the changing forms of animal life which are mingled around the fire-hearths and with the flints in the ascending levels.

(13) Eneolithic Age. Small, triangular dagger in copper.
(12) Azilian. Flint industry—Age of the Stag.
(11) Upper Magdalenian. Artistic engravings on stag-horn.
(10) Lower Magdalenian. Flints and fine engravings on bone. Reindeer bâton.
(9) Archaic Solutrean. *Feuilles de laurier*, retouched on one side only.
(8, 7, 6) Upper Aurignacian in three layers. Remains of the reindeer and *burins*.
(5) Lower Aurignacian. Implements of stone and bone. Remains of an infant.
(4) Upper Mousterian. Rich in small implements and large tools of quartzite. Merck's rhinoceros very abundant.
(3) Typical Mousterian flints and quartzites. Merck's rhinoceros.
(2) Early Mousterian industry. Bones of cave-bear and Merck's rhinoceros.
(1) Acheulean flints.

The entrance to this grotto is on the side of a high hill overlooking the valley and might easily have been barricaded against attack. In early Acheulean times, when the flint workers were on the very floor of the grotto, the lower entrance of the cavern was still open, leading far into the heart of the mountain. The successive accumulations of débris, cave loam, fire-stones, bones, and innumerable flints, together with great blocks falling over the entrance of the cavern, reached a height of 45 feet, so that during the Upper Palæolithic only the upper entrance to the cavern was used by the artists of Magdalenian times. The subsequent Azilian and Eneolithic cultures were crowded under the very roof of the grotto at the sides.

This station, repaired to and then abandoned by tribe after tribe over a period estimated at present as not less than 50,000 years, is a monumental volume of prehistory, read and interpreted by the archæologist almost as clearly as if the whole record were in writing.

The first positive evidences of the use of fire are the layers of charred wood and bones frequently found in the industrial deposits of early Acheulean times.

Geographic and Climatic Changes

During the early period of development of the Acheulean industry, the geography, the climate, and the plant and animal life continued to present exactly the same aspect as during Chellean times. The mammals which we find in Thuringia in the lower travertines of the valley of the Ilm, at Taubach, near Weimar, and at Ehringsdorf, mingled with flints of early Acheulean industry, are of the same species as those found in the valley of the Somme mingled with the implements of the Chellean industry. The southern mammoth occurs at Taubach, and we find the straight-tusked elephant (*E. antiquus*), Merck's rhinoceros, the hippopotamus, the lion, and the hyæna representing the ancient African-Asiatic migrants, while the north European and Asiatic life is represented by the giant deer, roe-deer, wild goat, brown bear, wolf, badger, marten, otter, beaver, meadow hamster, and shrew. Grazing in the meadows were the aurochs, or wild ox, and the wisent, or bison. There was one variety of horse, probably of the forest type. Thus, the fauna as a whole contains six Asiatic types, or eight if we include the bison and wild cattle. Of the forest life there are nine species, including the wild boar (*Sus scrofa ferus*) not mentioned above.

The layers of travertine are indicative of very important geographical changes which were occurring in central and southern Europe in the middle period of Third Interglacial times. The travertines of the Ilm and of other parts of central Germany were due to wide-spread volcanic disturbances and eruptions, accompanied by the deposition of travertines, gypsums, and tufas. To this volcanic disturbance in central France is attributed the deposition of the *tuf de La Celle-sous-Moret*, near Paris, which records the warm temperate climate of early Acheulean times, as well as the somewhat cooler succeeding climate of late Acheulean times. This uplift in the centre of Germany and France apparently left the region between France and Great Britain undisturbed, because there is evidence of continued free migration of the tribes and of the Acheulean cultures; but there appears to have been a wide-spread subsidence of the coasts of southern Europe by which the islands of the Mediterranean became isolated from the mainland, and the migrating routes between Europe and Africa across the central Mediterranean region were cut off. Thus, Italy, Sicily, and Sardinia were separated from the mainland after having received a large contingent of mammalian life from the continents both to the north and to the south. While descendants of the African and Asiatic mammals, as well as of the northerly European forest and meadow types, survive on these islands, there is, thus far, no indication that they were invaded by hunters carrying the implements of the Acheulean culture, although these Acheulean flint workers ranged over all parts of the Italian peninsula (Fig. 80), as indicated by the discovery of nine stations.

Distribution of Acheulean Stations

The Acheulean stations are widely distributed along the Seine, Marne, and Somme in northern France, where flint is abundant and well adapted for fine workmanship. In central and southern France, where large flints are scarce, the Acheulean tribes were forced to use quartz, which fashions into clumsier forms. In the north the Acheulean workers continued on the old Chellean sites at Chelles, St. Acheul, Abbeville, and Helin. In late Acheulean times were established the new stations of

Wolvercote on the Thames, near Oxford, and of Levallois on the Seine, near Paris, both famous for their 'Levallois' flint knives or blades. Near Levallois is the late Acheulean station of Villejuif, south of Paris, where the flints are buried in drifts of loess. In Normandy are the important stations of Frileuse, Bléville,

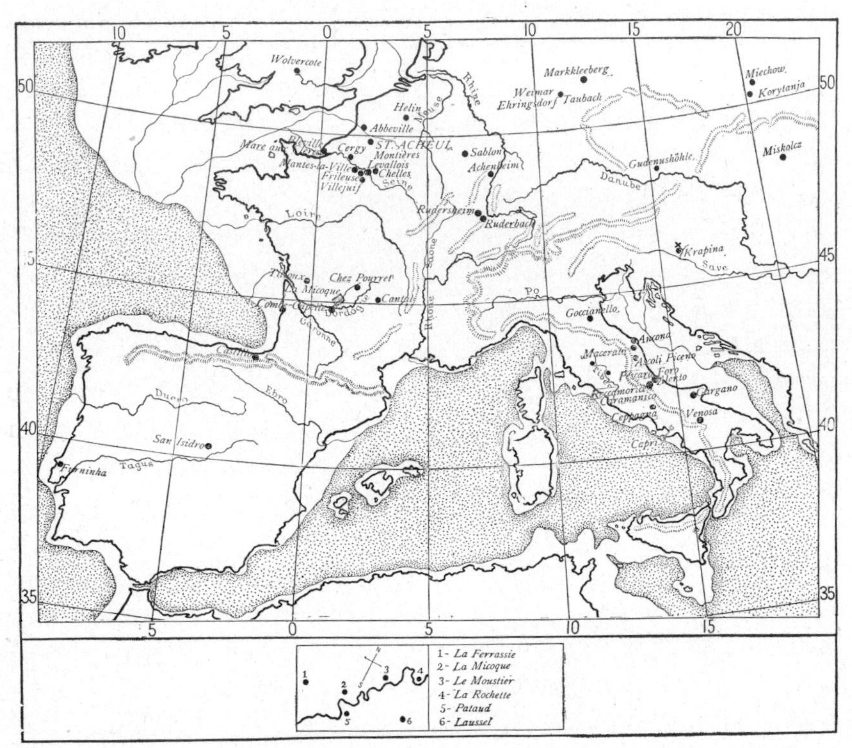

FIG. 80. Distribution of the principal Acheulean industrial stations in western Europe.

and La Mare-aux-Clercs, which give the whole Acheulean development, both early and late. On a small tributary valley of the Vézère, in Dordogne, in late Acheulean times there was established the station of La Micoque, which gives its name to a number of miniature flints of distinctive form which were first found there and are known as the 'type of La Micoque.' Other stations, such as Combe-Capelle, also show examples of this 'miniature' Acheulean workmanship.

Altogether, over thirty Acheulean stations have been found in France, two—Castillo and San Isidro—in northern and central

Spain, the single station of Furninha in Portugal, over eight in Germany, three in Austria, and three in Russian Poland. Especially remarkable is the wide distribution of this culture all over Italy, where explorations by no means exhaustive have resulted in the discovery of at least nine or ten very prolific stations extending from Goccianello in the north to Capri in the south, but not into Sicily as far as is at present known. Thus all of western

FIG. 81. Late Acheulean station of La Micoque, in Dordogne, where miniature flints of distinctive late Acheulean form are found. Photograph by N. C. Nelson.

Europe, excepting the area covered by the Scandinavian ice-fields on the north and by the Alpine ice-fields on the south, was penetrated by the workers of Acheulean flints, probably members, for the most part, of the Neanderthal race.

The general uniformity of Acheulean workmanship in all parts of western Europe is an indication that these Neanderthaloid tribes were more or less migratory and that the inventions of new and useful implements, such as the lance-pointed coup de poing of La Micoque and the flint-flakes of Levallois, which probably originated at an especial centre, or perhaps even in the inventive mind of a single workman, became widely distributed and highly distinctive of certain periods. The development of the implements in different regions is so uniform as to prove that the evolution of the early Palæolithic cultures extended all over western Europe and that the various types or stages were essentially contemporary.

Forms of Acheulean Implements

There is a close sequence between the coup de poing of the Chellean workers and its development into the finer and more

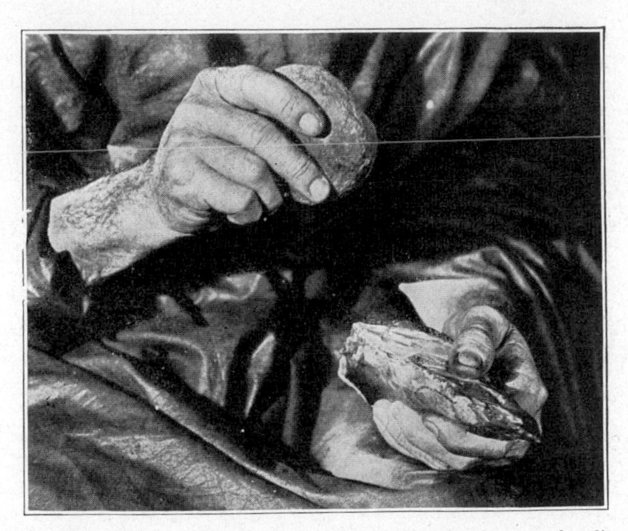

Fig. 82. Illustrating the method of 'flaking' flint implements by direct or indirect blow with a hammer-stone.

symmetrical forms of the Acheulean. The latter, according to Obermaier,[36] is distinguished by the flaking of the entire surface, by the far more skilful fashioning, and by the really symmetrical almond form which is attained by retouching both the surface and the edges. This more refined retouch becomes the means of producing symmetrical instruments, with straight, convex, or concave cutting edges, as well as finer and lighter tools.

The *early Acheulean* industry belonged to a warm temperate climatic period and directly succeeds the Chellean, as shown in a most perfect manner in the quarries of the type station of St. Acheul on the Somme. In these earlier strata the prevailing forms of coup de poing are the 'pointed oval' and the 'lance-pointed,' the latter showing very simple chipping, a broad point, and a thick base. The oval coups de poing are smaller than the Chellean tools of the same kind, carefully fashioned on all sides and round the base, and very symmetrical; there are four distinct varieties of these: the almond type, oval almond-shaped, elongate oval, and subtriangular—the latter evolving into the

FIG. 83. Illustrating the method of 'chipping' flint implements by pressure with a bone or wooden implement, to produce the finer retouch of the surfaces and edges.

finely modelled type of late Acheulean times. It may have been from these oval types that the disc form was finally evolved.

There is wide difference of opinion regarding the use of these thin ovaloid, triangular, and disc forms. Obermaier considers that they may have been clamped in wood, or furnished with a shaft, thus forming a spear head. Another suggestion is that they were used with a leather guard to protect the hand; and there is no doubt that in either case they would have served as effective weapons in chase or war. Another view is that of Commont,[37] who believes that not a single implement down to the very end of Acheulean times can be regarded as a weapon of war; this author maintains that many of these implements, including those dressed on both edges, were still in various ways grasped by the hand, although they do not present the firm, blunted grip of the ancient coups de poing.

We also note the development of a type of coup de poing, with cutting blade fashioned straight across the end: this primitive

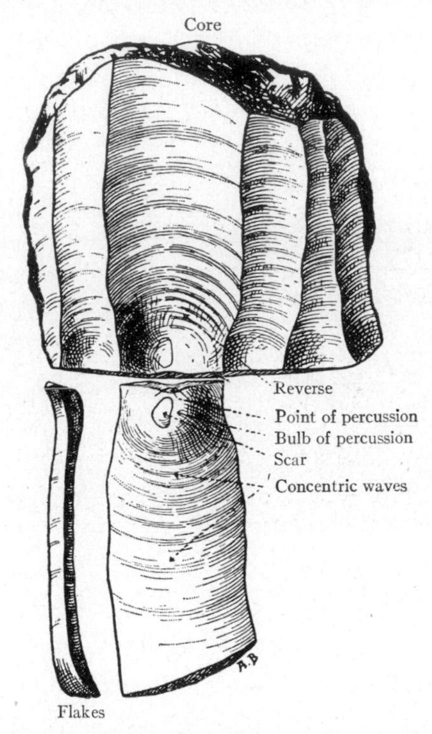

FIG. 84. Method of producing the long *flake* and the central *core* of flint by sharp blows at the indicated point of percussion. After R. R. Schmidt. In this case a series of flakes have been cut off the entire periphery of the core. The primitive use of the flake begins in the Pre-Chellean.

chisel or adze-shaped tool may have been used as a chopper, or as an axe, in fashioning wooden tools.

In the lance-pointed coup de poing of narrow, elongate shape, the flaking is very simple and the edges are continued into the short base, generally very thick, and often showing part of the original crust of the flint nodule, which is well adapted for the grip of the hand. This implement, which serves the original idea of the coup de poing, develops into the round-pointed and lance-pointed forms. There is no question that, whether in industrial use, in war, or in the chase, these implements were held only by the hand.

The small implements of the early Acheulean included a great variety of designs developing out of the far more primitive tools of Chellean and Pre-Chellean times, namely, the planing tool, the scraper, the borer, and the knife. Each of these types develops its own variety, often fashioned with great care, primitive blades, straight-edged cutting tools, with the back rounded or blunted for the grip of the fingers, scrapers with straight or curved edges, and perçoirs or borers. The scraping and planing tools, doubtless used for the dressing of hides, are now more carefully fashioned. We also observe the racloir and the scraper finished to a point which is the precursor of the graving tool of the Upper Palæolithic.[38]

INDUSTRIAL.

Coup de poing.
- Ovaloid.
- Double-edged.
- Subtriangular.
- Straight cutting blade across the end.
- Disc-shaped.
- Triangular—very thin and flat.

Hachette,	chopper.
Grattoir,	planing tool.
Racloir,	scraper.
Perçoir,	drill, borer.
Couteau,	knife.
'Pointe' (Levallois blade).	
'Pointe,'	point—oval and chisel-shaped.

WAR AND CHASE.

Coup de poing.
- Of pointed and lance-pointed types.

Pierre de jet,	throwing stone.
Couteau,	knife.
'Pointe,'	dart and spear heads.

Characteristic of this stage is the systematic use of large 'flakes' or outlying pieces of flint struck off from the core, which were used as scrapers or planes, or developed into small 'haches,' or coups de poing.

The *core* or *centre* of the flint nodule still constitutes the material out of which the large typical implements are fashioned; but the *flake* begins to lend itself to a great variety of forms, as witnessed in the evolution of the Levallois knives of the Upper Acheulean and the highly varied flake implements of the Mousterian and Aurignacian industries.

The 'pointe,' or point, is a special implement chipped out

of a short, sharply convex flake, taking the form of a blunt dart or spear head, pointed at one end and oval or flat at the other.

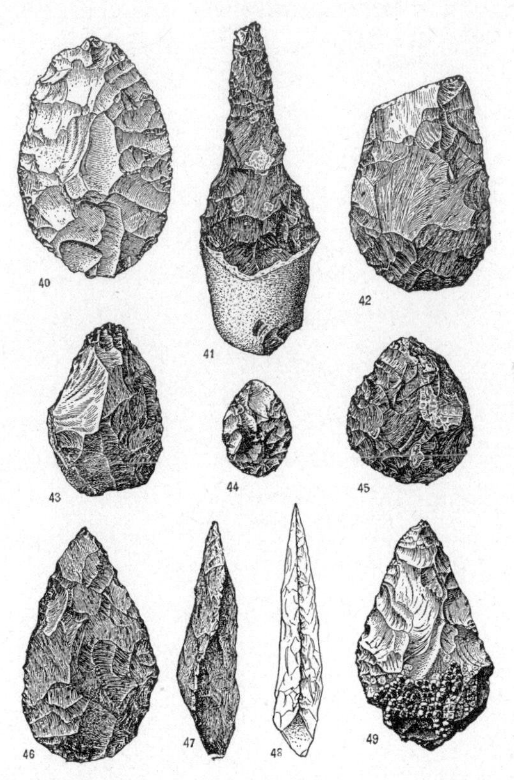

FIG. 85. Large, typical Acheulean implements, chiefly described as *coups de poing*, after de Mortillet. One-quarter actual size. One of these (41) shows at one end a part of the crust of the flint nodule left intact to afford a smooth, firm grip to the hand. Another (43) shows a part of the crust remaining along the left side, for the same purpose. Two of the coups de poing (47 and 48) show, the one a double-curved, the other a straight, lateral edge. Another coup de poing (49), from a submarine deposit near the shore at Havre, is partly covered by acorn shells.

Late Acheulean Climate

The Acheulean industry continued over a very long period, and by the time the late Acheulean culture stage had been reached a decided change of climate ensued in western Europe. Along the borders of the Danube and of the Rhine, in the valley of the Somme, and even in central and southern France there are indications of a cool dry continental climate, similar to that which is now found on the southern steppes of Russia, in the Ural Mountains, and in the vicinity of the Caspian Sea. Indications of this climate have been mentioned above, as seen in the plant life in the *tuf de La Celle-sous-Moret*, near Paris, where there are evidences that trees of a cool temperate climate took the place of the warm temperate forests of early Acheulean times.

That the climate should be considered as cool and arid rather than comparable with the bitter-cold climate of the 'upper loess' period, when a true steppe fauna entered Europe for the first time, is further indicated by the fact that late Acheulean implements are more frequently found in the centre and north of France than in the south.

To the far north, before the close of Acheulean times, the Scandinavian ice-fields had again begun to advance southward; the region bordering the glaciers was cold and moist and favored the migration from the tundra regions of the woolly mammoth and woolly rhinoceros to the locality still frequented by the Acheulean flint workers, for it is said [39] that Acheulean flints are occasionally associated even with the remains of these tundra mammals. At the very same time the Acheulean flint workers along the Somme may have enjoyed a more genial climate.

It is only through this interpretation of the various climatic and life zones in western Europe that we can explain the survival on the River Somme, or return to this river from the south, of a warm temperate fauna, hippopotami, rhinoceroses, and elephants, in the Mousterian period, which is even subsequent to the close of Acheulean times.

The valleys of the two great river-systems of southwestern France, the Dordogne draining the central plateau, and the Garonne draining the eastern Pyrenees, were now sought by the Acheulean flint workers. The valley of the Vézère, a northern tributary of the Dordogne, cuts through a broad plateau of limestone in which the streams have hollowed out deep beds with vertical sides. Here the landscape of late Acheulean times bore the same general aspect as at present.[40] Evidences of a change of climate are observed even in the sheltered valleys where the flint workers were seeking the warmer and sunnier river-slopes. The river channels were the same as they are to-day, and the quarries of the early Acheulean flint workers are found quite close to the streams; but as the period progressed they moved up nearer to the cliffs and shelters. Here, too, there is evidence that a dry continental climate prevailed. On the upper levels of

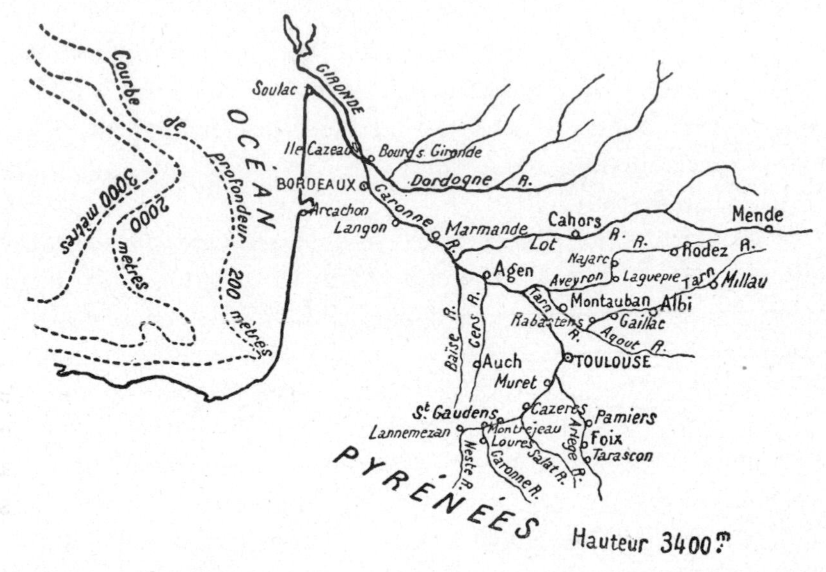

Fig. 86. "Valleys of the two great river-systems of southwestern France, the Dordogne draining the central plateau and the Garonne draining the eastern Pyrenees." After Harlé.

the old plateaus of Dordogne we still find the *Quercus ilex* occurring quite frequently, a tree which belongs to relatively dry regions and which in southern Russia is reckoned with the flora of the steppes. Yet the greater aridity toward the close of the Acheulean stage was probably not such as to prevent the growth of forests along the borders of the streams. Thus, in the mammalian life of the period there was, perhaps, a division between the more hardy forms which frequented the dry plateaus above and the forest-loving and less hardy forms which frequented the river-valleys.

The most convincing proof of an arid climate in the north of France with prevailing high westerly winds is found in the layers of 'loess' which occur on the 'terraces' of the Somme, the Seine, the Rhine, and the Danube. These 'lower loess' layers of Third Interglacial times frequently contain implements of the late Acheulean industry. Thus, at Villejuif, south of Paris, late

Fig. 87. "The valley of the Vézère, a northern tributary of the Dordogne, cuts through a broad plateau of limestone in which the streams have hollowed out deep beds with vertical sides," favorable to the formation of caverns, grottos, and shelters. "Here the landscape of late Acheulean times bore the same general aspect as at present." Photograph by N. C. Nelson.

Acheulean implements are found embedded in drifts of 'loess.' In the valley of the Somme, flints of the middle Acheulean stage are also found in the *loess ancien* and 'river-drift.' In the *tuf de La Celle-sous-Moret* the layer of 'loess' immediately overlies the tufa layer containing late Acheulean implements and proofs of a cooler climate.

Among the most famous of the 'loess' stations of late Acheulean times is that of Achenheim on the upper Rhine, west of Strasburg. Here the 'older loess' contains a typical Acheulean culture.

With this prolonged epoch of cooler temperature the hippopotamus and the southern mammoth retreated to the warmer portions of southern Europe, and their remains are no longer found associated with the late Acheulean flints. The more hardy straight-tusked elephant and Merck's rhinoceros still continued in the north, apparently well adapted to sustain a very considerable fall in temperature.

Forms of Late Acheulean Implements

The coups de poing of the *late Acheulean* exhibit a great advance upon the Chellean, being fashioned into dagger or lance forms, with all the edges carefully chipped. The ovaloid implements of late Acheulean times are often worked into fine and sharp blades, which may have been used like butcher-knives for dismembering the carcasses of game and for cutting up the pelts, while the fine almond and disc shapes may have been used as scrapers to cut off the tissues of the inner surfaces of the hides, which were finally dressed by the grattoir, or flint planing tool. In brief, the coup de poing reaches its acme of development in late Acheulean times, both in the fineness of flaking and retouching and in its symmetry of form. The use of large flakes of flint and the retouching both of the borders and of the extremities of these flakes shows a constantly improving technique. It is in the thin, flat, triangular blades and in the lance-pointed forms that the coup de poing reaches its culmination; but we still observe the development of the oval or almond-shaped forms and of the flattened discs. The implements of this time reach their greatest perfection in the north of France, where flint is so abundant.

The late Acheulean is further distinguished by an advance in all the finer and smaller implements and tools. The knives are now very fine and perfect, although they retain the broad, thick form of the original flint fragment and seldom attain the symmetrical shape which characterizes the blades of the Upper Palæolithic.[41] The 'points' are also of finer technique, with their edges converging from a broad base to a well-formed point. It is generally assumed that these were held in the bare hand, but it is quite as probable that they were attached to wooden shafts and used as dart or spear heads. By far the most numerous as well as the most varied of the smaller tools were the racloirs,

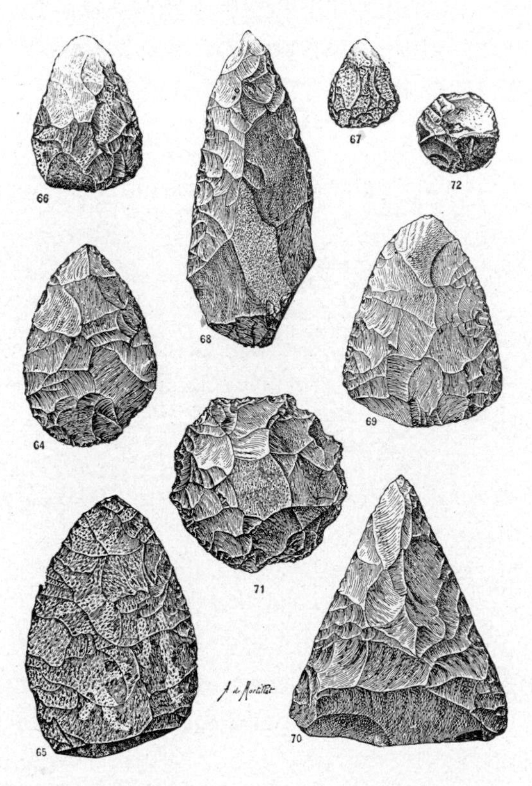

Fig. 88. Varied shapes of the Acheulean flints described as *coups de poing*, including some 'miniature' forms, after de Mortillet. The oval, the pointed, the almond, the triangular, the disc-shaped. The late Acheulean is distinguished by an advance in all the finer and smaller implements, tools, and weapons; yet the finest work of Acheulean times appears thick and clumsy when contrasted with the best Solutrean work of the Upper Palæolithic. One-quarter actual size.

or scrapers, which were developed, doubtless, by the increasing use of skins for clothing as a protection against the somewhat more rigorous climate of late Acheulean times. Probably the women of the tribe were employed in dressing hides by means of these scrapers, which were either flat and broad with crescent-shaped edges, flat and narrow, or double-edged with rounded ends. The development of other fine tools—borers, small discs, triangular and ovaloid shapes, miniature coups de poing, and many varied forms besides—is best witnessed in the station of La Micoque, close to the junction of the Vézère with the Dordogne. These miniature implements may well have been used in the final dressing of skins for clothing, in the chase of smaller kinds of game, or at feasts for splitting marrow-bones.

No bone implements whatever have been found even with

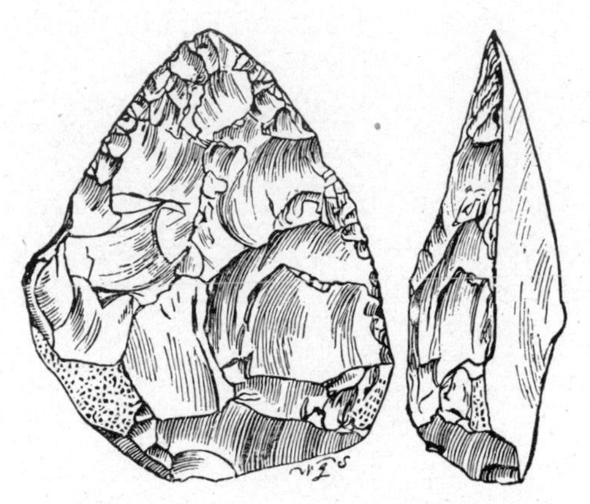

Fig. 89. The *chef-d'œuvre* of the Acheulean industry is the Levallois flake, which may have evolved from the large flakes of Chellean times. After Worthington Smith.

these late Acheulean flints, but it is important to observe that the majority of these stations are open and exposed to the weather and that bone implements would not be preserved here as they would in the sheltered grottos and caverns to which the flint workers repaired in the Mousterian and succeeding times.

As regards the finish of these flint implements, it is important to note that it is fine only by comparison with the crude work of the early Acheulean or the still coarser types of Chellean times and that the very finest work of Acheulean times appears thick and clumsy when contrasted with the finer work of the Upper Palæolithic.

The *chef-d'œuvre* of the late Acheulean industry is the Levallois flake, first found at Levallois-Perret, near Paris, which de Mortillet believed to be fashioned out of a divided coup de poing with a flat under-side, but which may have been evolved from the very large primitive flakes of Pre-Chellean date. These flakes date back earlier than the Chellean coup de poing but continued in use after its invention and may have been greatly perfected into the Levallois type. This type of 'couteau' is a large, wide, thin flake of fairly symmetrical shape, with a flat back formed by the original smooth surface of the flake. These implements are pointed, oval, or sharply rectangular in form and present the most characteristic tool of the closing stage of the Acheulean industry.

It is most interesting at this point to observe the two modes of evolution which seem to pervade all nature: first, the gradual perfection and modification in size and proportion of a certain older form; second, the sudden change or mutation into a new form, which in turn enters the stage of gradual improvement.

The late Acheulean is seen to present the climax of a gradual and unbroken development from the early Chellean industries and ideas; and to our mind this is strongly suggestive of a corresponding evolution of manual skill and mental development in the workmen themselves, who may have been partly of Pre-Neanderthaloid race.

The next industrial stage, namely, the Mousterian, which certainly presents the closing workmanship of the Neanderthal race, shows a marked retrogression of technique in contrast to the steady progression which we have observed up to this time. We have, in fact, witnessed a number of successive stages of progression, which are to be followed in the Mousterian by a stage of retrogression. Such a retrogression in industrial development may for certain known or unknown reasons occur in the same race. It is a noteworthy parallel that in the Upper Palæolithic, where the Solutrean culture represents the climax and perfection of flint working, the succeeding Magdalenian shows marked retrogression in the technique of flint retouch.

The Krapina Neanderthaloids

In northern Croatia, near the small town of Krapina, in the valley of the Krapinica River, is the now famous cavern of Krapina, where in 1899 was made the fourth discovery of the remains of men of the Neanderthaloid race in western Europe, twelve

Fig. 90. The grotto of Krapina, overlooking the valley of the Krapinica River, near Krapina, Croatia, in Austria-Hungary. After Kraemer.

years after the discovery of the men of Spy, in Belgium, and forty-three years after the discovery of the man of Neanderthal. Even now opinion is divided as to the age of the human remains found in this cavern. The discoverer, Professor Gorjanovič-Kramberger of Agram considered that the stone implements and chips were of Mousterian age, and Breuil still refers them to the early, or so-called warm, Mousterian period; this opinion is shared by Déchelette. Schmidt, however, regards Krapina as a true Acheulean station, lacking in some of the typical implements, and of the same age as the 'loess' station of Ehringsdorf.

The mammals found in the cavern certainly belong to the very late Acheulean period and include Merck's rhinoceros, the cave-bear, the urus, a species of horse, the giant deer (*Megaceros*), the beaver, and the marmot (*Arctomys marmotta*).

The cavern was originally washed out by the river, but now it is 82 feet above the present water-level. When found it was completely filled with sand and gravel deposits, weathered fragments from the roof and walls, and loose stones and boulders.[42] Enclosed in this mass. in separate strata which are perfectly

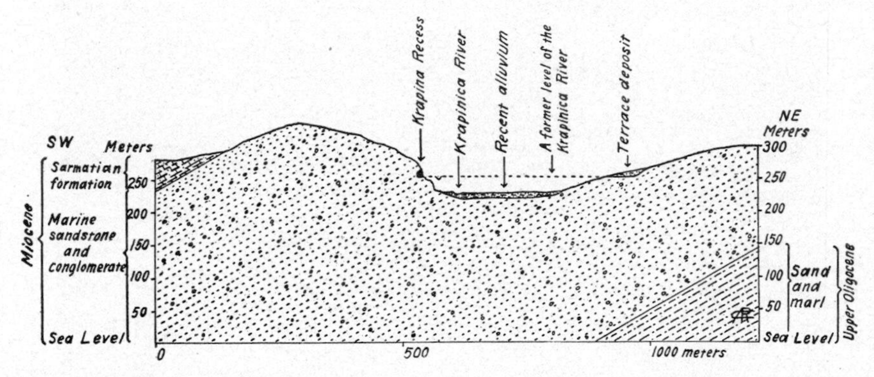

FIG. 91. Cross-section of the valley traversed by the Krapinica River showing the location of the grotto known as the Krapina recess on the bank to the left. Drawn by C. A. Reeds.

distinguishable, there lay, variously distributed through the different layers, thousands of animal bones, mingled with hundreds of human bones, and hundreds of stone implements and chips.

During the years 1899–1905 Gorjanovič-Kramberger made a thorough exploration of the contents of this cavern, and published a complete account of his researches in 1906.[43] There were about three hundred pieces of human bones, among them many small fragments, also many sizable pieces of skull and several entire limb bones perfectly preserved. The bones are of a strongly characterized type, and the lower jaws, face bones, bones of the thigh and arm, the teeth, and the bones of many children establish the Krapina race as belonging unquestionably in the same group with that of Neanderthal and of Spy.

The skull of the Krapina man (Fig. 93) is somewhat broader or more brachycephalic than that of any other members of the Neanderthal race. In general, the race is somewhat dwarfed, of broader head form and with less prominent supraorbital processes. The species is unquestionably *Homo neanderthalensis*, of which

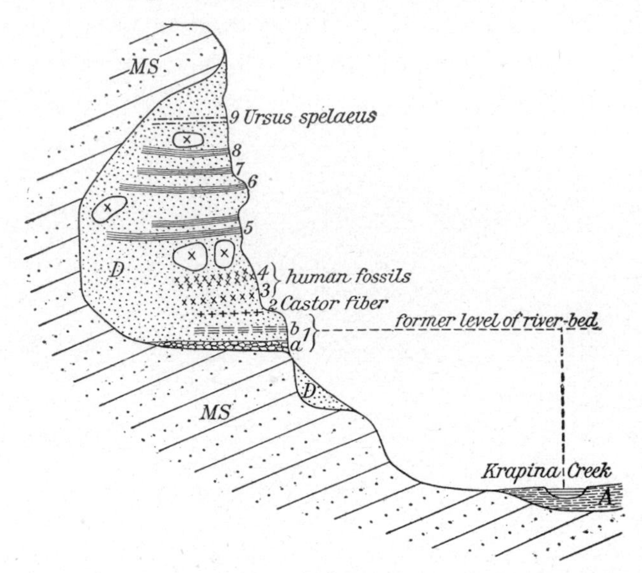

FIG. 92. Detail showing the interior contents of the Krapina grotto before its excavation in the years 1899 to 1905. After Gorjanovič-Kramberger.

the Krapina men constitute a local race. Schwalbe and Boule observe that the greater breadth of the Krapina skull is partly due to the manner in which the bones have been put together,[44] and they do not consider that the Krapina man represents a different subrace (*Homo neanderthalensis krapinensis*) as held by the discoverer. The cephalic index of one Krapina skull is recorded as 83.7 per cent (?) as compared with 73.9 per cent, the cephalic index of the true *H. neanderthalensis*, a difference which, as above noted, may be partly due to the restoration. The bones are in such a fragmentary condition that it is impossible to form a proper estimate of the brain capacity in either the males or females of this race; nor is it possible to estimate the stature. The space between the eyes is the same as in the Neanderthal race; the angle of the retreat of the forehead (52°) is nearly the same as in the Gibraltar female Neanderthal skull (50°), this high forehead being due to the lesser development of the supra-orbital ridges. That the brain was of a low, flat-headed Neanderthal type is shown by the close similarity of the index of the height of skull (42.2) to that of one of the men of Spy (44.3), as compared with the lowest index among the existing races of men (48.9); yet the Krapina man presents a considerable advance

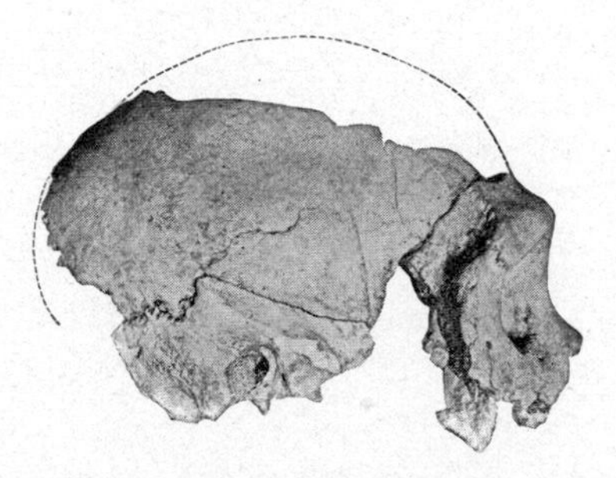

FIG. 93. Profile view, right side, of one of the skulls from Krapina. This skull is much broader than that of the typical Neanderthaloid. After Gorjanović-Kramberger. One-quarter life size.

over *Pithecanthropus*, in which the index of the height of skull is only 34.2.

The jaw is more slender than that of the Heidelberg man but is still thick and massive; the chin is receding, a characteristic of all the Neanderthal races.

The broken condition of all the human bones in this cavern, and the abundant indications of fire, have led to the charge that the Neanderthals of Krapina were cannibals, and that these mingled remains are the bones of animals and men collected here during cannibalistic feasts. Against this supposition Breuil observes that none of the human bones are split lengthwise, as is the usual practice when extracting the marrow, but they are broken crosswise. This is the only evidence of such practice that has been found during all Palæolithic times, and we should hesitate to accept it unless corroborated by other localities.

The various layers indicate that the cavern was successively occupied by man; in or near the hearths are found stone implements, broken and incinerated bones, and pieces of charcoal, which may indicate that this grotto was visited only at intervals, perhaps during the colder seasons of the year.

(1) Harlé, 1910.1.
(2) d'Ault du Mesnil, 1896.1, pp. 284–296.
(3) Obermaier, 1912.1, p. 146.
(4) Schmidt, 1912.1, pp. 118–126.
(5) Boule, 1888.1.
(6) Obermaier, 1912.1, pp. 327–329.
(7) Haug, 1907.1, vol. II, pp. 327–329.
(8) Geikie, 1914.1, p. 262.
(9) Morlot, 1854.1.
(10) Commont, 1906.1.
(11) Geikie, 1914.1, pp. 107–111.
(12) d'Ault du Mesnil, *op. cit.*
(13) Schmidt, 1912.1, pp. 124, 125.
(14) Obermaier, 1912.1, p. 118.
(15) Dawson, 1913.1; 1913.2; 1913.3.
(16) Kennard, 1913.1.
(17) Reid, 1913.1.
(18) Dawson, 1913.1, p. 123; 1914.1, pp. 82–86.
(19) Keith, A., 1913.1; 1913.2; 1913.3.
(20) Smith, G. E., 1913.1; 1913.2; 1913.3; 1913.4.
(21) Boule, 1913.1, pp. 245, 246.
(22) Schwalbe, 1914.1, p. 603.
(23) Osborn, 1910.1, pp. 404–409.
(24) Ewart, 1904.1; 1907.1; 1909.1.
(25) Obermaier, 1912.1, p. 120.
(26) de Mortillet, 1869.1.
(27) Obermaier, *op. cit.*, p. 116.
(28) Lyell, 1863.1, p. 164.
(29) Geikie, 1914.1, pp. 119, 263, 264.
(30) Schmidt, 1912.1, pp. 125, 126.
(31) Geikie, *op. cit.*, p. 228.
(32) Avebury, 1913.1, p. 342, Fig. 236.
(33) Schmidt, *op. cit.*, pp. 17–105.
(34) Breuil, 1912.5, p. 14.
(35) Obermaier, 1912.1, p. 164.
(36) Obermaier, *op. cit.*, pp. 124, 125, 127, 130.
(37) Commont, 1908.1.
(38) Déchelette, 1908.1, vol. I, pp. 80–90.
(39) Geikie, 1914.1, p. 255.
(40) Hilzheimer, 1913.1, p. 145.
(41) Obermaier, 1912.1, p. 127.
(42) Fischer, 1913.1.
(43) Gorjanović-Kramberger, 1901.1; 1903.1; 1906.1.
(44) Schwalbe, 1914.1, p. 597.

CHAPTER III

CLOSE OF THE THIRD INTERGLACIAL. TEMPERATE, AND ARID CLIMATE, ACHEULEAN INDUSTRY — ADVENT OF THE FOURTH GLACIATION, PROFOUND CHANGES IN ANIMAL AND PLANT LIFE — THE ARCTIC TUNDRA PERIOD OF MAMMALIAN AND PLANT LIFE — CHARACTERS OF THE NEANDERTHAL RACE, OF THEIR MOUSTERIAN FLINT INDUSTRY — SUPPOSED CAUSES OF EXTINCTION OR DISPERSAL

We now reach a prolonged and important stage in the prehistory of Europe, namely, the period of the fourth glaciation, of the final development of the Neanderthal race of man, of the Mousterian industry, of the beginnings of cave life, of the chase of the reindeer, and its use for food and clothing.

In all Europe the Acheulean industry appears to have come to a close during a period of arid climate, warm in some parts of western Europe and cool or even cold in others. The seasonal variations may well have been extreme, as on the steppes of southern Russia, where exceedingly hot summers may be followed by intensely cold winters, with high winds and snow-storms destructive of life.

It is this seasonal alternation, as well as the recurrence, either seasonal or secular, of milder climate, which explains the survival or return of the Asiatic fauna even after the close of the Acheulean industry and when the Mousterian industry was well advanced.

From deposits found at Grimaldi, in the *Grotte des Enfants* and in the *Grotte du Prince*, it has long been said that men of early Mousterian times lived contemporary with the hippopotamus, the straight-tusked elephant, and Merck's rhinoceros in the genial climate of the Mediterranean Riviera. More recently the same animals have been found as far north as the Somme valley in the 'river-drifts' of Montières-les-Amiens.[1] Here, again, we find remains of the hippopotamus, the stright-tusked elephant, and its companion, Merck's rhinoceros, in Mousterian deposits, a surprising discovery, because it had always been supposed that a cold climatic period had set in all over western Europe even before the close of the Acheulean culture. But there is also evidence of a temperate climate still prevailing in the Thames valley in the period of the Mousterian 'floors.'[2] Again, along the Vézère valley, Dordogne, we find that at the station of La Micoque, where the industry marks the transition between late Acheulean and early Mousterian times, Merck's rhinoceros is found in the lowest layers associated with remains of the moose (*Alces*).

There is evidence that Merck's rhinoceros and the straight-tusked elephant lingered in western Europe during the whole period of the early development of the Mousterian industry. As observed above, these animals were hardier than the southern mammoth, which was the first of the Asiatic mammals to disappear, soon to be followed by its companion, the hippopotamus. Even after the advent of the closely associated tundra pair, the woolly mammoth and the woolly rhinoceros, Merck's rhinoceros persists, as, for example, in the deposits of Rixdorf, near Berlin, where this ancient type occurs in the same deposits with the woolly mammoth, the woolly rhinoceros, the reindeer, and the musk-ox, as well as with the forest forms, the moose, stag, wolf, and forest horse. The extreme northern latitude of this deposit explains the absence of the straight-tusked elephant, which may at the time have been living farther to the south. The same mingling of south and north Asiatic mammals is found at Steinheim, in the valley of the Murr, some degrees to the west and south of Rixdorf, not far from Göttingen, where we find Merck's rhinoceros[3] and the straight-tusked elephant in association with the woolly mammoth, the woolly rhinoceros, the giant deer, and the reindeer.

Thus the Neanderthal races were entering the Mousterian stage of culture during the close of the Third Interglacial Stage and during the early period of the advance of the ice-fields from the great centres in Scandinavia and the Alps. As these ice-fields slowly approached each other from the north and from the south a very great period of time must have elapsed during which all the south Asiatic mammals abandoned western Europe or became extinct, with the exception of the lions and hyænas, which became well fitted to the very severe climate that prevailed over Europe during the fourth glaciation, and even during the long Postglacial Stage which ensued. The large carnivora readily become thoroughly adapted to cold climates, as they subsist on animal life wherever it may be found; tigers of the same stock as those of India have been found as far north as the river Lena, in latitude 52° 25′, where the climate is colder than that of Petrograd or of Stockholm, while the lion throve in the cold atmosphere of the upper Atlas range. Thus the cave-lion (*Felis leo spelæa*) and the cave-hyæna (*H. crocuta spelæa*) doubtless evolved an undercoating of fur as well as an overcoating of long hair, like the tundra mammals. In size the lion of this period in France often equalled and sometimes surpassed its existing relatives, the African and west Asiatic lion; it frequently figures in the art of the Upper Palæolithic artists and survived in western Europe to the very close of Upper Palæolithic times.

The Fourth Glaciation

Penck[4] has estimated that the first maximum of the fourth glaciation in the Alps was reached 40,000 years ago, and that after the recession period the second maximum ended not less than 20,000 years ago. This would extend the Mousterian industry over a very long period of time, for there can be no doubt that the Mousterian culture was practically contemporaneous with the fourth glaciation, even if a briefer period of time should be allotted to this great natural event.

The fourth glaciation, like the first, is believed to have been contemporaneous in Europe and North America,[5] a fact which is of especial importance to American anthropologists in connection with the question of the date of arrival of primitive man in America. In both countries the glaciation reached an early maximum, which was followed by a period of recession of the ice-fields, a time during which a somewhat more temperate climate prevailed, but this in turn gave way to a second advance of as great severity as the first.*

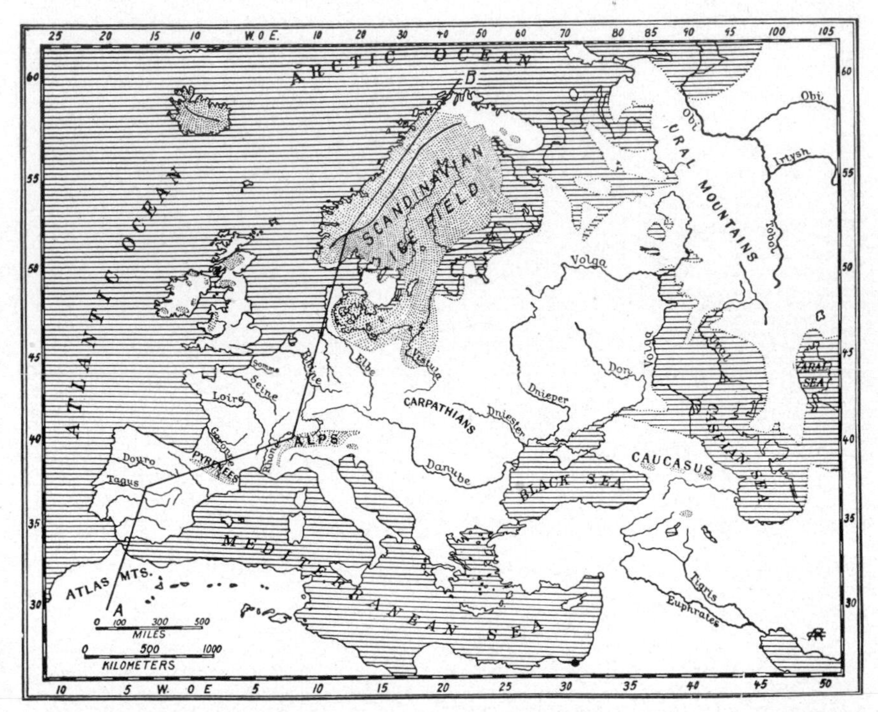

FIG. 94. Europe during the extension of the ice-fields and glaciers of the Fourth Glacial Stage. This is also supposed to have been a period of land depression and of extension of the inland seas of southern Europe. Britain was probably connected with France. The ice-covered areas in western Europe and Britain were far more limited than during the Third Glacial Stage, yet the climate appears to have been more severe than at any previous period. For the snow-level compare Fig. 13. Drawn by C. A. Reeds after Geikie and De Geer.

In the north, Scandinavia and Finland were again enshrouded in ice, and a great *mer de glace* occupied the basin of the Baltic Sea, sending its terminal moraines into Denmark and Schleswig-

*The entire fourth glaciation has been termed *Mecklenburgian* by Geikie;[6] the recession may correspond with his Fourth Interglacial Stage, the *Lower Forestian*. It is the *Würm* of Penck in the Alpine region, with a first and second maximum separated by the recession known as the *Laufenschwankung*. In America it is the early *Wisconsin* with the *Peorian* recession interval, followed by the late *Wisconsin*, which is the final great glaciation of America.

Holstein and over the northern provinces of Germany, but this great ice-field did not again become confluent with that of Great Britain.[7] At the commencement of the fourth glaciation large

FIG. 95. The two large tundra mammals, the woolly rhinoceros (upper), drawn from the work of Upper Palæolithic artists and from the specimen discovered at Starunia, in Galicia, Austria; and the woolly mammoth (lower). These hardy animals gradually replaced the African-Asiatic pair, Merck's rhinoceros and the straight-tusked elephant. Drawn by Erwin S. Christman. One-sixtieth life size.

glaciers descended over the Scottish mountain valleys and filled many of them even to the sea; the coast subsided at least 130 feet in this region. In southern Britain along the valley of the Thames there spread an arctic flora, with the polar willow (*Salix polaris*) and the dwarf birch (*Betula glandulosa*); an arctic plant bed has also been discovered in the valley of the Lea. Thus the tundra climate extended from the Scottish lowlands to the south of England, the land being bleak and almost treeless.[8] This, we believe, was also the period of the arctic flora at Hoxne, Suffolk, and of the arctic plant bed in the valley of the Thames. At this time the valley was frequented by the reindeer, the woolly rhinoceros, and the mammoth, whose remains are entombed in the low-level alluvia swept down from the sides of the valley, so that the remains of this arctic fauna may in places actually overlie those of the more deeply buried and far more ancient warm Asiatic fauna of Chellean times. Like the Somme, the Thames[9] was then from 10 to 25 feet below its present level, the bottom having since silted up with alluvial soil.

This was the period of the deposition of the 'upper drift' over the north German lowlands, the Alps, and northern England, also of the early and late *Wisconsin*, or 'upper drift,' which spreads very widely over the Eastern States, from Wisconsin southward and eastward to the latitude of New York. The gravels and sands of some of the 'lowest terraces' were also deposited.

Mammalian Life of Mousterian Times

The three successive phases of climate and environment surrounding the Neanderthal men during the period of the development of the Mousterian industry, were in descending order as follows:

3. *Extreme Cold Climate of the Last Great Glacial Advance.* Period of the late Mousterian industry of La Quina. Spread of all the arctic and tundra mammals over western Europe, including the musk-ox; migrations of the obi and banded lemming of the extreme north. Life and industry of the Neanderthal races, chiefly in the shelters, grottos, and entrances to the caverns.

2. *Cold Moist Climate.* Period of the middle or 'full Mousterian' industry of the Neanderthal races. Appearance of the tundra life, including well-protected mammals and birds from the arctic region, also descent of the Alpine types to the foot-hills and river borders. First forerunners of the steppe life; the full Eurasiatic forest and field life widely spread over

Europe. Life and industry chiefly in the shelters, grottos, and entrances to the caverns. Reindeer very abundant.

1. *Warm or Cool Arid Climate.* Transition from the Acheulean to the early Mousterian culture, as observed in the stations of La Micoque and of Combe-Capelle. The so-called 'warm Mousterian' fauna, including the surviving hippopotamus, Merck's rhinoceros, and the straight-tusked elephant in northern and southern France; herds of bison, cattle, and wild horses in southwestern France. Tribal life, with the industry partly in open stations, partly under sheltering cliffs.

This is the beginning of the 'Reindeer Period,' for this migrant from Scandinavia, with its companions of the northeastern tundras, the woolly mammoth and the rhinoceros, wandered slowly southward before the advancing Scandinavian ice-fields, which were greatly augmented by the increasingly cold and moist climate. Thus these animals are found in the north with flints of the Mousterian culture before they appear in the more genial region of Dordogne. In the somewhat older Acheulean-Mousterian station of La Micoque, along the Vézère, the fire-hearths contain almost exclusively the remains of horses and relatively few remains of bison and wild cattle, but no reindeer. A fireplace near the station of Combe-Capelle yields numerous remains of the bison, only a few of the horse, and the first of the reindeer. Before the appearance of the reindeer in the valley of the Vézère we may picture the meadow-lands as covered with bison and wild horses, the latter of the type which is now characteristic of the high plateaus of central Asia, while the bison of the period appears to be more similar to the American buffalo than to the surviving European form.

Gradually the tundra animals spread toward the south with the cold climate which for the first time swept all over western Europe. The whole aspect of the country slowly changed with the approach of the reindeer, and the northern flora of the spruce, the fir, and the arctic willow clad the more sheltered river-valleys and hillsides, while the plateaus and fields were partly or wholly deforested.

Thus the country became adapted chiefly to the tundra types of mammals; and in the middle Mousterian strata these herds,

Fig. 96. Typical tundra fauna. "Gradually the tundra animals pressed toward the south with the cold climate which for the first time swept all over western Europe." The wolverene, *Gulo luscus borealis;* the barren-ground reindeer, *Rangifer tarandus* (drawn from the living type); the arctic fox, *Canis lagopus;* the musk-ox, *Ovibos moschatus;* and the banded lemming, *Myodes torquatus*. One-twenty-fifth life size. The lemming (A) is also shown one-seventh life size. Drawn by Erwin S. Christman.

newly migrated from the far north and from the northeastern steppes bordering the Obi River, largely outnumber the steppe forms, which are limited to two or three species. Of these the principal types are the steppe horse, related to the Przewalski horse now living in the desert of Gobi, the steppe suslik (*Spermophilus rufescens*), and the steppe grouse, or moor-hen. The more characteristic forms of steppe life, such as the saiga antelope, the jerboa, and the kiang, were all later arrivals and did not appear until after the close of the Mousterian industry and the disappearance of the Neanderthal race.

This was due to the fact that the climate surrounding the Neanderthal race in Mousterian times was cold and moist, with heavy rainfalls in summer and snow-storms in winter, a climate thoroughly suited to the arctic tundra mammals with their heavy covering of hair acting as a rain shed and the undercoating of wool protecting them in the most severe weather.

The mammal life during the fourth glaciation, as it spread into the middle Rhine and Westphalian region, is fully recorded in the 'loess' deposits of Achenheim and in the famous grotto of Sirgenstein, on the upper Danube, lying northwest of Munich, where, together with traces of the most primitive Mousterian industry, are found remains of the mammoth, the bison, the reindeer, a species of wild horse, and the cave-bear. Following these mammals there is a record in the same deposit of the arrival of the Obi lemming, from northern Russia.

The fact that only seven Mousterian stations are known in all Germany, or eight if we include the site of the Neanderthal burial, may be accounted for by the relatively close proximity of the great Scandinavian glacier on the north, which was only 350 miles distant from the great Alpine glacier on the south. To the east were the plains of Bohemia and the vast lowland region stretching northeastward to the tundras and eastward to the steppes, through which came the great migrations of tundra and steppe life.

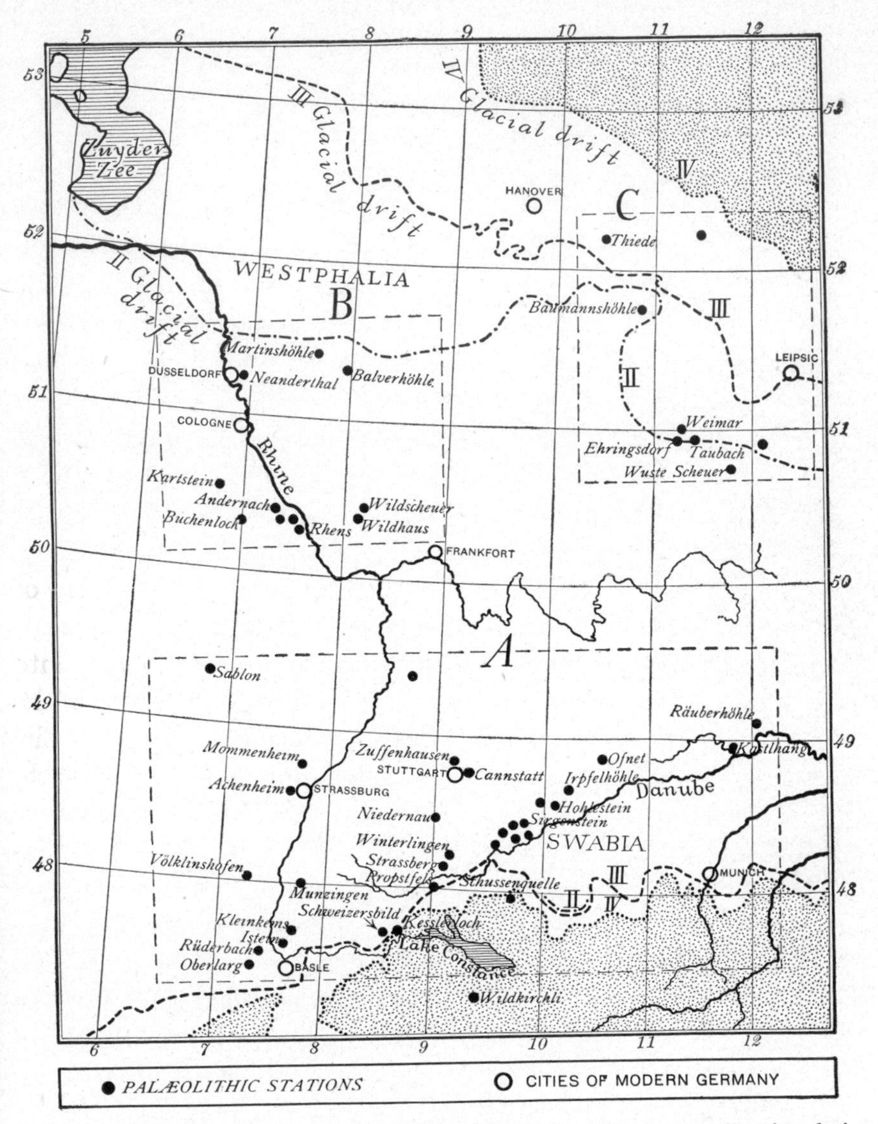

FIG. 97. The seven Mousterian stations of Germany lay between the Scandinavian glacier (IV) on the north and the Alpine glacier (IV) on the south (dotted areas). They include the grottos of *Sirgenstein*, *Irpfelhöhle*, and *Räuberhöhle*, along the valley of the Danube; *Kartstein* and *Buchenloch*, near the middle Rhine, and *Baumannshöhle*, south of Hanover; also the open loess station of *Mommenheim*. The Mousterian grotto of *Wildkirchli*, in Switzerland, lay within the limits of the Alpine ice-fields; and the burial at *Neanderthal*, near Düsseldorf, was probably of Mousterian age. After R. R. Schmidt, modified and redrawn.

Geographic and Climatic Environment of the Neanderthal Race

Let us first glance at Dordogne. Among the stations of the early Mousterian industry we have seen that the Neanderthals in the valley of the Vézère, at La Micoque, were in the midst of a fauna chiefly composed of the bison and of the wild horse, the remains found in the hearths being almost exclusively of the latter animal.* In the primitive Mousterian station of Combe-Capelle near by the fire-hearths yield remains of the bison but only a few of the horse.

Among the earliest caves inhabited by man[10] was that of Le Moustier, situated on the right bank of the Vézère, and about 90 feet above it. This shelter and cave were examined as early as 1860–3 by Lartet[11] and Christy and subsequently by de Vibraye,[12] Massénat,[13] and others. Besides the deposits in the floor of the grotto there, a deep Mousterian culture layer has been found under the cliff in front, and this has been selected for our representation of the life of the men of Mousterian times, and of the flora of the Vézère in this early period (see frontispiece). Peyrony observes that, here as elsewhere, the older and lower industrial camps were farther away from the shelters; indeed, in this very region there are evidences that the Chellean and Acheulean flint workers occasionally visited the plateaus above; but as time passed and the weather became more severe the Neanderthals began to work nearer to the overhanging cliffs and finally directly beneath them. At this classic station of Le Moustier, one of the most complete skeletons of Neanderthal man was unearthed by Hauser, in 1908. There was a continuous residence here in middle and upper Mousterian times, extending into the lower Aurignacian of the Upper Palæolithic. The contemporary fauna in these deposits included the mammoth, the reindeer, the giant deer (*Megaceros*), the horse, the bison, the woolly rhinoceros, and the

* Obermaier, Breuil, and Schmidt assign La Micoque to the transition between late Acheulean and early Mousterian times.

cave-bear. During the habitation of this typical station by man the climate was very cold and damp.

In this region is found the complete record of the course of Mousterian evolution, both in the implements and in the advent of new forms of life; the number of reindeer gradually increases in the ascending layers with the development of the Mousterian industry. There is a constant gradation from the Acheulean into the Mousterian industrial types; according to Cartailhac, this

FIG. 98. The type station of Le Moustier, on the right bank of the Vézère, Dordogne. The culture layer is on the middle terrace, overlooking the hamlet of Le Moustier. (Compare frontispiece, Pl. I.) Photograph by Belvès.

industry is all the work of the same people, with no sharp lines of division.

Thus at Combe-Capelle, where the début of the true Mousterian culture took place, we find a number of large coups de poing, pointing back to the early Acheulean implements. The gradations which are exhibited here in these successive layers are quite in contrast to the advance of the industry at the close of Mousterian times in the very same locality, where there is an abrupt cultural transition toward the Aurignacian.

Southern Britain tells of a similar sequence, which we may interpret as follows. Belonging either to the temperate climate of early Mousterian times, or to the period of the recession of the fourth glaciation, known in the Alps as the *Laufenschwankung*, are the Mousterian stations along the Lea and near the mouth of the Thames at Crayford (Worthington Smith,[14] Geikie[15]). These Palæolithic 'floors' of Mousterian times are buried be-

FIG. 99. Excavations of the Mousterian culture layer under the cliff of Le Moustier. Photograph by N. C. Nelson.

neath 4 to 5 feet of sand and loam and rest upon the surface of older river-gravels. Among the later river deposits several old land surfaces have been discovered; they consist of a few inches of angular gravel, crowded in places with unabraded implements and flakes which obviously occur just where they were left by Palæolithic workmen. At one point there is evidence that the flint maker squatted over his work, with his knees slightly apart, for the chips are thrown to the right and left in small piles. Here and there, mixed with these Mousterian implements, are more archaic forms which may have been drifted down from the older land surfaces above.

One such floor has been traced by Worthington Smith[16] through Middlesex and on both sides of the Thames. Plant remains occur plentifully on this old land surface, including impressions of portions of leaves, stems of grass, rushes, and sedges. The birch, alder, pine, yew, elm, and hazel have been recognized. The common male fern is of frequent occurrence, while the royal fern (*Osmunda regalis*) is found in profusion. Upon the whole, this assemblage of plants indicates a temperate climate. The flints described and figured by Worthington Smith are either of the late Acheulean 'Levallois flake' type or else of early Mousterian age. This writer[17] notes the great number of instruments known as trimmed flakes, which are found on the Palæolithic 'floor'; these are flakes of large size, trimmed to an implement-like form on one side, while the other side is left perfectly plain; the examples are remarkably constant to one form. The type of implement here described resembles the flakes of Levallois or Combe-Capelle, or even the typical 'point' from Le Moustier. Such flakes, shaped into the Mousterian forms of racloir, or scraper, are very common in the gravels of the Lea and of the Thames.

While the remains of the woolly mammoth are found here, there are also indications of the presence of a well-marked temperate flora. These high-level 'river-drifts' along the Thames[18] were certainly deposited when the climatic conditions were temperate, but they are succeeded by deposits indicating a renewed cold period, which may represent the cold 'full Mousterian' times of the Lower Palæolithic habitation of the Thames. Here we find the remarkable sheets of contorted 'drift' attributable to the movements of the frozen soil and subsoil when exposed to the heat of the summer sun. At the same time there may have been deposited along the Thames the alluvial loams and gravels, occasionally containing stones and rocks, which were brought down by ice-rafts; these low-level gravels are not to be confused with the underlying 'old river-gravels' which contain the warm temperate hippopotamus fauna, for they were accumulated under very cold conditions; they yield remains of the woolly rhinoceros and of the mammoth. Thus, on the high levels of the Thames as well as on the low levels we find evidences of the human culture and of the extinct fauna of the period of the fourth great glaciation.

The upper waters of the Rhine and Danube were also frequented by late Acheulean and early Mousterian flint workers. At a point far distant from southern England there is the cavern of Wildkirchli on the Santis Mountains, near Appenzell, in Switzerland; in Mousterian times this was in the very heart of the

Fig. 100. Mousterian cavern of Wildkirchli. After Bächler. Entrances indicated at 1, 2, and 3, in the side of the limestone cliff. Here, at a height of 4,500 feet above sea-level, Bächler discovered proofs of occupation by Mousterian man in the very heart of the Alpine ice-fields of the Fourth Glacial Stage.

north Alpine ice-field. The animal life here may indicate that this cavern was open during the period of recession between the two great advances of the fourth glaciation. Here, at a height of 4,500 feet, Bächler[19] between 1903–6, discovered proofs of occupation by Neanderthal man during Mousterian times; the flints are not well formed; the presence of crude bone implements may point to late Mousterian times; but the flints are considered by Bächler to be of the same stage as those of Le Moustier. It is asserted that when the Neanderthals followed the chase here the climate was more genial, because the animals found include the stag, Alpine wolf (*Cyon alpinus fossilis*), cave-bear, cave-lion, cave-leopard (*Felis pardus spelæa*), badger, marten, and otter, together with the typical Alpine forms, the ibex, chamois, and

FIG. 101. Entrance to the grotto of Sirgenstein. After R. R. Schmidt. "Of all the stations along the Danube by far the most important is that of Sirgenstein . . . which was first occupied by the Neanderthals in early Mousterian times and continued to be visited by the Lower and Upper Palæolithic men until the very close of the Upper Palæolithic."

marmot. But this fauna alone can hardly be taken as proof of a temperate climate, for at this Alpine height we should not expect to discover the tundra life of the period; in fact, it is entirely absent.

Of all the stations along the Danube, by far the most important is that of Sirgenstein, lying between the modern cities of Nuremberg and Augsburg, which was first occupied by the Neanderthals in early Mousterian times and continued to be visited by the Lower and Upper Palæolithic men until the very close of the

Upper Palæolithic. The continuous section of animal life and of human culture which this remarkable cavern yields afforded Schmidt,[20] who began his researches here in the spring of 1906, a key to the prehistory of all the eighteen caverns in the region of the upper Danube and upper Rhine. In Sirgenstein the primitive Mousterian culture of the early Neanderthals was found, together with remains of the mammoth, bison, reindeer, a species of wild horse, and the cave-bear; this Mousterian industry closed with a record of the arrival in this region of the Obi lemming from northern Russia. Later on the Crô-Magnon race of Aurignacian times left on the floor of the cavern remains of their flint industry and of their feasts, including the bones of the woolly rhinoceros, mammoth, stag, and reindeer. During Upper Palæolithic Solutrean times the cavern was not occupied; but early in Magdalenian times it was again inhabited by man, and coincident with his return is the arrival of a great migration of the banded lemming (*Myodes torquatus*) from the arctic tundras of the north. Finally, toward the end of the Upper Palæolithic, in late Magdalenian times, another climatic transition is indicated by the appearance of the pika, or tailless hare (*Lagomys pusillus*). During the Bronze Age this favorite grotto was again entered, and it was also inhabited during a portion of the Iron Age. The débris of these various cultures, hearths, and deposits of cave loam reach a total thickness of 8½ feet and mark Sirgenstein as first in rank among the Palæolithic stations of Germany.

Types and Migrations of the Mammals Hunted by the Neanderthals

This is the life of the period of the fourth glaciation, when a very cold and moist climate prevailed all over western Europe as far south as northern Spain and northern Italy. While the glacial fields were not so extensive as during the third or the second glaciation, the climate was very severe, as indicated by the southward migration not only of the arctic flora but of the mammals and birds of the tundra region bordering the southern shores of the Arctic Ocean. Two or three forms from the cold

Pl. V. The Neanderthal man of La Chapelle-aux-Saints, inhabiting the Dordogne region of central France in Mousterian times. Antiquity estimated as between 40,000 and 25,000 years. After the restoration modelled by J. H. McGregor. For the bodily proportions of this hunting race compare the frontispiece, Pl. I.

steppes of northern Russia also found their way into western Europe, but this was distinctly not a steppe period because of the prevailing moisture of the climate; in place of the westerly winds and great dust clouds of closing Acheulean times, cold mists and clouds heavy with moisture swept over the country, which during the winters was at times buried in snow, and subject to rapid changes of temperature. These climatic* conditions appear to be demonstrated by the predominance of the arctic tundra life, mammals which were adapted only to severe weather and attracted by the northern flora.

The summers were undoubtedly warm, like the present Arctic summers, but very much longer in these southerly latitudes. It is not improbable that there were seasonal migrations, northward and southward, of the mammoths, rhinoceroses, and reindeer, and also that the northern flint quarries along the Somme and the Marne may have been visited chiefly during the warm summer season. The Asiatic mammals had entirely disappeared from the regions of France and Germany during the first maximum of the fourth glaciation, but there are some who maintain that during the amelioration of climate that followed, an interval in the Alpine region termed the *Laufenschwankung* by Penck, the straight-tusked elephant and Merck's rhinoceros again migrated into northern France. It is true that occasionally we find the bones of these animals in close association with those of the woolly mammoth and the woolly rhinoceros. It is possible to explain such intermingling either as having occurred during the advance of the fourth glaciation, or as due to the northward and southward migration of the respective herds of mammals in the summer and winter seasons. As the period of the fourth glaciation continued it is certain that these Asiatic mammals entirely disappeared.

At the same time the Neanderthals had passed through the first stage of development of the Mousterian industry and had reached what is known as the 'full' or 'high' Mousterian, which,

* The *climate* of the *tundras* is extreme, the winter temperature falling on an average to 27° F. below zero, while in summer the temperature is about 50° F. In the subarctic steppes the average January temperature hardly exceeds 30° F., while that of July is 70° F.

with few exceptions, was carried on under the shelter of the overhanging cliffs or within the grottos.

The mammalian life of these 'full' Mousterian times, as found along the headwaters of the Danube, the Rhine, and the branches of the Dordogne and Vézère, is divided among the various faunal groups as follows:

Life of Middle Mousterian Times

Tundra Life.
- Woolly mammoth.
- Woolly rhinoceros.
- Scandinavian reindeer.
- Arctic fox.
- Arctic hare.
- Banded lemming.
- Arctic ptarmigan.

Alpine Life.
- Alpine marmot.
- Ibex.
- Alpine ptarmigan.

Steppe Life.
- Steppe horse.
- Steppe suslik.
- Moor-hen.

Asiatic Life.
- Cave-lion.
- Cave-hyæna.
- Cave-leopard.

Forest Life.
- Stag, lynx, wolf, fox, water-vole, brown bear, giant deer.
- Cave-bear.

Meadow Life.
- Bison.
- Wild cattle.

It would appear that the reindeer, the woolly mammoth, and the woolly rhinoceros were already widely distributed over western Europe, accompanied by the arctic fox (*Canis lagopus*), the arctic hare (*Lepus variabilis*), and the banded lemming (*Myodes torquatus*). There is no proof that the musk-ox had at this time reached its extreme southerly distribution, and it would appear that the arrival of the second type of northern lemming from the region of the river Obi (*Myodes obensis*) did not occur until the close of Mousterian times,[21] because the great migration of these animals is recorded by their abundant remains in the so-called 'lower rodent layer' of all the stations along the Rhine and Danube, such as Sirgenstein, Wildscheuer, and Ofnet, after the final stage of Mousterian industry. In fact, this remarkable little rodent appears to mark the second maximum or close of the fourth glaciation by its migration all over western Europe, and wherever its remains are found in the grotto deposits they furnish one of the most important and positive of prehistoric dates, namely, that of the 'lower rodent layer.' The lemmings surpass all other mammals in the great distances covered by their migrations, and it would appear that this northern species swept all over western Europe at the same time, leaving its remains not only in the caverns along the Danube but in those of Belgium and of Thiede, near Braunschweig. The latter station, Thiede, was not far from the southern border of the Scandinavian glacier; it was subjected to a very severe arctic climate, as the only associates of the Obi lemming were the banded lemming, the arctic fox, the arctic hare, the reindeer, the mammoth, and the musk-ox.

The woolly mammoth now reaches the height of its evolution and specialization; as preserved in the frozen tundras of northern Siberia, and as represented in very numerous drawings and engravings by the Upper Palæolithic artists, it is the most completely known of all fossil mammalia.[22] Its proportions, as shown in the accompanying figure, which represents the information gathered from all sources, are entirely different from those of either the Indian or African elephant. The head is very high and surmounted by a great mass of hair and wool; behind this a sharp depression separates the back of the head from the great hump on the back; the hinder portion of the back falls away very rapidly and the tail is short; the overcoat of long hair nearly reaches the ground, and beneath this is a warm undercoating of wool. It is not improbable that the humps on the head and the back were fat reservoirs. The color of the hair was a yellowish brown, varying from light brown to pure brown; woolly hair, from an inch to an inch and a half in length, covered the whole body; interspersed with the shorter hairs was a large number of longer and thicker hairs, which formed mane-like patches on the cheeks, chin, shoulders, flanks, and abdomen. A broad fringe of this

LIFE OF LATE MOUSTERIAN TIMES

Second Maximum of Fourth Glaciation

Tundra, Steppe, Alpine, Asiatic and Meadow life, as above.
Obi lemming.
Musk-ox.
Ermine.
Arctic ptarmigan.
Eversmann's weasel (Steppe weasel).

long hair extended along the sides of the body, as depicted in the work of the Upper Palæolithic artists in the Combarelles Cave. Especially interesting to us is the food found in the stomach and mouth of the frozen Siberian mammoths, which consists chiefly of a meadow flora such as flourishes during the summer in northern Siberia at the present day, including grasses and sedges, wild

FIG. 102. The woolly mammoth (*Elephas primigenius*) and the contemporary Neanderthal hunters (*Homo neanderthalensis*), after the drawings of Upper Palæolithic artists and the frozen mammoths found in northern Siberia. By Charles R. Knight, 1915.

thyme, beans of the wild oxytropis, also the arctic variety of the upright crowfoot (*Ranunculus acer*). This was the summer food. The winter food undoubtedly included the leaves and stems of the willow, the juniper, and other winter plants.

The woolly rhinoceros was the invariable companion of the mammoth, even as Merck's rhinoceros always associated itself with the straight-tusked elephant. This remarkable animal is related to the northern African group of white rhinoceroses, from which it branched off at a very remote period. The profile of its very long, narrow head, of its enormous anterior and lesser posterior horn, and its humped back resembles that of the existing

African form, but its protection against the arctic climate gave it a wholly different outward appearance; the hair of the face, of a golden-brown color, with an undercovering of wool, is preserved in the Museum of Petrograd. Through a discovery at Starunia, in eastern Galicia, in 1911, this animal is now completely known to us, except the tail; its remains were found here at a depth of 30 feet, and included the head, left fore leg, and the skin of the left side of the body. The Starunia specimen has a broad, truncated upper lip adapted to grazing habits, small oblique eyes, long, narrow, and pointed ears, a long anterior horn with oval base, and a shorter posterior horn, a short neck, on the back of which is a small, fleshy hump, quite independent of the skeleton; the legs are comparatively short. It differs from the living African form in the somewhat narrower muzzle, in its small, pointed ears, and in the presence of a thick coating of hair. Like the white rhinoceros, the woolly form was a plains dweller, living on grass and small herbs.[23] This rhinoceros kept more closely to the borders of the great ice-sheets than did the mammoth, arresting its migration in Germany and France; that is, it did not migrate so far to the south as the mammoth, which wandered down into Italy as far as Rome.

The reindeer was the herald or forerunner of all the arctic tundra fauna; it reached the valley of the Vézère at the beginning of the period of the true Mousterian culture and already had penetrated much farther south during the Third Glacial Stage, probably migrating along the borders of the ice-fields; in fact, it is found in northern Europe even during the second glaciation. It is the true Scandinavian or barren-ground species, which is now typified by two forms of the Old World reindeer (*R. tarandus*, *R. spitzbergensis*), and by the existing American barren-ground forms. The antlers are round, slender, and long in proportion to the relatively small size of the animal; the brow tines are palmated. There is little proof that the Neanderthals made much use of the bones of the reindeer, but there is every reason to suppose that they used the pelts, for the preparation of which the Mousterian scrapers and planers were especially well fitted.

In the Iberian peninsula the tundra fauna did not penetrate as far south as Portugal, although the Norwegian lemming (*Myodes lemmus*) reached the vicinity of Lisbon. The woolly mammoth, accompanied by the woolly rhinoceros, has been discovered in two localities on the extreme northern coast of Spain, in the province of Santander, bordering the Bay of Biscay. The

FIG. 103. The woolly rhinoceros (*Rhinoceros antiquitatis*), after the drawings of Palæolithic artists and the specimen from Starunia preserved in the museum of Lemberg, Galicia. By Charles R. Knight, 1915.

reindeer (*Rangifer tarandus*) is found in the cavern of Seriña, south of the Pyrenees; as early as Acheulean times it reached the region of Altamira, near Santander. Thus Harlé[24] concludes it is certain that the tundra fauna spread from France westward into Catalonia, along the northern coast of Spain, flanking the Pyrenees. It is generally believed that the cave-bear (*Ursus spelæus*) occupied many of the caverns before their possession by man, and developed certain peculiarities of structure in these haunts. Thus the phalanges bearing the claws are feebly developed, indicating that the claws had partly lost their prehensile function; the anterior grinding-teeth are very much reduced, and the cusps of the posterior grinders are blunted in a way which is indicative of an omnivorous diet; yet the front paws were of tremendous size, the body was thick-set and of heavier proportions than that of the larger recent bears (*Ursus arctos*) of Europe. Hence, it would appear that the Neanderthals drove out from the caves a type of bear less formidable than the existing species but nevertheless a serious opponent to men armed with the small weapons of the Mousterian period.

Customs of the Chase and of Cave Life

We have only indirect means of knowing the courage and activity of the Neanderthals in the chase, through the bones of animals hunted for food which are found intermingled with the flints around their ancient hearths. These include in the early Mousterian hearths, as we have seen, bones of the bison, the wild cattle, and the horse, which are followed at Combe-Capelle by the first appearance of the bones of the reindeer. The bones of the bison and of the wild horse are both utilized in the bone anvils of the closing Mousterian culture at La Quina. What we believe to be the period of the great mammalian life of the region of the upper Danube is found in the Mousterian levels of the grotto of Sirgenstein, from which it would appear that the Neanderthals hunted the mammoth, the rhinoceros, the wild horse, bison, and cattle, and the giant deer as well as the reindeer. We should keep in mind, however, that when these caves were for a time deserted, the beasts of prey returned, and so it often happens that the succeeding layers afford proofs of alternate occupation by man and by beasts of prey of sufficient size to bring in the larger kinds of game, while owls may be responsible for the deposits of the lemming, as in the 'lower rodent layer.'

Obermaier[25] has given careful study to the vicissitudes of cave life in Mousterian times. Long before these caves were inhabited by man, they served as lairs or refuges for the cave-bear and cave-hyæna, as well as for many birds of prey. For example, the cave of Echenoz-la-Moline, on the upper waters of the Saône, contained the remains of over eight hundred skeletons of the cave-bear, and no doubt it cost the Neanderthals many a hard-fought battle before the beasts were driven out and man possessed himself of the grotto. Fire may have been the means employed. It has been questioned whether the caves were not unhealthy dwelling-places, but it must be remembered that, except in certain caverns which had natural openings through the roof for the exit of smoke, there was no true cave life, but rather a grotto life, which centred around the entrance of the cave. The smallest cave, this author observes, was considerably larger and better ventilated than the small, smoky cabins of some of the European peasants, or the snow huts of the Eskimo. The most serious obstacle was the prevailing dampness, which varied periodically in the caverns, so that dry seasons were succeeded by abundant moisture seeping through the limestone roof and down the side walls. At such times the caverns were probably uninhabitable, and in the bones of both men and beasts many instances have been observed of diseased swellings and of inflammation of the vertebræ, such as are caused by extreme dampness. The compensating advantages were the shelter offered from the rain and cold, a constant temperature at moderate distances from the entrance, and also the fact that the caves were very easily defensible, because the entrance was generally small and the approach often steep and difficult; a high stone wall across the opening would have made the defense still easier, and a flaming firebrand would have prevented the approach of bears and other beasts of prey. On account of this shelter from the weather and wild beasts the grottos and the larger openings of the caverns were certainly crowded with the Mousterian flint workers during the inclement seasons of the year.

Yet the greater part of the life of the Neanderthals was undoubtedly passed in the open and in the chase. Throughout Mousterian times the commonest game consisted of the wild horse, wild ox, and reindeer. Both flesh and pelts were utilized, and the marrow was sought by splitting all the larger bones. Thus, frequently we find in the hearths the remains of the mammoth, the woolly rhinoceros, the giant deer, the cave-bear, and the brown bear. From these beasts of prey the Neanderthal hunters obtained pelts and perhaps also fat for torches used to light the caverns; there is no proof of the invention of the lamp at this period.

The work of the women undoubtedly consisted of preparing the meals and making the pelts into covers and clothing. Whenever possible this would be done in the daylight outside of the grottos, but in chilly, rainy weather, or the bitter cold of winter, the whole tribe would seek refuge in the grotto, gathering around the fire-hearths fed with wood; odd corners would serve as storehouses for fuel or dried meat, preserved against the days when extreme cold and blinding snow forbade the hunters to venture forth.

It appears that the game was dismembered where it fell and the best parts removed. The skull was split open for the brain; the long bones were preserved for the marrow; thus the bones of the flank and shoulder of game occur frequently in cave deposits, while the ribs and vertebræ are rare.

The pitfall may have been part of the hunting craft known to the Neanderthals. The chase was pursued with spears or darts fitted with flint points, also by means of 'throwing stones,' which are found in great numbers in the upper Mousterian levels of La Quina, in the Wolf Cave of Yonne, Les Cottés, and various places in Spain. If one imagines, as is quite possible, that the throwing stone was placed in a leather sling or in the cleft end of a stick, or fastened to a long leather thong, one can readily see it would prove a very effective weapon.

The methods of chase by the Neanderthals are, nevertheless, somewhat of a mystery. There was a very decided disparity between the size and effectiveness of their weapons and the strength and resistance of the animals which they pursued. None of the very heavy implements of Acheulean times was preserved; the dart and spear heads are not greatly improved, certainly they could not penetrate the thick hides of the larger arctic tundra mammals, heavily protected with hair and wool; the chase even of the horses, wild cattle, and reindeer was apparently without the aid of the bow and arrow and prior to the invention of the barbed arrow or lance head.

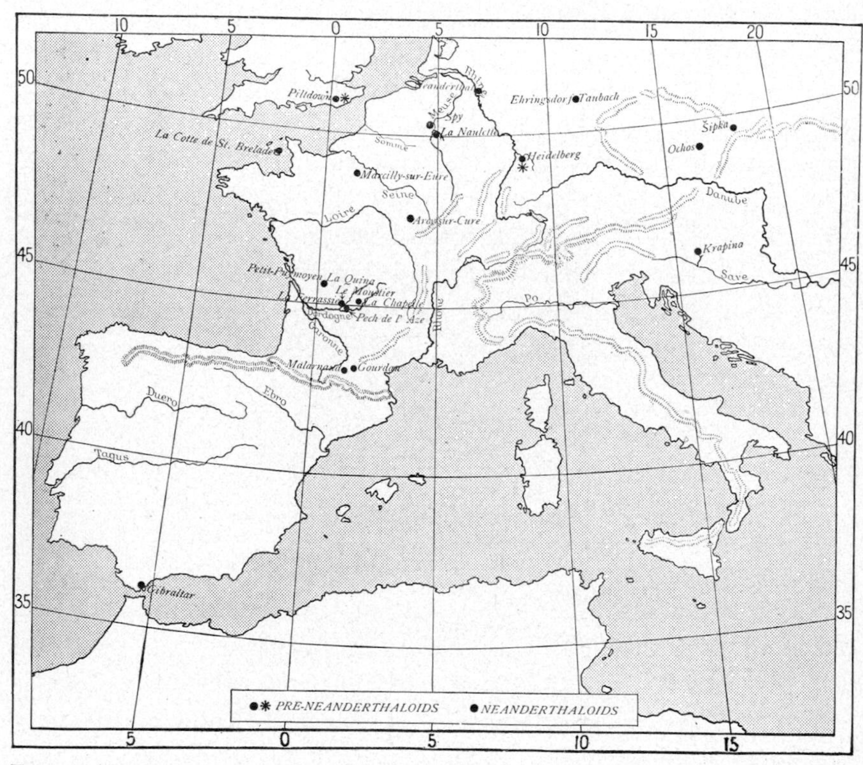

FIG. 104. Geographic distribution of Pre-Neanderthaloids and Neanderthaloids in western Europe, showing the localities where the remains of Pre-Neanderthaloid races (Heidelberg and Piltdown) and of true Neanderthaloids have thus far been discovered. (Compare table, p. 219.)

DISCOVERY OF THE NEANDERTHALOID RACES

The open-air or nomadic life of all the tribes of western Europe from Pre-Chellean nearly to the close of Acheulean times was very unfavorable to the preservation of human remains. It is possible that the bodies of the dead and of the aged were thrown out to the hyænas which surrounded the stations, as among some of the tribes of Africa to-day, but it is equally possible that they were interred in some manner. Skeletons buried near the surface in the river sands or gravels of the 'terraces' would not have been preserved. We have seen that the preservation of the Heidelberg and Piltdown remains was entirely due to chance, the bones having been washed down and mingled with those of the animals; nor has any evidence been found in the grotto of Krapina of ceremonial burial or of respect for the dead, but on the contrary there is some evidence of cannibalistic customs. Even before the close of early Mousterian times all this was changed. Perhaps the closer association en-

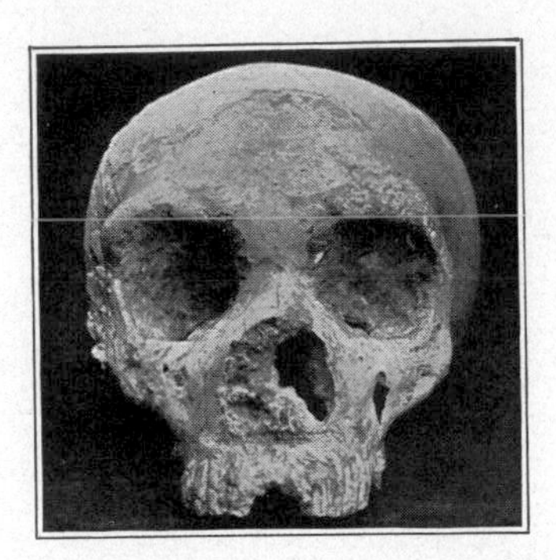

FIG. 105. Front view of the Neanderthaloid skull found at Gibraltar in 1848—the earliest discovery of a member of this race, now regarded as the skull of a woman. Photograph by A. Hrdlička from the original specimen. One-quarter life size.

forced by the more rigorous climate indirectly produced greater respect for the dead and led to the custom of burial or the orderly laying out of the remains of the dead in the floors of the partly protected grottos and caverns, to which custom we owe our present knowledge of the structure of Neanderthal man in Mousterian times.

The first discovery of a Neanderthaloid was made in 1848, eight years before the type of the Neanderthal race came to light. This was the Gibraltar skull[26] found by Lieutenant Flint, near Forbes Quarry, on the north face of the Rock of Gibraltar. It consists of a well-preserved skull, with the parietal bones only missing and the face and base of the cranium remarkably complete. In 1868 it was presented by Busk to the Museum of the

Royal College of Surgeons, in London, where it lies to-day. The exact site of the discovery can no longer be positively identified; it was probably found in a still existing cave, and although its archæologic age cannot be determined, yet as its anatomical features are those of the Neanderthal race, and as all the remains of this race which can be dated with certainty are of Mousterian age, it probably belongs to the Mousterian period. Of recent years its great importance in the history of man has been revealed in the studies of Sollas, Keith, and Schwalbe. Thus it has come

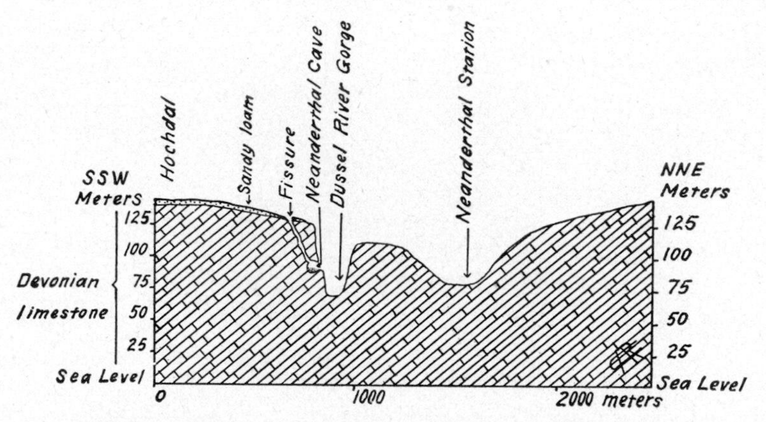

FIG. 106. Section of that part of the valley of the Düssel known as the Neanderthal, showing the location of the limestone grotto where the Neanderthal skeleton was discovered. Drawn by C. A. Reeds.

to be ranked among the Neanderthaloids and is considered of a particularly primitive form, because of the extremely small size of the brain. This feature and the slight development of the supraorbital ridges, so characteristic of the Neanderthaloids, are explained by the theory that the skull belonged to a female.

Sera[27] considers the Gibraltar skull to be the most ape-like of all human fossils and thinks it should not be classed with the Neanderthaloids at all, but should be regarded as Pre-Neanderthaloid; this view is shared by Keith. Boule, however, believes that this skull is of the same geologic age as that of Spy, La Chapelle, La Ferrassie, and La Quina; everything leads us to believe,[28] he remarks, that the skull of Gibraltar is a female skull of Neanderthal type. He elsewhere refers to the skulls of Gibraltar, of La Quina, and of La Ferrassie II as probably those of female Neanderthals.

The type skull of this great extinct race of men is that of Neanderthal—certainly the most famous and the most disputed of all anthropologic remains—appreciated by Lyell and Huxley, but passed over by Darwin, and finally established by Schwalbe as the most important missing link between the existing species of man (*Homo sapiens*) and the anthropoid apes. In 1856[29] some workmen were engaged in clearing a small loam-covered cave about six feet in height, the so-called Feldhofner Grotto, in the cretaceous limestone of the valley known as the Neanderthal, on the small stream Düssel flowing between Elberfeld and

FIG. 107. The original type skull of Neanderthal (left side) discovered in 1856. After Schwalbe. One-quarter life size.

Düsseldorf. They discovered some human bones, probably a complete skeleton representing an interment, which, unfortunately, were allowed to be scattered and crushed. Doctor Fuhlrott rescued the parts that remained, including the now famous skullcap, both thigh-bones, the right upper-arm bone, portions of the lower arm, bones of both sides, the right collar-bone, and fragments of the pelvis, shoulder-blade, and ribs. All the bones were perfectly preserved and are now to be found in the provincial museum of Bonn.

The discovery made a great sensation, but at first the age of these fossils remained doubtful; some 150 paces from the grotto, in a similar small cave were found bones of the cave-bear and rhinoceros. In 1858 Schaaffhausen's memoir[30] appeared, in which he gave the first detailed description of these remains as belonging to a primitive original race differing in every point from recent man, and he never wavered from this standpoint.

In 1863[31] Busk, Huxley, and Lyell also placed this skeleton in its true intermediate position between man and the anthropoid apes. The determined opinion of Virchow that this was not a normal type of man exerted so great an influence that not until the classic work of Schwalbe,[32] between 1899 and 1901, did this skeleton assume its commanding importance for all time, and even this was subsequent to the discovery of two other Neanderthaloid races.

At first, quite erroneously, this was associated with the so-called race of Cannstatt, but long before Schwalbe's work it was recognized by King,[33] in 1864, as a distinct species of man (*Homo neanderthalensis*) 'the man of the Neander valley.' Not long after the discovery of the Neanderthaloids of Spy, in Belgium, Cope,[34] in 1893, proposed the same specific name of *Homo neanderthalensis*. In 1897 Wilser[35] suggested the name of *Homo primigenius*, which has been widely adopted in Germany, while among French authors the same species of man is sometimes known to-day as *Homo mousteriensis*. This variety of names serves at least to record the unanimous opinion that this mid-Pleistocene man belongs to a distinct species.

Since the race was very widely distributed, we may speak of these people as the 'Neanderthals,' while races resembling the Neanderthal species may be characterized as 'Neanderthaloid.' The complete series of discoveries of members of this race is now very large indeed.

In the year 1887 the Belgian geologists Fraipont and Lohest[36] discovered in a grotto near Spy, not far from Dinant on the Meuse, the remains of two individuals which are now distinguished as Spy I and Spy II. In the same stratum with the skeletons, beneath a layer of tufaceous limestone, flint implements of Mousterian age were embedded, together with remains of the woolly mammoth, woolly rhinoceros, cave-bear, and cave-hyæna. This discovery is one of the most important in the history of anthropology, because it definitely dated the Spy men as belonging to the period of Mousterian industry, and also because the authors immediately recognized these men as belonging to the race of

DISTRIBUTION OF THE REMAINS OF THE NEANDERTHALS
(Compare Fig. 104)

	1. Of Unknown Lower Palæolithic Times		
1848.	Gibraltar.	Forbes Quarry.	Fragmentary skull.
1856.	Neanderthal.	Düsseldorf, Germany.	Skullcap and skeletal fragments.
1859.	Arcy-sur-Cure.	Yonne, France.	1 lower jaw.
1866.	La Naulette.	Belgium.	1 lower jaw.
1888.	Malarnaud.	Ariège, France.	1 lower jaw.
	?Gourdan.	Hautes-Pyrénées.	1 lower jaw.
1906.	Ochos.	Moravia.	1 lower jaw.
	2. With Late Mousterian Industry		
1887.	Spy I, II.	Near Dinant, Belgium.	Two skulls and skeletons.
1907.	Petit-Puymoyen.	Charente, France.	Fragments of upper and lower jaws.
1909.	Pech de l'Azé.	Dordogne, France.	Skull of a child.
1910.	La Ferrassie II.	Dordogne, France.	1 skeleton (female).
1911.	La Cotte de St. Brelade.	Isle of Jersey.	13 human teeth.
1911.	La Quina II.	Charente, France.	Skull and fragments of skeleton.
	3. With Middle Mousterian Industry		
1882.	Šipka.	Moravia.	Jaw of a child.
1908.	La Chapelle-aux-Saints.	Corrèze, France.	Almost complete skull and skeleton.
1909.	La Ferrassie I.	Dordogne, France.	Portions of one skeleton.
1910.	La Quina I.	Charente, France.	Foot bones.
	4. With Early Mousterian Industry		
1908.	Le Moustier.	Vézère Valley, Dordogne, France.	Skeleton of a youth.
1914.	Ehringsdorf.[37]	Near Weimar.	Lower jaw.
	5. With Mousterian or Acheulean Industry		
1899.	Krapina.	Croatia, Austria-Hungary.	Portions of many skeletons of adults and of children.
1892.	Taubach.	Near Weimar.	1 milk tooth.

Neanderthal and of Cannstatt, which at the time were supposed to be the same. Here for the first time the proportions of the cranium and the brain, the very primitive features of the lower jaw and of the teeth, the low stature, and several ape-like characters of the limb bones became known; here were observed the prominent supraorbital ridges of the Neanderthal type, the receding forehead, the cranial profile inferior to that of the lowest existing Australian races, the narrow, dolichocephalic skull.

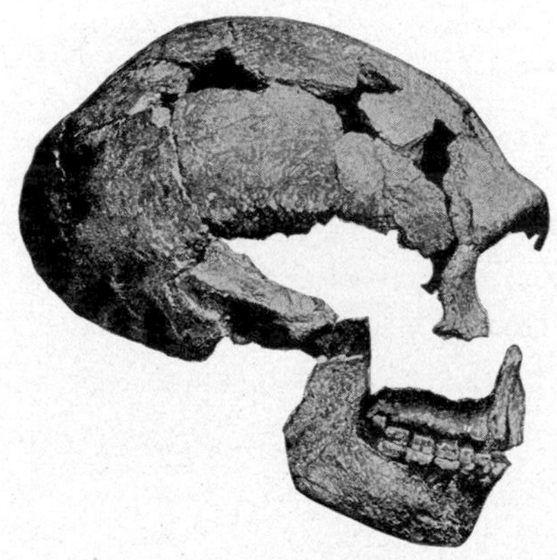

FIG. 108. Skull known as Spy I, discovered in 1887, in front of the grotto of Spy, near Namur, Belgium. After Kraemer. One-quarter life size.

The limbs were found to have retained the anthropoid disproportion between the thigh-bone and the shin-bone, and the important discovery was made that this short, massively built, heavy-browed, dull-visaged Neanderthal man was unable to stand absolutely erect, the structure of the knee-joint being such that the knees were constantly slightly bent. In other words, the Spy man had not yet fully acquired the erect position of the lower limbs.

This discovery may be said to have established the Neanderthals in all their characters as a very distinct low race, but twenty-two years elapsed before this was further confirmed by the finding of another and still earlier type of Neanderthaloid at Krapina, in northern Croatia, Austria-Hungary, as described at the close of Chapter II (p. 181 above); a type which with its local variations was soon determined as unquestionably belonging in the same group with the man of Neanderthal and the men of Spy.

Many years before, namely, in 1866, the Belgian anthropologist Dupont[38] had discovered the remains of another member of this race in a grotto on the bank of the River Lesse, near La Naulette, not far from Furfooz, in northern Belgium. This is now known as the La Naulette jaw and is found to be of Neanderthal type. It was associated with bones of the woolly mammoth, the rhinoceros, the reindeer, and a few fragments of other human bones.

Again, in 1882, Maška[39] found in a cave near Šipka, in Moravia, south of Sternberg, and six miles east of Neutitschein, fragments of a child's lower jaw, extraordinarily strong, thick, and large, and showing the incoming of the permanent teeth. From this very same region is the jaw of Ochos, Moravia, found by Rzehak[40] about 1906. Only the alveolar part of the jaw was found, but it served to demonstrate the very wide geographical distribution of the Neanderthal race.

At this time the Dordogne region, long known to be an intensive centre of Mousterian industry, from the time of Lartet's discovery of Le Moustier, in 1863, had not yielded a single skeleton, or any anatomical evidence of the type of man which in Mousterian times inhabited it. But beginning in the spring of 1908 there came in succession a whole series of such discoveries, mostly of ceremonial burials, at La Chapelle-aux-Saints, at the type station of Le Moustier itself, at La Ferrassie, another station on the lower Vézère, and at La Quina.

In October, 1910, was discovered the skull known as La Ferrassie II, of late Mousterian age; it is probably that of a female, and the remains were arranged in what was presumably a special form of ceremonial burial, because the bones, instead of being laid out straight in a certain direction, were in a crouching or flexed position (see Appendix, Note X).

The Le Moustier skeleton was found by Hauser in the lower grotto of Le Moustier, in the Vézère valley, in the spring of 1908, and carefully removed with the aid of Professor Klaatsch.[41]

It belonged to a youth some sixteen years of age. The most interesting feature of the discovery was the manner in which the skeleton was laid out.[42] The head rested on a number of flint fragments carefully piled together—a sort of stone pillow; the dead lay in a sleeping posture, with the head resting on the right forearm. An exceptionally fine coup de poing was close by the hand, and numerous charred and split bones of wild cattle (*Bos primigenius*) were placed around, indicative of a food offering. The flints were believed to belong to the Acheulean stage, which underlies the layer of true Mousterian industry, long known in

Fig. 109. Grotto of La Chapelle-aux-Saints, Corrèze, a few miles to the eastward of Le Moustier. After Boule.

this locality; but by French archæologists and by Schmidt these implements are regarded as of the earliest Mousterian age, in which it is well known that the Acheulean coup de poing still persisted. Unfortunately, the skeleton was not very well preserved and, while Klaatsch was entirely justified in classifying it with the Neanderthaloids, it should be regarded not as a distinct species (*Homo mousteriensis hauseri*) but rather as a member of the true Neanderthal race (*Homo neanderthalensis*). It also proves to be a rather stocky individual, robust and of low stature: the arms and legs are relatively short, especially the forearm and the shin-bone.

At the same time that the skeleton of Le Moustier was being disinterred, the Abbés A. and J. Bouyssonie, and L. Bardon[43] were exploring the Mousterian culture of the grotto near La Chapelle-aux-Saints, a few miles to the eastward of Le Moustier, and came upon a skeleton which has proved to be by far the finest of all the Neanderthaloid fossils, including a remark-

FIG. 110 Entrance to the grotto of La Chapelle-aux-Saints, where the finest of all the Neanderthaloid fossils was discovered in 1908. After Boule.

ably well-preserved skull, almost the entire back-bone, twenty ribs, bones of the arm and of the greater part of the leg, and a number of the bones of the hands and feet. This was also a ceremonial burial of an individual between fifty and fifty-five years of age, most carefully laid out in an east-and-west direction in a small, natural depression. With it were found typical Mousterian flints, also a number of shells and remains chiefly of the woolly rhinoceros, the horse, the reindeer, and the bison. The finding of a mature skull with the bones of the face in position, and in a relatively perfect state of preservation without distortion of the entire cranium, afforded for the first time the opportunity of finally determining not only all the skeletal characters and proportions of Neanderthal man but also the actual size and proportions of the brain. This superb specimen was sent to the Paris Museum, and Boule's preliminary descriptions[44]

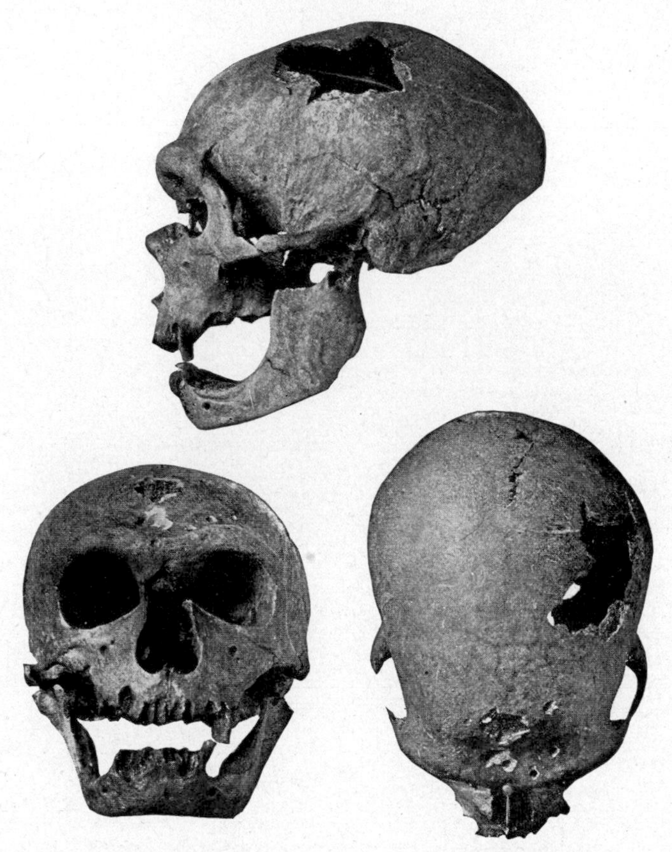

FIG. 111. The Neanderthaloid skull from La Chapelle-aux-Saints—side, front and top views. After Boule. One-quarter life size.

and finally his almost faultless monograph[45] aroused world-wide interest in the Neanderthal race.

A year later a third Neanderthal skeleton was discovered in the cave of La Ferrassie not far from Le Bugue, Dordogne, by Peyrony. The bones were badly shattered, and the proofs of ceremonial burial were not perfectly clear, but at a glance the skeleton was clearly recognized from the characters of the skull, and particularly from those of the forehead, as belonging to the Neanderthal race.

In the succeeding year, 1910, in the cavern of La Quina, Department of Charente, to the north of the Vézère region[46] were found the foot bones of a man precisely resembling the La Chapelle type, and again in 1911 several parts of the skeleton of another entirely typical member of the Neanderthal race were discovered in the earliest Mousterian strata. The skull bones were somewhat separated at the sutures. This was certainly not a

Fig. 112. Human teeth of Neanderthaloid type, discovered in a cave on the Isle of Jersey. After Marett and Hrdlička.

case of ceremonial burial. Like the Gibraltar skull, this is supposed to be that of a female.

Of especial geographic interest is the discovery by Nicolle and Sinel[47] of thirteen human teeth in a Mousterian cavern on St. Brelade's Bay, on the Island of Jersey,[48] which furnishes proof of the extension of the Neanderthal race to the Channel Islands, when these were, in all probability, still a part of the mainland. The teeth were associated with bones of the woolly rhinoceros, of the reindeer, and of two varieties of the horse, as well as with evidences of Mousterian hearths and flint implements. The distinctive features of the Neanderthal grinding-teeth are the stout size, deep implantation, and expanded form of the roots, which, with the heavy jaw, point to the toughness of the food and to the muscular strength exerted in mastication.

The roots, instead of tapering to a point below, as in modern man, form a broad, stout column, supporting the crown, adapted to a sweeping motion of the jaw. This special feature alone would exclude the Neanderthals from the ancestry of the higher races.

Thus, through a long series of discoveries, beginning in 1848 and rapidly multiplying during the last few years, we have found the materials for a complete knowledge of the skeletal structure of the men, women, and children of the Neanderthal race; we know the relative brain development as well as the stature of the sexes; we have determined that this race, and this only, extended over all western Europe during late Acheulean and the entire period of Mousterian times, and we have also learned that it was a race imbued with reverence for the dead and therefore probably animated by the belief in some form of future existence.

Characters of the Neanderthal Race

The skulls and skeletons[49] of Neanderthal, Spy, Krapina, Le Moustier, La Chapelle, La Ferrassie, and Gibraltar have so many distinctive features in common that it is beyond question that they must be classed in a closely related group. The distinctive features of this group are:

First, features found also in the different existing races of man, but never in the anthropoid apes, and therefore human; second, features, all of which have never been found combined in any race of recent man, the group, therefore, represents a distinct species of man; third, features outside of the limits of variation in the recent races of man, and intermediate between them and the variation limits of the anthropoid apes.

Before looking at Neanderthal man as a whole, we may turn our attention especially to a number of these peculiar features of the race. All the earliest observers were impressed by the heavy, overhanging brows and retreating forehead. In recent man there is often a decided prominence above the eyes, from the glabella or median point above the nose outward toward each side, but generally the outer third of the margin of these prominences turns upward beneath the outer line of the eyebrows. In the Neanderthals, on the contrary, these prominences beneath the eyebrows surround the whole upper edge of the eye socket, extending outward around the external borders of the forehead, so that they may be called '*tori supraorbitales*'; the extent of this prominent ridge above and to the sides forms a veritable roof over the eye sockets, which appear like two deep, lateral caverns. Such lateral prominences do occur, though rarely, in recent man; they are observed, for example, in certain Australians.

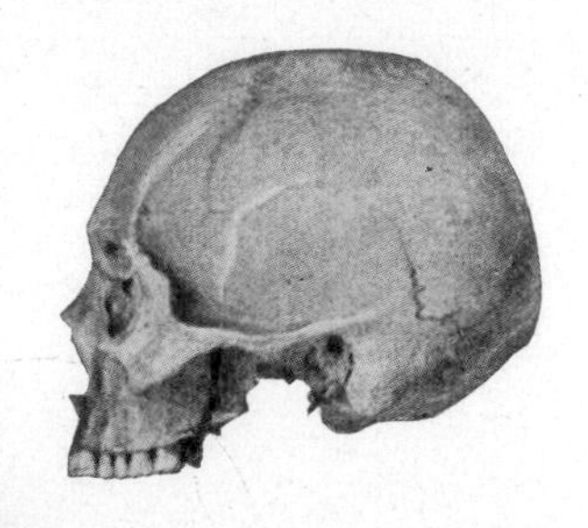

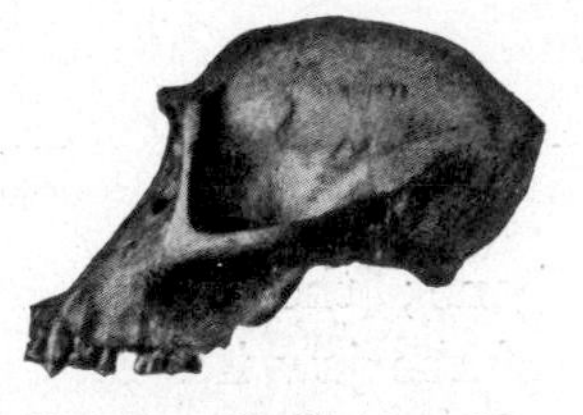

FIG. 113. Skulls of a chimpanzee (left), of La Chapelle-aux-Saints (centre), and of a modern Frenchman (right), showing the gradual disappearance of the eyebrow ridges and projecting face. After Boule.

The front view of the Neanderthal face, as seen in the female Gibraltar skull, in which these eyebrow ridges are by no means so prominent as in the male skulls, is no less remarkable for the great height of the face as compared with the flatness of the forehead. Placing the skull side by side with that of the Australian,[50] we observe at once the enormous difference in the proportions of the face and the cranium in these two types, although the Australian represents one of the lowest existing races of *Homo sapiens;* we observe in the Gibraltar skull the very wide space between the eyes and the very large size of the narial opening, which indicate a broad, flattened nose; there is a correspondingly long space between the bottom of the narial opening and the line for the insertion of the incisor teeth, indicating a very long upper lip.

The jaw is less powerful than that of the Heidelberg man. The Heidelberg jaw we have seen to be distinguished by its general strength and clumsiness and its lack of chin, or rather a chin without the slightest indication of a prominence; on the inside of this very thick, rounded chin plate, the characteristic chin spine (*spina mentalis*) is lacking; instead, a double groove is present as the point of attachment for the muscles which con-

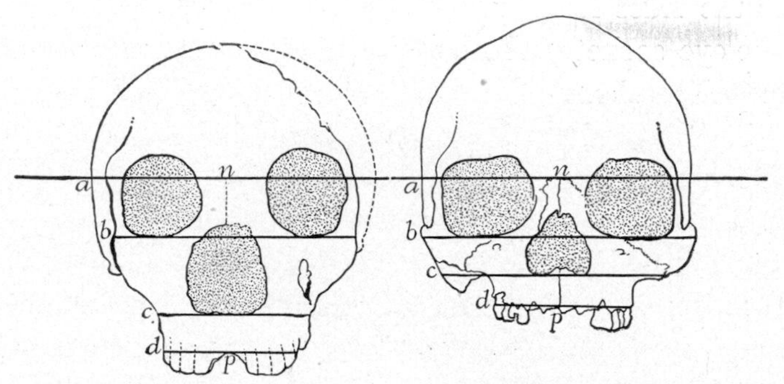

FIG. 114. Face view of the Gibraltar skull (left) after Hrdlička, and of a modern Australian skull (right) after Schwalbe, displaying the high, large visage of the former, which suggests that of the anthropoid apes. Both one-quarter life size. The comparative horizontal lines are across the (*a*) *nasion*, or root of the nose, the (*b*) lower edges of the orbits, the (*c*) lower edge of the nasal aperture, and the (*d*) top of the front teeth.

nect the chin and tongue with the hyoid bone; the ascending process for the attachment of the muscles of the jaw is seen to be unusually broad, 60 mm., in contrast to about 37 mm. in the recent jaw; finally, the condyle for attachment with the skull is particularly large.[51]

Like the Heidelberg jaw, that of the Neanderthals is distinguished by great thickness and massiveness. In general the contours are similar; in a few instances the chin process is suggested by a slight prominence, but in general the chin is strongly receding, and it agrees with that of Heidelberg in lacking the *spina mentalis*. In other characteristics there are decided differences in the Heidelberg and Neanderthal jaws. The form of the latter is now known from the specimens of Krapina, of Spy, of La Naulette, of Ochos, and of Šipka, and from the perfect examples of Le Moustier and La Chapelle. The Šipka specimen proves that even in a child ten years of age the jaw was remarkable for thickness and strength. Boule[52] entirely agrees with Gorjanovič-Kramberger[53] that the chin in the Neanderthal jaw was only in process of formation, and throughout life attained no more than an infantile form, that the Neanderthals may be ranked, however, as *Homines mentales*, whereas the Heidelbergs, in which the chin is entirely lacking, may be regarded as *Homines amentales*.

The proportions of the teeth in the Neanderthals are equally distinctive, especially in the size of the true grinders and cutting teeth. As in the Heidelberg jaw, they form a closely set row, from which the canine does not project as in the Piltdown dentition; in fact, the contour of the jaw and the proportions of the teeth are distinctly human when compared with the orang-like jaw of the Piltdown man. The grinding surface of the teeth has many layers of enamel, and the cusps are well developed. Unlike those of recent man, the incisors display folds of enamel on the inner or lingual surfaces, a condition rarely observed in the modern cutting teeth. In the teeth of the Heidelberg jaw, the pulp cavities are exceptionally large, whereas in the teeth of the Krapina race there is the unique feature that the molars have no normal roots, the roots having been more or less absorbed, a very rare occurrence in recent man. The dentition of La Chapelle is also distinctly human, but extraordinarily massive, corresponding with the general massiveness of the skull and masticating apparatus; in detail it is not that of civilized races, but an exaggerated form of the type called *macrodont*.[54] The elongation of the crown is also similar to what is termed hypsodont.

The grinding-teeth do not all show this massive size and columnar form, for about fifty per cent of the Krapina teeth have distinct roots and are more like normal modern grinders. In the Neanderthaloids of Spy the teeth are small and the roots are of moderate size.[55]

This study of the forehead and of the eyebrow ridges, of the great depth of the face, and of the peculiarly high, square form of the eye sockets prepares us for a profile view of the skull of

La Chapelle in contrast with that of the most highly developed and intellectual European type, namely, the profile of the distinguished American palæontologist, the late Professor Edward D. Cope, who bequeathed his skull and skeleton for purposes of scientific study and comparison. In La Chapelle we at once notice the platycephaly, or flattening of the skullcap, the retreating forehead, the great prominence of the eyebrow ridges resembling that of the anthropoid apes, the lengthening of the face as

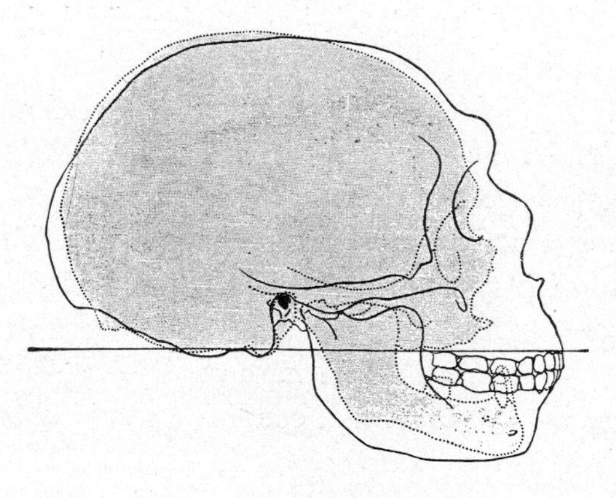

Fig. 115. Skull of La Chapelle-aux-Saints (outline) in comparison with that of a high modern type (shaded); illustrating the projecting eyebrows and prognathous, ape-like face of the Neanderthaloids. After Boule. One-quarter life size.

compared with the flattening of the cranium, the great prominence or prognathism of the face as a whole, and the special prominence of the rows of cutting teeth as compared with the vertical or indrawn line, and the recession of the tooth row in the Cope profile. This comparison also brings out the striking contrast between the high chin prominence of *Homo sapiens* and the deeply receding chin of the Neanderthals. The contrast is hardly less remarkable in the superior view of the skull in which the Neanderthal type is seen to be extremely *dolichocephalic*, the back of the skull being relatively broad and the front narrowing in the region of the forebrain until it suddenly expands in the prominent supraorbital processes.

As shown in the diagram on page 8, Fig. 1, the greatest

length of the Neanderthal skull is found on the horizontal line directly through the brain chamber, known as the *glabella-inion line*, a line drawn from a prominence between the eyebrow ridges to a point at the back of the skull known as the external occipital protuberance, or inion. This is also the longest line in the skulls of Spy and of La Chapelle, as well as of the anthropoid apes,[56] but in the north Australian skull, Fig. 1, owing to the greater expansion of the upper part of the brain, the greatest length of

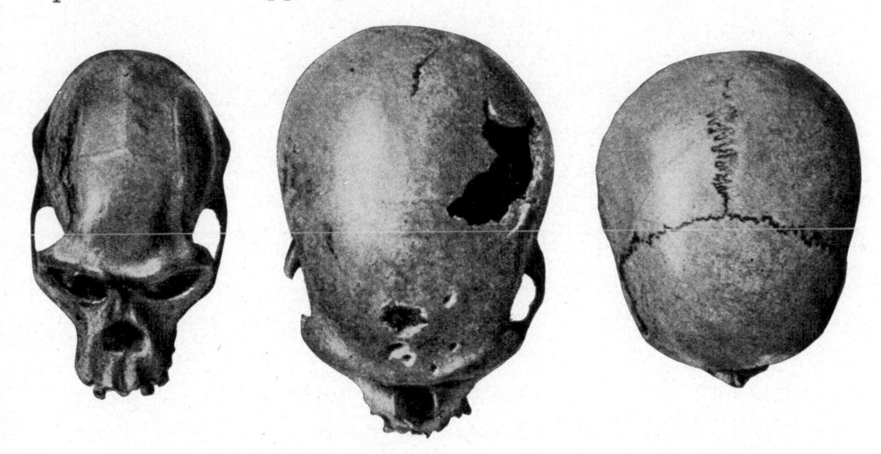

FIG. 116. Top view of three skulls—of a chimpanzee (left), of the man of La Chapelle aux-Saints (centre), and of a modern Frenchman (right)—showing the retreat of the projecting face and prominent eyebrow ridges. After Boule.

the skull is at a point considerably above the *glabella-inion* line. The median section of the skull of the chimpanzee, of the Neanderthal, and of the north Australian displays in a very striking manner the generalization made by Schwalbe, in 1901, that the Neanderthal skull is truly an intermediate or half-way form between that of the anthropoid apes and that of *Homo sapiens*. We observe in this illuminating section the growth of the dome of the skull, that is, the great brain-bearing cavity above the *glabella-inion* line *g–i*, by noting the contrast in the length of the vertical line of the *cranial height*, as compared with the space below the *glabella-inion* line indicated by the letters. This very important vertical line terminates below at the opening, where the spinal cord enters the base of the brain (see Fig. 1).

In many characteristics the Neanderthal skull is shown to be nearer to that of the anthropoid apes than to that of *Homo sapiens*. This conclusion arrived at by Schwalbe, in 1901,[57] has been more than confirmed by Boule's masterly study[58] of the very complete skull of La Chapelle. After his detailed review, he concludes: As to the unity of the Neanderthal head form, these features are not peculiar to the skull of La Chapelle; in every case they are also found in the skulls of Neanderthal, Gibraltar, Spy, Krapina, La Ferrassie, which witness to the homogeneity of that human fossil type called Neanderthal. These features show a structural affinity between the fossil men of the Mousterian period and the anthropoid apes. It must be noted that many of these features may be found also in recent human skulls of the inferior races, but that they are very rare, very scattered, very isolated, and occur only as aberrations. It is the accumulation of all these features in every skull of a whole series which constitutes an assemblage entirely new and of great importance. In the skull, as in other parts of the anatomy of the Neanderthals, we should not expect to find every character intermediate between the anthropoids and recent man. The long Neanderthal face is somewhat similar to that of the Eskimo and is in contrast with the very short face of the existing Australians and Tasmanians. The depression at the root of the nose, just below the glabella, is very marked in all Neanderthals; there is less of the nose bridge than in any recent races, except those of the male Australians, yet the nose is not flattened but somewhat arched or aquiline. This feature is not characteristic of all the anthropoid apes, and in this respect the Neanderthals, Australians, and Tasmanians are more different from the anthropoid apes than are some of the white races; thus the Neanderthal nose, far from resembling that of the anthropoids, differs from it more than does that of some recent human types.[59] Many anatomists, following Huxley, have described the Australian and Tasmanian skulls as more or less Neanderthaloid, and some authors have gone so far as to regard these races as surviving Neanderthals. It is true that some of the skulls in these existing races are extraordinarily platycephalic and show a retreating forehead, that others show supraorbital ridges almost as prominent as in the Neanderthals, that sometimes the prominence of the occipital inion is very marked, that certain jaws show a very retreating chin. Thus one or another of these Neanderthal features has been observed in these lower existing races, but all of these characteristics have never been combined in one race as constant features, and invariably associated, as in all the skulls of the Neanderthals known to us.

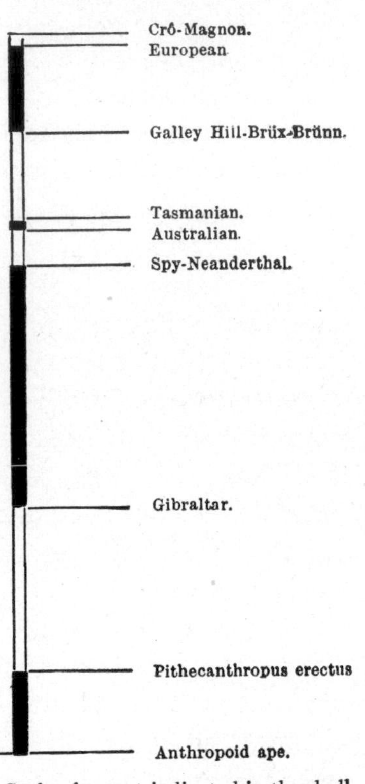

Fig. 117. Scale of ascent indicated in the skull form of eleven races of fossil and living men, based on the result of twelve different characters of comparison. At the bottom stands the anthropoid ape, and above this *Pithecanthropus*, the ape-man of Java. A wide range is observed between the Neanderthaloid skulls of Gibraltar and of Spy-Neanderthal. Not far above these in the scale of ascent stand the modern Australians and the recently extinct Tasmanians. Above these low races are found the fossil Upper Palæolithic races of Galley Hill, Brüx, Brünn, and Předmost. At the top stand the modern European races, beside which the Upper Palæolithic Crô-Magnon race takes a high rank. After Büchner.

In brief, the Australian type of head has nothing in common with that of the Neanderthals except in a small number of characteristics in the region of the forehead and of the nose. The distinguishing traits of the Neanderthal head and face are platycephaly, a retreating forehead, flattening of the occiput or lower portion of the skull, prominence of the supraorbital ridges, chin retreating or lacking, projection of the entire face owing to the peculiar form of the upper jaw, and the relatively small size of the frontal lobes of the brain. In fact, concludes Boule: "All these modern so-called 'Neanderthaloids' are nothing but varieties of individuals of *Homo sapiens*, remarkable for the accidental exaggeration of certain anatomical traits which are normally developed in all specimens of *Homo neanderthalensis*. The simplest explanation of these accidents in most cases is atavism or reversion. We cannot assert that there has never been an infusion of Neanderthaloid blood in the groups belonging to species *Homo sapiens*, but what seems to be quite certain is that any such infusion can have been only accidental, for there is no recent type which can be considered even as a modified direct descendant of the Neanderthals."

This opinion is confirmed by the latest and most exhaustive researches of Berry and Robertson,[60] who conclude that neither Australians nor Tasmanians have any direct relationship with *Homo neanderthalensis;* the superficial points of cranial resemblance are explicable solely on the grounds of the remoteness of the ancestry. The Australians and Tasmanians are descendants not of the Neanderthal stock but of a late Pliocene or early Pleistocene stock, which, following Sergi, may be called *Homo sapiens tasmanianus*, of which the Tasmanian aboriginal, now extinct, was the almost unchanged offspring. In respect to 'low' characters, as shown in the diagram, Fig. 117, the Spy-Neanderthal skulls stand quite close to the Tasmanians and Australians, and the Gibraltar skull stands midway between this type and *Pithecanthropus* with respect to twelve different characters of comparison.

It is interesting to note* that the Tasmanians were found in a stage of flint industry very similar to that practised by the Neanderthals in Mousterian times; their flints were made from artificially produced flakes, including a few examples[61] that exhibited a neatness of edge trimming and resultant regularity of outline, whereas the greater part were characterized by an unskilful trimming and irregular outline; the low status of the Tasmanian implements can most correctly be described by the word Pre-Aurignacian, that is, of Mousterian or of an earlier stage, but not by any means 'Eolithic.'

* The last of this very primitive race of the great island of Tasmania became extinct in 1877.[62]

The brain of Neanderthal man was known to be of large size even when estimated from the original skullcap of the Neanderthal type. Darwin was compelled to admit that the famous skull of Neanderthal was well developed and capacious, and Broca offered an ingenious explanation of the otherwise inexplicable fact that the mean capacity of the skull of the ancient cave-dweller is greater than that of many modern Frenchmen, namely, that the average capacity of the skull in civilized nations must be lowered by the preservation of a considerable number of individuals, weak in mind and body, who would have been promptly eliminated in the savage state, whereas among savages the average includes only the more capable individuals who have been able to survive under extremely hard conditions of life. The skulls of La Chapelle and of Spy afforded an opportunity of determining this very interesting problem, and the results entirely confirm the earlier estimates of Schaaffhausen and of Broca as to the great cubic capacity of the Neanderthal brain. The estimates in descending order are as follows:

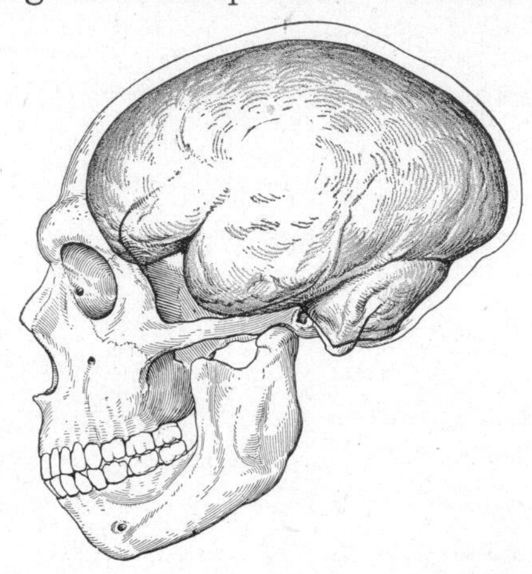

FIG. 118. The Neanderthaloid skull of La Chapelle-aux-Saints, with the right half removed to show the shape of the brain, as restored by J. H. McGregor. One-quarter life size.

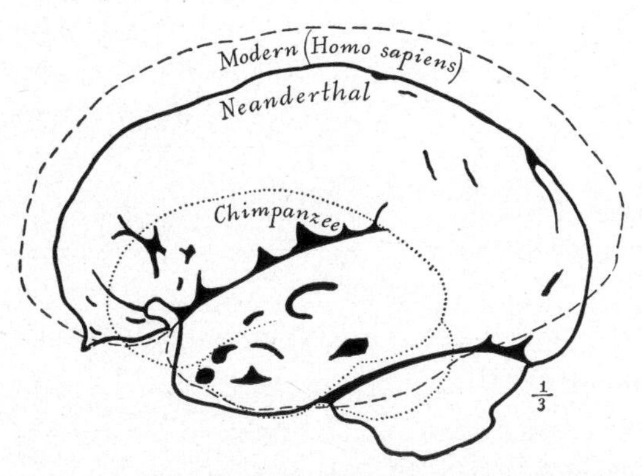

FIG. 119. Outline of the left side of the Neanderthaloid brain of La Chapelle-aux-Saints, compared with similar brain outlines of a chimpanzee and of a high type of modern man. One-third life size.

Skull of Spy II (Fraipont)	? 1723 c.cm.
" La Chapelle (Boule, Verneau, and Rivet)	1626 "
" Spy I (Fraipont)	? 1562 "
" Neanderthal	1408 "
" La Quina, female (Boule approximation)	1367 "
" Gibraltar, female (Boule estimate)	1296 "

The size of the brain in the existing races of *Homo sapiens* varies from 950 c.cm. to 2020 c.cm.[63] Thus in respect to the

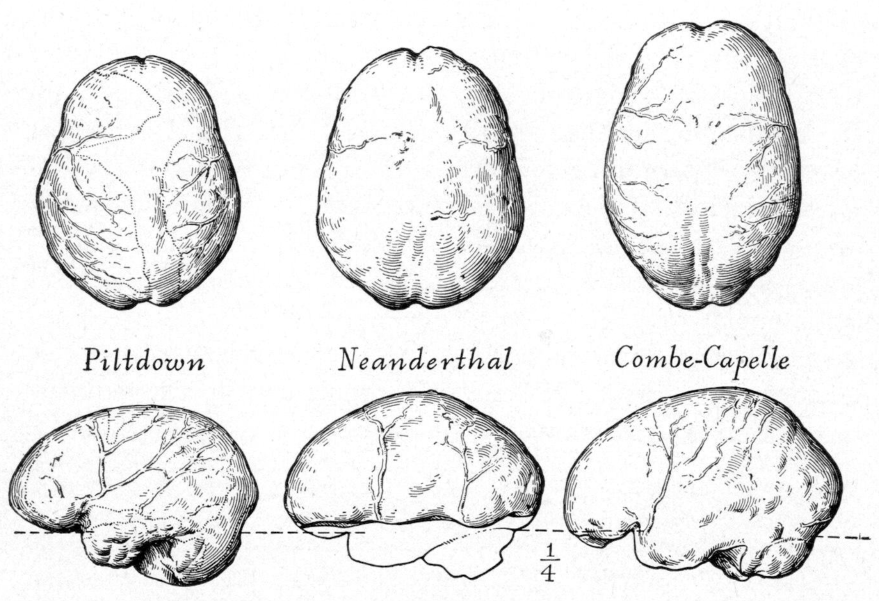

FIG. 120. Brains of Lower and Upper Palæolithic races compared (top and left side views). Piltdown (left), as restored by J. H. McGregor; Neanderthal (centre) brain, cast from the type skull; Combe-Capelle (right) from the base of the Upper Palæolithic, after Klaatsch. The Combe-Capelle brain, though unnaturally compressed, shows a relatively broad frontal area. One-quarter life size.

volume of cerebral matter the brain of the Neanderthal man is surely human, but in form the brain lacks the proportions characteristic of the superior organization of the brain in recent man. In another important respect it is human: in the larger size of the left hemisphere, indicating the development of the use of the right hand. In its general form the brain is more like that of the anthropoid apes in the relatively smaller size of the frontal portion, in the simplicity and length of the convolutions, and in the position and direction of the great fissures at the side known as the 'fissures of Sylvius' and of 'Rolando.' As studied by Boule and Anthony[64] there are many primitive characteristics in the brain of the Neanderthals. The front of the forebrain, the so-called prefrontal area, which is the seat of the higher faculties, is not fully developed but has a protuberance as in the brain of the anthropoids. The left frontal lobe in particular, which is associated with the power of speech, is not much developed in the lower part, so that a limited development of the faculty of speech is inferred. The lateral fissure of Sylvius is relatively wide and open, and this and other features suggest the brain of the anthropoid. The brain of the skull of La Quina, which is believed to be that of a female, also shows many primitive features.[65] The absolute cubic capacity of the brain is less significant of intelligence than the relative development of those portions of the brain which are concerned in the higher processes of the mind.

The stature of the various examples of the Neanderthal race is estimated somewhat differently by Boule and by Manouvrier, and also varies with the sex:

Neanderthal (Boule)	1.55 m.	5 ft. 1 in.
" (Manouvrier)	1.632 m.	5 ft. 4 1/5 in.
La Chapelle (Boule)	1.57 m.	5 ft. 1 4/5 in.
" (Manouvrier)	1.611 m.	5 ft. 3 2/5 in.
Spy (Manouvrier)	1.633 m.	5 ft. 4 3/10 in.
La Ferrassie I (Manouvrier)	1.657 m.	5 ft. 5 1/5 in.
Average of Neanderthals supposed male	1.633 m.	5 ft. 4 3/10 in.
La Ferrassie II (female)	1.482 m.	4 ft. 10 3/10 in.

The Neanderthal head is very large in proportion to the short, thick-set body, which we observe rarely exceeds 5 feet 5 inches in height in the male, and 4 feet 10 inches in the female. The proportions of the body and limbs of the Neanderthals throw a surprising light on their ancestral history as well as upon their defects as a race dependent upon the chase. In proportion to the length of the thigh, the lower leg is much shorter than in any existing human race. The tibia or shin-bone is only 76.6 per cent of the length of the femur or thigh-bone, whereas in the existing races with the shortest shin-bone, such as the Eskimos and the majority of the yellow races, it is never less than 80 per cent of the length of the thigh-bone. In this respect the Neanderthal man is not like the anthropoid apes but has a relatively *shorter* shin-bone, because the gorillas have an index of 80.6 per cent, the chimpanzees of 82 per cent, the orangs and gibbons of above 83 per cent; thus all the anthropoid apes and the lower races of man have a relatively longer leg from the knee down than has the Neanderthal race.

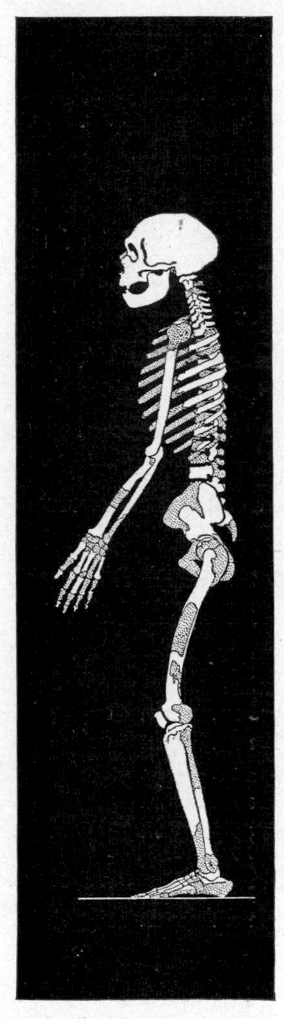

FIG. 121. Skeleton of the Neanderthaloid man of La Chapelle-aux-Saints. About one-seventeenth life size. After Boule.

The shortness of the shin-bone as compared with the length of the thigh-bone is proof that the Neanderthals were very clumsy and slow of foot, because this proportion is characteristic of all slow-moving animals, whereas a long shin-bone and a short thigh-bone indicate that a race is naturally fleet of foot.

Similarly the Neanderthal man has a very short forearm, only 73.8 per cent of the upper arm; it approaches the proportions seen in the Eskimos, Lapps, and Bushmen.[66] Here, again, the Neanderthal man differs from the anthropoid apes, among which the shortest forearm is that of the gorilla, having a ratio of 80 per cent.

There are other features which would tend to show that the ancestors of the Neanderthaloids had been ground dwellers rather than tree dwellers back into a very remote period of geologic time; the arms are much shorter than the legs, whereas in tree dwellers they are much longer. Thus, we have observed in the anthropoid apes that the arm is very long in proportion to the leg; in the chimpanzee, which has relatively the shortest arms among the anthropoid apes, the index is 104 per cent, that is, the arms are slightly longer than the legs. On the contrary, in the Neanderthals the arm length is only 68 per cent of the leg length; thus it is very far removed from the anthropoid-ape type and comes nearest to the Australian and African negro types.

Thus, to sum up the bodily proportions of the Neanderthals:

Arm short in proportion to leg, average index 68 per cent.
Forearm short in proportion to upper arm, average index 73.8 per cent.
Shin-bone short in proportion to thigh-bone, average index 76.6 per cent.
Stature extremely short in proportion to size of head.

The structure of the shoulder and of the chest is full of interest. All the ribs are remarkably robust and of large volume, and, whereas in existing races they exhibit a flattened section, in the Neanderthals the section is distinctly triangular in form. This implies a very muscular and robust torso in correlation with the gigantic head and stout limbs. The collar-bones are correspondingly long, presenting a ratio to the humerus exceeding 54 per cent, which is much higher than that among the average existing races; this indicates a very broad shoulder. The shoulder-blade is also very different in type from that of the higher races of men, and even from that of the higher Primates; it is extremely short and broad.

While, as noted above, the arm of the Neanderthals is relatively short and thus non-anthropoid, it presents a mingling of human and ape characters. The upper arm, or humerus, is truly of the human type, the torsion angle upon its axis being 148°, whereas in the anthropoid apes the angle of torsion never passes 141°. Among the bones of the lower arm the most significant is the radius, with which the turning movement of the hand is correlated; the structure of the head of the radius has more resemblance to that of the anthropoid apes than to that of existing species of man. The structure of the other bone of the forearm, the ulna, is also very primitive, exhibiting certain monkey characteristics.

The structure of the hand is a matter of the highest interest in connection with the implement-making powers of the Neanderthals. The hand is remarkably large and robust, comparable

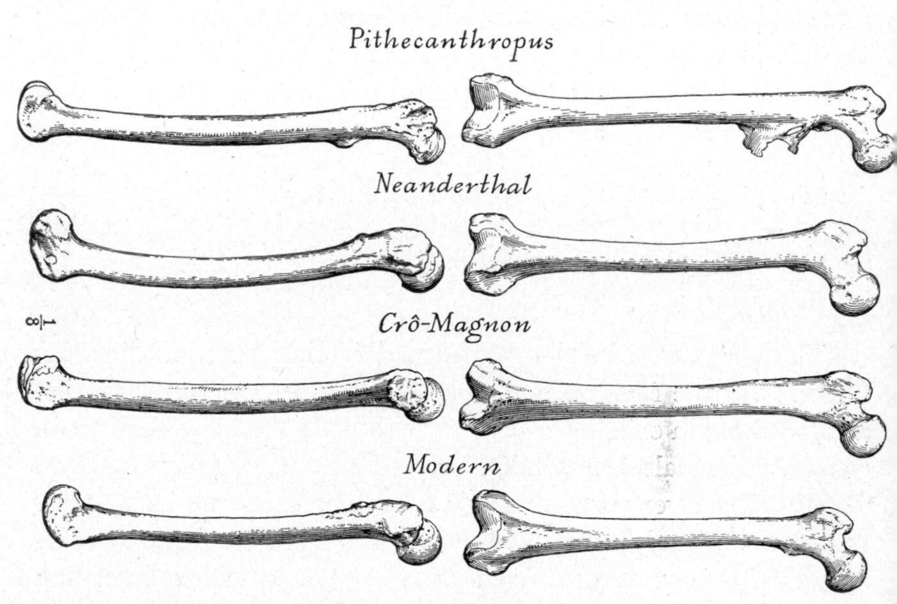

FIG. 122. Thigh-bones, or *femora*, of the Trinil, Neanderthal, and Crô-Magnon races, compared with one of modern type. The Neanderthal femur seems to be short and stout, whereas that attributed to *Pithecanthropus* is relatively long, slender, and straight. Of the *femora* illustrated the Neanderthal and Trinil are those of the type specimens, the Crô-Magnon is from the skeletal fragments of La Madeleine. After Dubois, Boule, Lartet, and Christy. One-eighth life size.

in size with that of men of very large stature in existing races. With respect to the opposition power of the thumb against the fingers by means of the opponens muscle, a distinctively human characteristic, the stage of Neanderthal development is decidedly lower than that of existing races, because the joint of the metacarpal bone which supports the thumb is of a peculiar form, convex, and presenting a veritable convex condyle, whereas in the existing human races the articular surface of the upper part of the thumb joint is saddle-shaped, that is, concave from within backward, and convex from without inward. Thus the highly perfected motions of the thumb in *Homo sapiens* were not attained in *Homo neanderthalensis*. Two phalanges which are preserved in the Chapelle-aux-Saints skeleton show that the fingers were relatively short and robust.

In the structure of the hip-girdle our fossil man is altogether human; nevertheless, some of its characters are very primitive and distinctive.

Similarly, the thigh-bone shows several primitive characters which are only rarely seen in existing races, such as the third trochanter and the strong, general forward curvature.

The structure of the knee-joint in relation to the shin-bone is very peculiar, because it shows that the shin was always retroverted or bent backward. Two other features of the shin-bone are its extreme abbreviation as compared with the femur, and the absence of flattening, or platycnemism. Where the shin-bone joins the ankle-bone (astragalus) are shown two facets, such as are preserved only in those races of existing men which have retained the habit of squatting or the folded position of the limbs; these facets are not found in races which have the habit of sitting. They indicate that the resting position of the Neanderthals while engaged in industrial work was squatting, as shown in our restoration of one of the Neanderthals at Le Moustier.

Associated with these powerful and peculiarly shaped limbs is the particularly short and thick-set vertebral column, each bone of which is remarkable for its abbreviation. The neck especially is entirely different in construction from that of existing races of men. It would appear that the concave curvature of the back in the Neanderthals was carried directly upward and continued into the concave curvature of the neck, as among the anthropoid apes, and especially in the chimpanzee. The vertebræ of the neck, especially the fifth, sixth, and seventh, and the first dorsal, resemble those of the chimpanzee far more closely than those of the modern European; the spinous processes are directed backward instead of downward. This caused the habitual stooping of Neanderthal man at the neck and shoulders and prevented him from ever holding his head entirely erect. Whereas in the back-bone of existing races the erect position is maintained by four graceful curvatures, two toward the front, and two toward the back, in the Neanderthals, as in the newly-born members of the higher races, we observe only three curvatures, two concave

FIG. 123. Restoration of the head of the Neanderthal man of La Chapelle-aux-Saints, in profile, after model by J. H. McGregor. One-quarter life size.

toward the front, namely, the back and neck curvature, just described, and a sacral or pelvic curvature; there is also a convex lumbar curvature in the lower part of the Neanderthal back-bone, which, however, is less pronounced than in existing species of man.

Summing up the characters of the back-bone in the Neanderthals, certain of them are very primitive, such as the structure of the vertebræ of the neck and the robust development of the spinous processes, the absence of marked curvature in the lower part of the back-bone and the very gentle curvature of the bones of the sacrum.

The total aspect of Neanderthal man may be characterized in the following manner:[67] An enormous head placed upon a

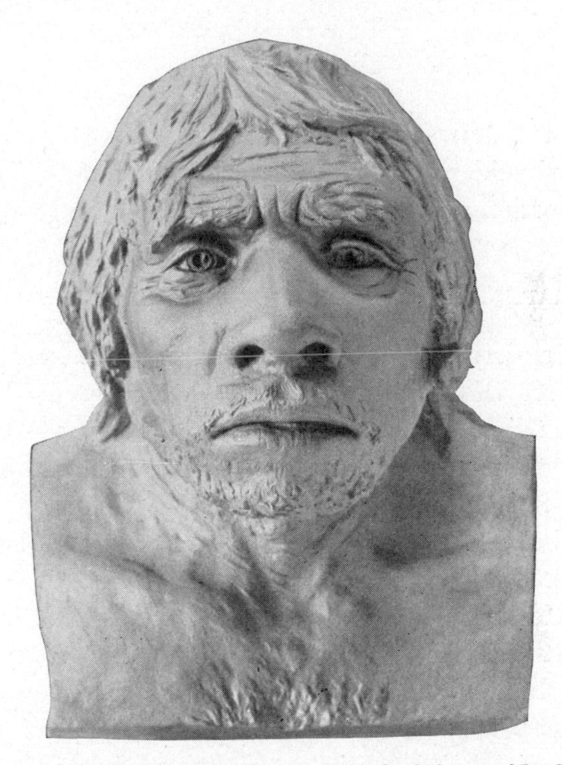

FIG. 124. Restoration of the head of the Neanderthal man of La Chapelle-aux-Saints, in front view, after model by J. H. McGregor. One-quarter life size.

short and thick trunk, with limbs very short and thick-set, and very robust; the shoulders broad and stooping, with the head and neck habitually bent forward into the same curvature as the back; the arms relatively short as compared with the legs; the lower leg, as compared with the upper leg, shorter than in any of the existing races of men; the knee habitually bent forward without the power of straightening the joint or of standing fully erect; the hands extremely large and without the delicate play between the thumb and fingers characteristic of modern races; the resort to a squatting position while occupied in flint-making and other industries. Thus the ordinary attitudes characteristic of *Homo neanderthalensis* would be quite different from our own and most ungainly. The heavy head, the enormous development of the face, and the backward position of the foramen magnum, through which the spinal cord connects with the brain, would tend to throw the upper part of the body forward, and this tendency, with the lesser curvature of the neck, the heavy shoulders, and the flattened form of the head, would give this portion of the body a more or less anthropoid aspect.

Geographic Distribution of Mousterian Stations

The Neanderthal race of Mousterian times established stations all over western Europe, of which upward of fifty have already been discovered, as compared with the fifty-seven or more Acheulean stations known. At some points the old open camps of the Acheulean flint workers were still visited, as along the Thames, the Somme, and the Marne. Thus Abbeville, St. Acheul, Montières, and Chelles, in northern France, show a succession of Mousterian industry following the Acheulean, the Chellean, and, at St. Acheul, even the Pre-Chellean. These may well have been summer stations, visited at favorable seasons of the year because of their abundant supply of flint. About 125 miles to the east of St. Acheul, in Belgium, on a small tributary of the Meuse, is the grotto of Spy, which, together with Mousterian implements, has yielded two human fossil skeletons of the Neanderthal race.

In southern Devonshire is the famous cavern of Kent's Hole, near Torquay, discovered as long ago as 1825 by MacEnery and described in 1840 by Godwin-Austen.[68] It is interesting to note that teeth of the sabre-tooth tiger (*Machærodus latidens*) have been found in this cavern, leading Boyd Dawkins to believe that this animal survived to late geologic times: it will be recalled as a contemporary of the early Chellean flint workers at Abbeville. The animal life of Kent's Hole, as originally described by Godwin-Austen, included remains of "elephant, rhinoceros, ox, deer, horse, bear, hyæna, and a feline animal of large size"—fauna now known to belong to the period of the fourth glaciation.*

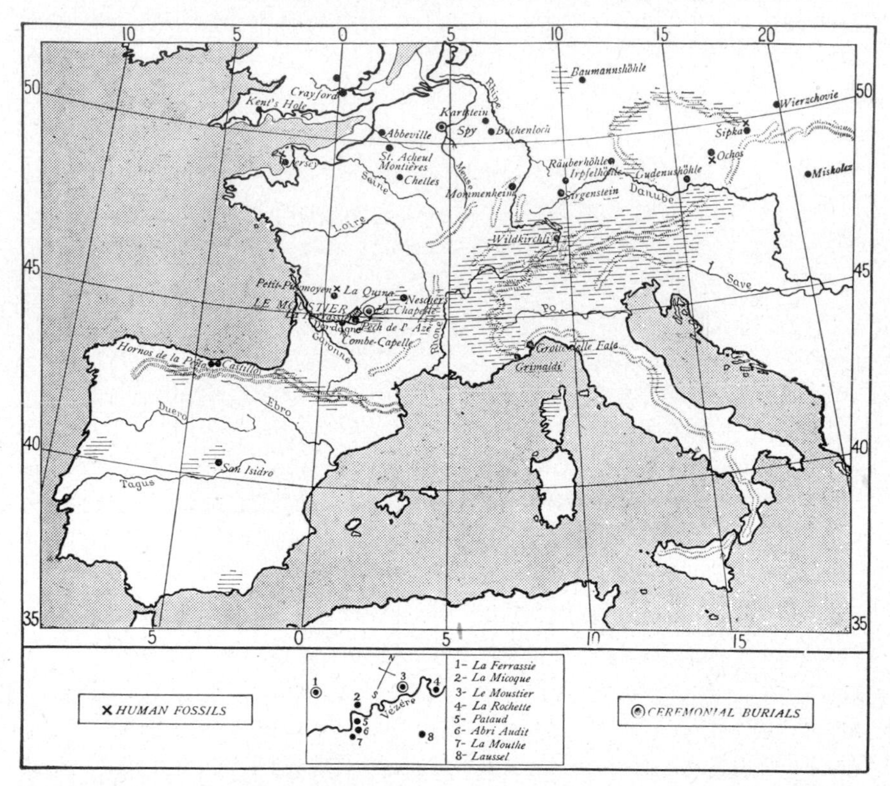

FIG. 125. Geographic distribution of the principal Mousterian industrial stations in western Europe, attributed to the Neanderthal race.

To the south are three stations, one of which, La Cotte de St. Brelade, on the present isle of Jersey, then part of the mainland, has yielded Mousterian flakes and thirteen human teeth of Neanderthal type.

Still farther to the south, in the Dordogne region, is found the type station described on a previous page, of Le Moustier, the

* This cavern, like many of those discovered in the early days of anthropological research, was not carefully explored in reference to the all-important horizontal bedding of the layers of flint flakes and of animal remains.

centre of a group of eight sites crowded along the north and south shores of the Vézère, which have become famous for the knowledge they yield of the successive stages in the development of the Mousterian implements, beginning with the primitive culture station of La Micoque, and including La Ferrassie, Le Moustier, La Rochette, Pataud, La Mouthe, Laussel, and finally the Abri Audit, which marks the closing stage in the development of

Fig. 126. The Mousterian cave of Hornos de la Peña, in the Cantabrian Mountains of northern Spain. Photograph by N. C. Nelson.

the Mousterian industry and, in the opinion of many archæologists, its transition to the Aurignacian. At several of these places important discoveries have been made, both of human fossils and of noteworthy transitions in the progress of invention. Circling round this Vézère group are the stations of Petit-Puymoyen, La Quina, where implements of the closing stage of Mousterian industry have been found as well as a human fossil of the Neanderthal type, and La Chapelle-aux-Saints, which has yielded the only complete skeleton of a Neanderthal man so far discovered.

In Spain is the station of San Isidro, near the headwaters of the Tagus, and the beautifully situated grottos of Castillo and Hornos de la Peña, on the northern slopes of the Cantabrian Mountains.

As contrasted with the very numerous Acheulean sites of Italy, it is surprising to note that only two Mousterian grottos have thus far been discovered in this region: the Grotte delle Fate in the mountains of Liguria, and the very important group of caves on the Riviera, near Mentone, known as the Grottes de Grimaldi, close to the seashore and at the very point where the Italian Alps abut upon the sea. Crossing to the north, we

FIG. 127. Outlook from the cave of Hornos de la Peña. Photograph by N. C. Nelson.

note the superb Swiss grotto of Wildkirchli, on the headwaters of the Rhine, 5,000 feet above sea-level.

In all Germany there are only about seven stations of unquestioned Mousterian age. Of these six are grottos, and the seventh, Mommenheim, is a fluvial redeposit of loess along a small stream, where only *one* implement has been found.[69] It is interesting to observe that in Germany these Mousterian sites occupy the great wedge of territory between the Scandinavian ice-fields on the north, and the Alpine on the south, and that Wildkirchli was actually within the area of glaciation; while the caves of Räuberhöhle and Šipka were not far from the glaciers which clothed the Carpathian Mountains, and Baumannshöhle was not so very remote from the great Scandinavian ice-field. In the region of the headwaters of the Rhine and Danube the industry of the

Neanderthal race has thus far been traced only at the stations of Irpfelhöhle, Räuberhöhle, and Sirgenstein. The latter cavern is of especial importance because it comprises the entire Palæolithic history of this region, presenting a series of successive culture layers from Mousterian times up to the arrival of the Neolithic race. Further to the east are the Gudenushöhle, near Krems, in Lower Austria, and Ochos and Šipka, in Moravia, while over the Russian border are Wierschovie and Miskolcz. Well to the northwest of Wildkirchli are the stations of Mommenheim and Kartstein, and to the north that of Baumannshöhle.

Workmanship of the Neanderthals

The dense communal life of Mousterian times may have favored a social evolution, the development of the imagination and of tribal lore, and the beginnings of the religious belief and ceremonial of which apparent indications are found to be wide-spread among the entirely different races of Upper Palæolithic times. The life is not, however, marked by industrial progress or invention.

The successive stages of the Mousterian industry have not as yet been so clearly defined as those of the Acheulean (Schmidt[70]). In the open Mousterian stations and caverns of Belgium and England Schmidt has observed the stages of early, middle, and late Mousterian. Breuil and Obermaier consider La Micoque as belonging to the close of the Acheulean but as marking the transition into the Mousterian. Breuil considers the industry of the Combe-Capelle station as representing the oldest true Mousterian culture. The researches which have been carried thus far would appear to justify the following subdivisions of the Mousterian culture in southwestern France:

6. Abri Audit culture, marking the transition from late Mousterian to early Aurignacian industry.
5. Late true Mousterian industry. La Quina type of implements with scrapers and bone anvils.
4. Middle Mousterian industry, with a predominance of handsome, large Mousterian points carefully 'retouched' on the edge and sometimes on one side, a 'retouch' at times approaching the superior Solutrean technique.

3. Primitive early Mousterian industry, with a limited inventory of implements.
2. Combe-Capelle stage, with heart-shaped coups de poing and typical Mousterian 'points.' (Arrival of reindeer.)
1. La Micoque culture, transitional from Acheulean to Mousterian times. (No reindeer.)

The flint industry, although very different in its outward appearance, is recognizable as a direct evolution from the Acheulean, with the suppression or decline of certain implements and the improvements of others. It is the product of the same kind of mind at work with the same materials, but under different climatic conditions and with new demands, especially for clothing as protection against the severe weather. We also cannot avoid the feeling that the abandonment of the free, open life of Chellean and early Acheulean times and the crowding of the Neanderthal tribesmen beneath the shelters and in the grottos had a dwarfing effect both upon the physique and upon the industry itself. The Mousterian implements, as compared with the Acheulean, impress one as the work of a less muscular and vigorous race.

In addition to the many fine transitions that one observes[71] between the Acheulean and Mousterian industries at St. Acheul, strong evidence is also furnished in favor of a close connection between these cultures by the discoveries at Laussel, on the Vézère, near Les Eyzies. There, broad and deep before this shelter of Laussel, lies the Mousterian layer, and directly beneath it is a true Acheulean layer close to the waters of the valley of the Beune. This proves that in Acheulean times this valley was deepened to the same degree as to-day, and a close union of the Acheulean to the Mousterian is here again evident. In the valley of the Somme near St. Acheul Commont has also observed proofs of a similar close connection between these cultures. With such records in northern and southern France, the Neanderthal race, which is known toward the end of Acheulean times and especially covers the entire period of Mousterian time, comes much nearer to us. If we assign the Mousterian industry to the last glacial period, we give it a duration of some 30,000 years, and this is about the reckoning which thoughtful anatomists have already assigned for the Neanderthal man.

SPECIAL MOUSTERIAN IMPLEMENTS

Two instruments are especially typical of the Mousterian industry from beginning to end; these are the 'pointe' and the 'racloir.' The former, pointed and spear-shaped, is from 1 to 4

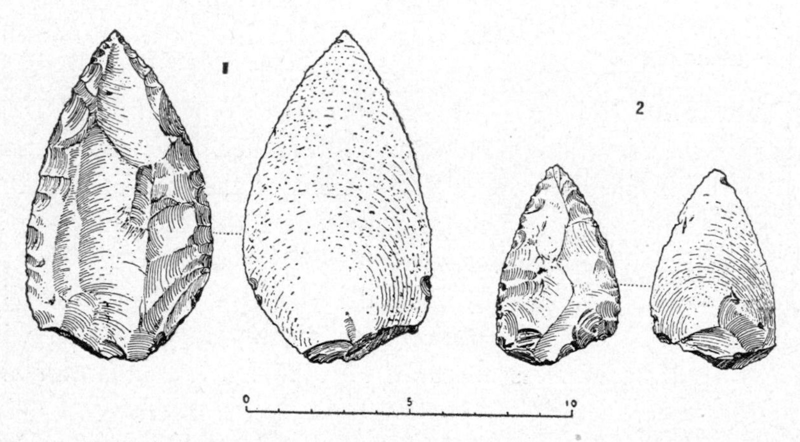

FIG. 128. Typical Mousterian 'points' from the type station of Le Moustier, made of a large flake of flint struck off from the nodule and retouched on only one side, leaving on the opposite side a smooth, conchoidal surface. After Déchelette, by permission of M. A. Picard, Librairie Alphonse Picard et Fils.

inches in length; the latter is a broad scraper, from 1 to 2 inches in width; and both have the distinctive peculiarity of being composed of a large flake of flint struck off from a larger bulb or nodule and of being retouched only on one side, leaving on the opposite side the smooth conchoidal surface of the flake.[72] This point and scraper are highly characteristic not only of the early stages but of the Mousterian industry throughout its entire course, including even the late La Quina types, and their manner of making is obviously a modified usage of the late Acheulean discovery of the flakes of Levallois.

A matter of the greatest interest in the industrial development of western Europe at this time is the fact that this discovery of the *utilization of the flake*, whether in the 'lames de Levallois' or in the Mousterian point and scraper, led to the decline of the coup de poing. The retouched flakes of various shapes were easier to make and to repair and served equally well the purposes of skinning and dismembering game which had been previously served by the ancient coup de poing.[73]

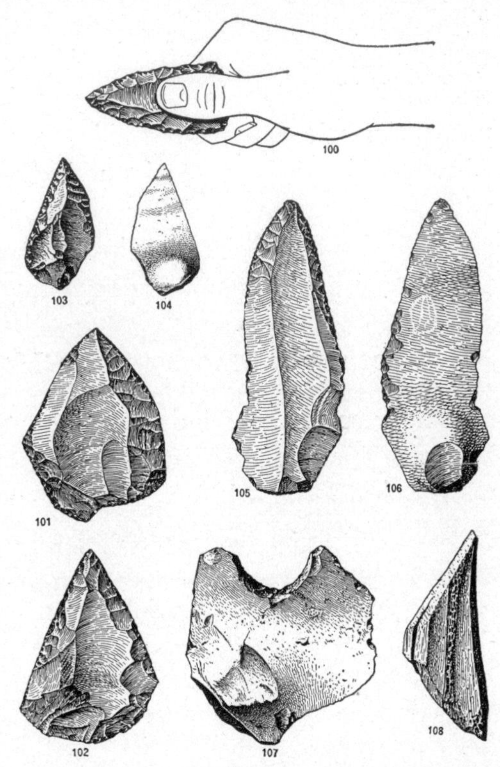

FIG. 129. Mousterian 'points' and scrapers from various parts of Europe, as interpreted by de Mortillet. In some cases both sides of the implement are shown; all are one-quarter actual size except 101, which is one-half actual size. 100—De Mortillet's theory of the manner of using the Mousterian 'point,' which was held in the hand and not shafted. 101—Mousterian point from Suffolk, England. 102—Mousterian point from Umbria, Italy. 103, 104—A single flake point from the Crimea, in southern Russia. 105, 106—A long, narrow Mousterian point from Oise, France. 107—A curved-in scraper, or *grattoir*, from Dordogne, France; perhaps an implement for dressing a wooden spear or lance. 108—Bone splinter, broken for the marrow, but not shaped.

In consequence, the coup de poing, fashioned from the core of the nodule, begins to play a very secondary rôle and occurs but rarely in the Mousterian levels. Even at St. Acheul, the very centre of its former reign, we begin to find decadent forms and poor workmanship, which make it difficult to recognize that these are the successors of the finely retouched Acheulean coups de poing. While the coups de poing at the type station of Le Moustier continue to retain the old Acheulean patterns—the oval, the heart-shaped, the sharp-pointed—they are all of smaller size and rather coarsely retouched. Thus, after thousands of years of development and employment, the coup de poing falls into a period of degeneration and of final disuse. The history of this implement, which we have traced from its Pre-Chellean prototypes, presents a most interesting analogy with the course of evolution observed in so many animal and plant forms. It passes through many stages of improvement and reaches a climax of perfection and adaptation; it then comes into competition with another form evolving on a fundamentally different and superior plan and disappears in the struggle for existence through the greater usefulness of the replacing type.

Successive Stages in the Mousterian Industry

The succession of industrial stages is best shown along the Vézère. The oldest Mousterian industry is that of Combe-Capelle with its heart-shaped, roughly fashioned coups de poing, entirely lacking, however, any evidence of a surface prepared for the grasp of the hand.

In the valley of the Somme Commont[74] has observed the three following stages in the advance of the Mousterian industry:

3. A late Mousterian culture which lies on the upper layers near the top of the same gravel deposit and which shows entirely new technical elements. The old coup-de-poing culture is no longer valued, and all the implements found here are of flakes worked only on one side and with an extraordinarily fine retouch.
2. A middle Mousterian horizon which lies in the lower layers of a gravel deposit, belonging to the 'newer loess,' and which contains only *one* small coup de poing.
1. An early Mousterian, with quite numerous lance-shaped coups de poing, lies at the base of the 'newer loess,' showing that the coup-de-poing tradition still lingers and the coup-de-poing type is still preserved. With these are associated the new types of implements and especially the 'hand-points,' which are so typical of the Mousterian industry.

The more recent levels (2, 3) contain longer flakes, which already exhibit a tendency toward the blades, or 'lames,' of the Upper Palæolithic.

In the shelters and caverns of Dordogne the same industrial sequence may be observed, although the chronological succession of the strata is not always clearly defined. At the grotto of Combe-Capelle the heart-shaped coups de poing retain most strongly the old traditions, but even here these are outnumbered by the well-fashioned Mousterian 'points,' chipped only on one side.

The further development of the Mousterian industry may be observed in the type station of Le Moustier, where the lower levels show a primitive Mousterian consisting mostly of very fine, irregularly fashioned flakes, made into small scrapers, triangular points, borers, and disks. The overlying layer includes very carefully worked Mousterian points which are frequently retouched on one side over the entire surface; here the Mousterian technique reaches its highest development, so that Schmidt designates it as 'high Mousterian.'[75] Above this layer, again, is a level of typical late Mousterian forms, quite unlike the small primitive flakes of the lower level and resembling the characteristic forms of La Quina, the dominant type being the finely shaped La Quina racloir. The few diminutive coups de poing which occur in this level at Le Moustier furnish the only distinction between the industry here and that of La Quina, where no coups de poing are found. At Le Moustier also occur the typical bone anvils which were first recognized at La Quina.

The Mousterian industry of the Neanderthals was thus devoted mainly to the development of the smaller forms of implements, for the most part retouched on one side only, and with a constant improvement of technique. Yet the chief types of Mousterian implements remain the same as in Acheulean times, as shown in the accompanying table.

The implement known as the *pointe*, or the 'hand-point,' is a principal and very characteristic Mousterian form further perfected from its Acheulean stage. It is spear-headed in shape and chipped on one side only, and continues into late Mousterian times, being still found in the Mousterian levels of Spy, in Belgium.

The *pointe double*, a double-pointed, spear-shaped form, at times almost attains the elongate shape of the Solutrean *pointe de laurier*, though never its slenderness, symmetry, and perfection of technique.

There are five or six well-defined varieties of the racloir, or scraper, carefully fashioned out of flakes. The principal form is crescentic in shape, with outward-curved edge. Other forms are saw-like with straight edges or knife-edged. Another form with very neatly and symmetrically incurved borders has its edges sharply retouched, as if for the smoothing down of bone or wooden shafts. The borer is also fashioned of an elongate flake and sometimes finished with a very fine point at one of its extremities. It is noteworthy that the grattoir, or planing tool, so well developed in the Upper Palæolithic industries, appears only sporadically in Mousterian times. For example, at La Quina, in the closing stages of the Mousterian industry, out of 220 implements collected at hazard, there were 166 scrapers of six different forms, 45 'hand-points' of five different forms, and 5 double points, as compared with 5 grattoirs, or planing tools. There are very few knife-shaped forms. It would appear that the racloir and the perçoir were the principal implements employed in the preparation of skins for clothing.

INDUSTRIAL.

Coup de poing (decadent),	hand-stone.
ovoid.	
heart-shaped.	
sharp-pointed.	
Hachette,	chopper.
Grattoir,	planing tool.
Perçoir,	drill, borer.
Couteau,	knife.
Racloir,	scraper.
knife-edged.	
curved-out edge.	
saw-edged.	
double-edged.	
beak-shaped.	
many-edged.	
Pointe,	'hand-point.'
Percuteur?	hammer-stone?

WAR AND CHASE.

Pointe,	'hand-point.'
Pointe double,	spear head?
Coup de poing,	hand-stone.
Pierre de jet,	throwing stone.
Couteau,	knife.

In early Mousterian times the coup de poing may still have been used by the Neanderthals in the chase, and the fine, spear-headed 'point' and the rarer 'double point' may have been developed in response to the needs of hunters, who now ventured the chase of the bison, the urus, the wild horse, and the reindeer.

The most striking features of all the implements which may have been used in the chase are: first, the absence of any definite proof of their attachment to a shaft or handle; and second, the absence of any barbed or headed type of point. The use of the barb, as we shall see, appears to be a relatively recent discovery of the later cultures of Upper Palæolithic times.

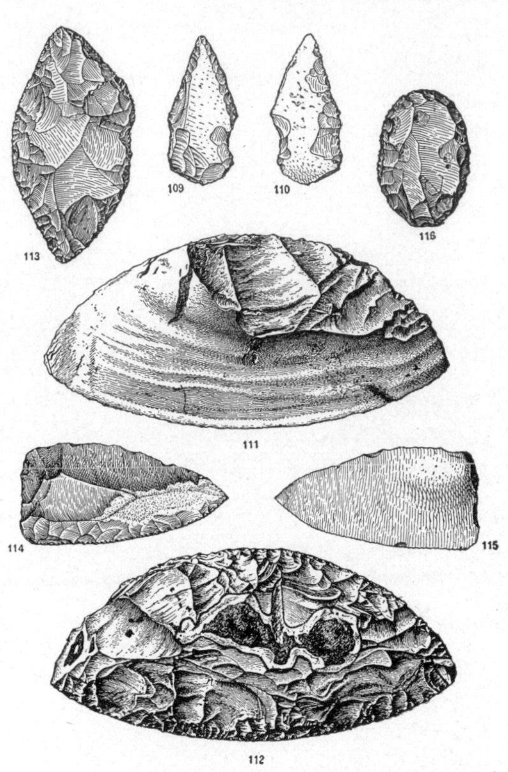

FIG. 130. Late Mousterian implements, after de Mortillet, one-quarter actual size. 109, 110—Point, finely retouched at one end, from Seine-et-Marne, France. The reverse shows a retouch on the flaked surface which suggests the double-face Solutrean retouch. 111, 112—A very large *racloir*, or scraper, from La Quina, Charente, France; part of the bulb of percussion has been chipped off. 113—Double-ended point from Le Moustier, retouched on both surfaces. 114, 115—Combination point and scraper from Le Moustier, Dordogne, France. 116—Double scraper, or *racloir*, with *grattoir*, or planing end.

The transition from the Mousterian to the Aurignacian appears in the Abri Audit, which also lies in the valley of the Vézère. Here we still find irregularly fashioned coups de poing, decadent followers of the heart-shaped types of the earliest Mousterian industry; this is nearly the last phase in the decline of the old coup-de-poing manufacture. While the lance-shaped coup de poing of the late Acheulean never appears in any true Mousterian industry, the shorter, more heart-shaped type of Combe-Capelle traverses the entire Mousterian and, after further stages of degeneration, passes into the Abri Audit culture and even lingers into the early Aurignacian. At this latter station the typical Mousterian 'points' are almost wanting.

The Mousterian, observes Schmidt,[75] which preserves the traditions of the Lower Palæolithic coup-de-poing culture, is one of the most interesting phases in the development of Palæolithic industry, in that its successive stages exhibit the very last phases of the great coup-de-poing industry, of which only the almond and oval scraper types appear, and that very rarely, in the early Aurignacian. On the other hand, in the late Mousterian we observe a trend toward the blade (*lame*) industry of the Upper Palæolithic. Careful study and observation of the subdivisions of Mousterian culture have thus far been limited to central and southern France, and they have not yet been traced in Spain; but in the grottos of Belgium and England the early, middle, and late Mousterian types are known to exist.

Bone anvils, fashioned out of the hard surfaces of the foreleg and foot bones of the bison and horse, were discovered at La Quina in 1906. They show a flattened surface with cross incisions too regular to be accidental and too far from the articulation to be the result of an inexpert attempt to sever the joint.[76] This was not the only use of bone in Mousterian times, however, for primitive pointed implements of bone are occasionally found in Dordogne, mingled with Mousterian flints. A variety of rudely fashioned bone implements also occurs at Wildkirchli, in Switzerland.

Disappearance of the Neanderthal Race

We have seen that the Neanderthals dwelt in Europe for a very long time, many thousands of years, during which they doubtless underwent considerable evolution from lower to higher types, and into varieties, under the modifying influences of climate, food, and racial habits. Consequently the known remains of Neanderthals exhibit a decided variation in head form, as well as in dentition: some are more primitive and ape-like; others, such as Spy II, are more like the modern races. The Krapina variety is more broad-headed than the typical Neanderthal variety. The Gibraltar variety is in many respects of low type. The individual known as Spy II is of higher type than the other Neanderthals. The variations in stature so far as known are slight.

For these and other reasons Hrdlička,[77] who has recently made a broad comparative study of the chief Neanderthal remains of Europe, is of the opinion that the Neanderthals partly evolved into the lower races of *Homo sapiens;* being not only in some measure ancestral to such very primitive forms as the Brünn or Předmost race of Upper Palæolithic times, but even contributing to the higher race of the Crô-Magnons. He also holds that traces of Neanderthal blood and physiognomy are not lacking even among modern Europeans.

A contrary view is set forth in the present volume; namely, that the Neanderthals represent a side branch of the human race which became wholly extinct in western Europe. This view the author shares with Boule and with Schwalbe. Certainly the evidence afforded by the known Upper Palæolithic burial sites does not support the theory that the Neanderthals persisted. It is possible, however, that the Upper Palæolithic skeletons discovered at Předmost, and now awaiting description by Maška, may modify this conclusion and demonstrate Hrdlička's theory that the Neanderthals survived and left descendants or men of mixed Neanderthal and *Homo sapiens* race along the valley of the Danube.

Whatever may have been their fate in other regions, certainly the most sudden racial change which we know of in the whole prehistory of western Europe is the disappearance of the Neanderthal race at the close of the Mousterian culture stage, which was the latest industrial period of Lower Palæolithic times, and their replacement by the Crô-Magnon race. From geologic evidence the date of this replacement is believed to have been between 20,000 and 25,000 years before our era. So far as we know at present, the Neanderthals were entirely eliminated; no trace of the survival of the pure Neanderthal type has been found in any of the Upper Palæolithic burial sites; nor have the alleged instances of the survival of the Neanderthal strain or of people bearing the Neanderthal cranial characters been substantiated. We incline to agree with Boule and Schwalbe that the supposed cases among modern races of the transmission of Neanderthal characters are simply low or reversional types, which, upon close analysis, are never found to present the highly distinctive and peculiar combination of Neanderthal characteristics.

There is some reason to believe that the Neanderthals were degenerating physically and industrially during the very severe conditions of life of the fourth glaciation, but the consequent inferiority and diminution in numbers would not account for their total extinction, and we are inclined to attribute this to the entrance into the whole Neanderthal country of western Europe toward the close of Lower Palæolithic times of a new and highly superior race. Archæologists find traces of a new culture and industry in certain Mousterian stations preceding the disappearance of the typical Mousterian industry. Such a mingling is found in the valley of the Somme in northern France.

From this scanty evidence we may infer that the new race competed for a time with the Neanderthals before they dispossessed them of their principal stations and drove them out of the country or killed them in battle. The Neanderthals, no doubt, fought with wooden weapons and with the stone-headed dart and spear, but there is no evidence that they possessed the bow and arrow. There is, on the contrary, some possibility that the newly arriving Crô-Magnon race may have been familiar with the bow and arrow, for a barbed arrow or spear head appears in drawings of a later stage of Crô-Magnon history, the so-called Magdalenian. It is thus possible, though very far from being demonstrated, that when the Crô-Magnons entered western Europe, at the dawn of the Upper Palæolithic, they were armed with weapons which, with their superior intelligence and physique, would have given them a very great advantage in contests with the Neanderthals.

(1) Commont, 1912.1, p. 294.
(2) Smith, W., 1894.1, chap. XV.
(3) Dietrich, 1910.1, pp. 329, 330.
(4) Penck, 1909.1.
(5) Leverett, 1910.1, pp. 306–314.
(6) Geikie, 1914.1.
(7) *Op. cit.*, p. 272.
(8) *Op. cit.*, pp. 265–266.
(9) Keith, 1911.1, p. 23, Fig. 5.
(10) Munro, 1912.1, pp. 46, 47.
(11) Lartet, 1861.1; 1875.1.
(12) De Vibraye, 1864.1.
(13) Massénat, 1868.1.
(14) Smith, W., 1894.1, chap. XIV.
(15) Geikie, 1914.1, p. 119.
(16) Smith, W., *op. cit.*, pp. 196, 197.
(17) *Op. cit.*, p. 224.
(18) Geikie, 1914.1, p. 118.
(19) Bächler, 1912.1.
(20) Schmidt, 1912.1, pp. 18–32, 165–171.
(21) *Op. cit.*, Table opposite p. 270.
(22) Osborn, 1910.1, pp. 419, 420.
(23) Niezabitowski, 1911.1.
(24) Harlé, 1908.1, p. 302.
(25) Obermaier, 1912.1, p. 135.
(26) Keith, 1911.2.
(27) Boule, 1913.1, pp. 220, 221.
(28) *Op. cit.*, p. 64.
(29) Fischer, 1913.1, pp. 336, 337.
(30) Schaaffhausen, 1875.1; 1858.1.
(31) Lyell, 1863.1, pp. 80–92.
(32) Schwalbe, 1897.1; 1901.1; 1901.2; 1904.1.
(33) King, 1864.1.
(34) Cope, 1893.1.
(35) Wilser, 1898.1.
(36) Fraipont, 1887.1.
(37) Schwalbe, 1914.2.
(38) Dupont, 1866.1.
(39) Maška, 1886.1.
(40) Rzehak, 1906.1.
(41) Fischer, 1913.1.
(42) Klaatsch, 1909.1.
(43) Bouyssonie, 1909.1.
(44) Boule, 1908.1; 1908.2; 1909.1; 1911.1; 1912.1.
(45) Boule, 1913.1.
(46) Martin, H., 1911.1.
(47) Nicolle, 1910.1.
(48) Keith, 1911.1.
(49) Fischer, 1913.1, p. 352.
(50) Schwalbe, 1914.1, p. 544, Figs. 4 and 5.
(51) Fischer, *op. cit.*
(52) Boule, 1913.1, p. 85.
(53) Gorjanovič-Kramberger, 1909.1.
(54) Boule, 1913.1, p. 104.
(55) Tomes, 1914.1, pp. 588–598.
(56) Schwalbe, 1901.2; 1914.1, pp. 534, 535.
(57) Schwalbe, 1901.1.
(58) Boule, 1913.1.
(59) *Op. cit.*, pp. 66, 67, 72, 75.
(60) Berry, 1914.1.
(61) Johnson, 1913.1.
(62) Quatrefages, 1884.1, p. 394.
(63) Martin, R., 1914.1, p. 645.
(64) Boule, 1910.1; 1911.1.
(65) Anthony, 1912.1.
(66) Boule, 1913.1, p. 119.
(67) *Op. cit.*, p. 120.
(68) Geikie, 1914.1, p. 130; Godwin-Austen, 1840.1.
(69) Schmidt, 1912.1, pp. 23, 32, 66, 75, 76, 101, 169.
(70) *Op. cit.*, p. 128.
(71) Schuchhardt, 1913.1, p. 144.
(72) Déchelette, 1908.1, vol. I, pp. 98–101.
(73) Obermaier, 1912.1, p. 130.
(74) Commont, 1909.1.
(75) Schmidt, 1912.1, pp. 126–128.
(76) Déchelette, 1908.1, vol. I, pp. 104, 105.
(77) Hrdlička, 1914.1

CHAPTER IV

OPENING OF THE UPPER PALÆOLITHIC — THE GRIMALDI RACE — ARRIVAL OF THE CRÔ-MAGNON RACE AND OF THE AURIGNACIAN INDUSTRY — GEOGRAPHIC AND CLIMATIC CONDITIONS — MAMMALIAN LIFE — CHARACTERISTICS AND HABITS OF THE CRÔ-MAGNONS — DISTRIBUTION OF THE AURIGNACIAN INDUSTRY — THE BIRTH OF ART — ORIGIN AND DISTRIBUTION OF THE SOLUTREAN INDUSTRY — BRÜNN RACE — SOLUTREAN INDUSTRY AND ART.

In the whole racial history of western Europe there has never occurred so profound a change as that involving the disappearance of the Neanderthal race and the appearance of the Crô-Magnon race. It was the replacement of a race lower than any existing human type by one which ranks high among the existing types in capacity and intelligence. The Crô-Magnons belonged to *Homo sapiens*, the same species of man as ourselves, and appear to have been the chief race of the Upper Palæolithic Period up to the very close of Magdalenian times, after which they apparently underwent a decline.

Although there were one or more other races which influenced the industrial development of western Europe, the Crô-Magnons were certainly dominant, as shown both by the abundance of their skeletal remains and by the wide distribution of their industry and art; the Upper Palæolithic may almost be said to be the period of the Crô-Magnons as the Lower Palæolithic is that of the Neanderthals and the Pre-Neanderthals. Their arrival toward the end of Mousterian times effected a social and industrial change and a race replacement of so profound a nature that it would certainly be legitimate to separate the Upper Palæolithic from the Lower by a break equal to that which separates the former from the Neolithic.[1]

The arrival of the Crô-Magnons and the introduction of the

Aurignacian industry are the first events of the prehistory of Europe to which we can assign a date with any degree of confidence; they correspond geologically with the close of the fourth glaciation and the beginning of Postglacial time, the duration of which has been estimated by geologists from evidence of many different kinds, but which brings us, nevertheless, to substantially similar conclusions. It seems that 25,000 years is a conservative estimate for the duration of the Postglacial Period; this is supported by the independent observations of Lyell, Taylor, Penck and Brückner, and Coleman; it is within the estimates made by Chamberlin and Salisbury, Fairchild, Sardeson, and Spencer; it is somewhat larger than the estimates of Gilbert and Upham.* Thus, with considerable confidence we may record man of the modern type of *Homo sapiens* as entering western Europe between 25,000 and 30,000 years ago.

The Lower Palæolithic industrial cycle, comprising the Chellean, Acheulean, and Mousterian, seems to have been similar in evolution both around the Mediterranean coasts and in the northern portions of Europe. From the fact that the Crô-Magnons arrived with the Aurignacian industry it would appear that they came through Phœnicia and along the southern coasts of the Mediterranean, through Tunis, into Spain; also perhaps along the northern coasts of the Mediterranean through Italy. Their evolution had probably taken place somewhere on the continent of Asia, for their physical structure is entirely of Asiatic type, and not in the least of African or Ethiopian type; that is, they exhibit no negroid characters whatever. The reason that Breuil considers that the Aurignacian did not come in through central or eastern Europe is that there are no early Aurignacian stations in either region, whereas the Aurignacian is abundantly developed along the Mediterranean coasts, both of Europe and Africa. The passage of the Crô-Magnons along these coasts was, therefore, like the subsequent wave of the true Mediterranean race, dark-haired, long-headed, narrow-faced people, which followed this coast in early Neolithic

* See Appendix, Note VI.

times, or, again, like the wave of the Arabian or Moslem advance, which pressed forward along the northern coast of Africa and into southwestern Europe.

Some support of this theory of migration along the north coast of Africa is given by the presence of the skeletons of two members of an entirely distinct race, which are commonly known

FIG. 131. Entrance to the great *Grotte du Prince* at the base of the limestone promontory known as the *Baoussé Roussé*, with a view of Mentone in the distance. After Davanne.

as the 'negroids of Grimaldi' because of their discovery in the *Grottes de Grimaldi* near Mentone, and because they alone among all the Upper Palæolithic races thus far discovered in Europe display a number of resemblances to the African negroid race. Anatomically they are related neither to the Neanderthals nor to the Crô-Magnons. Their archæologic age appears to be early Aurignacian because they are found immediately above the layer which marks the close of Mousterian time and the last climate favorable to the warm fauna of mammals.

This sunny coast where modern France joins Italy has supplied some of the most valuable records of the racial and industrial transition from the Lower to the Upper Palæolithic. Of the nine *Grottes de Grimaldi* three at least show evidences of occupation in closing Mousterian times, probably by men of the Neanderthal race, although no skeletal remains of Neanderthals have been found here. Four of the grottos, namely, the *Grotte des Enfants*, the *Grotte de Cavillon*, the *Barma Grande*, and the *Baousso da Torre*, have yielded altogether the skeletal remains of sixteen individuals, all associated with implements of Aurignacian culture and evidently representing a number of ceremonial burials. Fourteen of these skeletons are attributed by Verneau to the Crô-Magnon race; the other two are the 'negroids of Grimaldi' above referred to. This is, therefore, a prehistoric record of the greatest significance, which we shall now examine more in detail.

Racial Succession along the Ancient Riviera

Where the southern spurs of the Alps descend into the Mediterranean and separate France from Italy we find a limestone promontory, known as the *Baoussé Roussé*, projecting in a long cliff, beneath which the rocky shore descends abruptly into the sea. Opening toward the south, and at intervals along the base of this cliff are the nine *Grottes de Grimaldi*. Doubtless the Neanderthals migrated along these shores at a time when the hippopotamus, the straight-tusked elephant (*E. antiquus*), and Merck's rhinoceros (*R. merckii*) still abounded as the last representatives of the great African-Asiatic fauna. These hunters of Mousterian times entered the sea-swept floor of the great *Grotte du Prince** (Fig. 131), with a ceiling height at that time perhaps of over 80 feet, carrying in their game to the fire-hearths, and leaving Mousterian implements in the accumulating deposits. In the succeeding layers of this grotto the changing forms of animal life demonstrate the effect of the fourth gla-

* Named in honor of the reigning Prince of Monaco, whose generous gifts and personal interest made the adequate exploration of these grottos possible.

ciation and the cooling of the climate toward the close of Mousterian times.

The smaller *Grotte des Enfants* (Fig. 132), which lies to the west of the Prince's Grotto, was apparently occupied at a somewhat more recent period, because the lowest fire-hearths contain, together with the Mousterian implements, remains of Merck's rhinoceros only—apparently the last survivor here, as well as in other parts of western Europe, of the warm African-Asiatic fauna. The hippopotamus and the straight-tusked elephant had either become extinct or had been driven farther south by the time the hunters first occupied this grotto. In the overlying layers of this and several other grottos the fire-hearths contain remains of a rich forest fauna which includes the wild boar, stag, roe-deer, wild horse, wolf, and bear. The first signs of increasing cold in the mountains to the north is the appearance of remains of the chamois and ibex driven from the Alpine heights. Then in still higher layers appears the reindeer, harbinger of the tundra climate.

The Grimaldi Race

Verneau is inclined to regard the Grimaldi as a very ancient race, antedating the Crô-Magnon.[2] He believes that they belong to a new ethnic type which played an important rôle in Europe and enjoyed a wide geographic distribution. There does not, however, seem to be much support for this opinion, because, unlike some other races, no traces of the Grimaldis have been found elsewhere, and it would appear more probable that they were, as their skeletal characters indicate, true negroids which perhaps found their way from Africa but never became established as a race in western Europe.

The type consists of two skeletons found in the *Grotte des Enfants* by Verneau in 1906. One skeleton is that of a middle-aged woman; the other is that of a youth of sixteen or seventeen. Both are referred to the existing species of man, *Homo sapiens*. The layer which contained them is on a level two feet

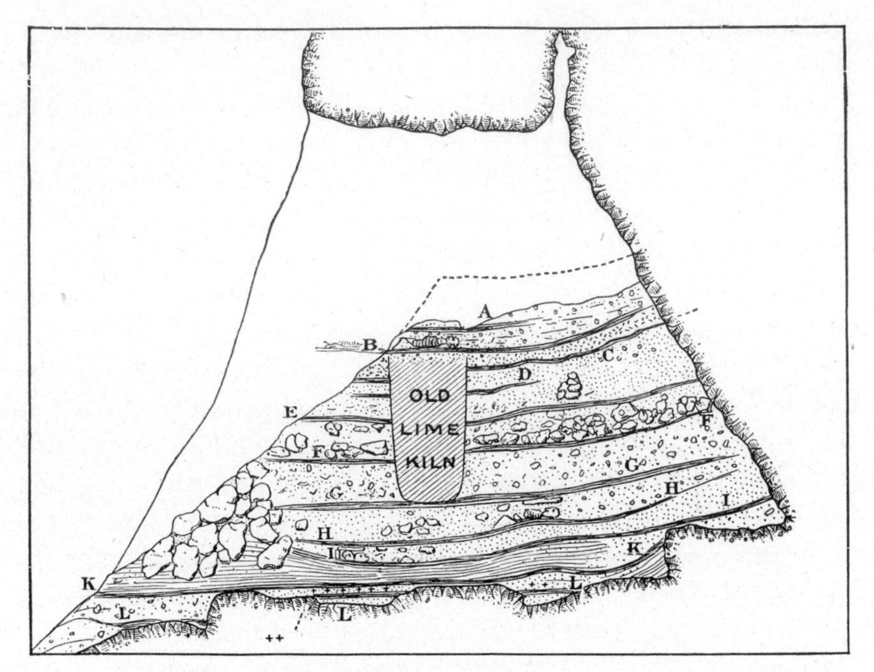

FIG. 132. Section of the *Grotte des Enfants*, after Tschirret. In deposits which accumulated to a thickness of over 30 feet this grotto contains in its ascending strata a complete epitome of the vicissitudes of climate, together with four burials of members of the Crô-Magnon Race, and, near the base, the burial of the two Grimaldi skeletons. The layers in descending order are as follows:

A. Burial of two infant skeletons. Remains of forest and alpine (*Ibex*) mammals.

B. Burial of the skeleton of a Crô-Magnon woman. Remains of forest and alpine mammals.

C. Fire-hearths containing forest mammals—the wild boar, also the reindeer.

D. Fire-hearths with flints of Aurignacian type. Remains of forest fauna—the marten.

E. Layer containing a cairn or artificial pile of stone. Remains of ibex, horse, wolf, cave-lion, and fox.

Intermediate layer. Remains of the wild ass, perhaps of the steppe type, and of the reindeer; also of the ibex, the wild horse, and forest fauna—the wild boar.

F. Large fragments fallen from the cave roof. No evidence of habitation.

G. Fire-hearths. Remains of the moose, roe-deer, fallow deer, stag, wild cattle, ibex, fox, leopard, and rabbit.

H. Burial of a very tall skeleton of the CRÔ-MAGNON RACE (see Fig. 144, p. 297). Fire-hearths containing remains of the forest fauna, also the alpine chamois and marmot, the cave-hyæna, and the leopard.

I. Burial of two skeletons of the GRIMALDI RACE (see Fig. 133, p. 267). Flints of Aurignacian type and remains of a forest fauna which includes the deer, also of the wild horse, the alpine ibex, and the hyæna.

K. Traces of charcoal and disturbed fire-hearths.

K–L. Remains of Merck's rhinoceros and of the hyæna. Alpine (*Ibex*) and temperate forest fauna.

L. Traces of fire-hearths with Mousterian implements, chiefly of quartzite, probably left by members of the NEANDERTHAL RACE on the ancient floor of the grotto, following the recession of the sea. Evidence of previous occupation by hyænas.

lower than any which contained Crô-Magnons, and immediately above the culture layer of Mousterian times.

The Grimaldi characters present a wide contrast to those of the Crô-Magnon. The two known skeletons, of a woman and a youth, are of inferior stature, not exceeding 5 feet 3 inches:

Grimaldi female estimated at	1.57 m.	5 ft. 2 in.
" youth " "	1.55 m.	5 ft. 1 in.

These measurements, however, are only slightly inferior to those of the Crô-Magnon woman and youth, which rise to 5 feet 5 inches. There are many negroid characters in the skull, in the structure of the hip-girdle, and in the proportions of the limbs; there are also some characters in common with the anthropoid apes, namely, the long forearm, the curved thigh-bone, and the marked prognathism, or projection of the tooth row; the face is low and broad, and extremely prognathous; the nose is platyrhine, or broad and flat; the jaw is heavy, with large teeth and without the chin prominence; the head form, like that of the Crô-Magnons, is dolichocephalic and somewhat disharmonic; that is, while the head is long, the face is short and relatively broad. Yet the cranial capacity is relatively high, being estimated at 1,580 c.cm. Unlike the Crô-Magnons, the Grimaldis have a relatively long forearm and a negroid type of pelvis. The proportions of the leg are, however, somewhat similar to those of the leg of the Crô-Magnon, the thigh-bone being short and the shin-bone long, the index being 83.8 per cent. In addition to the long forearm, which approaches in form that of the living anthropoid apes, there is a curved femur, distinctly of anthropoid-ape character.

"In its body and tooth characters," observes Verneau,[3] "this negroid race in many respects shows a greater resemblance to the anthropoid apes than does the Neanderthal race." He continues: "The fact remains that at a very remote period of the Pleistocene there existed in Europe, beside the Neanderthal race, a type of man that in many of his cephalic characters, in the structure of his pelvis, and in his limb proportions showed striking analogies to the negro of to-day. In their remarkable proportions they exaggerate some of the peculiarities of the recent negroes; the teeth resemble those of the Australian types.

FIG. 133. The Grimaldi skeletons found in the lower Aurignacian layer of the *Grotte des Enfants*—the youth to the right and the woman to the left. After Verneau.

There is evidence of the establishment and spread of the Grimaldi race throughout western Europe, namely, in cases of partial reversion to this type among the skeletal remains of the Neolithic Age, the Bronze Age, and the early Iron Age in Brittany,

Switzerland, and northern Italy. Extreme prognathism is the characteristic that most frequently appears, and in some instances there is the broad nose, with the same osteological peculiarities that mark the Grimaldi type. In every instance these individuals show dolichocephaly, nearly always combined with a short, broad face. Until the discovery of the Grimaldi type we were at a loss to explain the existence of these individuals among a population from which they differed so radically."

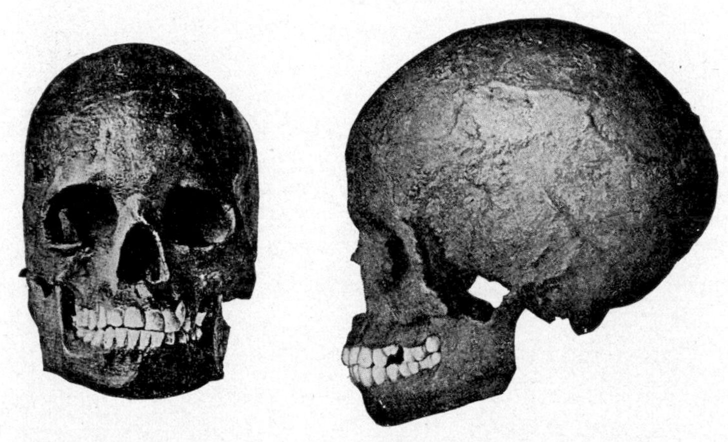

FIG. 134. Skull of the Grimaldi youth in front and in profile. After Verneau, one-quarter life size.

Against this opinion of Verneau we should weigh the entire absence of any trace of this Grimaldi race in any part of western Europe among all the burials and other human remains of Upper Palæolithic age known at the present time. Setting aside any such records which are of doubtful authenticity or difficult to diagnose on account of their fragmentary nature, there remains a number of human fossils representing at least ninety individuals discovered at over fifteen widely distributed localities. None of these shows any features of the Grimaldi race.

In describing the Grimaldi skeletons, Keith[4] agrees that they are of a mixed or negroid type; the shallow, projecting incisor part of the upper jaw and the characters of the chin are features of recent negroid races; so are the wide opening of the nose, the prominent cheek-bones, the flat and short face. Yet the bridge of the nose is not flat as in negroes, but rather prominent as in Europeans, and the capacity of the skull in the woman (1,375 c.cm.) is ample. In the boy the teeth are large and of the negro type; he bears a striking resemblance to the woman, and his cranial capacity (1,580 c.cm.) indicates a distinctly modern brain; the prominences of the forehead do not meet across the median line as in certain negroids and in the Neanderthals. Keith concludes that the Grimaldi people represent an intermediate type in the evolution of the typical white and black races.

MAIN FEATURES OF THE ENTIRE UPPER PALÆOLITHIC HISTORY

Having now considered the opening of the Upper Palæolithic, also the single appearance of the Grimaldi race of which no further trace is known, it is desirable to briefly review the entire Upper Palæolithic history before we attempt to follow in detail its successive phases beginning with the appearance of the Aurignacian industry.

There is evidence of various kinds that the Crô-Magnons arrived in western Europe, bringing in their Aurignacian industry, while the Neanderthals were still in possession of the country and practising their Mousterian industry. Thus in the valley of the Somme, Commont believes he has recognized a level of flints, exhibiting the primitive Aurignacian 'retouch' of Dordogne, but occurring beneath a late Mousterian level. Additional evidence of a contact between the industries of these two races is found at the stations of La Ferrassie, of Les Bouffia, and especially of the Abri Audit, where there is a distinct transition period, in which the characteristic types of the late Mousterian are found intermixed with a number of flints suggesting the early Aurignacian;[5] here it would appear that the development of the Aurignacian is partly a local evolution, and not an invasion of wholly new types of implements. Breuil[6] suggests that these mixed layers may perhaps be explained by the supposition that we have here degenerate or modified Mousterian tools, more or less influenced by contact with the Aurignacian industry of the Crô-Magnon race.

THE STONE IMPLEMENTS CHARACTERISTIC OF LOWER AND UPPER PALÆOLITHIC TIMES

The Typical Stone Implements		Lower Palæolithic				Upper Palæolithic				
		Pre-Chellean	Chellean	Acheulean	Mousterian	Aurignacian	Solutrean	Magdalenian	Azilian	Tardenoisian
A.—WAR AND CHASE										
*1. Microlithique?	Arrow Point? etc.	..	..	..	..	..	..	=	=	+
2. Pointe	Point..........	..	..	=	+	+	=	=	=	..
3. Pointe à Soie	Lance or Knife.	..	..	..	..	=	+	=	..	..
4. Pointe à Cran	Lance-Head.....	..	..	..	..	=	‡‡	?	..	..
5. Pointe de Laurier	" "	..	..	..	..	?	‡‡	?	..	..
*6. Coup de Poing	Hand-Axe, Poniard, etc...	..	+	‡‡	=	..	..	..	..	..
7. Pierre de Jet	Throwing Stone.	?	?	=	=	?	?	=	..	..
*8. Couteau	Knife..........	=	=	=	=	=	=	=	=	=
B.—INDUSTRIAL AND DOMESTIC										
9. Lampe	Lamp..........	..	..	..	..	..	..	=	..	..
10. Lissoir	Polisher........	..	..	..	..	..	=	=	..	..
11. Mortier	Mortar.........	..	..	..	..	..	..	=	..	..
12. Hachette (Tranchette)	Chopper........	..	?	=	=	..	..	..	..	..
*13. Coup de Poing	Hand-Axe, etc...	..	+	‡‡	=	..	..	..	..	..
14. Grattoir	Planing Tool....	=	=	=	=	=	=	=	=	=
15. Racloir	Scraper........	=	=	=	‡‡	+	=	=	=	..
16. Perçoir	Drill, Borer....	=	=	=	=	=	=	=	=	..
*17. Couteau	Knife..........	=	=	=	=	=	=	=	=	=
18. Enclume	Anvil Stone.....	..	..	..	..	=	?	=	..	..
19. Percuteur	Hammer-Stone...	=	=	?	?	=	=	=	=	=
C.—ART, SCULPTURE, ENGRAVING										
*20. Microlithique	Drill, Graver, and Etcher....	..	..	..	..	=	=	=	‡‡	=
21. Ciseau	Chisel..........	..	..	..	..	=	=	=	..	..
22. Gravette	Etching Tool....	..	..	..	..	+	+	=	=	..
23. Burin (also Mortar, Hammer-Stone, and Polisher)	Graver.........	..	..	..	..	‡‡	=	=	?	..

* = twice mentioned (in different classifications).
+ or ‡‡ denotes an unusual or culminating development.

Again, the burial customs of the Neanderthals were in many respects followed by the Crô-Magnons; they chose, in fact, the same kind of burial sites, namely, at the entrances of grottos or in proximity to the shelters. Some degree of ceremony must have marked these burials, for with the remains were interred implements of industry and warfare together with offerings of food. Most of the Neanderthal burials were with the body extended; the two burials of the Grimaldi race were with the

THE BONE IMPLEMENTS APPEARING AT THE CLOSE OF THE LOWER PALÆOLITHIC AND HIGHLY CHARACTERISTIC OF THE UPPER PALÆOLITHIC

The Typical Bone Implements		Lower Palæolithic				Upper Palæolithic				
		Pre-Chellean	Chellean	Acheulean	Mousterian	Aurignacian	Solutrean	Magdalenian	Azilian	Tardenoisian
A.—WAR, CHASE, FISHING										
*1. Lames	Blades	..	..	..	..	=	?	=	..	..
2. Poignard	Dagger	..	..	..	..	..	=	=	..	..
3. Hameçon?	Fish-Hook?	..	..	..	..	?	?	?	..	..
4. Propulseur	Spear Thrower	..	..	..	..	..	..	=	..	..
5. Harpon	Harpoon	..	..	..	..	..	=	‡‡	=	..
6. Pointe de Sagaie	Javelin Point	..	..	..	..	=	=	=	..	..
7. Pointe de Lance	Spear Point	..	..	..	..	=	=	=	=	..
B.—INDUSTRIAL AND DOMESTIC										
8. Spatule	Spatula	..	..	..	..	..	=	=	..	..
9. Navette	Shuttle	..	..	..	..	..	..	=	..	..
10. Epingle	Pin	..	..	..	..	..	..	=	..	..
11. Aiguille	Needle	..	..	..	..	=	+	‡‡	..	..
*12. Lames	Blades	..	..	..	..	=	..	‡‡	..	..
13. Compresseur	Anvil	..	..	..	=	..	..	..	..	..
14. Lissoir	Smoother	..	..	..	..	=	=	=	=	..
15. Coin	Wedge	..	..	..	..	=	..	=	..	..
16. Ciseau	Chisel	..	..	..	..	=	..	=	=	..
17. Poinçon	Awl	..	..	..	=	=	=	=	=	..
C.—CEREMONIAL, SOCIAL										
18. Bâton de Commandement	Ceremonial Staff	..	..	..	..	=	+	‡‡	..	..
19. Baguette	Wand	..	..	..	..	..	..	=	..	..

* = twice mentioned (in different classifications).
+ or ‡‡ denotes an unusual or culminating development.

limbs in a flexed position and tightly bound to the body, probably with skin garments or thongs. The Crô-Magnon burials are either with the body extended, as in the Grottes de Grimaldi, or with the limbs flexed, as in the Aurignacian burial of Laugerie Haute.

Whether the Neanderthals were exterminated entirely or whether they were driven out of the country is not known; the encounter was certainly between a very superior people, both physically and mentally, who possibly had the use of the bow and arrow, and a very inferior and somewhat degenerate people that had been already reduced physically and perhaps numerically by the severe climatic conditions of the fourth glaciation. The Neanderthals were dispossessed of all their dwelling-places and industrial stations by this new and vigorous race, for at no less than eighteen points the Aurignacian immediately succeeds upon the Mousterian industry and in a few instances Crô-Magnon burials occur very near the Neanderthal burial sites.

In the racial replacements of savage as well as of historic peoples the men are often killed and the women spared and taken into families of the warriors, but no evidence has thus far been found that even the Neanderthal women were spared or allowed to remain in the country, because in none of the burials of Aurignacian times is there any evidence of the crossing or admixture of the Crô-Magnons and the Neanderthals.

The chief source of the change which swept over western Europe lay in the brain power of the Crô-Magnons, as seen not only in the large size of the brain as a whole but principally in the almost modern forehead and forebrain. It was a race which had evolved in Asia and which was in no way connected by any ancestral links with the Neanderthals; a race with a brain capable of ideas, of reasoning, of imagination, and more highly endowed with artistic sense and ability than any uncivilized race which has ever been discovered. No trace of artistic instinct whatever has been found among the Neanderthals; we have seen developing among them only a sense of symmetry and proportion in the fashioning of their implements. After prolonged study of the works of the Crô-Magnons one cannot avoid the conclusions that their capacity was nearly if not quite as high as our own; that they were capable of advanced education; that they had a strongly developed æsthetic as well as a religious sense; that their society was quite highly differentiated

Pl. VI. The head of the Crô-Magnon type of *Homo sapiens*, a race inhabiting southwestern Europe from Aurignacian to Magdalenian times. Antiquity in western Europe estimated as at least 25,000 years. After the restoration modelled by J. H. McGregor. For the bodily proportions of this finely developed race compare Pl. VII.

along the lines of talent for work of different kinds. One derives this impression especially from the conditions surrounding the development of their art, which are still mysterious and an interpretation of which we shall attempt to give in the following chapter.

Cultural, Racial, and Climatic Divisions

The Upper Palæolithic covers the greater part of the 'Reindeer Epoch' as it was conceived by Lartet and Christy, who began their systematic study and exploration of the caves of Dordogne in 1863. They were soon joined by Massénat and the Marquis de Vibraye, while Dupont took up the work in Belgium and Piette made the artistic development, especially in the Pyrenees, his chosen field.

Lartet was the first to perceive that the culture of the grotto of Aurignac was quite distinct from that of the Lower Palæolithic in northern France; he also recognized in the shelter of Laugerie Haute, in Dordogne, that there was still another culture, which is now known as the Solutrean; also that in the shelter of Laugerie Basse, in Dordogne, there was yet another industry, that which we now know as Magdalenian. M. de Mortillet was the first to recognize the superiority of the Solutrean industry in stone, which in this period reached its height, and its succession by the Magdalenian period, in which the industry in bone and horn reached a climax; but he failed to recognize the very important preceding position of the Aurignacian, and it was not until 1906 that the clear presentation by Breuil of the entire distinctness of the Aurignacian industry led to the adoption by the Archæological Congress at Geneva of three cultural divisions of the Upper Palæolithic. In the meantime Piette had discovered that in the Mas d'Azil there was a distinct cultural phase, the Azilian, following the Magdalenian, and thus a fourfold division of the Upper Palæolithic (Breuil,[7] Obermaier[8]) was established, as follows:

AZILIAN.—Industry of the surviving Crô-Magnon and other resident races, and of newly arrived brachycephalic and dolichocephalic races in western Europe; decadent forms of flint and bone workmanship; entire absence of art. *Daun* stage of Postglacial retreat; Europe with a milder climate and forest and meadow fauna like that of early historic times.

MAGDALENIAN.—Closing stage of the industry and art of the Crô-Magnon race; bone implements highly developed; marked decline in the flint industry. Close of Postglacial Period; climate alternately cold and moist (corresponding with the *Bühl* and *Gschnitz* Postglacial advances of the ice in the Alpine region), or cold and arid; Europe covered with the tundra and steppe fauna; life chiefly in the shelters and grottos.

SOLUTREAN.—Culminating stage of flint industry; apparent invasion in eastern Europe of the Brünn (Brüx, Předmost, and [?] Galley Hill) race. The highly developed flint industry of the Solutrean types; art development of the Crô-Magnon race partly suspended. Dry, cold climate; life largely in the open.

AURIGNACIAN.—Appearance of the Crô-Magnon race in southwestern Europe, succeeding the Mousterian industry; art of engraving and drawing and sculpture of human and animal forms developing. Animal life the same as during the fourth glaciation; climate cold and increasingly dry; life chiefly in the grottos and shelters.

The successive phases of development of Upper Palæolithic industry and art have been traced with extraordinary precision in Dordogne, in the Pyrenees, in northern Spain, and along the Danube and upper Rhine by a host of able workers—Cartailhac, Capitan, Peyrony, Bouyssonnie, Lalanne, and others. Breuil has made himself master especially of the Aurignacian and has succeeded Piette as the great historian of Upper Palæolithic art. Obermaier's chief service has been the comparison of the Upper Palæolithic of the Danubian region with that of Dordogne and northern Spain both in regard to the geologic age and the archæologic and racial succession. The labors of Schmidt along the upper Rhine and Danube have not only brought this region into definite prehistoric relation with the Dordogne and the Pyrenees but have given us by far the clearest evidence of the relation between the human and the industrial development and the succession of climatic phases in northern Europe. Finally, the explorations of Commont along the River Somme have proved that this region, too, was frequented throughout all Upper Palæolithic times, during which it exhibits an industrial development hardly less important than that of the Lower Palæolithic.

There are two very distinct lines of thought among these archæologists: the first is shown in the tendency to regard the industries as mainly *autochthonous*, or as following local lines of development; the exponents of this theory dwell most strongly on the transitions between the Mousterian, the Aurignacian, and the Solutrean industries. For example, the chief object of Schuchhardt's tour[9] through the Palæolithic stations of Dordogne was to observe the transitions from one period to another and the evidence afforded of successive changes of climate. This writer is impressed with the transitions; he notes that the typical curved knives of the Abri Audit furnish a transition from the Mousterian scrapers to the Aurignacian 'points' of La Gravette and La Font Robert; that the Solutrean takes up all the fine threads of the Aurignacian culture and spins them further into Magdalenian times. Thus we get an Aurignacian-Solutrean-Magdalenian industrial cycle which is comparable to the Chellean-Acheulean-Mousterian cycle.

Breuil, on the other hand, from the archæologist's standpoint—because he is not especially interested in the matter of racial development—is a strong exponent of the idea of *successive invasions* of cultures, either from the south or Mediterranean region or from the central region of Europe, which he calls the 'Atlantic'; and he distinguishes sharply between these two great areas of Upper Palæolithic evolution, namely, the *southern* and the *central* European, pointing out that it was only after the establishment of more genial climatic conditions, like those of modern times, that there was an added element of northern or Baltic invasion. Certainly the archæologic testimony strongly supports this culture-invasion hypothesis and it appears to be strengthened in a measure by the study of the human types, although this study has not progressed beyond the stage of hypothesis. When the Upper Palæolithic races have been studied with as close attention as those of the Lower Palæolithic we may be able to establish positively the relation between these human types and the advance of certain cultures and industries.

Distribution of Upper Palæolithic Human Fossils

Our present view, as drawn from a consideration of the facts before us, is that western Europe in Upper Palæolithic times was entered by four or five distinct races, all belonging to *Homo sapiens*, only three of which became established:

5. The *Furfooz* (Ofnet, and [?] Grenelle) *race*, extremely broad-headed, entering central Europe possibly from central Asia, bringing an Azilian culture, without art or developed flint industry. (Alpine type.)

4. A *dolichocephalic race* with a narrow face, associated with the Furfooz race, either connected with the Brünn and Brüx, or an advance wave of one of the dolichocephalic Neolithic races. (Mediterranean type.)

3. The *Brünn* (Brüx, Předmost, and [?] Galley Hill) *race*, long-headed, with a narrow, short face, probably entering central Europe directly from Asia through Hungary and along the Danube; bringing a perfected Solutrean culture; inferior in brain development to the Crô-Magnons, in industrial contact with them but not displacing them.

2. The *Crô-Magnon race*, long-headed with a very broad face, entering Europe in closing Mousterian or early Aurignacian times, probably from the south along the Mediterranean coast, and bringing in an Aurignacian flint industry and art spirit characteristic especially of Aurignacian and Magdalenian times; greatly reduced in number in closing Magdalenian times, but leaving descendants in various colonies in western Europe.

1. The *Grimaldi race*, in the transition between the Mousterian and the Aurignacian; negroid or African in character; apparently never established as a race of any influence in western Europe.

The presence of these five races, and perhaps of a sixth if the 'Aurignacian man' of Klaatsch proves to be distinct from the Crô-Magnon, is firmly established by anatomy. It is most important constantly to keep before our minds certain great principles of racial evolution: (1) that the development of a racial type, whether long-headed or broad-headed, narrow-faced or broad-faced, of tall or of short stature, must necessarily be very slow; (2) that this development of the races which invaded western Europe took place for the most part to the eastward in the vast continent of Asia and eastern Europe; (3) that, once established through a long process of isolation and separate evolution, these racial types are extremely stable and persistent; their head form, their bodily characters, and especially their psychic characters and tendencies are not readily modified or altered; nor are they in any marked degree blended by crossing. Crosses do not produce merely blends; they chiefly produce a mosaic of distinct characters derived from one race or the other.

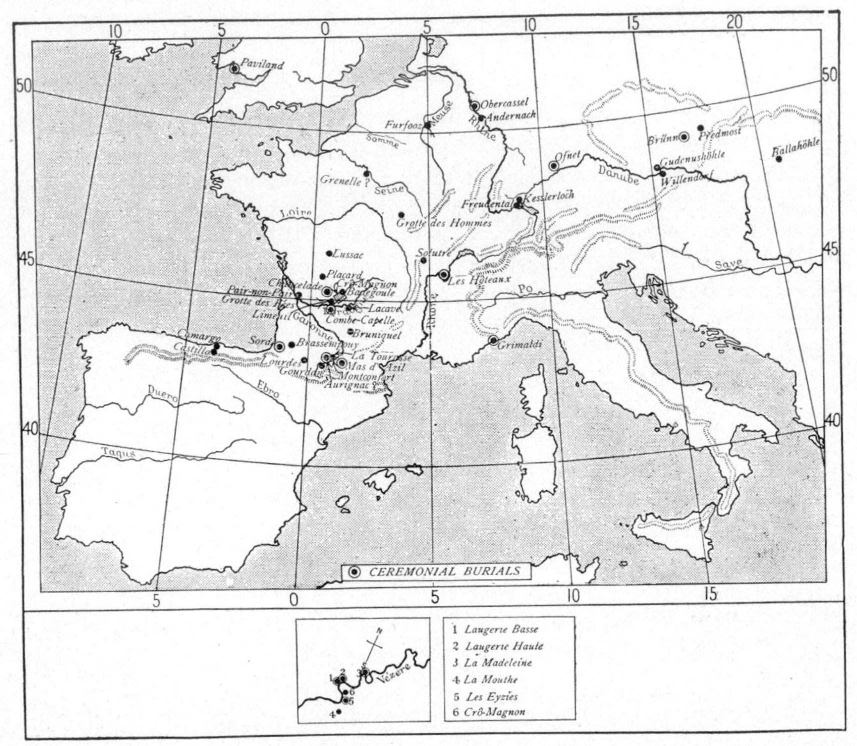

FIG. 135. Geographic distribution of Upper Palæolithic human fossils in western Europe.

We must therefore imagine western Europe in Upper Palæolithic times again as a terminal region; a great peninsula toward which the human migrants from the east and from the south came to mingle and superpose their cultures. These races took the great migration routes which had been followed by other waves of animal life before them; they were pressed upon from behind by the increasing populations of the east; they were attracted to western Europe as a fresh and wonderful game country, where food in the forests, in the meadows, and in the streams abounded in unparalleled profusion. The Crô-Magnons especially were a nomadic hunting people, perfectly fitted by their physical structure for the chase and developing an extraordinary appreciation of the beauty and majesty of the varied forms of animal life which existed in no other part of the world at the time. Between the retreating Alpine and Scandinavian glaciers Europe was freely open toward the eastern plains of the Danube,

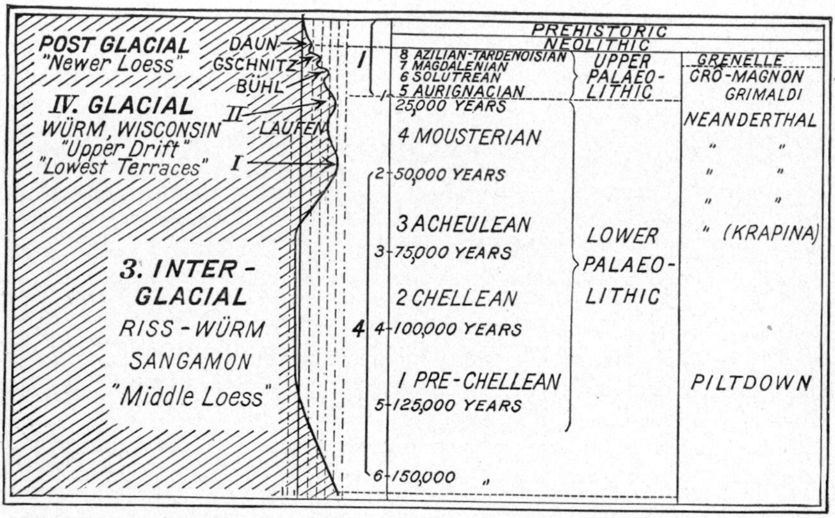

FIG. 136. Epitome of human history in western Europe during the Third Interglacial, Fourth Glacial, and Postglacial Stages; showing also the three Postglacial advances and retreats which succeeded the close of the Fourth Glacial Stage in the Alpine region, theoretically corresponding with the climatic vicissitudes of Postglacial time. From the data of Penck and Schmidt. Drawn by C. A. Reeds. (Compare Fig. 14.)

extending to central and southern Asia; on the north, however, along the Baltic, the climate was still too inclement for a wave of human migration, and there is no trace of man along these northern shores until the close of the Upper Palæolithic, nor of any residence of man in the Scandinavian peninsula until the great wave of Neolithic migration established itself in that region.

The climatic and cultural relations of Upper Palæolithic times may be correlated* in descending order as follows:

* This correlation agrees in the main with that of Schmidt in his *Diluviale Vorzeit Deutschlands*.[10]

6. The *Daun* or final Postglacial advance of the glaciers of the Alps, estimated at 7,000 B. C. Europe with its modern or prehistoric forest fauna, the lion lingering in the Pyrenees, the moose in Spain. AZILIAN-TARDENOISIAN, closing stage of the Upper Palæolithic culture; western Europe peopled by the broad-headed race of Furfooz and Ofnet, also by a narrow-headed race. Baltic Migration, MAGLEMOSE culture.

5. The *Gschnitz* stage in the Alps or second Postglacial advance. Climate still cold and moist but gradually moderating. Decline of the Magdalenian. Period of the retreat of the tundra and steppe animals; mammoth, reindeer, and arctic rodents becoming more rare; Eurasiatic forest mammals becoming more abundant.

Close of steppe period. Crô-Magnon race still dominant in western Europe in the LATE MAGDALENIAN stage of culture.

4. Interval between the *Bühl* and *Gschnitz* Postglacial advances in the Alps. A renewed steppe and 'loess' period. Climate cold and dry. Mammoth and woolly rhinoceros, reindeer, full tundra and steppe fauna very abundant. Crô-Magnon race in the stage of MIDDLE MAGDALENIAN culture.

3. The *Bühl* stage of Postglacial advance in the Alps; renewal of severe conditions of cold moist climate, and spread all over western Europe of the arctic banded and Obi lemmings of the *Upper Rodent Layer*. *Bühl* moraines in Lake Lucerne estimated as having been deposited between 16,000 and 24,000 years B. C. Crô-Magnon race dominant in the EARLY MAGDALENIAN stage of culture.

2. Period of the first Postglacial interval or *Achen* retreat of the glaciers in the Alpine region. A dry cold climate. Crô-Magnon and Brünn races in the stage of SOLUTREAN culture.

1. Close of fourth glaciation, between 24,000 and 40,000 years B. C. Cold and moist but increasingly dry climate succeeding the fourth glaciation and deposition of *Lower Rodent Layer*, or first invasion of the arctic tundra rodents. Crô-Magnon and possibly Aurignacian race in the stage of AURIGNACIAN culture.

BEGINNING OF THE UPPER PALÆOLITHIC

THE AURIGNACIAN INDUSTRY

We now glance at western Europe as it was between 25,000 and 30,000 years ago, at the opening of the Upper Palæolithic.

During Aurignacian times France was still broadly connected with Great Britain.[11] The British Islands were not only united with each other but with the continent, while the elevation of the Scandinavian peninsula converted the Baltic Sea into a great fresh-water lake, the old shores of which are readily traced. Geikie also maintains that the rise of land in Scotland after the fourth glaciation was accompanied by an amelioration of climate and the advent of more genial conditions; a strong forest growth covered the lowlands, hence this is termed the *Lower Forestian* stage of the physiographic history of northern Britain; it corresponds to the temporary period of the retreat of the glaciers in the Alpine region, which Penck has named the *Achenschwänkung*. The latter author is not inclined to connect any marked rise of temperature in the Alpine region with this interval of time; to our knowledge no fossil plant beds have been preserved which would give us such indications, and the animal life, as we shall see, certainly affords only a very slight indication of a rise in temperature in the retreat of certain of the snow-loving tundra and northern steppe lemmings to the north; the greater number of tundra forms remained. The continental elevation of the northern coast-line of Europe would explain the advent of a dry continental climate and the renewal of high prevailing winds, at least during the warmer and drier summer seasons, for it is certain that atmospheric conditions such as produced the great dust-storms and deposition of 'loess' after the second and third glaciations prevailed again in western Europe after the fourth glaciation. This gave rise to deposits of what is known among geologists as the 'newer loess,' and we find these sheets of 'newer loess' spreading immediately above the Mousterian culture at a number of different points in western Europe.

When the Crô-Magnon race entered this part of Europe the climate was becoming more dry and stimulating; the summers were warm or temperate, the winters very severe. Great ice-caps still spread over the Scandinavian peninsula and also over the Alps, but the borders of the ice-fields no longer reached the plains; in a sense, the Glacial Epoch had not yet closed, for during the whole period of Postglacial time the glaciers of the

Alps, beginning in early Magdalenian times, developed three renewed advances, each somewhat less vigorous than the preceding one, with intervening stages of a drier climate.

The greater number of the Aurignacian stations, like those of Mousterian times, were under the shelters or within the

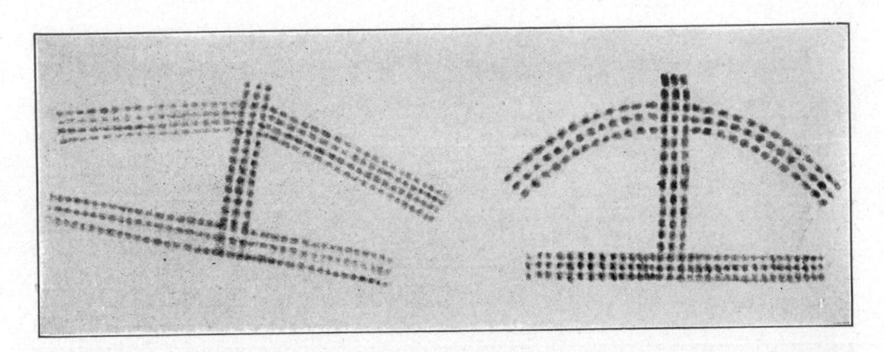

Fig. 137. 'Tectiforms'—schematic drawings in lines and dots believed to represent huts and larger shelters built of logs and covered with hides. From the walls of the cavern of *Font-de-Gaume,* Dordogne. After Breuil.

entrances of the grottos and caverns; all the stations in southwestern France are of this character. There was, however, a great open camp at Solutré, which was a most famous hunting station for the wild horse in Aurignacian times. In northern France there are several open stations, such as those of Montières and St. Acheul, along the River Somme, and to the east, along the middle Rhine, there are several open 'loess' stations, such as those of Achenheim, Völklinshofen, Rhens, and Metternich. It may very well be that these open stations were visited only during the mild summer season. The continued choice of sites which naturally afforded the greatest protection from the weather, in France, Britain, Belgium, and all along the Danube, as well as in the genial region of the Riviera, is a sure indication of a prevailing severe climate. It is hardly possible, however, that the closed or protected stations were the only residences of these people; they merely indicate the points where the flint industry was continuously carried on and also the vast foyers and gathering places; but there is little doubt from the evidence afforded by the signs on the walls of the caverns, known as 'tectiforms,' that huts and large shelters built of logs and covered with hides were grouped around most of these stations and scattered through the country at points favorable for hunting and fishing. These would be the only dwelling-places possible in such vast open camps, for example, as Solutré.

Climate and Life of Aurignacian Times

3. *First Postglacial Retreat, Achenschwänkung* in the Alpine region. Period of Solutrean industry. A cold dry climate, with dust-storms and wide-spread deposition of 'loess' in western Europe. Flint workers seeking many open stations. Horses and wild asses numerous on the prairies; reindeer and wild cattle very abundant.

2. *Recession of the Ice-Fields of the Fourth Glaciation.* Period of Aurignacian industry. Climate cold and increasingly dry; renewal of the dust-storms and deposits of the 'newer loess.' Flint industry in the caverns, grottos, shelters, and a few open stations. Opening of the Upper Palæolithic period. Arrival of the Crô-Magnon race.

1. *Final Stage of Fourth Glaciation.* Close of the Lower Palæolithic Mousterian culture. Gradual extinction of the Neanderthal race.

The arrival of the Crô-Magnon race and the beginning of the Aurignacian industry took place during the period of retreat of the ice-fields of the fourth glaciation. As we pass from the levels of the early Aurignacian industry into those of the middle and upper Aurignacian, we find that the mammal life of Mousterian times continued in its prime all over western Europe, with the addition, one by one, of some new forms from the tundras, such as the musk-ox, and the successive arrival from the mountains and steppes of western Asia of such characteristic forms as the argali sheep and the wild ass, or kiang.

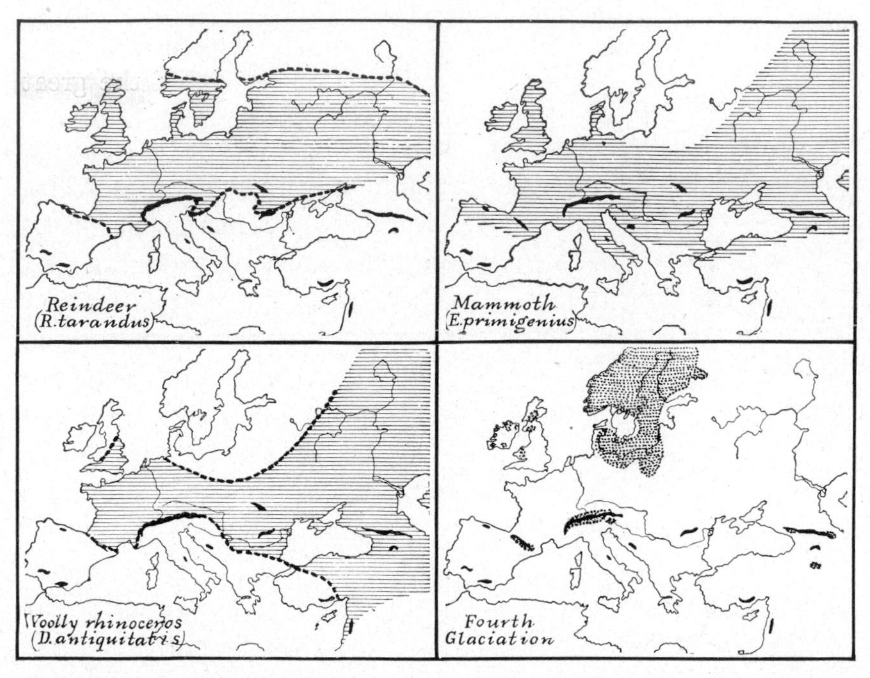

FIG. 138. Geographic distribution (horizontal lines) of the reindeer, mammoth, and woolly rhinoceros, the three chief mammals of the tundra fauna, with reference to the retiring ice-fields (dots) of the Fourth Glacial Stage. After Boule and Geikie. (Compare Figs. 95 and 96.)

The extremely cold and moist climate of the fourth glaciation had passed, and a somewhat drier but still extremely cold climatic condition prevailed throughout western Europe. During the early Aurignacian the two northern types of lemming, the banded lemming (*Myodes torquatus*) and the Obi lemming (*Myodes obensis*), were still found along the upper Danube, as in the grottos of Sirgenstein, Ofnet, and Bockstein. From middle Aurignacian on through Solutrean times these denizens of the extreme north disappear from this region of Europe. Further evidence of a dry, cold climate is found in the recurrence of dust-storms and in the great deposits of 'newer loess' beginning in certain parts of Europe at the very close of the Mousterian industry and extending through both middle and late Aurignacian and Solutrean times in all the region of the upper Rhine, along both shores of the Danube, and westward in the valley of the Somme, in northern France. This period is therefore believed to correspond with the *Achen* retreat of the great glaciers still covering the Alpine region.

Another striking proof of the amelioration of climate is the return of the flint workers to many of the open stations, old and new, in various parts of western Europe, the climate being more endurable because less humid. In Mousterian times the open stations were very rare and were perhaps visited during the summer season only; in Aurignacian times they were more abundant, there being twelve open stations out of a total of about sixty stations thus far discovered; in Aurignacian and Solutrean times the type station of Solutré was much frequented, and many other open camps are found in various parts of western Europe.

This is still the Reindeer Period; in fact, it is the typical 'Reindeer Epoch' of Lartet, and the predominant forms of life are the woolly mammoth and the woolly rhinoceros; but for a time the reindeer seems to have been less abundant, and Aurignacian times are marked apparently by a very greatly increased number of horses. The animal life throughout retains its northern or arctic character; the tundra species predominate, the hardy forms of the forests and meadows of Eurasia are next in number, and then are found a few of the steppe forms, with here and there forms characteristic of the Alps. The entire fauna of the Aurignacian may be summed up as follows:

The wild ass, or kiang, of the Asiatic deserts appears in late Aurignacian times in the region of the upper Rhine and upper Danube, as seen in the deposits of Wildscheuer, Thaingen, Kesslerloch, and Schweizersbild, and also there probably arrived in Europe at this time the Elasmothere (*E. sibericum*), a gigantic rhinoceros, distinguished from all others that we have been considering by the entire absence of the anterior horn and by the possession of an enormous single horn situated on the forehead above the eyes, also by the elaborate foldings of the dental enamel, to which the name 'Elasmothere' refers; its teeth were especially adapted to a grassy diet; it apparently wandered into Europe from the arid grassy plains of central and western Asia, and its appearance is connected with the extensive deforestation accompanying the tundra and steppe periods of mammalian life.

TUNDRA LIFE.

Reindeer, woolly mammoth, woolly rhinoceros, musk-ox (rare), arctic fox, arctic hare, arctic wolverene, arctic ptarmigan.

Banded and Obi lemmings in lower Aurignacian only.

ALPINE LIFE.

Argali sheep, ibex, alpine ptarmigan.

STEPPE LIFE.

Steppe horse, kiang, central Asiatic ass.

FOREST LIFE.

Red deer, roe-deer, giant deer, brown bear, cave-bear, wildcat, wolf, fox, otter, lynx, weasel.

MEADOW LIFE.

Bison, wild cattle.

ASIATIC LIFE.

Cave-hyæna, cave-lion, ? cave-leopard.

These periodic arrivals from central Asia suggest the existence of migration routes which may also have been followed by tribes of Palæolithic hunters.

There is no evidence at this time of the presence of the more characteristic animals of the steppes, such as the saiga antelope, the jerboa, and the steppe hamster, which enter Europe during the later period of Magdalenian culture. As an indication, perhaps, of the dryness of the climate we observe that the moose (*Alces*) is no longer recorded, although it reappears in western Europe in later Magdalenian times. The giant deer (*Megaceros*) appears in southern Germany with the early Aurignacian culture, but this would seem to be the time of its extinction, because it does not occur in association with any of the later industries. For a time the bison in Dordogne, in southern Germany, and in Austria appears to be far more abundant than the wild cattle; the latter animals are not recorded either by Schmidt or Déchelette in association with the Aurignacian culture, but they reappear in the moister period of Magdalenian times.

The remains of similar late Pleistocene mammals lie scattered over a large area in Britain, and we must conclude from their presence, observes Dawkins,[12] that Britain was still broadly connected with the mainland of Europe. This is proved by the occurrence of the mammoth fauna in various places now covered by the sea, as in Holyhead Harbor, off the coasts of Devonshire and of Sussex, and in the North Sea. On the Dogger Bank the accumulation of bones, teeth, and antlers is so great that the fishermen of Yarmouth have collected in their nets and dredges more than three hundred specimens. They belong to the bear, wolf, cave-hyæna, giant deer, Irish elk, reindeer, stag, bison, urus, horse, woolly rhinoceros, mammoth, and beaver, and are to be viewed as the remains of animals deposited by river currents, as in the case of similar accumulations on land. Had they been deposited by the sea they would have been sifted by the action of the waves, the smaller being heaped together in one place and the larger in another. The carcasses had evidently been collected in the eddies of a river that helped to form the Dogger Bank, which now rises to within eight fathoms of the sea-level.

One of the animals of the Aurignacian period which is best known is the 'horse of Solutré.' Around the great Aurignacian camp at Solutré there accumulated the remains of a vast number of horses, which are estimated at not less than 100,000; the bones are distributed in a wide circle around the ancient camp, consisting of broken or entire skeletons compacted into a veritable magma, with which occur also remains of the reindeer, the urus, and the mammoth interbedded with all the types of Aurignacian implements. The majority of these horses belong to the stout-headed, short-limbed forest or northern type, measuring 54 inches (13.2 hands) at the withers, and about the size of the existing pony.[13] The joints and hoofs were especially large, and the long teeth and powerful jaws were adapted to feeding on coarse grasses; the greater part of the remains are those of horses from five to seven years of age. There is no evidence that the men of Aurignacian times either bred or reared these animals; they pursued them only for food. The discovery that the horse might be used as an animal of transport appears to have been made in the far East, and not in western Europe.

The animal and plant life of the Aurignacian station near Krems, on the Danube, above Vienna,[14] includes a strong element of the tundra forms—the arctic fox, wolverene, mammoth, rhinoceros, musk-ox, reindeer, hare, and ptarmigan. The steppe fauna, on the other hand, is rare, including only the suslik, but not the saiga antelope or any of the other characteristic steppe types. The principal objects of the chase were not only the mammoth, which was extraordinarily abundant, but also the reindeer and wild horses; the ibex is rare.

Obermaier observes that the chart of the geographic distribution of the Aurignacian shows this culture to belong essentially to the provinces surrounding the entire Mediterranean, from Syria (the grottos of Lebanon) through north Africa (Algiers) to Spain. It also has a strong development throughout France, entering middle and southern Germany and passing along the Danube to Austria, Poland, and southern Russia (Mezine) north of Kiev. There is no doubt that the mammoth hunters of Krems belonged in this wide-spread distribution; the shells used for ornaments, which unmistakably recall those of the Riviera, are only in part local from the neighborhood of Vienna; the larger part is from the Mediterranean. We may imagine that these shells passed through several hands among this race of nomadic hunters, and this is not surprising in view of the girdle which the Aurignacian stretched around the entire Mediterranean Sea.

Discovery of the Crô-Magnon Race

The earliest discovery of a member of this race was that by Buckland, in the cave of Paviland, which opens on the face of a steep limestone cliff, about a mile east of Rhossilly, on the coast of Gower, Wales.[15] As described by Sollas, a painted skeleton, long known as the 'Red Lady,' was found in the kitchen midden which forms the floor of this cave; recent investigation has proved that this skeleton belongs to a man of the Crô-Magnon race; the associated implements are of Aurignacian type. Pavi-

FIG. 139. Section of the sepulchral grotto of Aurignac, the type station of Aurignacian culture, as restored by Lartet from the description of the original condition of the grotto as it was in 1852. After Lyell.

land cave is thus the first Aurignacian station discovered in Britain and marks the most westerly outpost of the Crô-Magnon race.

In 1852 the sepulchral grotto of Aurignac, on the nearest spur of the Pyrenees, in Haute-Garonne, was accidentally discovered by a laborer. It was almost filled with bones, among which were two entire skulls and many fragments, numbering altogether no less than seventeen skeletons of both sexes and of all ages. The mayor of Aurignac ordered all the bones to be taken out and re-interred in the parish cemetery. Thus, in 1860, when Lartet visited this grotto and determined it as the type station of a distinct industry, all the human remains had been lost beyond recovery, and with them all possibility of learning to what race, culture, and geologic age they belonged. On a sloping terrace in front of the grotto was the hearth containing one hundred flint implements, mingled with the remains of a typical reindeer fauna.

In 1868 Lartet explored a grotto in the little hamlet of Crô-Magnon, near Les Eyzies, on the Vézère, where he found five

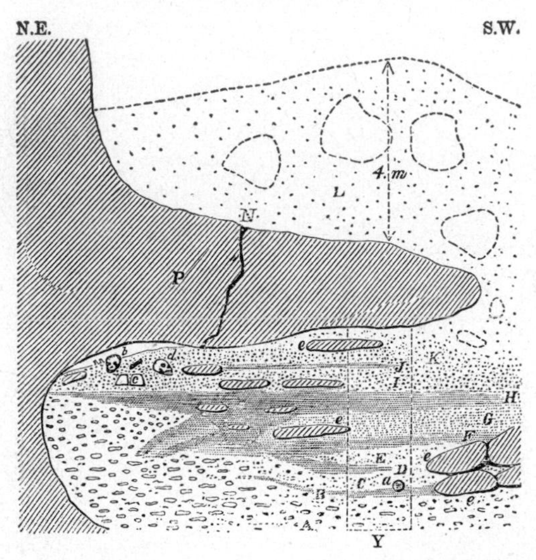

FIG. 140. Section of the Grotto of Crô-Magnon, in which the fossilized skeleton of the 'Old Man of Crô-Magnon,' type of the Crô-Magnon race, was discovered in 1868, together with the remains of four other individuals. After Louis Lartet. Scale = 1–125.

skeletons, which have become the type of the great Crô-Magnon race of Upper Palæolithic times. The grotto was accidentally discovered by workmen building a road in the Vézère valley. Here Lartet found the skeleton of an old man, now known as the 'old man of Crô-Magnon'; then that of a woman, whose forehead bore the mark of a wound from some heavy blow; close to her lay the fragments of a child's skeleton and near by those of two young men. Flint implements and perforated shells were found with these skeletons.

In May, 1868, the material was first described by Broca,[16] his excellent account being later reprinted and amplified in the *Reliquiæ Aquitanicæ* of Lartet and Christy.[17] Broca referred to these skeletons as incontestable proofs of the contemporaneous existence of man and the mammoth. The associated mammalian life was that of the reindeer and the industry is now known to be of the Aurignacian stage. In his classic original description of this type Broca remarks upon the high stature, the face very

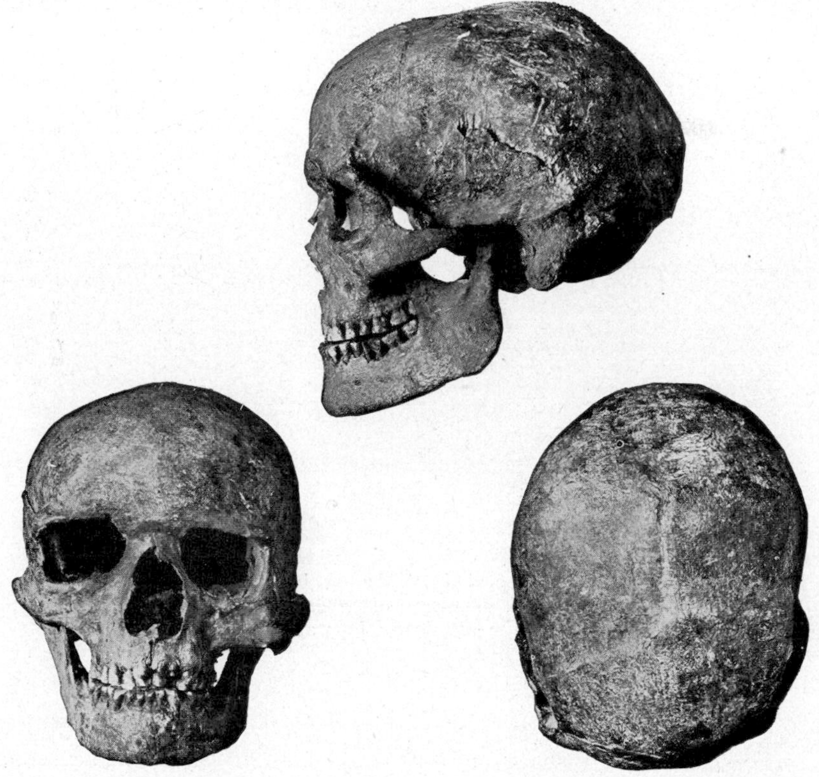

FIG. 141. Head of the very tall skeleton of Crô-Magnon type discovered in the *Grotte des Enfants*. After Verneau. One-quarter life size.

broad in relation to its height, with very long and very narrow orbits; the large and markedly dolichocephalic skull, with an unusually large brain capacity, noting that the brain capacity of the Crô-Magnon woman surpasses that of the average male of to-day; the forehead correspondingly broad, vertical, convex on the median line; the bones of the limbs robust, and the shin-bones flattened transversely; altogether a very high racial type of skeleton belonging to the species *Homo sapiens*.

Verneau,[18] in his description of the Crô-Magnon type, emphasizes the *disharmonic* form of the head, for the dolichocephalic form of the skull is combined with a face very broad for its height, and this, in fact, is the unique and most distinctive feature of the Crô-Magnon race. The cheek-bones are both broad and high. It is curious that in this face, so broad across the cheek-

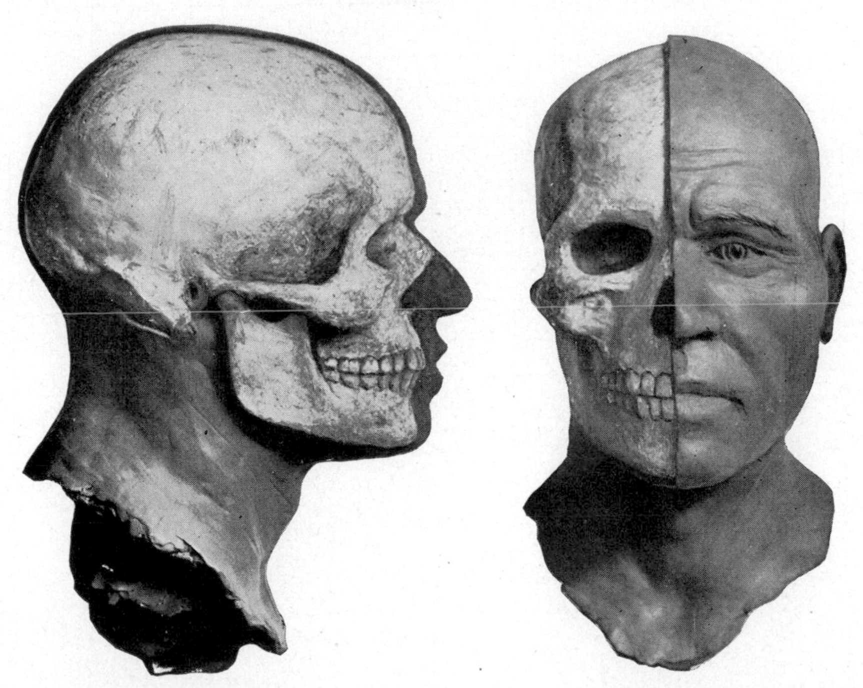

Fig. 142. Head of the 'Old Man of Crô-Magnon,' rejuvenated by the restoration of the teeth, showing the method of restoration of the features adopted in all the models by J. H. McGregor. The diameter of the head across the cheek-bones is seen to be greater than that across the cranium. (Compare Figs. 146 and 147, also Pl. VI.)

bones and cheek arches, the space between the eyes is small, the nose is narrow and aquiline, and the upper jaw is noticeably narrow; it is no less remarkable that this upper jaw projects forward, while the upper part of the face is almost vertical, as in the highest types of *Homo sapiens*. The eye sockets, which are remarkably broad, are rather shallow, and their angles are but slightly rounded off, so that the form suggests a very long rectangle; the mandible is thick and strong, and the chin massive, triangular, and very prominent; the marks of muscular attachment denote great muscular development around the thick, strong jaws, in which the parts for the attachment of the vertical

DISCOVERIES CHIEFLY OF THE CRÔ-MAGNON AND GRIMALDI RACES*

REFERRED TO AURIGNACIAN TIMES

Date of Discovery	Locality	Number of Individuals	Culture Stage
	CRÔ-MAGNON AND (?) AURIGNACIAN RACE		
1823.	Paviland cave, western Wales.	One skeleton. Burial.	Aurignacian.
1852.	Aurignac, Haute-Garonne, Pyrenees, France.	Seventeen skeletons. Burial.	? "
1868.	Crô-Magnon, Dordogne, France.	Three incomplete skeletons and fragments of two others. ? Burial.	"
1872–1884.	Grottes de Grimaldi, Baoussé-Roussé, Italy.	Burial.	
	1. Grotte des Enfants (Grotte de Grimaldi).	Four skeletons.	"
	2. Grotte de Cavillon.	One "	"
	3. Barma Grande.	Six "	"
	4. Baousso da Torre.	Three "	"
1909.	Combe-Capelle, Dordogne.	Type of *Homo aurignacensis*, Klaatsch. Burial.	"
1909.	Laugerie Haute, Dordogne.	One skeleton. Burial.	? "
	Solutré.	Fragments.	? "
	Camargo (Santander), Spain.	Fragment of skull.	"
	Willendorf, Austria.	Fragments.	Late Aurignacian.
	Cave of Antelias (Syria).	Scattered bones.	Aurignacian.
	GRIMALDI RACE		
1906.	Grottes de Grimaldi, Baoussé-Roussé, Italy.		
	1. Grotte des Enfants (Grotte de Grimaldi).	Two skeletons.	Aurignacian or Late Mousterian.

* Obermaier,[19] R. Martin.[20]

muscles are unusually large. I would add, says Verneau, to these essential characteristics the surprising capacity of the cranium, which Broca estimated as at least 1,590 c.cm. The majority of these features are found in almost all of the skulls of the Crô-Magnon race in the Grottes de Grimaldi. The top view of the skull is unusual on account of the extreme prominence of the eminences of the parietals, which give the skull a pentagonal effect when seen from above. The eyebrow ridges show decided prominences above the orbits but disappear completely in the median line and at the sides and thus differ totally from those in the Neanderthal head.

Of the numerous skeletons found in the Grottes de Grimaldi, or Baoussé-Roussé, near Mentone, the one first discovered is most widely known as the 'man of Mentone,' which was found in the Grotte de Cavillon, in 1872, by Rivière; hence this is sometimes spoken of as the Mentone race; but, as Verneau shows, while the measurements of the skulls of Baoussé-Roussé show some variety, they do not exceed what might be expected in individual variation, and we conclude that all the men of tall stature found in the Grottes de Grimaldi belong to the Crô-Magnon race, which is not to be confused with the very distinct dwarf *Grimaldi race* discovered in the Grottes de Grimaldi by Verneau, in 1906, in a lower level than any of the skeletons of the Crô-Magnon type.

In Aurignacian times, lofty stature seems to have been a general characteristic of this race, but there appears to have been a gradual decrease in height, so that in later industrial times the race in general is somewhat smaller in stature. The heights are as follows:

Crô-Magnon type of Dordogne	1.80 m.	5 ft. 10¾ in.
" woman slightly inferior in size.		
Baoussé-Roussé, Grottes de Grimaldi.		
Adult males of		
Cavillon	1.79 m.	5 ft. 10½ in.
Barma Grande II	1.82 m.	5 ft. 11½ in.
Baousso da Torre II	1.85 m.	6 ft. ¾ in.
Barma Grande I	1.93 m.	6 ft. 4 in.
Grotte des Enfants	1.94 m.	6 ft. 4½ in.
Average	1.87 m.	6 ft. 1½ in.
Woman of Barma Grande estimated at	1.65 m.	5 ft. 5 in.
Youth of 15 years, Barma Grande, estimated at	1.65 m.	5 ft. 5 in.

The woman had not reached complete development. As there is a variation of 6 inches in the height of the various male skeletons, it is evident that we cannot reach a trustworthy conclusion from a single subject; but there would seem to be quite a disparity in height between the sexes.

The very large skeleton from the *Grotte des Enfants*, measuring 6 feet 4½ inches, was found associated with the remains of

FIG. 143. The *abri* or shelter of Laugerie Haute, Dordogne, France, where the Aurignacian burial of a skeleton referred to the Crô-Magnon race, was discovered in 1909. Photograph by Belvès.

the reindeer, 15 feet below the surface, from which it would appear probable that the skeleton antedates the Aurignacian skeleton of Laugerie Haute, and even of Crô-Magnon. Thus the so-called man of Mentone may be an ancestor of the race which was found in Crô-Magnon and other regions of Dordogne. It is these men of great height, found in Barma Grande and the Grotte des Enfants, which Verneau selects for his description of the primitive members of the Crô-Magnon race, which at this time lived along the Riviera and in the valley of the Vézère and later spread over a vast area in western Europe. It is probable that in the genial climate of the Riviera these men obtained their finest development; the country was admirably protected

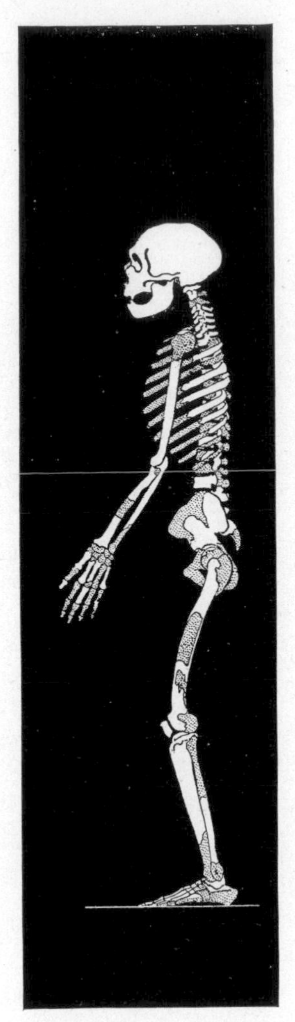

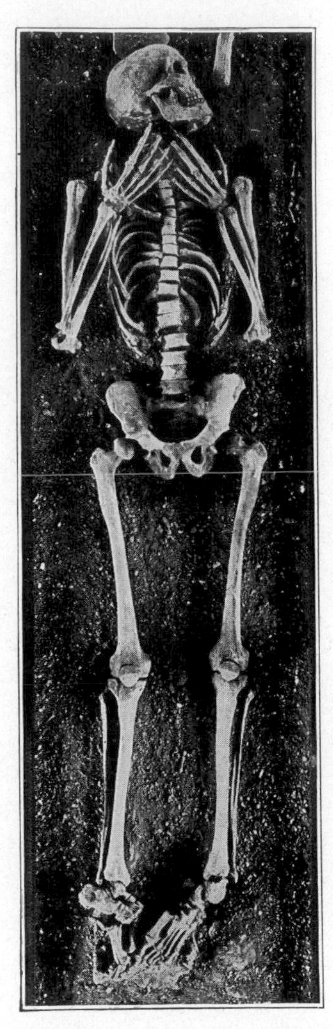

FIG. 144. Comparative view of the Neanderthal skeleton (left) from *La Chapelle-aux Saints*, and of the skeleton of a very tall member of the Crô-Magnon race (right) discovered in the *Grotte des Enfants*. After Boule and Verneau. Both figures are approximately one-seventeenth life size.

from the cold winds of the north, refuges were abundant, and game by no means scarce, to judge from the quantity of animal bones found in the caves. Under such conditions of life the race enjoyed a fine physical development and dispersed widely.

With an average height of 6 feet 1½ inches, these cave-dwellers may be said to demonstrate one of the most striking traits of the Crô-Magnon race. In the proportions of the limbs and in the great size of the upper part of the chest these men are removed from the modern European type and approach some of the African negroid types, although there is not the least resemblance to the negro type in the skull or in the dentition. In contrast with the Neanderthals are three characters of the limbs:

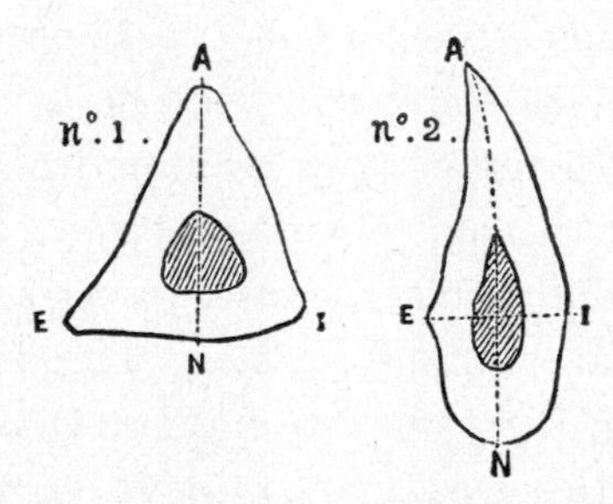

Fig. 145. Sections of the tibia or shin-bone, (1) the normal triangular type; and (2) the extremely platycnæmic flattened type characteristic of the Crô-Magnon race. After Broca.

the leg was very long in comparison with the arm; they show a remarkable lengthening of the forearm in proportion to the upper arm and a still more remarkable lengthening of the lower leg or shin-bone in proportion to the thigh-bone; the tibia has an index of 81–86 per cent as compared with the femur, which is relatively greater than that of the average modern European, with a tibio-femoral index of 79.7 per cent. This long shin-bone indicates that these men were swift of foot, quite in keeping with their undoubted nomadic habits and wide distribution. The flatness of the tibia, which is strongly marked in 62 per cent of the skeletons, may well be due to the habit of squatting while engaged in fashioning flints and in other industrial occupations. The leg, long in comparison with the arm, and the thigh-bone, strongly developed, are both characters of a hunting race. The foot has a very protruding heel, but the sole and the toes are of moderate length. The hip-girdle is of a type which has nothing negroid about it, but is as fine as that of the most civilized whites; it is marked by its strength, the augmentation of all the vertical and transverse diameters, and the reduction of the anteroposterior diameters. The shoulders are exceptionally broad. The fact that the arms are relatively short as compared with the legs is also a high racial character. The upper arm is very robust, and in some cases the left arm is more largely developed, in others the right.

In all the skulls from these grottos near Mentone, the face shows the essential features of the Crô-Magnon race, its breadth being due to the development of the cheek-bones and the zygomatic arches, for the upper jaws are narrow, and the nose is thin or leptorhine. At the root the nose shows a marked depression, but it rises immediately to a considerable prominence; it thus undoubtedly had an aquiline profile. The orbits always present the form of a long rectangle, so characteristic of the race along the Vézère. All these characters leave no doubt of the racial affinity of the skeletons from the Grottes de Grimaldi with the original Crô-Magnon type. It must be concluded, therefore, that certain peculiar features noted in the type of the 'old man of Crô-Magnon' are purely individual, and that we are not justified in assuming the admixture of a foreign element to account for the weakness of some characteristics which we notice in the majority of the Crô-Magnon subjects from the caves of Grimaldi.

The highly evolved characters of the skeleton in this race are in keeping with the extraordinarily great cranial capacity. Broca estimated the 'old man of Crô-Magnon' as having a cranial capacity of 1,590 c.cm., and in the female the brain is estimated at 1550 c.cm. Verneau estimates the five large male skulls of Crô-Magnon type at Grimaldi as having an average capacity of 1,800 c.cm., the lowest being 1,715 c.cm., and the highest 1,880 c.cm. This race, observes Keith,[21] was one of the finest the world has ever seen. The wide, short face, the extremely prominent cheek-bones, the spread of the palate and a tendency of the upper cutting teeth and incisors to project forward, and the narrow, pointed chin recall a facial type which is best seen to-day in tribes living in Asia to the north and to the south of the Himalayas. As regards their stature the Crô-

FIG. 146. Restoration of the head of the 'Old Man of Crô-Magnon,' in profile, modelled after the type skull of Crô-Magnon, Dordogne, with the teeth restored and the head given a younger appearance. After the model by J. H. McGregor. One-quarter life size.

Magnon race recalls the Sikhs living to the south of the Himalayas. In the disharmonic proportions of the face, that is, the combination of broad cheek-bones and narrow skull, they resemble the Eskimo. The sum of the Crô-Magnon characters is certainly Asiatic rather than African, whereas in the Grimaldis the sum of the characters is decidedly negroid or African.

We shall trace this great race through the Solutrean and

Magdalenian stages of the Upper Palæolithic and consider its disappearance and possible distribution at the close of Magdalenian times. It will then be interesting to consider the evidence of the survival of the descendants of this race in various

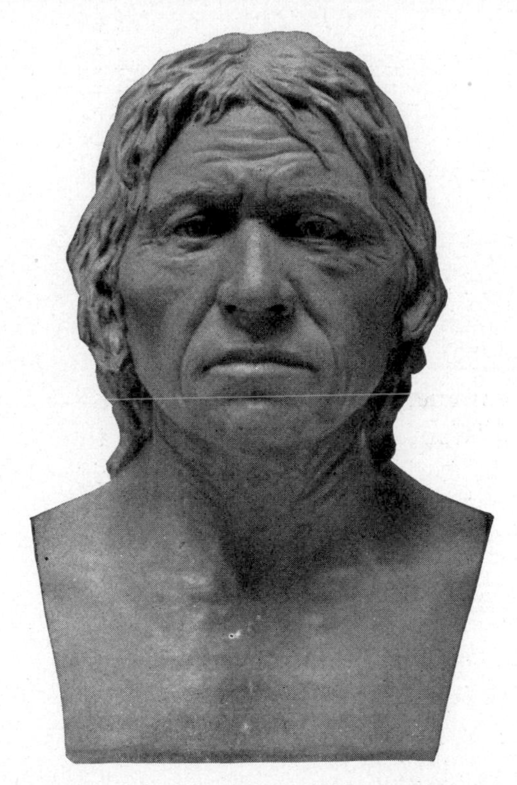

FIG. 147. Restoration of the head of the 'Old Man of Crô-Magnon,' front view. After the model by J. H. McGregor. One-quarter life size.

parts of western Europe and possibly among the primitive inhabitants of the Canary Islands, known as the Guanches.

EVIDENCE OF OTHER RACES

It is a mooted question whether the Crô-Magnons were the only people inhabiting Europe in early Aurignacian time or whether there were also two other races, the *Grimaldi* and the *Aurignacian*. As we have seen in the preceding pages, there is no evidence that the negroid Grimaldi race ever became established in Europe; the idea of the presence of a negroid race has taken the fancy of archæologists like Breuil and Rutot, when seeking an African, Egyptian, or Bushman analogy in certain phases of early Aurignacian art; but it rests merely on the slender evidence afforded by the isolated skeletons of a woman and of a boy.

The case of the Aurignacian race is different; this is held by competent anatomists (Klaatsch,[22] Keith[23]) to be distinct from the Crô-Magnon race and to bear some resemblance to the Brünn (Brüx, Předmost, [?] Galley Hill) race which, we know, became established in central Europe certainly as early as Solutrean times, if not before.

The so-called Aurignacian race (*Homo sapiens aurignacensis*), described as a subspecies of existing man, is based upon a type found in the shelter of Combe-Capelle near Montferrand, Périgord, in the summer of 1909 by O. Hauser.[24] It is commonly known as the 'Combe-Capelle' man from the scene of its discovery, or as the Aurignacian man (*Homo aurignacensis*); if a subspecies, it certainly belongs to *Homo sapiens*. The adult male skeleton was discovered lying undisturbed in the lowest stratum of an Aurignacian industry and was carefully disinterred by Klaatsch and Hauser. It was apparently a case of ceremonial burial; a great number of unusually fine flints of early Aurignacian type was found with it, also a necklace of perforated shells (*Littorina*, *Nassa*); the limbs were bent.[25] Water saturated with lime had dripped upon the burial-place, resulting in the remarkable preservation of the skeleton. This skeleton is compared by Klaatsch with that of Brünn, Moravia, and of Galley Hill, near London, from which he concludes that it represents a distinct type, the Aurignacian race; the stature is 5 feet 3 inches, as compared with 6 feet 1½ inches, the average in the five Crô-Magnon males of Grimaldi; the brain case is well arched and falls within the variation limits of *Homo sapiens*. The skull is very long and narrow, the cephalic index being 65.7 per cent; in some points it shows a striking similarity to that of Brünn, in others it varies from it in the direction of the recent European form; the face is not narrow nor is it prognathous; the lower jaw is small with a well-developed chin. Klaatsch finds many characteristics resembling those of the Crô-Magnon race, including the Chancelade type which is a late Crô-Magnon. He suggests that the Crô-Magnon type may be considered a further development of the Aurignacian. It seems probable that the Aurignacian man is a member of the true Crô-Magnon race and that additional evidence is required to establish it as distinct. Schliz[26] considers that this

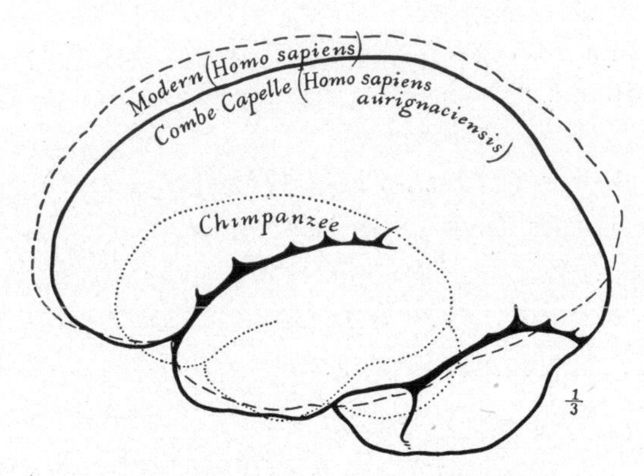

FIG. 148. Brain outline of the man of the so-called Aurignacian race discovered at Combe-Capelle in 1909 (after Klaatsch), as compared with the brain outlines of a chimpanzee and of *Homo sapiens*.

skull is an intermediate form between that of the Crô-Magnon and the Brünn race, an indication that these two races were undergoing a parallel development.

Burial Customs

Similar customs of burial prevailed widely in Aurignacian times, as we have observed from the use of color in the Paviland interment of western Wales and in the Brünn interment of Moravia. This is a feature seldom found in the Neanderthal burials, although the latter are accompanied by signs of great reverence and by an abundance of ornaments and finely finished flints. Up to the present time the races of the Upper Palæolithic have been studied with far less anatomical precision than those of the Lower, and the attribution of many of the burials to the Crô-Magnon race awaits verification.

We have little record of the Paviland burial except that the skeleton was that of a man of the Crô-Magnon race and colored red. Of the burial of Aurignac we have no record other than that seventeen skeletons were placed close together; it would appear that this compound burial may have been the sequel of a battle or, less probably, that of an epidemic. The type skeletons of the Crô-Magnon race were simply lying on the surface of a deep shelter; thus there has always been some doubt as to their exact archæological age; a large number of perforated shells was found among the bones, as well as pendants of ivory.

The most remarkable Crô-Magnon burials of undoubted Aurignacian age are those of the Grottes de Grimaldi; the infant skeletons found here are neither colored nor decorated, but occurred with a vast number of small perforated shells (*Nassa*), evidently forming a sort of burial mantle. Similarly, the female skeleton was enveloped in a bed of shells not perforated; the legs were extended, while the arms were stretched beside the body; there were a few pierced shells and a few bits of silex. One of the large male skeletons of the same grotto had the lower limbs extended, the upper limbs folded, and was decorated with a gorget and crown of perforated shells; the head rested on a block of red stone. In the 'man of Mentone,' found in 1872, the body rested on its left side, the limbs were slightly flexed, and the forearm was folded; heavy stones protected the body from disturbance; the head was decorated with a circle of perforated shells colored in red, and implements of various types were carefully placed on the forehead and chest. Similarly in the burial of Barma Grande three skeletons were found placed side by side in a layer of red earth containing a large quantity of peroxide of iron; two of the skeletons rested on the left side, the limbs extended or slightly flexed; the forehead and chest and one of the limbs were encircled with shells.

In the burial of the so-called Aurignac man of Combe-Capelle, described above, the limbs were outstretched and the body was decorated with a necklace of perforated shells and surrounded with a great number of fine Aurignacian flints. It appears that in all the numerous burials of these grottos of Aurignacian age and industry of the Crô-Magnon race we have the burial standards which prevailed in western Europe at this time.

We must infer that the conception of survival after death was among the primitive beliefs, attested by the placing with the dead of ornaments and of weapons and in many instances of objects of food. It is interesting to note that the grottos and shelters were so frequently sought as places of burial, also that the flexed limbs or extended position of the body prevailed throughout western Europe into Neolithic times, as well as the use of color through the Solutrean into Magdalenian times. It is probable from their love of color in parietal decorations, and from the appearance of coloring matter in so many of the burials, that decoration of the living body with color was widely practised, and that color was freshly applied, either as pigment or in the form of powder, to the bodies of the dead in order to prepare them for a renewal of life.

Aurignacian Flint and Bone Industry

As pointed out in the introduction of this chapter, the geographical distribution of the early Aurignacian industry is especially interesting in its bearing upon the routes by which the Crô-Magnon race entered Europe. "We can hardly contemplate an origin directly from the east," says Breuil,[27] "because these earlier phases of the Aurignacian industry have not as yet been met with in central or eastern Europe." A southerly origin seems more probable, because the Aurignacian colonies appear to surround the entire periphery of the Mediterranean, being found in northern Africa, Sicily, and the Italian and Iberian peninsulas, from which they extended over the larger part of southern France. In Tunis we find a very primitive Aurignacian like that of the Abri Audit of Dordogne, with implements undoubtedly similar to those of Chatelperron, in France. Even far to the east, in the cave of Antelias, in Syria, as well as in certain stations of Phœnicia,[28] culture deposits are found which are characteristically Aurignacian. Again, in southern Italy implements of typical Aurignacian form, tending toward the superior stage, are found in the grotto of Romanelli, Otranto.

On the other hand, in favor of the theory of local or autochthonous evolution of this culture is the direct succession described below of Aurignacian prototypes and early Aurignacian implements above the older Mousterian layers in the various stations of Dordogne. In fact, the relation of the Aurignacian industry to the preceding Mousterian is one of the most important in the history of Palæolithic archæology, because of the change of race which occurred at this time. How far is it derivative and autochthonous, how far is it new and influenced by invasion and the handicraft of a new and superior race?

Art.

Microlithique,	microlith.
Burin,	graver (first appearance).

Industrial.

Coup de poing,	hand-stone (rare and degenerate).
Pointe,	point.
* Chatelperron (curved).	
double-pointed.	
Racloir,	scraper.
convex.	
concave.	
straight.	
double-edged.	
triple-edged.	
Grattoir,	planing tool.
Perçoir,	drill, borer.
Couteau,	knife, blade.
Enclume,	anvil stone.
Percuteur,	hammer-stone.

War and Chase.

Pointe,	point.
Pierre de jet,	throwing stone.
Couteau,	knife, blade.
Pointe de lance,	bone lance-heads.

First, as for transition from the older culture, it is important to note throughout that the 'Aurignacian retouch' is identical with the Mousterian; this retouch is on one side of the flake only and gives it a short, abrupt, and blunt edge. As we shall see, it is essentially different from that discovered by the Solutrean flint workers and employed in Solutrean times, a superior technique which produced a sharp, thin edge, many of the implements

* Denotes very frequent occurrence of a typical form.

being dressed on both sides. On the other hand, Breuil concludes that the early Aurignacian industry can only in part be derived from the late Mousterian and that it is partly due to the invasion of a race which ranks much higher in the scale of intelligence than the Neanderthal.

The pure *early Aurignacian* industry is seen in the regions of Dordogne and the Pyrenees in the layers of Chatelperron, Germolles, Roche au Loup, Haurets, and Gargas. The cave of

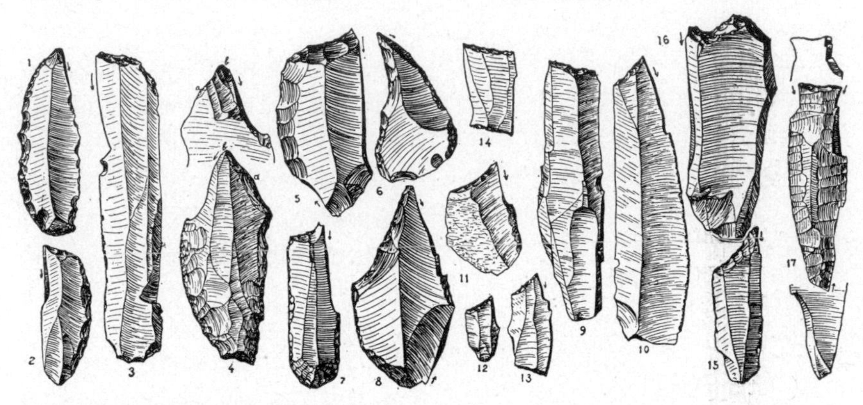

Fig. 149. Implements designed for engraving and sculpture. Evolution of the angulate graving-tool or *burin*, from the early Aurignacian of Chatelperron (left), to the late Solutrean of Placard (right). After Breuil. About one-third actual size. These small implements, chiefly made from elongated flakes and distinguished by a sharp angulate edge at one end suitable for graving on bone or stone, are especially characteristic of the Aurignacian stage of culture, in which they first appear. 1, 2. Chatelperron points. 6. Prototype of the Magdalenian 'parrot-beak.' Some of these *burins*, such as 7, are made into *grattoirs* or planing tools at the other end.

Gudenushöhle, near Krems, in Lower Austria, exhibits a very primitive phase of the early Aurignacian. Here numerous small flints were found, resembling those found at Brive by the Abbés Bardon and Bouyssonie; similar microliths are also found at Pair-non-Pair, Gironde, at various stations in Dordogne, and at the Grottes de Grimaldi, on the Riviera, in layers of corresponding age.

The chief invention of this stage is the 'Chatelperron point' (Fig. 149), a direct development from the curved point of the Abri Audit (Fig. 151) and a dominant type of the early Aurignacian culture. Small almond-shaped 'coups de poing' are still met with at Chatelperron and a few other localities, but Breuil suggests that these may not be real examples of Aurignacian industry but implements carried off from older stations.

The use of elongated flakes is another feature of this early industry, but the retouch of the edges cannot compare with the fine 'grooved retouch' of the middle Aurignacian; as yet the flakes are thick and large. Many of the scrapers are 'keeled' (*grattoirs carénés*).

An entirely new implement appears in addition to the triangular and elongate flakes of flint shaped into points and scrapers of forms; this is the primitive graving-tool, or *burin*, which at first is quite rare, but which we know was designed by the Crô-Magnon artists for their early engravings on stone (Fig. 149).

A fourth highly distinctive feature of the early Aurignacian is the use of a variety of implements of bone and horn consisting chiefly of javelin points and drills and of coarse, spatula-like tools.

In the *middle Aurignacian* the flake industry reaches its perfection of form and technique; the edges of the flakes are shaped all around with the 'grooved retouch' resulting in symmetrical forms such as the oval, double-ended 'points,' the leaf-shaped 'points,' and the double scrapers; this, in fact, is the culmination of the 'Aurignacian retouch,' which afterward begins to decline. The retouch of the long flakes is

Art Implements.

Microlithique,	microlith.
* *Burin,*	graver.
Ciseau,	chisel.
* *Gravette,*	etching tool (first appearance).

New Industrial Implements.

Pointe,	point (leaf-shaped).
* *Grattoir carêné,*	keeled scraper.
Perçoir,	drill, borer. * curved (first appearance).
Couteau,	knife, blade. * curved-in edges.
Poinçon,	awl (bone).

New Implements of War and Chase.

Pointe à cran,	shouldered point (stone).
Pointe de sagaie,	javelin point (bone).

* Denotes very frequent occurrence of a typical form.

fine and parallel, but as yet the flakes themselves are generally thick and heavy, so that their ends are, perforce, much broader than those of the Solutrean and Magdalenian fashion. One of the most distinctive forms of this middle Aurignacian industry is the 'keeled scraper' (*grattoir caréné*) with an abruptly grooved retouch (Fig. 150).

Still more significant in connection with the rapid artistic development of these people is the remarkable increase in the

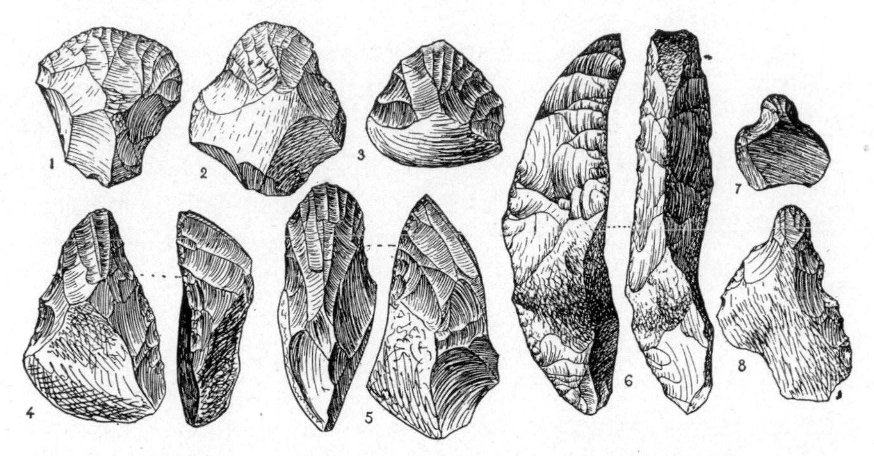

FIG. 150. Implements suitable for the dressing of hides and for sculpture. The keeled scraper or planing tool—*grattoir caréné*—characteristic of the Aurignacian culture. After Breuil. About two-fifth actual size. 1, 2, 3. Short and broad types appearing in the middle Aurignacian. 4, 5. More elongated types of the advanced middle Aurignacian from Crô-Magnon, Dordogne. 6. Elongated type (*pic*) of the close of the middle Aurignacian. 7, 8. Small *grattoirs* with handles, suitable for sculpture.

number and variety of graving-tools, including numerous curved gravers. Almost all the chief types of gravers (burins) have now been invented, and tools of bone have become extremely numerous and varied. To engraving and linear design have been added the art of sculpture and the primitive use of color (Breuil,[29] Schmidt[30]).

In the Dordogne region this evolution of the middle Aurignacian is exemplified at Le Ruth, Le Roc de Combe-Capelle, and the principal layers of the Abri Audit as well as at the shelter of Laussel. It is well developed also at Le Trilobite, on the headwaters of the Seine.

In the *late Aurignacian* (Breuil,[31] Obermaier[32]) there is a notable departure from the Mousterian fashion of chipping the flakes; even the distinctive blunt 'Aurignacian retouch' is somewhat weakened; but at the same time the work on the elongated flakes becomes more facile and skilful. For delicate, artistic work there appear extremely small implements or 'microliths' of various shapes.

The early and middle Aurignacian 'point' and the 'grattoir,' sharpened all around, as well as the incurved flake become less frequent. The grattoirs, or planing tools, are somewhat higher and narrower than those of the early Aurignacian but not very different in form; two forms of grattoir are recognized, one long and not very thick, the other high and keel-shaped (*grattoir caréné*).

Art.

Microlithique,	microlith.
Burin,	graver.
Ciseau, (of stone and bone).	chisel
Gravette,	etching tool.
Pic, (triangular or quadrangular, for sculpture).	pick

Ceremonial.

Bâton de commandement, (first appearance).	ceremonial staff

New Industrial Implements.

Grattoir, * long but not thick.	planing tool
Aiguille, (bone, first appearance).	needle

New Implements of War and Chase.

Lance and spear head types, of stone:

(*a*) Pointe à cran,	shouldered point.
(*b*) Pointe à soie, (Font Robert type).	tongued point
(*c*) Pointe de laurier(?),	laurel-leaf point(?).
Couteau, (bone, first appearance).	knife, blade

Among the perçoirs a curved form is very characteristic, and we also note a variety of small knives, or couteaux.

The inventive genius of this people is displayed in the rapidly increasing variety of flint implements designed for fishing or for the chase. Toward the end of the Upper Aurignacian there appears the shouldered spear head (*pointe à cran*), and also a

* Denotes very frequent occurrence of a typical form.

lance form of which the most perfect types have been found at Willendorf, in Austria, and at Grimaldi, on the Riviera. More or less sporadically there appear specimens of the tongued spear heads (*pointes à soie*), such as are found at Spy, Font Robert, and Laussel. This type of flint is constantly found associated with rudely formed prototypes of the Solutrean laurel-leaf point.

Decorative art has now become a passion, and graving-tools of great variety of shape, curved, straight, convex, or concave,

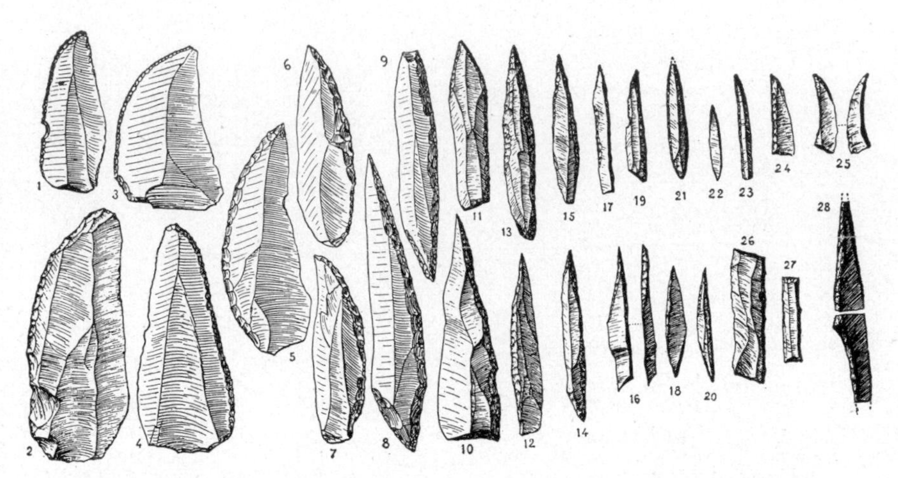

FIG. 151. Implements of industrial use, of the chase, and of fishing; also suitable for fine engraving and etching on stone or bone. Evolution of the Aurignacian *pointe* with abrupt retouch along one edge, from the base to the summit of the Aurignacian. After Breuil. About one-third actual size. 1–4. Primitive curved points from the *Abri Audit*, Dordogne. 5. More evolved curved point from Gargas. 6, 7. Points from Chatelperron, at the base of the middle Aurignacian. 11–28. Microlithic points from *La Gravette* and *Font Robert*. The form of 28 suggests that of the *pointe à cran* or 'shouldered point' characteristic of the late Solutrean.

diversified both in size and in style of technique, are very numerous. We may imagine that the long periods of cold and inclement weather were employed in these occupations. The use of the reindeer horn is developing, and the decoration of the bone with very fine lines drawn by the microlithic tools is at times very remarkable. Here appear the earliest examples of the so-called *bâton de commandement*, which is supposed to have served as a ceremonial staff or wand; it is made of the reindeer antler with a great hole bored at the point where the brow tine unites with the main beam; some of these *bâtons* are ornamented with rude engravings, but not as yet with sculpture.

Strong and very sharp graving-tools were also needed for the sculpture out of ivory and soapstone of such human figures and figurines as the statuettes found in the Grottes de Grimaldi and at Willendorf and still more powerful tools for such work as the large stone bas-reliefs of Laussel. At this time the Crô-Magnons were also fashioning stronger tools for the engraving of

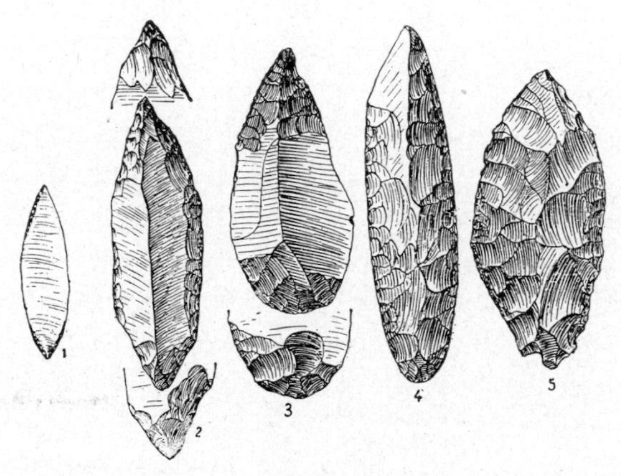

FIG. 152. Prototypes of the Solutrean laurel-leaf point, probably an implement of war or the chase. After Breuil. Large symmetrical flakes chipped over the entire surface. 1, 2. Late Aurignacian types from *Font Robert.* 3, 4, 5. Points from the Proto-Solutrean layer of the *Grotte du Trilobite.*

animals in stone, for shallow forms of bas-relief on the walls of the caves, and for other animal outlines. The most evolved animal figures of this period arouse the thought of Magdalenian art in its beginnings.

As this industrial evolution widens it is apparent that we witness not the local evolution of a single people but rather the influence and collaboration of numerous colonies reacting more or less one upon the other and spreading their inventions and discoveries. These people were essentially nomadic and no doubt carried the latest types of implements from point to point or bartered them in trade. Thus there is not only a definite succession in such places as Dordogne, but in more remote regions the form of the implements may take on some important differences.[33] There are also other localities where the industry seems for a while to be suspended; thus in the Cantabrian Mountains of Spain we find only the early and the late Aurignacian.

Stations similar in culture to those of Dordogne extend northward into Germany and Belgium and eastward into Austria and Poland. Thus the characteristic flint spear heads, known as the *pointe à soie* and *pointe à cran* extend from Laussel along the Vézère to Willendorf, in Austria; and the female figures of Baoussé-Roussé (Grimaldi) and of Willendorf represent the same stage of evolution as the large stone bas-relief of Laussel. Again, we observe some relations between the Aurignacian cultures of Austria and of the Italian peninsula, such as the *pointe à cran*, derived from the *gravette* and found both in various stations of northern Italy and at Willendorf. In western Russia the Aurignacian station of Mezine, Chernigov, shows clearly the types of the superior Aurignacian in the graving of bone and ivory, in the small bâtons recalling those of Spy, in Belgium, and of Brassempouy, in southwestern France, in the large bone piercers perforated at the head, suggesting the primitive needles from the shelter of Blanchard, and in the degenerate statuettes resembling the type of Brassempouy.

Distribution of the Aurignacian Industry

When the general geographic distribution of the Aurignacian (Fig. 153) is compared with that of the Mousterian (Fig. 125) it is surprising to find how many of the stations are identical; it would appear as if the Crô-Magnons had driven the Neanderthals from their principal stations over all of western Europe for the pursuit of their own industries and of the chase. We have already spoken of the invasion of the Mousterian stations along the Riviera, in the Pyrenees, in the Cantabrian Alps, and along the Dordogne and the Somme; this occupation also extends along the Meuse, the Rhine, and the Danube; but, whereas there are only six stations in all Germany of unquestioned Mousterian age, there are more than double that number in

Aurignacian times. The Crô-Magnons entered the grottos of Sirgenstein and Räuberhöhle, near the headwaters of the Danube; northwest of Sirgenstein they established the open 'loess' station of Achenheim, west of Strasburg; in the lower layers of

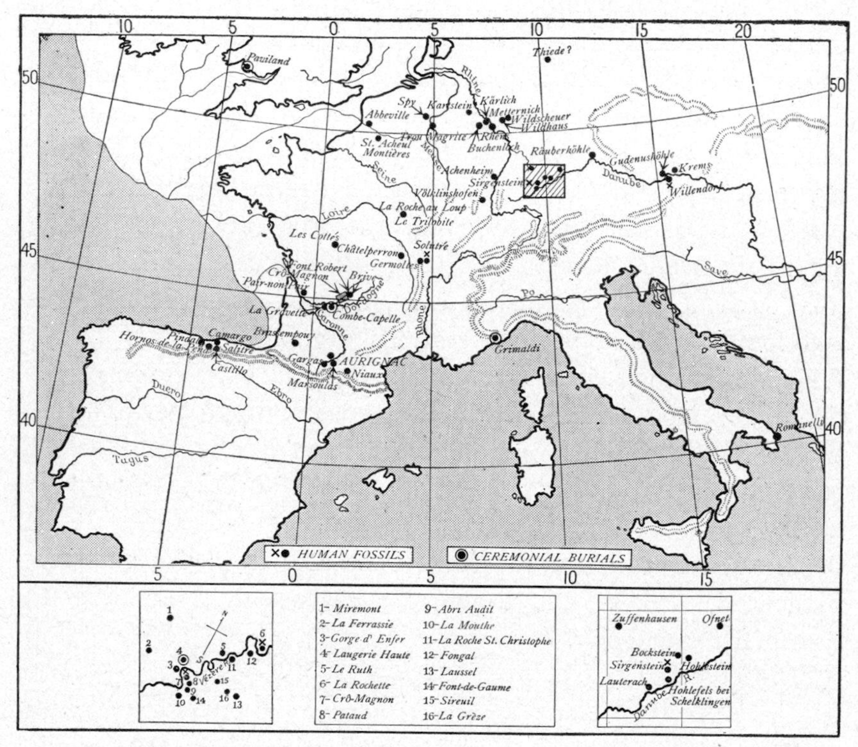

Fig. 153. Geographic distribution of the principal Aurignacian industrial stations in western Europe.

the 'newer loess' was also the station of Völklinshofen, south of Achenheim; along the middle Rhine were the 'loess' stations of Rhens and Metternich, and to the far north, close to the borders of the Scandinavian glacier, was the somewhat doubtful Aurignacian station of Thiede. The Crô-Magnon men entered the Sirgenstein grotto and scattered the implements of their culture above the 'lower rodent layer,' composed of the Obi lemming, and also left remains of the woolly rhinoceros, the woolly mammoth, the stag, and the reindeer on the floor of the cavern. The Upper Aurignacian also extends down the Danube as far as Willendorf, and possibly to Brünn, Moravia, which last, however, may be of Solutrean age. Altogether be-

FIG. 154. Outlook over the Bay of Biscay from the entrance of the cavern of Pindal, in the province of Asturias, northern Spain. Photograph by N. C. Nelson.

tween seventeen and twenty Aurignacian stations have been discovered in the region north of the Danube and along the Rhine.

AURIGNACIAN ART*

The strongest proof of the unity of heredity as displayed in the dominant Crô-Magnon race in Europe from early Aurignacian until the close of Magdalenian times is the unity of their

* Breuil,[34] Schmidt.[35]

art impulse. This indicates a unity of mind and of spirit. It is something which could not pass to them from another race, like an industrial invention, but was inborn and creative. These people were the Palæolithic Greeks; artistic observation and representation and a true sense of proportion and of beauty were instinct with them from the beginning. Their stone and bone industry may show vicissitudes and the influence of invasion and of trade and the bringing in of new inventions, but their art shows a continuous evolution and development from first to

FIG. 155. Outline of a mammoth painted in red ochre in the cavern of Pindal, and attributed by Breuil to the Aurignacian. Only two limbs are represented. After Breuil.

last, animated by a single motive, namely, the appreciation of the beauty of form and the realistic representation of it.

This art, as first discovered by Lartet and further made known through the brilliant studies of Piette and Breuil, is industrial (*l'art mobilier*), consisting of the decoration of small personal belongings, ornaments, and implements of stone, bone, and ivory. According to the later researches of Sautuola, Rivière, Cartailhac, Capitan, and Breuil it is also mural or parietal (*l'art pariétal*), consisting of drawings, engravings, paintings, and bas-reliefs on the walls of caverns and grottos. It remained for Breuil especially to demonstrate that the mobile and the parietal art are identical, the work of the same artistic race, developing along closely similar lines, step by step. Thus the art becomes a new means not only of interpreting the psychology of the race but of establishing the prehistoric chronology.

Dating of the Art

One of the first questions which rises in our mind is this—how is this art dated; how can these steps be positively determined?

The age of these engraved or painted designs on the walls of the caverns is determined in a number of ways described by Breuil.[36] The simplest method is where the wall designs of one period are covered by the archæological layers of succeeding periods. This has been observed in four cases, as at Pair-non-Pair, Gironde, where primitive engravings of horses, caprids, and bovids are buried under flints characteristic of the late Aurignacian mingled with bones of the mammoth, rhinoceros, lion, hyæna, bison, and reindeer. Again, the deeply engraved bison on the wall of the grotto of La Grèze, Dordogne, is found beneath a talus of Solutrean flints associated with remains of the bison, reindeer, and rhinoceros. In the Grotte de la Mairie, Dordogne, are found several finely engraved middle Magdalenian figures of animals buried beneath late Magdalenian implements associated with the reindeer fauna.

Very important, indeed, is the age of the sculpture and bas-reliefs found in Laussel. The human sculptures are determined to be of late Aurignacian age, because they are buried in an early Solutrean talus. The splendid wall sculptures of the series of horses in the Cap-Blanc shelter, near the Laussel shelter, are shown to be of middle Magdalenian age, because of the upper Magdalenian strata which covered and partly concealed them.

In other instances we can date a drawing in a cavern by the period at which the opening was closed; for example, the cave of La Mouthe, Dordogne, was closed in by a Magdalenian layer of flints which touched the roof and firmly sealed up the entrance until recent times. Again, at Gargas, Hautes-Pyrénées, we know that the last occupation by the Crô-Magnons was near the end of Aurignacian times, as indicated by a hearth filled

Fig. 156. Primitive painted outlines of animals from the cavern walls of *Font-de-Gaume*, Dordogne, attributed by Breuil to the early Aurignacian. The outlines represent the horse, ibex, cave-bear, wild cattle, and reindeer. After Breuil.

with late Aurignacian flints and with the remains of the bear, hyæna, horse, and reindeer; the opening of the grotto was buried beneath these foyers, which obstructed the entrance until the cave was rediscovered at a comparatively recent date. Also at Marsoulas, Haute-Garonne, there are two hearths, one late Aurignacian, the other late Magdalenian; the grotto was then closed until recent times. The grotto of Niaux, on the Ariège, which contains fine examples of drawings of middle Magdalenian times at a distance of 1,800 feet from the entrance, was protected for a long period by a lake 6 feet deep and several hundred feet long. At Altamira, near Santander, the superb frescoed ceiling was buried, long before Neolithic times, by the

Fig. 157. The woolly rhinoceros, painted in red ochre with shading and partial representation of the hair, in the cavern of *Font-de-Gaume*, Dordogne. Attributed by Breuil to the late Aurignacian. Possibly Magdalenian. After Breuil.

closing up of the entrance, which was rediscovered only about thirty years ago.

A third method of dating the art is still more significant; it is through a similarity in the engravings on bone, found in the old hearths associated with flints, to the mural decorations which are found upon the walls. Thus, at Altamira, engravings on bone associated with Solutrean and Magdalenian flints enabled Alcalde del Rio and Breuil to date the engravings on the limestone walls. Hence, in grottos which have never been closed up and which have been frequented at different times from the Palæolithic to the present epoch one observes that the mural designs in the caverns are invariably accompanied by Upper Palæolithic implements with a similar style of decoration; and this is the case at Font-de-Gaume, Combarelles, Portel, Mas d'Azil, Castillo, Pasiega, and Hornos de la Peña. The bone engravings of the female red deer found at Altamira are identical in their artistic period with those found on the walls of the same grotto. The excavations at Castillo, where numerous shoulder-blades of the deer were found engraved in the same style as those of Altamira, prove that all these engravings and drawings are to be referred to ancient Magdalenian rather than to upper Solutrean times. The engravings upon the walls in the grotto of Hornos de la Peña, of Aurignacian times, are dated through the discovery at the base of the layer of Aurignacian flints of an engraved equine figure similar to the engravings at Altamira.

A fourth method applies to those not infrequent cases when two or three designs are superposed one upon the other, from which it necessarily follows that the underlying designs must antedate those above.

Through the application of these four methods Breuil has succeeded in dating all the steps in the advance of art from Aurignacian into Magdalenian times.

Engraving, Painting, and Sculpture

In the archaic drawings of the caverns of Pair-non-Pair, La Grèze, and La Mouthe most of the animal figures are somewhat heavily and deeply engraved; the proportions are not true; the head is usually too small, with a large, short body which is often lightly modelled, resting on thin extremities. Quadrupeds are frequently represented with but two legs, as in the case of the mammoth. That the powers of observation were only gradually trained is shown by the fact that details which in later drawings are well observed are here overlooked; the profile drawings of animals, with one fore leg and one hind leg represented, are quite like those of children.

Progress toward a true representation of animal form in drawing begins very early; even in middle Aurignacian times primitive drawing and engraving commences to replace sculpture. Both the flint 'burins' and the engravings on the walls of the grottos show that the beginnings of drawing may be traced back to early Aurignacian times. While the Palæolithic artists early in the Aurignacian had obtained a certain facility in plastic work, their drawings, which are solely contours—somewhat imperfect and deeply engraved lines—show a gradual development. The degree of skill attained in late Aurignacian times we know from the engraving of a horse on a stone fragment from Gargas, and from a sketch of the hinder quarter of a horse found in the cave of Hornos de la Peña, which is engraved on the frontal bone of one of the wild horses; the latter is strikingly similar to one of the engravings found at the entrance to the same grotto. The engravings on a slab of slate of the heads of two woolly rhinoceroses[37] (Fig. 161) probably belong to the late Aurignacian. Similar attempts are found in the Abri Lacoste. Ornamentation develops in the middle Aurignacian, but retains a simple geometric character.

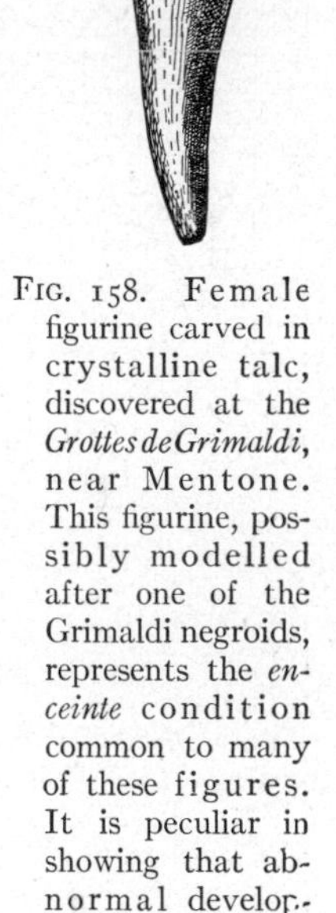

Fig. 158. Female figurine carved in crystalline talc, discovered at the *Grottes de Grimaldi*, near Mentone. This figurine, possibly modelled after one of the Grimaldi negroids, represents the *enceinte* condition common to many of these figures. It is peculiar in showing that abnormal development behind the hips known as steatopygy. After Reinach.

The parietal art on the walls of the caverns, mostly deep engravings, consists of stiff profiles in single lines and in red or black coloring. The animals represented are the ibex, the horse, the bison, and rarely the mammoth. The caves where these are found are Pair-non-Pair, La Grèze, La Mouthe, Bernifal, Font-de-Gaume, Altamira, and Marsoulas. Crucibles for grinding the color are found in the grotto of Marsoulas, the color being made by grinding up the red and yellow oxides of iron.

The development of art during the whole Aurignacian is continuous and is undoubtedly the work of one race; Breuil considers it the work certainly either of the tall Crô-Magnons or of the small Grimaldis; there is, however, no evidence of the survival of the Grimaldi race, and we may safely attribute this entire art development to the Crô-Magnons.

The creative spirit manifested itself along many different lines. In the fashioning of bone in early Aurignacian times there begins a new industry capable of great possibilities; out of combinations of lines there develop geometric figures; in animal figures there is an attempt at simple symmetric relations, but a full, free composition is not attained. With further experience in working with bone and ivory, we find in the middle Aurignacian the first plastic representations of the human figure in the round.

FIG. 159. Statuette in limestone from the grotto of Willendorf, Lower Austria, attributed to the late Aurignacian. This female figurine, possibly an idol and generally known as the 'Venus of Willendorf,' is about four and one-half inches in height. After Szombathi.

The Crô-Magnon artist undertook this plastic work, choosing chiefly for his subject the female figure. These small plastic models were probably designed as idols; the figures are often misshapen; in the face the eyes frequently are not indicated at all; in some cases the ear is indicated; they recall the style of the modern cubists. More care is given to the sculpture of the form of the body than of the face. The ivory statue known as the Venus of Brassempouy lies at the base of the middle Aurignacian; of the same epoch are the female statuettes of Sireuil, and the torso from Pair-non-Pair, whereas the soapstone figurine of Mentone and the ivory statuettes of Trou Magrite, Belgium, belong to the late Aurignacian. The spread of these idols, which are altogether characteristic of the earlier period of the Upper Palæolithic, is traced eastward to Willendorf, Austria, and to Brünn, Moravia.

Breuil's great contention is a certain similarity to north African art, which would seem to agree with his theory that the Crô-Magnon people followed the southern shores of the Mediterranean, bringing with them the Aurignacian industry and the glyptic art of the female statuettes similar to those of baked clay which are found along the valley of the Nile. These figurines have in common the great development of all the parts connected with maternity, and in some cases a coiffure or headdress very much like that found in the most primitive Egyptian work. The extreme corpulence of all the figurines has been compared with the 'steatopygy,' or development of what

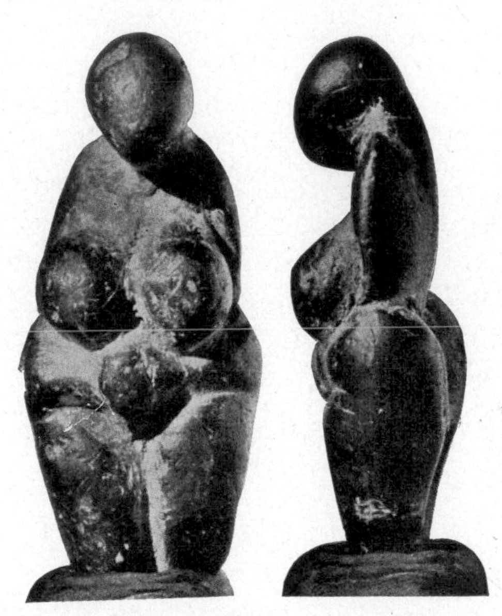

FIG. 160. Female figurine in soapstone, discovered at the *Grottes de Grimaldi*, near Mentone, and attributed to the late Aurignacian. After Obermaier. This seems to be a prototype of modern cubist art.

are politely known as the 'posterior curves,' of the female in many African races. But only one of these Aurignacian figurines is truly 'steatopygous'; the others are simply corpulent, a condition due to eating large quantities of fat and marrow, and probably to a very sedentary life. It is noteworthy that none of the male figures in drawing and sculpture is corpulent. While the art of the statuettes appears to come to a close in late Aurignacian times, it may extend into the Solutrean at Brünn, Moravia, and at Trou Magrite, Belgium. With due regard for analogies, it would rather appear probable that this archaic sculpture was autochthonous.

The art of engraving and drawing was almost certainly autochthonous, because we trace it from its most rudimentary beginnings. This northern art developed from the beginning of Upper Palæolithic times over the whole of southwestern France and in the northwest of Spain, being contemporaneous with the descent of the alpine fauna from the Pyrenees and the Alps and

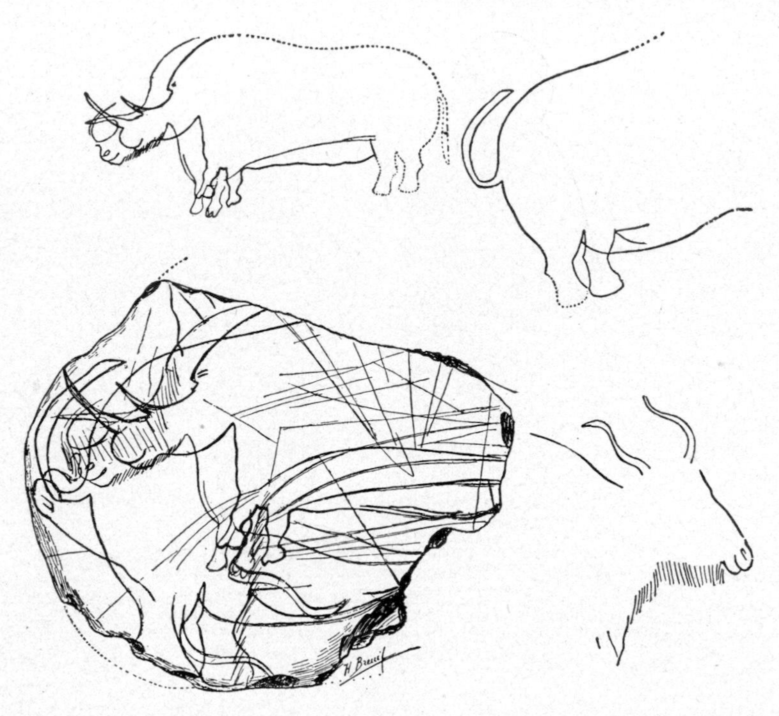

FIG. 161. Superposed engravings of various mammals on a slab of slate found in the *Grotte du Trilobite*, Yonne, France. In detail are seen the profiles of two woolly rhinoceroses superposed on the rump of a mammoth with tail upturned. After Breuil.

the presence all over western Europe of the tundra fauna. It was, by preference, an animal art, begun by the Aurignacians but largely suspended in Solutrean times.

Painting[38] also had its birth in the Aurignacian, in the simple contours of the hand pressed against a wall surface or outlined with color, accompanied by primitive attempts at linear drawing in color and painted groupings; for example, the crude outlines of the bison in the grotto of Castillo are of Aurignacian age, also the black linear designs of the deer and of the ibex in the cavern of Font-de-Gaume, Dordogne, the striking red linear design of the mammoth in the grotto of Pindal, in northern Spain, representing the animal as with two limbs, and the red outlines of wild

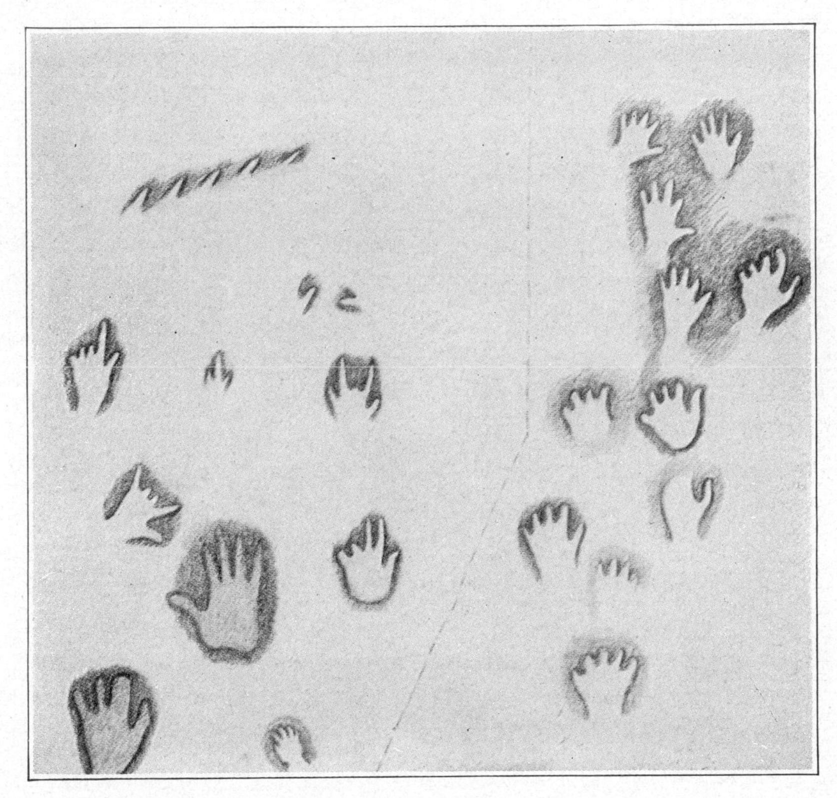

FIG. 162. Silhouettes of complete and of partly mutilated hands from the walls of the grotto of Gargas in the Pyrenees. After Breuil.

cattle in Castillo. Breuil also attributes to Aurignacian times the spirited figure of the woolly rhinoceros in red ochre in the cave of Font-de-Gaume, as well as the outline of the stag in red color.

We are impressed throughout with three qualities in this Aurignacian design: first, the very close observation of the animal form; second, the attempt at realistic effect produced with very few lines; third, the element of motion or movement in these animals. For example, the two heads of the woolly rhinoceros in the slab engravings of the Trilobite grotto (Fig. 161) are remarkably correct in proportion; there is an attempt with fine lines to indicate the wool hanging along the lower surface of the head; behind these two figures is the rump of an elephant

FIG. 163. The long, overhanging cliff of Laussel on the Beune is a typical rock shelter, first sought in Acheulean times, and also visited during the Mousterian, Aurignacian, and Solutrean stages. Photograph by N. C. Nelson.

with the tail upturned, an adaptation of the artist to the form of the slate fragment; the outlines of the feet both of the rhinoceros and the mammoth are remarkably accurate representations of these pachyderms.

In the more advanced development of draftsmanship in late Aurignacian times the engravings of these animals not merely approach the truth, but characteristic features are strikingly represented; and with a few sure lines the proportions of the body as a whole are better preserved, while the complicated curves of the hoofs and of the head show very close observation.

In the grotto of La Grèze overhanging the Beune, a small tributary of the Vézère, was found an archaic Aurignacian outline of the bison deeply incised on the limestone walls. The grotto of Gargas,* Hautes-Pyrénées,[39] is one of the most famous stations; it was entered in closing Mousterian times and was occupied at intervals during the Aurignacian stage. Beneath the Mousterian layer is a deep deposit of entire skeletons of the cave-bear without any traces of human industry. These layers lie beyond the grotto in the vast foyer which opens above into

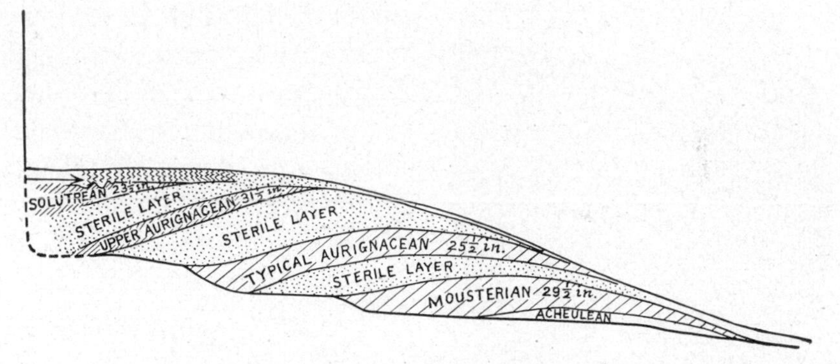

FIG. 164. Section of the rock shelter of Laussel, showing the superposed industrial layers from Acheulean to Solutrean times. After Lalanne.

a great chimney, so that this is one of the true cavern habitations. The drawings along the walls of the cave include a large number of figures in a very unequal style, which belong chiefly to middle and upper Aurignacian times. Among these are two figures of birds, several mammals, a few primitive drawings of wild cattle, the bison, the ibex, and numerous representations of the horse. A long serpentine band of color meanders among some of these drawings. Most interesting are the silhouettes of the hand in black and red produced by pressing the hand against the limestone wall and covering the surrounding surface with color. It would appear that the fingers were mutilated or cut off at the middle joint, because one, two, three, and four of the fingers are wanting, but the thumb is never mutilated. This mutilation

* The writer had the privilege of visiting all these caverns in the company either of Professor Emile Cartailhac, or of the Abbé Breuil.

of the hand may be compared with similar practices prevailing among some Australian tribes.

In the cavern of Marsoulas, on the headwaters of the Garonne, the conditions are altogether different; the parietal art here represents two cultural stages, the late Aurignacian and the late Magdalenian. There is a small entrance grotto with two hearths, corresponding to these two industries. The entrance to the cave is well up on the side of the hill, and the drawings which belong with the upper Aurignacian culture are somewhat damaged. Again, we find designs extending along the wall below the drawings. There are numerous outlines of the bison in black, the entire side of the body being covered with splashes of red.

Fig. 165. Bas-relief of a woman with a drinking horn, sculptured on the face of a boulder within the shelter of Laussel, and attributed to the late Aurignacian. After Lalanne. About one-eighth actual size.

The great abri of Laussel, on the Beune, was first visited by the Neanderthals, for there are two Mousterian layers and above them two Aurignacian layers, the lower belonging to the middle Aurignacian industry and the upper to the closing Aurignacian period. This long, overhanging cliff of Laussel is a typical shelter, first sought in Acheulean times, revisited in Mousterian times, then again in middle or late Aurignacian, in Solutrean, and finally in Magdalenian times. As these successive layers rise they approach the shelter of the cliff, so that the Magdalenian flint workers were directly beneath the overhanging rock shelter, which opened outward toward the sun.

In the upper Aurignacian layer Lalanne discovered two bas-reliefs representing the figures of a man and of a woman. The bas-relief of the woman represents a nude figure holding the horn of a bison in the right hand; this is cut from a block of limestone with a relief of about two centimetres, and it measures forty-six centimetres in height; with the exception of the head, the entire body is polished, and at certain points there remain traces of red coloring. A little farther on the artist had modelled the figure of a man in three-quarter view in the attitude of casting a spear or of an archer drawing the bow; the top of the head and the extremities of the limbs have been broken away; the figure measures forty centimetres in height. These bas-reliefs of Laussel are regarded as sincere representations, for the artist has presented as accurately as possible the contemporary human figure; both the man and the woman are represented in motion. On the technique employed in this primordial sculpture, Doctor Lalanne observes that we find at Laussel a series of tools perfectly adapted to attain this result, many of which would have been inexplicable unless found to occur in connection with the sculpture itself. It is curious to note how many analogies there are between the flint utensils of the primitive sculptor and those of the sculptors of our own day. First, we find tools designed to remove the rock, there are points, pickaxes, chopping tools for shaping the rock, saws, and coarse stone planers; all of these are perfectly adapted to the hand, from which we may conclude that our artist was right-handed. There is a great number of graving-tools, or burins, all forms being represented

Fig. 166. Bas-relief of a spear thrower or hunter, sculptured on the face of a boulder within the shelter of Laussel. After Lalanne. About one-sixth actual size.

—plain, double, fine, coarse, and combinations of the burin and grattoir. Some of the burins show the sharp-angled point centred at the extremity of a blade; these are the ordinary types; but in many the blade ends with a terminal retouch, which may be transverse, oblique, ccncave, or convex with the point to one side. The grattoirs, or planers, are equally numerous, with examples of all the known forms. Many of these are formed at the end of a blade; a few are circular, and others are at the opposite end of a pointed blade; the latter are particularly fine and are retouched around the entire edge. But the artist did not merely carve his subjects; he also coated them with a paint made of ochre and manganese; he crushed his coloring matter on a palette of schist, and we have found one of these unbroken and still bearing the red and ochre colors. This palette is 10½ inches long and 6 inches wide; it is oblong in form.

Distribution of the Solutrean Industry

The period of the Solutrean industry is one of the most difficult to interpret in the whole prehistory of western Europe. The remains of this industry in several localities lie directly between those of the Aurignacian and the Magdalenian; in others, as at Solutré, they directly follow the Aurignacian. There is no doubt that this represents a very long and a very important epoch in Upper Palæolithic development. From the cultural standpoint it represents a climax in the flint industry, but a period of suspension or of arrested development in art.

A glance at the maps of the Mousterian (Fig. 125), the Aurignacian (Fig. 153), and the Solutrean (Fig. 167) culture stations shows that the geographic distribution of the Solutrean is entirely unique; whereas the Aurignacian culture may be said to girdle the Mediterranean, both on its southern and northern coasts, the Solutrean culture is absent in this entire region. The interpretation of this strange phenomenon offered by Breuil, that the Solutrean culture entered Europe directly from the east and not from the south, may be connected with the theory that toward the end of Aurignacian times a new race from the central east was working westward through Hungary and along the Danube—a race of inferior mental type, but extremely expert in fashioning the flint spears and lances with what is known as the Solutrean 'retouch.' This may be the race of Brünn,

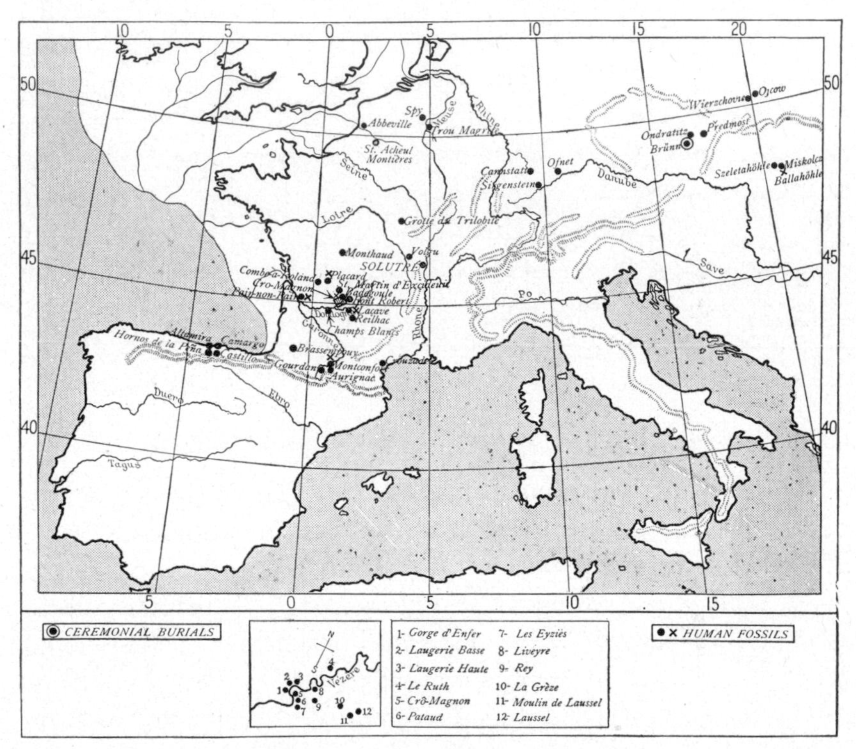

FIG. 167. Geographic distribution of the principal Solutrean industrial stations in western Europe.

Brüx, and Předmost, the remains of which are found in two localities associated with these highly perfected flint spear heads. Either by the invasion of this race or, more probably, by the invasion of the highly perfected spear-head industry itself, the type station of Solutré, on the Saône, was established and the region of Dordogne reached, where this industry progressed at twelve different stations.

There is no doubt whatever that the new and entirely distinct Brünn race penetrated the Danubian region at this time, but there is no evidence from skeletal remains that it reached France. It is quite possible that some of the flint workers adept in the Solutrean 'retouch' migrated into the far western stations of Dordogne, bringing with them their beautiful technique, but without leaving traces of their skeletal remains through ceremonial burial. This unsettled problem affords one of the many reasons why the anatomy of all the Upper Palæolithic men of western Europe should be most carefully studied and compared.

Another mystery of Solutrean times is the arrest of the artistic impulse which had animated the Crô-Magnons throughout the entire Aurignacian. Evidences of artistic work in Solutrean times are very rare, and some drawings which have been attributed to the Solutrean, as at Altamira, have now been referred to the Magdalenian. Is it possible that the Crô-Magnon race for a time suspended its artistic endeavor only to renew it under the different conditions of environment of Magdalenian times? Unfortunately, the Solutrean burials afford very little evidence on this point. One interpretation which may be offered is that the Solutrean was evidently a period of open-air life, and that the new implements of the chase of Solutrean type absorbed the industrial energies of these people, for the weapons were fashioned in enormous numbers. Consistent with this theory of climatic influence is the fact that the return of the severe climate of Magdalenian times, which crowded the men again into the shelters and grottos, was accompanied by a renewal of the artistic development continuing from the point where it had been interrupted in closing Aurignacian times. That Aurignacian and Magdalenian art is the work of one race there can be no question whatever; that this race was the Crô-Magnon is now absolutely demonstrated.

The climate of Solutrean times is generally believed to have been cold and dry. In the region of Dordogne throughout this period the reindeer was still far more numerous than any other animal; so we may safely conclude that this was the principal object of the chase and of food; in fact, it would appear that the reindeer were resident forms in the valley of the Vézère, hunted and consumed throughout the year.[40] Here we also occasionally find the northern steppe or Obi lemming, an animal which at the same time extends along the borders of the Volga River toward southern Russia. It would appear that in Solutrean times in southwestern France there prevailed a dry, cold continental subarctic climate like that of the Caspian, Volga, and Ural steppes of the present day. With the mammoth and the reindeer occur a great variety of northern European forest forms—the true fox, the hare, the stag, the brown bear, the wolf, the bison, and the urus. Most interesting is the identification of the jackal belonging to the ancient species *C. neschersensis*. In the type industrial locality of Solutré the reindeer is very abundant in the fire-hearths associated with the lower Solutrean industry, but less abundant in the upper levels; an antelope, perhaps the saiga antelope, is said to be found among the crude engravings on bone.

Solutrean Races

There were certainly two distinct races of men in Europe during Solutrean times, to the east the race of Brünn and to the west the race of Crô-Magnon. Remains attributed to the Crô-Magnons have been found in the Departments of Charente, Gironde, Lot, Haute-Garonne, Tarn, and Dordogne. But most of these remains are very fragmentary and cannot readily be determined racially. The fragments of ten skulls and a few other bones found in the Grotte du Placard, Charente, are attributed to late Solutrean and to early Magdalenian times and constitute one of the most exceptional discoveries which have thus far been made in France; the interments probably date from the early Magdalenian (p. 380), but are probably of a race surviving from the Solutrean. The section of the cave deposit is from 23 to 26 feet in thickness and is highly instructive; it shows eight cultural layers, separated by layers of débris and succeeding each other in the following order:

8. Neolithic layer.

7–4. Magdalenian layers; in the lowest layer is the ceremonial burial of four skulls.

3. Solutrean layer with shouldered points (*pointes à cran*) and a few laurel-leaf points (*pointes de laurier*).

2. Solutrean layer with laurel-leaf points but no shouldered points; knives, grattoirs, scrapers, borers, in great numbers, together with javelin points and awls in bone and ornamented with notches, and fragments of red chalk and black lead found embedded with the Solutrean points.

1. Mousterian layer.

Race of Brünn, Brüx, Předmost, and (?) Galley Hill

In 1871 a skullcap, now in the Royal Museum of Vienna, was discovered in the course of coal mining at Brüx, Bohemia. In 1891[41] a skeleton, apparently of the same race, was discovered at Brünn, Moravia, deeply embedded in loess along with bones of the woolly mammoth and other great Pleistocene mammals. In 1892 it was described by Makowsky,[42] who a few years before had excavated from the loess sand in the neighborhood of Brünn the fragmentary skull now known as Brünn II. Both these skulls are of a somewhat low racial type, and for a long time they were regarded as transition forms between the Neanderthals and *Homo sapiens*, but in 1906 Schwalbe[43] showed the affinity between the skulls of Brüx and Brünn and at the same time their entire distinctness from the Neanderthal skull and their approach to lower forms of *Homo sapiens*. The chief distinction of these skulls is their extreme elongation or dolichocephaly, the ratio of width to length being 69 per cent in the Brüx skull, and 68.2 per cent in the Brünn skull. The latter ranks lower in racial type than the Australian negroids. The chief distinction from the Neanderthal skull is in the index of the height of skull (51.22 per cent) and in the absence of the prominent ridges extending across the eyebrow region above the nose;* the forehead, in brief, is more modern, the frontal

* Despite Schwalbe's statement, the supraorbital ridges in this skull appear to form a complete bridge. Doctor Hrdlička regards the related Předmost skull as distinctly showing Neanderthaloid affinity.

angle being 74.7–75 per cent. The brain capacity in this race is estimated, according to Makowsky,[44] at 1,350 c.cm. Both the Brüx and Brünn skulls are *harmonic;* they do not present

FIG. 168. The type skull known as Brünn I—supposed male—discovered at Brünn, Moravia, in 1891. It was found deeply imbedded in loess along with bones of the woolly mammoth, woolly rhinoceros, giant deer, reindeer, and other Pleistocene mammals, and is believed to be of Solutrean age. After Makowsky. One-third life size.

the very broad, high cheek-bones characteristic of the Crô-Magnon race, the face being of a narrow, modern type, but not very long. There is evidence that the neck and shoulders were powerful and muscular; the prominence of the chin is pronounced; the dentition is macrodont, that is, the last lower molar is of exceptionally large size; there was no prognathism or protrusion of the jaws. The second Brünn skull (Brünn II) may represent a female type of the Brünn race, the cephalic index being estimated at 72 per cent.

DISCOVERIES CHIEFLY OF THE CRÔ-MAGNON AND BRÜNN RACES*

REFERRED TO SOLUTREAN TIMES

Date of Discovery	Locality	Number of Individuals	Culture Stage
	CRÔ-MAGNON RACE (?)		
	Grotte du Placard, Charente, France.	Fragments of ten skulls and a few other bones.	Late Solutrean and early Magdalenian.
	Pair-non-Pair, Gironde, France.	Skull fragments.	Solutrean.
	Lacave, Lot, France.	" "	"
	Montconfort, Haute-Garonne, France.	" "	"
	Roset, Tarn, France.	" "	Late Solutrean.
	Badegoule, Dordogne, France.	Bones.	Solutrean.
	BRÜNN-BRÜX-PŘEDMOST RACE		
1880.	Předmost, Moravia, Austria.	Portions of twenty skeletons.	Solutrean.
1891.	Brünn, Moravia, Austria.	Male skeleton (Brünn I). (?) Female skeleton (Brünn II).	"
	Ballahöhle, Miskolcz, Hungary.	Skeleton of infant.	(?) "
	(?) Galley Hill.	One skeleton.	Unknown.

* Obermaier,[45] R. Martin.[46]

There is a possibility[47] that the Brünn race was ancestral to several later dolichocephalic groups which are found in the region of the Danube and of middle and southern Germany. Schliz characterizes the Brünn skull as distinguished by the retreating forehead, by massive eminences above the orbits separated by a cleft in the median line, by broad, low orbits, and prominent chin. These characters are met with again in one of the dolichocephalic skulls found in the interment at Ofnet, at the very close of Upper Palæolithic times. It would thus appear that the Brünn race is distinct from the Crô-Magnon race, that it represents a long-headed type which became established along the Danube as early as Solutrean times, and that it may possibly be connected with the introduction of some of the peculiar features of the Solutrean culture.

One of the skeletons of Brünn, found at a depth of 12 feet below the surface of the 'loess,' was lavishly adorned with tooth-shells, perforated stone discs, and bone ornaments made from the ribs of the rhinoceros or mammoth and from the teeth of the mammoth; associated with these was an ivory idol, apparently of a male figure, of which only the head, the torso, and the left arm remain. The skeleton and many of the objects found with the sepulture were partly tinted in red. An ivory figurine belongs to the Eburnéen stage of Piette and appears to indicate that the burial was of Aurignacian rather than of Solutrean age.

The Předmost 'mammoth hunters' also probably belonged to this race. They are represented by the remains of six individuals excavated since 1880 at Předmost, Moravia, by Wankel, Kříž, and Maška. The bones were found in a very much shattered condition. Maška has since discovered a collective burial of fourteen human skeletons, with remains of six others; the bodies were covered with stones, but no flints or objects of art were buried with them. The dimensions of the limbs indicate a race of large stature. The skeletons were deeply buried in 'loess,' and above and below the rich archæological layer were abundant débris of the mammoth, representing between eight and nine hundred specimens. Along with the numerous flints, including laurel-leaf spear heads of middle Solutrean type, were found other objects and even primitive works of art in bone and ivory. There is no question that the human remains belong to the middle Solutrean stage.[48]

With this race is also associated by many authors (Schwalbe, Schliz, Klaatsch, Keith) the Galley Hill skull, which was found in 1888, buried at a depth of 8 feet in the 'high terrace' gravels

90 feet above the Thames.[49] Sollas thinks it highly probable that the remains were in a natural position and of the same age as the high-level gravels and the Palæolithic flints and remains of extinct animals which they contained, but Evans and Dawkins regard the Galley Hill man as belonging to a long-headed Neolithic race interred in a Palæolithic stratum. The gravels of the 'high terrace' in which the Galley Hill skull was buried are by no means of the geologic antiquity of 200,000 years assigned to them by Keith;[50] they are probably of Fourth Glacial or of Postglacial age, and lie within the estimates of Postglacial time, namely, from 20,000 to 40,000 years.

The antiquity of the Galley Hill cranial type has been maintained with ability by Keith. The skull is extremely long or hyperdolichocephalic, the cephalic index being estimated by Keith at 69 per cent;[51] the brain capacity is estimated at between 1,350 c.cm. and 1,400 c.cm.; the cheek-bones are not preserved, so that no judgment can be formed as to this most distinctive character of the Crô-Magnon race. With this Galley Hill race Keith also compares the Combe-Capelle, or Aurignacian man of Klaatsch,[52] although he mistakenly considers the Combe-Capelle man of much less geologic antiquity. He continues: "Thus, while the writer is inclined to agree in provisionally assigning the Combe-Capelle man to the Galley Hill race, he believes that further discoveries will show that the Combe-Capelle man belongs to a branch marked with certain negroid features."

Solutrean Flint Industry

The 'Solutrean retouch' marks one of the most notable advances in the technique of flint working; it is altogether distinct from the 'Aurignacian retouch,' which is an heritage from the Mousterian.[53] The flint is chipped off by *pressure* in *fine, thin flakes* from the entire surface of the implement, to which in its perfected form the craftsman can give a thin, sharp edge and perfect symmetry. This is a great advance on the abrupt Aurignacian retouch, in which the flint is chipped back at a rather blunt angle to make a sharp edge. According to de Mortillet,

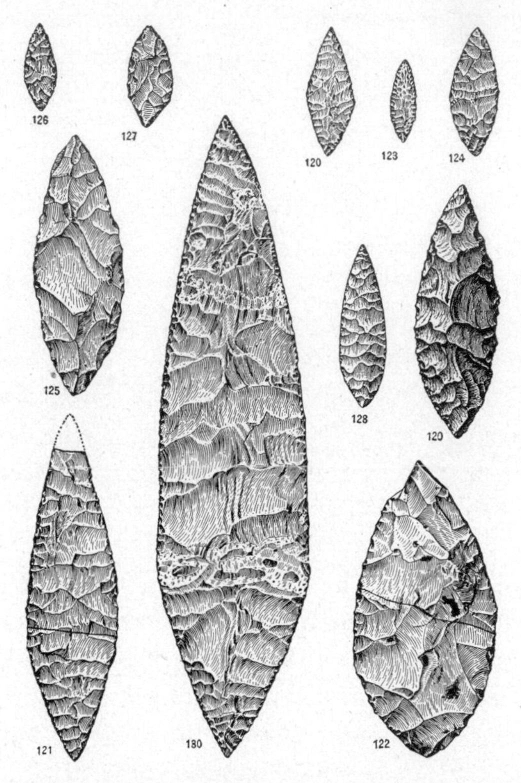

Fig. 169. Typical Solutrean implements of war and chase. After de Mortillet. *Pointes en feuille de laurier*, or laurel-leaf points, artistically retouched on both surfaces, at both ends, and on both borders; regarded by de Mortillet rather as blades of poniards than as javelin heads. 120. Lozenge-shaped form from the type station of Solutré, Saône-et-Loire. 121. Elongate form found at Solutré. 122. The largest *pointe* discovered at Solutré. 123. One of the smallest points found at Solutré. 124. Solutrean point from Laugerie Haute, Dordogne. 127. Point from Gargas, Vaucluse. 128. Point of exceptionally fine workmanship. 130. One of eleven very large Solutrean laurel-leaf points found in a *cache* at Volgu; probably a votive offering, as the flints are too slender to be of any use and one at least shows traces of coloring. All the flints are shown one-quarter actual size, except 129, which is one-half actual size.

the Solutrean method of pressure made possible the execution of much more delicate work.

The question at once arises, did this industrial advance take place in France or was it an invention brought from the east? On this point Breuil observes[54] that in the highest Aurignacian levels in Belgium, in Dordogne, and at Solutré the Solutrean technique becomes faintly apparent either in the 'stem' points (*pointes à soie*) of Font Robert, La Ferrassie, and Spy or in the double-edged points tending toward the laurel-leaf type of the Solutrean, but that all the other implements remain purely Aurignacian.

Relations and Subdivisions of Solutrean Culture

Lower (Early) Magdalenian.
Prototypes of bone harpoons.
Beginnings of animal sculpture.
Absence of any trace of the laurel-leaf spear heads of Solutrean times.

Upper (Late) Solutrean.
Typical shouldered points (*pointes à cran*)—elongate flakes worked on one or both sides and notched. Small laurel-leaf spear heads.
Bone javelin points, awls, and needles, very finely worked. Placard. Lacave.

Middle (High) Solutrean.
Large 'laurel-leaf' spear heads worked on both sides. Climax of Solutrean flint industry. Placard.

Lower (Proto-) Solutrean.
Primitive 'laurel-leaf' and 'willow-leaf' spear heads, most of them worked on only one side. Grotte du Trilobite.

Transition from Aurignacian.
Pedunculate spear heads (*pointes à soie*) of primitive Font Robert type.
Climax of human sculpture.

As to the chief source of Solutrean influence, the same author remarks that, since this culture is entirely wanting in central and southern Spain, in Italy, in Sicily, in Algeria, and in Phœnicia, we should certainly not look to the Mediterranean for its origin but rather to eastern Europe; for in the grottos of Hungary we find a great development of the true Solutrean, while so far the Aurignacian has not been found here, although we do find traces of the earlier transitional stages below the levels of the true laurel-leaf points. We must admit, therefore, that in all probability the Solutrean culture reached Europe from the east and that its source is as mysterious as that of the Aurignacian, which, as we have seen, was of southern and probably of Mediterranean origin. It is not impossible that the evolution of the laurel-leaf point took place in Hungary, for it was certainly not evolved in central or western Europe.

At Předmost, in Moravia, we observe an advanced Aurignacian industry which had adopted a Solutrean fashion in its spear heads. Here the laurel-leaf implements are few, while the implements of bone are abundant; but in the Solutrean stations of Hungary there are no bone implements. As the Solutrean technique comes to perfection the laurel-leaf spear head, so characteristic of the full Solutrean industry, is created and is met with in Poland, in Hungary, in Bavaria, and then in France, where the industry extends southward to the west and east of the central plateau. In France it appears quite suddenly in the Grotte du Trilobite (Yonne), and also in Dordogne and Ardèche, where the Proto-Solutrean types show marked impoverishment, both in the variety and in the execution of most of the flint implements, the only exception being the flattened spear heads, *pointes à face plane*, which show a regular Solutrean retouch, beautiful but monotonous. Laurel-leaf points discovered at Crouzade, Gourdan, and Montfort denote the presence of the true Solutrean culture, but this culture does not approach the stations in the neighborhood of Brassempouy. Toward the north the grotto of Spy, in Belgium, affords examples of Proto-Solutrean types, which have also been traced in several British caverns, but it is not certain that true Solutrean implements are found in Britain.

In Picard a Proto-Solutrean layer has been found, but no laurel-leaf points. In the type station of Solutré in southeastern France Breuil discovered two Solutrean layers, quite different from each other: one rich in bone implements and graving-tools, with small flint laurel leaves retouched on only one face; the other poor in bone implements but with large laurel-leaf spear heads.

The Solutrean culture never penetrated to the south of the great barrier of the Pyrenees, but, passing through the Vézère valley, in Dordogne, it spread along the western coast to the northern slopes of the Cantabrian Mountains into the province of Santander, Spain. Here the laurel-leaf points of the middle Solutrean are found at Castillo, while the shouldered points, *pointes à cran*, typical of the later Solutrean, are found at Altamira, together with bone implements. None the less, it should be noticed that in the southwest of Europe the earlier phases

FIG. 170. The type station of Solutrean culture, near the present village of Solutré, in south central France, sheltered on the north by a steep rocky ridge and with a fine sunny exposure toward the south.

of the Solutrean are characterized by a decrease in the use of bone, which, however, increases again in the upper levels.

The type station of the Solutrean culture is the great open-air camp of Solutré, near the Saône, sheltered on the north by a steep ridge and with a fine, sunny exposure toward the south. The traces of this great camp, which is the largest thus far discovered in western Europe, cover an area 300 feet square and are situated within a short distance of a good spring of water. As explored, in 1866, by Arcelin,[55] Ferry, and Ducrost, this station had already been occupied in Aurignacian times; and two sections, taken at two different points, showed the deposits of the old camp to be from 22 to 26 feet in thickness, representing superposed Aurignacian and Solutrean fire-hearths with thick layers of intermediate débris. In the Aurignacian level is found the vast accumulation of the bones of horses already described.

FIG. 171. Centre of the great open camp of Solutré, covering an area 300 feet square, with the village of Solutré in the distance. First occupied in Aurignacian times, and a favorite and densely inhabited camp throughout the Aurignacian and Solutrean stages. In Aurignacian times the remains of thousands of horses were accumulated around this station.

In the middle Solutrean levels great fireplaces are found with flint utensils and the remains of abundant feasts among the charred débris. The fauna includes the wolf, the fox, the hyæna, both the cave and the brown bear, the badger, the rabbit, the stag, wild cattle, and two characteristic northern forms —the woolly mammoth and the reindeer; the remains of the last are the most abundant in the ancient hearths.

In all the Solutrean stations, beside the bone implements,[56] we find two distinct classes of flints. The first belongs to the entire 'Reindeer Epoch' and consists of single and double scrapers, drills, burins, retouched flakes, and plain ones of small dimensions.

The second is composed of the 'leaf' types, which are solely characteristic of the Solutrean and which degenerate and entirely disappear at its close; these latter are the arrow and lance head forms, many of which are fashioned with a rare degree of perfection and exhibit the beautiful broad Solutrean retouch across the entire surface of both sides of the flake, together with perfect symmetry, both lateral and bilateral; they are commonly known as the willow-leaf (narrow) and the laurel-leaf (broad) forms. The explorers of the type station of Solutré have discovered five principal shapes, as follows: (1) irregular lozenge; (2) oval, pointed at both ends; (3) oval, pointed at one end; (4) regular lozenge; (5) arrow-head form with peduncle, doubtless for attachment to a shaft. The perfected Solutrean laurel-leaf spear heads do not reappear in any other Upper Palæolithic period, but their resemblance to Neolithic flints is very marked.

The 'willow-leaf' spear heads (*pointes de saule*), chipped on only one side, characteristic of the *early Solutrean*, may possibly be contemporary with the closing Aurignacian culture of Font Robert. At Solutré layers have also been discovered rich in bone implements and in graving-tools, as well as small 'laurel-leaf' points worked on only one face. As regards the general tendencies of the early Solutrean culture in Dordogne, at the Grotte du Trilobite (Yonne), and in Ardèche, there is a marked decline in the work in bone and in the variety and workmanship of all the implements, excepting only that of the primitive flattened spear heads, made of flakes, retouched in Solutrean fashion, but on one side only. Typical deposits of early Solutrean culture are found at Trou Magrite, in Belgium, at Font Robert, Corrèze, and in the third level of the Grotte du Trilobite, Yonne; in the second level we find flints with the nascent Solutrean retouch.

The distinctive implement of the 'high' or *middle Solutrean* is the large 'laurel-leaf' point, flaked and chipped on both sides and attaining a marvellous perfection in technique and symmetry.

The finest examples of these spear heads are the famous *pointes de laurier*, fourteen in number, discovered at Volgu, Saône-et-Loire, in 1873: they were found together in a sort of cache and, it would seem probable, were intended as a votive offering, for one at least was colored red, and all were too fragile and delicate to be of any use in the chase. They are of unusual size, the smallest measuring 9 inches, and the largest over 13½. In workmanship they are equalled only by the marvellous Neolithic specimens of Egypt and Scandinavia.

At Solutré and other stations implements of bone are also found, although by no means of such frequent occurrence as in the later divisions of the Solutrean. While the most easterly Solutrean stations of Hungary exhibit no bone implements, these are abundant at Předmost, in Moravia, where the culture altogether is of an advanced Aurignacian type, with the Solutrean retouch used in the shaping of its flint spear heads. The bone industry includes a number of awls and smoothers, as well as numerous 'bâtons de commandement.' On this level at Předmost a few works of art are found consisting of the representations of four animals sculptured on nodules of limestone, the subjects apparently being reindeer, and also of one single engraving on bone.

The chief invention of the *late Solutrean* is the 'shouldered point' (*pointe à cran*), a single notched and very slender dart. These notches are the first indication of the value of the barb in holding a weapon in the flesh. Here also is a *stem* for the attachment of the shaft of the dart. In earlier stages of the Solutrean one finds flints where the unsymmetrical base of the 'point' shows a small obtuse tongue or stem. The elongate peduncle at the base of such spear heads (*pointes à soie*) is developed into the *pointe à cran*, or shouldered point, made of long, fine flakes, with a short retouch on one or both sides, and found in the late Solutrean at the grotto of Lacave, at Placard, and at many of the stations in Dordogne. No example of the *pointe à cran* has ever been found at the type station of Solutré, but it is of frequent occurrence at the stations between the Loire and the

Cantabrian Pyrenees, being found at Altamira, at Laugerie Haute, at Monthaud (Indre), in Chalosse and Charente, while the great cave of Placard has yielded no less than 5,000 specimens, whole and broken.

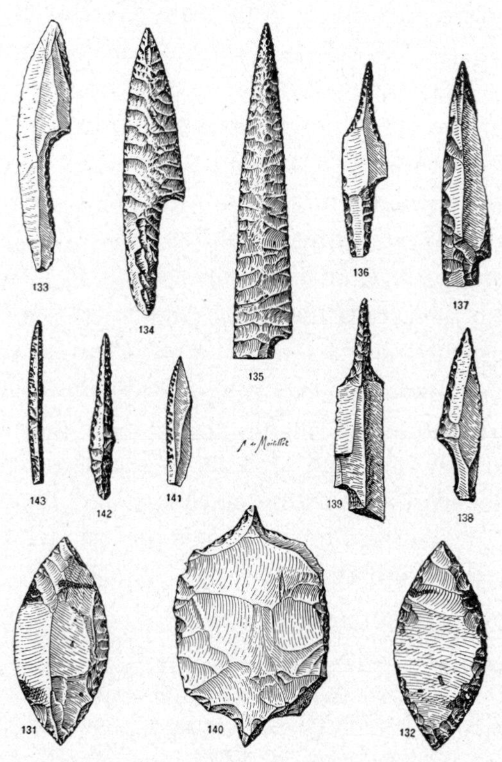

FIG. 172. Typical Solutrean implements of the chase, of fishing, and of industry. After de Mortillet. 131, 132. A laurel-leaf point retouched on both sides. 133–138. Various forms of the *pointe à cran*, or 'shouldered point,' a type distinctive of the late Solutrean. It has an elongated peduncle or stem at one side adapted for the attachment of a wooden shaft, and was probably an implement of the chase, being suitable for fishing or for hunting small game. The examples figured show a great variety of finish and retouch. 137 is from Placard and 138 from the *Grottes de Grimaldi*. 139. *Poinçon*, or awl, beautifully shaped. 140. *Perçoir*, drill or borer. 141. Flake retouched on one border, recalling the style of the Aurignacian points. 142, 143. Finely retouched points, suitable for engraving or etching. All the flints are shown one-half actual size.

At Monthaud there are also found bone implements including a number of *poinçons* (awls) and a series of *sagaies* (javelin points). Solutrean sagaies, however, are very rare and very primitive as compared with the Magdalenian.

The successive phases of Solutrean industry are all shown in southern France. As to its stratigraphic relations, the type station of Solutré exhibits lower and middle Solutrean above Aurignacian hearths and deposits; that of Placard, Charente, shows the middle and upper Solutrean overlaid by a Magdalenian layer. In the Grotte du Trilobite the Solutrean layer lies between one of Aurignacian and one of primitive Magdalenian; it is here that we find the clearest transition from the Aurignacian culture in the appearance of prototypes of the laurel and willow-leaf points, made of flakes, retouched on only one side. At Brassempouy the Solutrean lies immediately beneath a Magdalenian layer, with engraved bones and Magdalenian flints. Needles, which are particularly abundant in the Magdalenian epoch, are also found in a number of the Solutrean stations. In the grotto of Lacave, Lot, in an upper Solutrean layer, Viré has found beautiful bone needles, pierced at one end and of fine workmanship, and engraved utensils of reindeer horn; here also was found the head of an antelope engraved on a fragment of reindeer horn. The local fauna of this period included the horse, the ibex, and the reindeer.

Solutrean Engraving and Animal Sculpture

The artistic work of Solutrean times is not so rich as that of the Aurignacian. This, as we have suggested, may be partly attributable to the less wide-spread distribution of the Solutrean culture, as well as to the great importance which was attached to the careful fashioning of the stone weapons. None the less we can trace indications of the development of both phases of art, the linear and the plastic, and especially the beginnings of animal sculpture. From the full, round sculpture of Aurignacian times there follows in Solutrean times a development of carving in bone of the *Rundstabfiguren* (bâton, or ceremonial staff), and of high relief. The lion[57] and the head of a horse at Isturitz, in the Pyrenees, which Breuil attributes to a late Solutrean period, are typical examples of this work.

Relatively rare are the parietal and mobile engravings as well as the schematic representations, such as are found at Placard and Champs Blancs. According to Alcalde del Rio, there are found at Altamira, in northern Spain, very simple, finely engraved figures of the doe on the bone of the shoulder-blade; the head and neck are covered with lines, and both the eye and the nostril as well as the form of the ear are very characteristic of the animal. Breuil, however, considers these as belonging rather to earlier Magdalenian times.

Decorative art certainly makes some advances over the Aurignacian work, because the arrangement of the geometric figures is quite clear, and the execution shows marked progress in the technique of engraving.

At Předmost, near the site of the human burial described above, there has been discovered a statuette of the mammoth sculptured in the round, in ivory, which proves that animal sculpture was well advanced in Solutrean times. The statuette was found six to nine feet beneath the surface of the 'loess,' in an undoubted Solutrean layer. The accompanying fauna is of a truly arctic character: the mammoth being extraordinarily abundant; the tundra forms including the mammoth, woolly rhinoceros, musk-ox, reindeer, arctic fox, arctic hare, glutton, and banded lemming; the Asiatic forms including the lion and leopard; the forest and meadow fauna embracing the wolf, fox, beaver, brown bear, bison, and wild cattle, moose, and horse, also the ibex. Among the remnants of 30,000 flints there are a dozen points (*feuilles de laurier*) and other pieces with the Solutrean 'retouch.' The industry in ivory, bone, and reindeer horn is also varied, including numerous poniards, polishers, piercers, dart-throwers, and bâtons de commandement.

This ivory sculpture of the mammoth indicates very accurately the characteristic contours of the top of the head, and of the back; the striations on the side represent the falling masses of hair. Other sculptured figures representing the mammoth are believed to be of Magdalenian age, the best known being the figures found in the grottos of Bruniquel and Laugerie Basse, a fragment from Raymonden, Dordogne, and a bas-relief in the grotto of Figuier, Gard. All these sculptures of the mammoth have in common the indication of a very small ear—similar to that in the Předmost model—feet shaped like inverted mushrooms, bordered with short, coarse hairs, the tail terminating in

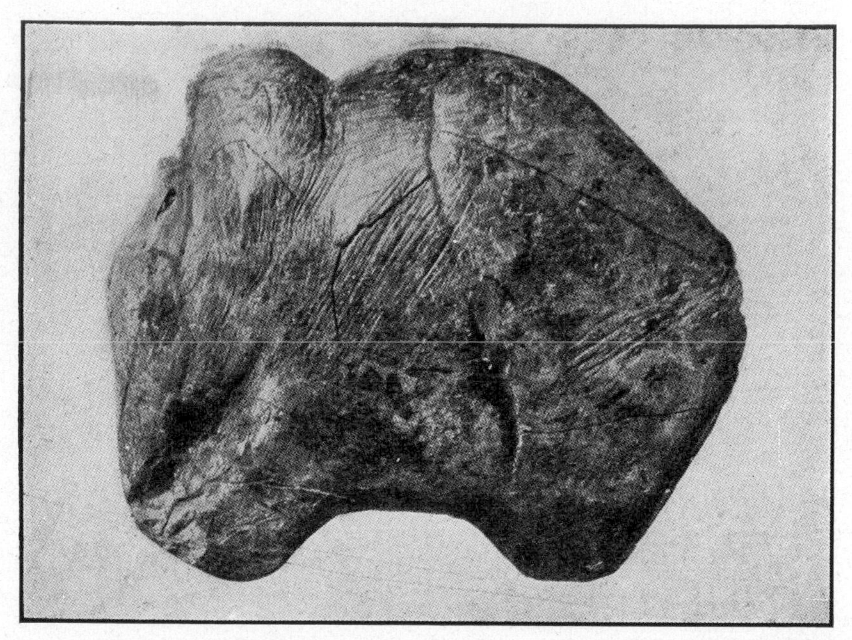

FIG. 173. Mammoth sculptured on a fragment of ivory tusk from the Solutrean station of Předmost, Moravia. After Maška. This figure is covered with fine lines representing the long, hairy coating, and measures about four and one-half inches.

a long tuft of hairs. If the figure of Předmost is of Solutrean age, it is by far the earliest of all the sculptured or engraved animal representations in the mobile art, and is also the most complete of the animal figurines of this group. It is certainly of more recent date than the engraved designs of Aurignacian age in the grottos of Gargas and of Chabot or than the red or black tracings of the mammoth, also of Aurignacian age, at Castillo, Pindal, and Font-de-Gaume. It is probable that the mammoth figures of Combarelles are of later date than the Předmost sculpture and belong to the beginning of Magdalenian times, while those at Font-de-Gaume belong to the end of Magdalenian times and are the most recent of all the parietal designs. Despite the differences in age and technique, all the designs of the mammoth are undoubtedly the work of artists of a single race; they agree in faithfully portraying the external form of this great proboscidian which wandered over the steppes and prairies of western Europe from the beginning of the fourth glaciation until near the close of Postglacial times.

(1) Breuil, 1912.7.
(2) Verneau, 1906.1, pp. 202–207.
(3) *Op. cit.*, p. 204.
(4) Keith, 1911.1, p. 60.
(5) Obermaier, 1912.1, p. 178.
(6) Breuil, 1912.7, p. 174.
(7) *Op. cit.*, pp. 165–168.
(8) Obermaier, 1912.1, pp. 177, 178.
(9) Wiegers, 1913.1.
(10) Schmidt, 1912.1, p. 266.
(11) Geikie, 1914.1, p. 278.
(12) Dawkins, 1880.1, pp. 148, 149.
(13) Ewart, 1904.1.
(14) Obermaier, 1909.2, p. 145.
(15) Sollas, 1913.1, p. 325.
(16) Broca, 1868.1.
(17) Lartet, 1875.1.
(18) Verneau, 1886.1; 1906.1, pp. 68, 69.
(19) Obermaier, 1912.2.
(20) Martin, R., 1914.1, pp. 15, 16.
(21) Keith, 1911.1, p. 71.
(22) Klaatsch, 1909.1.
(23) Keith, *op. cit.*, p. 56.
(24) Hauser, 1909.1.
(25) Fischer, 1913.1.
(26) Schliz, 1912.1, p. 554.
(27) Breuil, 1912.7, p. 175.
(28) *Op. cit.*, p. 183.
(29) *Op. cit.*, pp. 177–180.
(30) Schmidt, 1912.1, p. 266.
(31) Breuil, *op. cit.*, p. 178.
(32) Obermaier, 1912.1, p. 181.
(33) Breuil, 1912.7, p. 169.
(34) Breuil, 1912.1, pp. 194–200.
(35) Schmidt, 1912.1.
(36) Breuil, *op. cit.*
(37) Schmidt, 1912.1, p. 142.
(38) Breuil, 1912.1, p. 202.
(39) Breuil, 1912.6.
(40) Hilzheimer, 1913.1, p. 151.
(41) Fischer, 1913.1.
(42) Makowsky, 1902.1.
(43) Schwalbe, 1906.1.
(44) Makowsky, *op. cit.*
(45) Obermaier, 1912.1, pp. 342–355.
(46) Martin, R., 1914.1, pp. 15, 16.
(47) Schliz, 1912.1.
(48) Déchelette, 1908.1, vol. I, p. 28.
(49) Keane, 1901.1, p. 147.
(50) Keith, 1911.1, p. 30.
(51) *Op. cit.*, pp. 28–45.
(52) *Op. cit.*, pp. 51–56.
(53) Obermaier, 1912.1, p. 93.
(54) Breuil, 1912.7, p. 188.
(55) Arcelin, 1869.1.
(56) Déchelette, 1908.1, vol. I, pp. 137–141.
(57) Schmidt, 1912.1, p. 144, Tafel B.

CHAPTER V

MAGDALENIAN TIMES — CLIMATE AND MAMMALIAN LIFE OF EUROPE — CUSTOMS AND LIFE OF THE CRÔ-MAGNONS; THEIR INDUSTRY IN FLINT AND BONE; THEIR DISTRIBUTION — DEVELOPMENT OF THEIR ART, ENGRAVING, PAINTING, SCULPTURE — ART IN THE CAVERNS — CLIMAX OF THE MAGDALENIAN ART AND INDUSTRY OF THE CRÔ-MAGNONS — APPARENT DECLINE OF THE RACE.

THE art and industrial epoch of Magdalenian times is by far the best known and most fascinating of the Old Stone Age. This period forms the culmination of Palæolithic civilization; it marks the highest development of the Crô-Magnon race preceding their sudden decline and disappearance as the dominant type of western Europe. The men of this time are commonly known as the Magdalenians, taking their name from the type station of La Madeleine, as the Greeks in their highest stage took their name from Athens and were known as the Athenians.

We would assign the minimum prehistoric date of 16,000 B. C. for the beginning of the Magdalenian culture, and since we have assigned to the beginning of the Aurignacian culture the date of 25,000 B. C., we should allow 9,000 years for the development of the Aurignacian and Solutrean industries in western Europe.

INTRODUCTION. INDUSTRIAL AND ARTISTIC DEVELOPMENT

Well as this culture is known, its origin is obscured by the fact that it shows little or no connection with the preceding Solutrean industry, which, as we have noted (p. 331), seems like a technical invasion in the history of western Europe and not an inherent part of the main line of cultural development. Thus Breuil[1] observes that it appears as if the fundamental elements of the superior Aurignacian culture had contributed by some unknown route to constitute the kernel of the Magdalenian civilization while the Solutrean episode was going on elsewhere. Again, early Magdalenian art bears striking resemblances to the superior Aurignacian art of the Pyrenees, especially the parietal art, as shown by comparing the Aurignacian engravings of Gargas with the early Magdalenian of Combarelles. Moreover, the same author observes that, if there is one certain prehistoric fact, it is that the first Magdalenian culture was not evolved from the Solutrean—that these Magdalenians were newcomers in western France, as unskilful in the art of shaping and retouching flints as their predecessors were skilled. Ancient Magdalenian hearths are found in many localities close to the levels of the upper Solutrean industries with their shouldered spear points (*pointes à cran*) and highly perfected flint work. Yet the Magdalenians show a radical departure from the Solutrean type of flint working; both in Dordogne (Laugerie Haute and Laussel) and in Charente (Placard) the splinters of flint are massive, heavy, badly selected, often of poor quality, and poorly retouched, sometimes almost in an Eolithic manner; at the same time, the chance flints, that is, the piercers and graving-tools made from splinters of any accidental shape, are abundant. To these people flint implements appear to be altogether of secondary importance; although the flints are very numerous, they are not finished with any of the perfection of the Solutrean technique; the laurel-leaf spear head and shouldered dart head have disappeared entirely, but a great variety of smaller graving and chasing forms are employed for fashioning the implements of bone and horn. What a contrast to the beautiful flints so finely retouched and of such carefully selected materials, found in the very same stations in middle and upper Solutrean layers!

Thus Breuil, always predisposed to believe in an invasion of culture rather than in an autochthonous development, favors the theory of eastern origin for the Magdalenian industry, because this is not wanting either in Austria or in Poland; two sites of ancient Magdalenian industry have been found by Obermaier in the 'loess' stations of Austria, while in Russian Poland the grotto of Mašzycka, near Ojcow, exhibits workings in bone resembling those found at the grotto of Placard, Charente, in the layers directly succeeding the base of the Magdalenian. The fact that near the Ural Mountains there has also been found a peculiar Magdalenian culture, the origin of which is not western, inclines us to believe that the Magdalenian culture extended from the east toward the west, and then, later, toward the Baltic.

This theory of the eastern origin of the Magdalenian industry has, however, to face, first, the very strong counter-evidence of

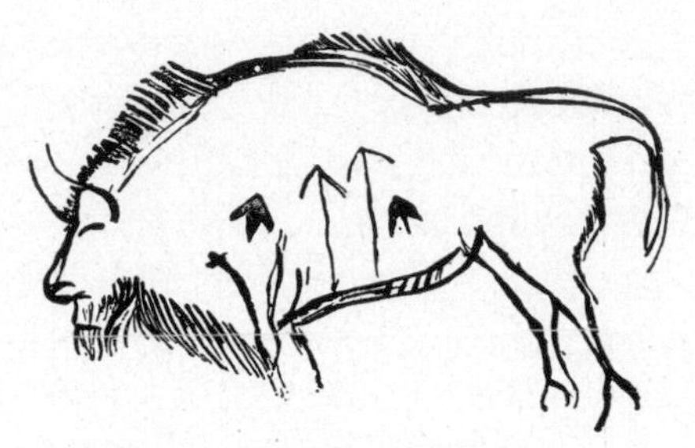

FIG. 174. One of the large bison drawings in the cavern of Niaux, on the Ariège, showing the supposed spear or arrow heads with shafts on its side. The artist's technique consists of an outline incised with flint followed by a painted outline in black manganese giving high relief. After Cartailhac and Breuil. Greatly reduced.

the close affinity between Aurignacian and Magdalenian art, which Breuil himself has done the most to demonstrate; second, the physical, mental, and especially the artistic unity of the Crô-Magnon race in Aurignacian and Magdalenian times. The recent discovery of two Crô-Magnon skeletons together with two carved bone implements of Magdalenian type, at Obercassel, on the Rhine, links the art with this race and with no other, because, as we remarked above, an artistic instinct and ability cannot be passed from one race to another like the technique of a handicraft. Breuil[2] himself has positively stated that the whole Upper Palæolithic art development of Europe was the work of one race: if so, this race can be no other than the Crô-Magnon.

We must, therefore, revert to the explanation offered in a preceding chapter, that the Solutrean technique was an intrusion or an invasion either brought in by another race or acquired from the craftsmen of some easterly race, perhaps that of Brünn, Brüx, and Předmost. Why the art of fashioning these perfect Solutrean spear, dart, and arrow heads was lost is very difficult to explain, because they appear to be the most effective implements of war and of the chase which were ever developed by Palæolithic workmen.

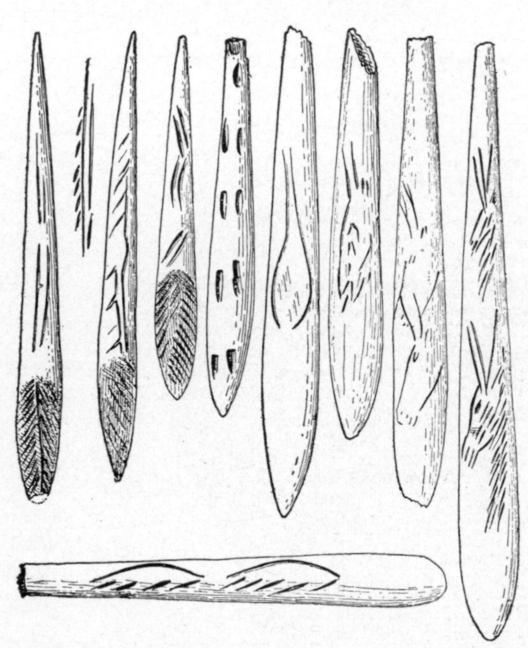

FIG. 175. Decorated *sagaies*, or javelin points, of bone; pointed at one end and bevelled at the other for the attachment of a shaft. After Breuil.

It is possible, although not probable, that the bow was introduced at this time and that a less perfect flint point, fastened to a shaft like an arrow-head and projected with great velocity and accuracy, proved to be far more effective than the spear. The bison in the cavern of Niaux show several barbed points adhering to the sides, and the symbol of the *flèche* appears on the sides of many of the bison, cattle, and other animals of the chase in Magdalenian drawings. From these drawings and symbols it would appear that *barbed* weapons of some kind were used in the chase, but no barbed flints occur at any time in the Palæolithic, nor has any trace been found of bone barbed arrow-heads or any direct evidence of the existence of the bow.

In compensation for the decline of flint is the rapid development of bone implements, the most distinctive feature of Magdalenian industry. In the late Solutrean we have noted the occasional appearance of the bone javelin points (*sagaies*) with their decorative *motifs;* these become much more frequent in Magdalenian times. They occur in the most ancient Magdalenian levels of the grotto of Placard, Charente, which are prior even to the appearance of prototypes of the harpoon, the evolution of which clearly marks off the early, middle, and late divisions of Magdalenian times. These primitive javelins, decorated

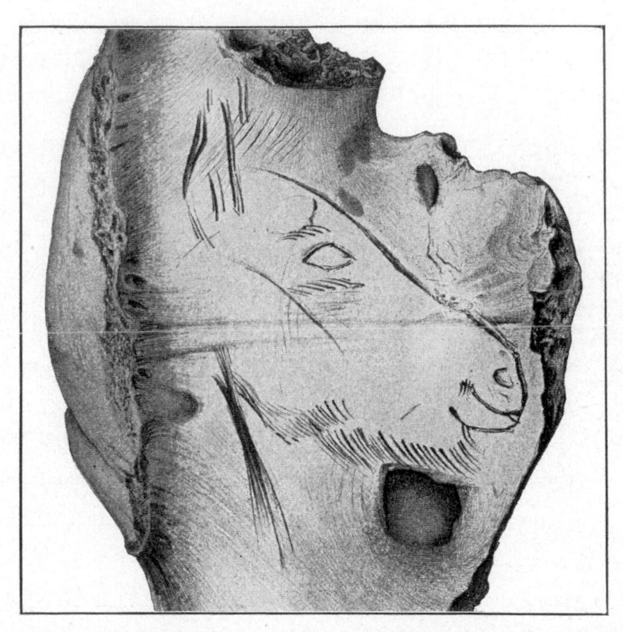

FIG. 176. Head of the forest or of the steppe horse engraved on a fragment of bone, from the Grotte du Pape, Brassempouy. After Piette.

in a characteristic fashion, are found in Poland, at the grotto of Kesslerloch and other places in Switzerland, at many stations in Dordogne and the region of the Pyrenees in southern France, and in the Cantabrian Mountains of northern Spain.

It is only above the levels where early types of these javelin points occur that the rudimentary harpoons of the typical early Magdalenian are found. The discovery of the bone harpoon as a means of catching fish marks an important addition to the food supply, which was apparently followed by a decline in the chase. Later, to the javelin, lance, and harpoon is added the dart-thrower (*propulseur*), which gradually spreads all over western

Europe, where also the evolution of these bone implements and of the decoration with which they are richly adorned enables the trained archæologist to establish corresponding subdivisions of Magdalenian time.

From the uniform character of Palæolithic art in its highest forms of engraving, painting, and animal sculpture we may infer the probable unity of the Crô-Magnon race, especially throughout western Europe. During Magdalenian times various branches of art reached their highest point and were the culmination of

FIG. 177. Polychrome wall-painting of a wolf from the cavern of Font-de-Gaume. After Breuil.

a movement begun in the early Aurignacian. The artist, whose life brought him into close touch with nature and who evidently followed the movements both of the individual animals and of the herds for hours at a time, has rendered his observations in the most realistic manner. Among the animals represented are the bison, mammoth, wild horse, reindeer, wild cattle, deer, and rhinoceros; less frequent are representations of the ibex, wolf, and wild boar, and there are comparatively few representations of fishes or of any form of plant life; the nobler beasts of prey, such as the lion and the bear, are often represented, but there are no figures of the skulking hyæna, which at that time was a rare if not almost extinct animal. While many figures are of real artistic worth and reach a high level, others are more or less crude attempts; the composition of figures or of groups of animals is rarely undertaken.

The artistic sense of these people is also manifest in the decoration of their household utensils and weapons of the chase. Here the smaller animals of the chase, the saiga, the ibex, and

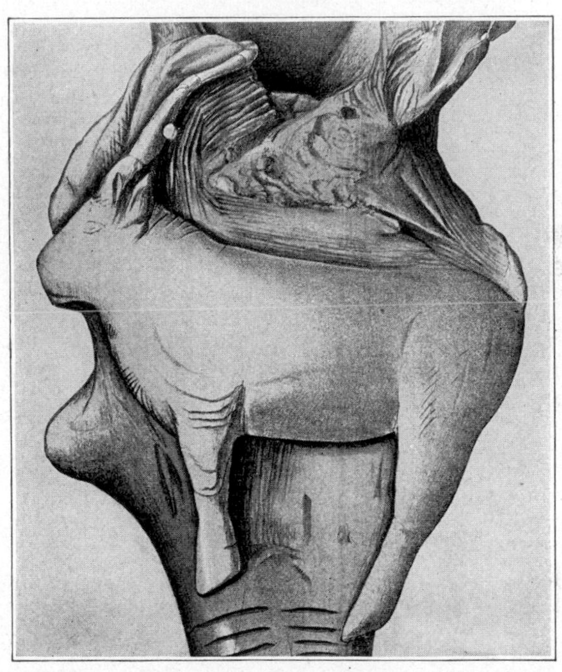

FIG. 178. Crude sculpture of the ibex, from the Magdalenian deposit at Mas d'Azil on the right bank of the Arize. After Piette. A little less than actual size.

the chamois, are executed with a sure hand. Sculpture of animal forms in the large, which begins in Solutrean times, is continued and reaches its highest point in the early Magdalenian. At this period the use of sculpture as a means of decoration arises and extends into the middle and late Magdalenian. These latter divisions are also distinguished by the reappearance of human figurines, nude, like the Aurignacian, and occasionally somewhat more slender. Thus it would appear that the artistic spirit, more or less dormant in Solutrean times, was revived.

In the variety of industries we find evidences of a race endowed with closely observant and creative minds, in which the two chief motives of life seem to have been the chase and the pursuit of art. The Magdalenian flints are fashioned in a somewhat different manner from the Solutrean: long, slender flakes or 'blades' with little or no retouch are frequent, and in other implements the work is apparently carried only to a point where the flint will serve its purpose. No attempt is made to attain perfect symmetry. Thus the old technical impulse of the flint industry seems to be far less than that among the makers of the Solutrean flints, while a new technical impulse manifests itself in several branches of art: arms and utensils are carved in ivory, reindeer horn and bone, and sculpture and engraving on bone and ivory are greatly developed. We find that these people are beginning to utilize the walls of dark, mysterious caverns for their drawings and paintings, which show deep appreciation for the perfection of the animal form, depicted by them in most lifelike attitudes.

We may infer that there was a tribal organization, and it has been suggested that certain unexplained implements of reindeer horn, often beautifully carved and known as 'bâtons de commandement,' were insignia of authority borne by the chieftains.

There can be little doubt that such diversities of temperament, of talent, and of predisposition as obtain to-day also prevailed then, and that they tended to differentiate society into chieftains, priests, and medicine-men, hunters of large game and fishermen, fashioners of flints and dressers of hides, makers of clothing and footwear, makers of ornaments, engravers, sculptors in wood, bone, ivory, and stone, and artists with color and brush. In their artistic work, at least, these people were animated with a compelling sense of truth, and we cannot deny them a strong appreciation of beauty.

It is probable that a sense of wonder in the face of the powers of nature was connected with the development of a religious sentiment. How far their artistic work in the caverns was an expression of such sentiment and how far it was the

PL. VII. Crô-Magnon man in the cavern of Font-de-Gaume, Dordogne, restored in the act of drawing the outlines of one of the bisons on the wall of the *Galerie des Fresques*. Drawn under the direction of the author by Charles R. Knight.

outcome of a purely artistic impulse are matters for very careful study. Undoubtedly the inquisitive sense which led them into the deep and dangerous recesses of the caverns was accompanied by an increased sense of awe and possibly by a sentiment which we may regard as more or less religious. We may dwell for a moment on this very interesting problem of the

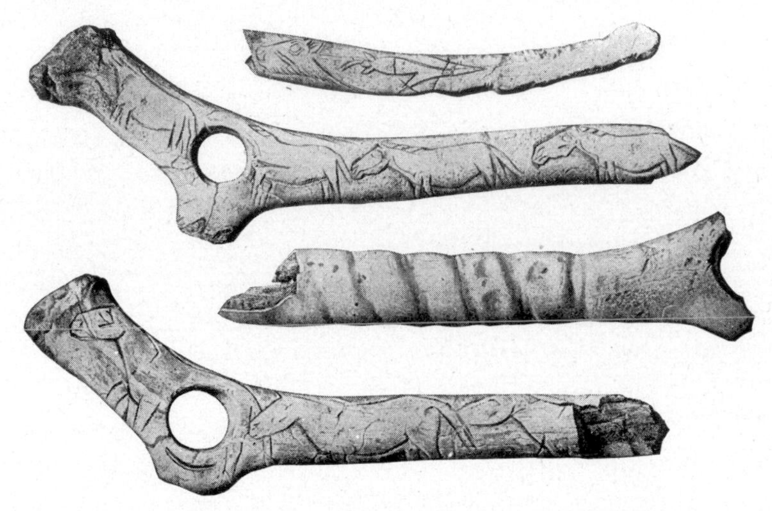

Fig. 179. Decorated *bâtons de commandement* carved from reindeer horn with a large perforation opposite the brow tine. After Lartet and Christy.

origin of religion during the Old Stone Age, so that the reader may judge for himself in connection with the ensuing accounts of Magdalenian art.

"The religious phenomenon," observes James,[3] "has shown itself to consist everywhere, and in all its stages, in the consciousness which individuals have of an intercourse between themselves and higher powers with which they feel themselves to be related. This intercourse is realized at the time as being both active and mutual. . . . The gods believed in—whether by crude savages or by men disciplined intellectually—agree with each other in recognizing personal calls. . . . To coerce the spiritual powers, or to square them and get them on our side, was, during enormous tracts of time, the one great object in our dealings with the natural world."

The study of this race, in our opinion, would suggest a still earlier phase in the development of religious thought than that considered by James, namely, a phase in which the wonders of nature in their various manifestations begin to arouse in the primitive mind a desire for an explanation of these phenomena, and in which it is attempted to seek such cause in some vague supernatural power underlying these otherwise unaccountable occurrences, a cause to which the primitive human spirit commences to make its appeal. According to certain anthropologists,* this wonder-working force may either be personal, like the gods of Homer, or impersonal, like the *Mana* of the Melanesian, or the *Manitou* of the North American Indian. It may impress an individual when he is in a proper frame of mind, and through magic or propitiation may be brought into relation with his individual ends. Magic and religion jointly belong to the supernatural as opposed to the every-day world of the savage.

We have already seen evidence from the burials that these people apparently believed in the preparation of the bodies of the dead for a future existence. How far these beliefs and the votive sense of propitiation for protection and success in the chase are indicated by the art of the caverns is to be judged in connection with their entire life and productive effort, with their burials associated with offerings of implements and articles of food, and with their art.

The Three Climatic Cycles of Magdalenian Times

The culture of the Crô-Magnons was doubtless influenced by the changing climatic conditions of Magdalenian times, which were quite varied, so that we may trace three parallel lines of development: that of environment, as indicated by the climate and the forms of animal life, that of industry, and that of art.

The entire climatic, life, and industrial cycle of which the

* From notes by Doctor Robert H. Lowie (Nov. 16, 1914) of the American Museum of Natural History on the opinions of Marett (*Anthropology*) and of James.

Magdalenian marks the conclusion has been presented in Chapter IV (p. 281). After a very long period of cold and somewhat arid climate following the fourth glaciation, it would appear that western Europe in early Magdalenian times again experienced a stage of increasing cold and moisture accompanied by the renewed advance of the glaciers in the Alpine region, in Scandinavia, and in Great Britain. This is known as the *Bühl* stage in the Alps, in which the snow-line descended 2,700 feet below its present level and the great glaciers thrust down along the southerly borders of Lake Lucerne a series of new moraines distinctly overlying those of the fourth glaciation. Another indication of the lowered temperature and increased moisture in the same geographic region is found in the return of the arctic lemmings from the northern tundras; these migrants have left their remains in several of the large grottos north of the Alps, especially in Schweizersbild and Kesslerloch, composing what is known as the *Upper Rodent Layer*, with which are associated the implements and art objects of the early Magdalenian culture stage.

We have adopted the minimum estimate of 25,000 years since the fourth glaciation, but Heim[4] has estimated that the much more recent prehistoric event of the advance of this minor *Bühl* glaciation began at least 24,000 years ago, that it extended over a very long period of time, and that the *Bühl* moraines in Lake Lucerne are at least 16,000 years of age.

The three climatic changes of Magdalenian times are therefore as follows:

First, the *Bühl* Postglacial Stage in the Alps, which corresponds with what Geikie has named the Fifth Glacial Epoch, or *Lower Turbarian*, in Scotland; for he believes that a relapse to cold conditions in northern Britain was accompanied by a partial subsidence of the coast lands, that snow-fields again appeared, that considerable glaciers descended the mountain valleys, and even reached the sea. At this time the arctic alpine flora of Scotland also descended to within 150 feet of the sea-level. The result of this renewed or fifth glaciation in western Europe was the advent of the great wave of tundra life and the descent to the plains of all the forms of Alpine life.

Second, it would appear that in middle Magdalenian times, after the *Bühl* advance, there occurred a temporary retreat of the ice-fields, and that during this period the full tide of life from the steppes of western Asia and eastern Europe for the first time

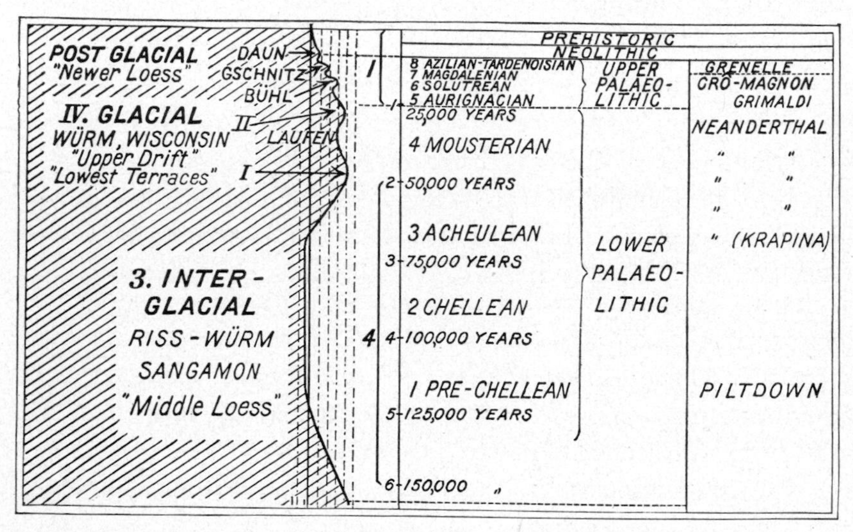

FIG. 180. Correlation of the Postglacial climatic changes with the four stages of Upper Palæolithic culture: the Aurignacian coincident with the final retreat of the fourth glaciation; the Solutrean coincident with the interval preceding the *Bühl* advance; the Magdalenian coincident with the *Bühl* and *Gschnitz* Postglacial advances; and the Azilian coincident with the *Daun* or third Postglacial advance. (Compare Fig. 14.)

spread over western Europe, including especially such animals as the jerboa and the saiga antelope, the dwarf pika and steppe hamster. Correlation is very hazardous, but this ice retreat may correspond with the *Upper Forestian*, or Fifth Interglacial Stage in Scotland, described by Geikie, the stage which he mentions as marked by the elevation of the Scottish coast with the retreat of the sea beyond the present coast-lines; geographic changes which were accompanied by the disappearance of perennial snow and ice, and the return of more genial conditions. The tundra fauna still prevailed; such a typical arctic animal as the musk-ox wandered as far south as Dordogne and the

Pyrenees, and became one of the objects of the chase. During what is known as the middle or 'full Magdalenian' the tundra, steppe, alpine, forest, and meadow faunæ spread over the plains and valleys throughout western Europe.

Third, the second Postglacial advance, known as the *Gschnitz* stage in the Alpine region, appears to have been contemporaneous with the closing period of Magdalenian culture. This was the last great effort of the ice-fields to conquer western Europe, and in the Alpine region the snow-line descended 1,800 feet below the present levels; it marked the closing stage of the long cold climatic period that had favored the presence of the reindeer, the woolly mammoth, and the woolly rhinoceros in western Europe, as well as the close of the 'Reindeer Epoch' of Lartet. Again, in the north of Britain Geikie observes an *Upper Turbarian* or Sixth Glacial Epoch, accompanied by a partial subsidence of the Scottish coast, and the return of a cold and wet climate; there is evidence of the existence of snow glaciers upon the high mountains only. The *Gschnitz* stage marks the end of glacial conditions in Europe, the retreat of the tundra and steppe faunæ, and the predominance of the forest and meadow environment and life.

In the Alps there was, however, still a final effort of the glaciers, known as the *Daun* stage, which, it is believed, broadly corresponds with the period of the Azilian-Tardenoisian industry, and a climatic condition in Europe favorable to the spread of the Eurasiatic forest and meadow life.

The key to this great prehistoric chronology is found in palæontology. The arctic tundra rodents especially are the most invaluable timekeepers; according to Schmidt[5] there is no doubt whatever that the *Upper Rodent Layer*, composed of the animals of the second invasion from the arctic tundras, corresponds, on the one hand, with the beginning of the Magdalenian industry and, on the other, with the renewed glacial advance in the Alpine region, known as the *Bühl* stage, and probably also with that in the north. The *Upper Rodent Layer* of Magdalenian times is found in the remarkably complete succession of deposits at the stations of Schweizersbild and Kesslerloch, which are more recent in time than the 'low terraces' bordering the neighboring River Rhine. The fossil animals prove that after the extreme cold of early Magdalenian times the tundra fauna gradually gave way to a wide-spread steppe fauna. Along the Rhine and the Danube the banded lemmings become less frequent; the jerboas, hamsters, and susliks of the steppes become more abundant. Exactly similar changes are observed in Dordogne. In Longueroche, on the Vézère, there occur for the first time in western Europe great numbers of rabbits (*Lepus cuniculus*); numerous hares (*Lepus timidus*) are also observed at the type station of La Madeleine, especially in the uppermost and lowermost culture layers. These small rabbits probably came from the Mediterranean region and denote a slight elevation of temperature. But it is only in the very highest Magdalenian layers that the animal life of western Europe begins to approach that of recent times, namely, that of the prehistoric forest and meadow faunæ.

Mammalian Life of Magdalenian Times

Thus it is very important to keep in mind that during Magdalenian times there were both cold and moist periods favorable to tundra life and cold and arid periods favorable to steppe life. In the latter were deposited the sheets of 'upper loess.'

The mammalian life of Magdalenian times is of interest not only in connection with the climate and environment of the Crô-Magnon race, but with the development of their industry and especially of their art. It is noteworthy that the imposing forms of animal life, the mammoth among the tundra fauna and the bison among the meadow fauna, made a very strong impression and were the favorite subjects of the draftsmen and colorists; but the eye was also susceptible to the beauty of the reindeer, the stag, and the horse and to the grace of the chamois. The artists and sculptors have preserved the external appearance of more than thirty forms of this wonderful mammalian assemblage, which accord exactly with the fossil records preserved in the fire-hearths of the grottos and shelters, and with the deposits assembled by beasts and birds of prey in the uninhabited caverns.

No artists have ever had before them at the same time and in the same country such a wonderful panorama of animal life as that observed by the Crô-Magnons. Their representations in drawing, engraving, painting, and sculpture afford us a view of a great part of the life of the period, including its contingent of

FIG. 181. Reindeer with outlines first engraved and then retraced with heavy lines of black manganese finely finished with a wash of gray tone, from the *Galerie des Fresques* at Font-de-Gaume. After Breuil.

forms from the tundras, steppes, Alpine summits, and Eurasiatic forests and meadows, and the one surviving member of the Asiatic fauna, the lion.

The paintings and drawings of Dordogne chiefly represent the mammoth, reindeer, rhinoceros, bison, horses, wild cattle, red deer, ibex, lion, and bear. The caverns of the Pyrenees of southern France present chiefly bison, horses, deer, wild cattle, ibex, and chamois; the reindeer and mammoth are relatively rare, and in some cases entirely wanting in the parietal art; this is singular because in the Pyrenees the reindeer constituted the principal food of the authors of the drawings and frescos. In the caves of the Cantabrian Mountains representations of the reindeer are entirely absent, while the doe and stag of the red deer are frequently pictured; there are only a few representations of the mammoth and one of the cave-bear. In the drawings of eastern Spain deer and wild cattle are abundantly represented, and there is undoubtedly a representation of the moose at Alpera.

Favorite Art Subjects

TUNDRA LIFE.
- Mammoth.
- Woolly rhinoceros.
- Reindeer.
- Musk-ox.

STEPPE LIFE.
- Steppe horse.
- Saiga antelope.
- Wild ass, kiang.

ASIATIC LIFE.
- Lion.
- Desert horse.

ALPINE LIFE.
- Ibex.
- Chamois.

MEADOW LIFE.
- Bison.
- Wild cattle.

FOREST LIFE.
- Red deer, stag.
- Forest horse.
- Cave-bear.
- Wolf.
- Fox.
- Wild boar.
- Moose.
- Fallow deer.

SEA LIFE.
- Seal.

REPTILES, BIRDS, FISHES.
(Rarely depicted.)

As regards the sources of this great fauna, we have observed that in late Aurignacian and Solutrean times, at Předmost, Moravia, and elsewhere, the steppe fauna was not richly represented in western Europe, for it included only the steppe horse and the wild Asiatic ass or kiang; that the contemporary tundra fauna lacked two of the smaller but most characteristic forms, the banded and the Obi lemmings, although all of the large tundra forms were still widespread and freely intermingled with the forest and meadow life; and that preying upon these herbivorous mammals were the surviving Asiatic lions and hyænas.

The successive faunal phases of Magdalenian times, beginning with the early cold and moist or tundra period, have been determined with wonderful precision by Schmidt from the animal remains found associated with the lower, middle, and upper Magdalenian cultures in the grotto and cavern deposits of northern Switzerland, of the upper Rhine, and of the upper Danube. This region was lacking in some of the characteristic animals seen in Dordogne, yet these invaluable records show that throughout the entire period of Magdalenian times, probably extending over some thousands of years, the forests, meadows, and river borders of western Europe maintained the entire existing, or rather prehistoric, forest and meadow faunæ. The royal stag,

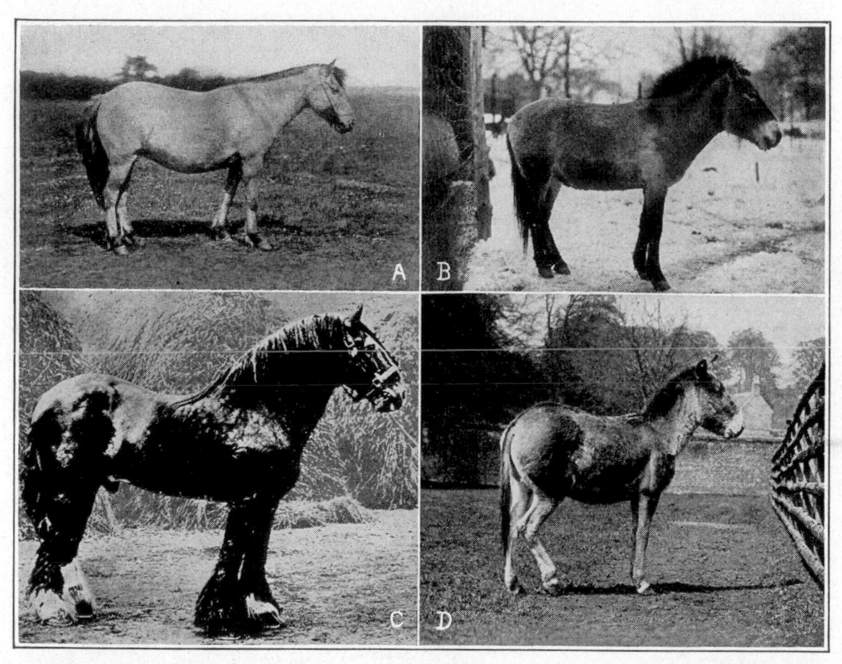

FIG. 182. Modern descendants of the four principal types of the horse family which roamed over western Europe in Upper Palæolithic times: (*A*) the plateau, desert, or Celtic horse, (*B*) the steppe or Przewalski horse, (*C*) the forest or Nordic horse, and (*D*) the kiang or wild ass of the Asiatic steppes.

or red deer (*Cervus elaphus*), was no longer accompanied by the giant deer (*Megaceros*), which apparently left this region of Europe in Aurignacian times, but the maral or Persian deer (*Cervus maral*) occasionally appears; both the stag and the roe-deer (*Capreolus*) were especially abundant in southwestern Europe and the Cantabrian Mountains of northern Spain, where the stag became the favorite subject of the Magdalenian artists at the same time that the reindeer was the favorite subject in the region of Dordogne. In the forests were also the brown bear, the lynx, the badger, the marten, and in the streams the beaver; tree squirrels (*Sciurus vulgaris*) appear for the first time; and in Dordogne rabbits and hares become numerous. Among birds we observe the grouse and the raven. The wild boar (*Sus scrofa ferus*) was occasionally found in the region of the Danube and the Rhine, but abounded in southwestern Europe and the Pyrenees. The two

FIG. 183. The desert or Celtic horse, with delicate head, long, slender limbs, and short back, from a painting on the ceiling of Altamira, in northern Spain. The horse is painted in red ochre with black manganese outlines. The eye, ear, mouth, nostrils, and chin are carefully engraved. After Breuil.

dominant forms of meadow life surviving from the earliest Pleistocene times, and widely distributed throughout the Magdalenian are the bison (*B. priscus*) and the wild cattle (*Bos primigenius*); of these animals the bison appears to have been the more hardy, and seeking a more northerly range, while the urus was extremely abundant in southwestern France and the Pyrenees.

In connection with art, the majestic form of the bison seemed to strike the fancy of the artist more than the less-imposing outlines of the wild cattle; there are perhaps fifty drawings of the bison to one of the *Bos*. Among the forest and meadow life, not recognized in the fossil remains, but clearly distinguished in the work of the artists, are two types of horses, the forest or Nordic horse, related to the northern or draught horse, and the diminutive plateau or desert horse (*E. caballus celticus*) related to the Arab. With the forest life should also be numbered the cave bear (*Ursus spelæus*) of southwestern Europe and the moose

FIG. 184. Heads of four chamois engraved on a fragment of reindeer horn, from the grotto of Gourdan, Haute-Garonne. After Piette.

(*Alces*), indicated by the artists of Aurignacian times as present in the Cantabrian Pyrenees.

It is the above entire Eurasiatic forest and meadow fauna which survived all the climatic vicissitudes of Pleistocene time, and which alone remained in western Europe to the very close of the Upper Palæolithic culture, and into the period of the arrival of the Neolithic race.

The descent of the European and Asiatic alpine types of mammals to the lower hills and valleys is one of the most striking episodes of Magdalenian times. The argali sheep (*Ovis argaloides*) of western Asia had already appeared in the upper Danubian region during the Aurignacian; it is replaced in Magdalenian times by the ibex (*Ibex priscus*), and by the chamois, which descended along the northern slopes of the Alps and of the Pyrenees, and became numbered among the most highly favored subjects of the Magdalenian artists, especially in the mobile art of ivory and bone, and in the decoration of their spear throwers and *bâtons de commandement.* From the mountains also come the pikas or tailless hares (*Lagomys pusillus*), the alpine marmot (*Arctomys marmotta*), the alpine vole (*Arvicola nivalis*), and the alpine ptarmigan (*Lagopus alpinus*).

The Tundra Climate of Early Magdalenian Times

In the first cold moist period the full wave of arctic tundra life appeared in the whole region between the Alpine and Scandinavian glaciers during the renewed descent of the ice-fields; this was the tundra stage of early Magdalenian times, accompanying the *Bühl* advance. At the stations of Thaingen, Schweizersbild, Kastlhäng, and Niedernau, appears the musk-ox, together with the woolly mammoth, the woolly rhinoceros, and the reindeer. The discovery of the grotto of Kastlhäng, a reindeer hunting station in the Altmühltale of Bavaria[6] fills out what has long been a gap in the geographic distribution of the early Magdalenian. The principal objects of the chase here were the reindeer, the wild horse, the arctic hare, and the ptarmigan; the royal stag is very rare, and the bison is wanting entirely; a strong arctic character is given to the fauna by the presence of the banded lemming, the arctic wolverene, and the arctic fox. From this region the musk-ox migrated far to the southwest, reaching the northern slopes of the Pyrenees. At the same time the arctic grouse, the whistling swan, and other northern birds entered the region of the Rhine and the Danube. But the surest indicators of a cold tundra climate prevailing during the period of the *Bühl* advance are the banded lemming (*Myodes torquatus*) and the Obi lemming (*Myodes obensis*), which are found in the same deposits with the arctic hare, the reindeer, and the woolly mammoth mixed with the implements of the early Magdalenian industry at the stations of Sirgenstein, Wildscheuer, and Ofnet along the upper and middle Danube. There also appear the ermine and the arctic wolverene; in fact, almost all the characteristic forms of tundra

FIG. 185. Characteristic forms of alpine life, which descended from the mountains or migrated from the highlands of western Asia in Aurignacian and Magdalenian times: the ibex, the chamois, the alpine ptarmigan, the argali sheep, and the (*A*) alpine vole, all shown one-twenty-fifth life size; and the (*A*) alpine vole also one-fifth life size.

life except the polar bear, which only enters the northern tundras in the summer season.

The regions of the northern Alps bordering the great glaciers of the *Bühl* and *Gschnitz* advances, were barren stretches of rock, and the valleys and plateaus now free from ice became tundras, where the swamps alternated with patches of polar willows and stunted fir-trees, while other areas were covered with low, scrubby birches, or reindeer moss and lichens. The return of these hard conditions of life undoubtedly exerted a great influence both upon the physical and mental development of the Crô-Magnon race; it was at the very period when the life conditions in western Europe were most severe that the artistic development of these people began to revive. Forced to return to the shelters and grottos, which certainly were less frequented in Solutrean times, there was time for the development of the imagination and for its expression both in the mobile and parietal arts. There was a less vigorous development of the flint industry, and apparently a degeneration in physique and stature.

In Germany and northern Switzerland, on the headwaters of the Rhine and the Danube, the entrance and departure of the northern waves of life are recorded, especially in the grottos of Sirgenstein, Schussenquelle, Andernach, Schmiechenfels, and Propstfels. It would appear that the woolly mammoth and the woolly rhinoceros were not hunted in this region, for their remains are not preserved in any of the grottos or stations mingled with the middle or late Magdalenian cultures. On the other hand, we find the steppe horse, the kiang, the stag, and the reindeer very abundant indeed. The bison is absent, and wild cattle are very rare; so that this region is not typical of the mammalian life of Magdalenian times as found in Dordogne and in the Pyrenees.

The migration of the woolly mammoth and woolly rhinoceros along the Pyrenees and westward into the Cantabrian Mountains, and the crossing of the Pyrenees by the reindeer, have already been described. In the mural frescos of Font-de-Gaume, Dordogne, it is noteworthy that the very latest engravings are those of the mammoth superposed on the fine polychromes which belong to the period of middle Magdalenian art.

The Dry Steppe Climate of Middle Magdalenian Times

The cold, dry period, when the full tide of steppe life reached western Europe, is of somewhat uncertain date; it probably began during the stage of the middle Magdalenian industry and continued into the late or high Magdalenian. There was certainly an environment attractive to these peculiar and very highly specialized mammals, which at the present time are neutral in color, swift of foot, inured to existence on very sparse vegetation, and adapted to extremes of heat and cold. Among the smaller steppe forms were the suslik or pouched marmot of the steppes (*Spermophilus rufescens*) and the steppe hamster (*Cricetus phæus*), also the Siberian vole (*Arvicola gregalis*); still more characteristic was the great jerboa (*Alactaga jaculus*), with long, springy hind legs, and the saiga antelope (*Antilope saiga*). With these mammals appeared the steppe grouse (*Perdix cinerea*), which is found along the Danube in late Magdalenian strata; another bird characteristic of the northern steppes and tundras is the 'woodcock owl' (*Brachyotus palustris*). Accompanying these mammals was undoubtedly the steppe horse (*Equus przewalski*), now restricted to the desert of Gobi; it is said to occur in the grottos of northern Switzerland.

It would appear that the saiga antelope may have reached eastern Europe in late Solutrean times, for its outline is said to be found in an engraving at Solutré. Widely spread over Europe was the giant Elasmothere; it would seem very unlikely that this animal was present in Magdalenian times, for it certainly would have attracted the attention of the artists. Neither have we any positive artistic records of the wild ass, or kiang, although certain of the drawings in the grottos of Niaux and Marsoulas, of the middle Magdalenian, also of Albarracin, in Spain, may be interpreted as representing this animal. Thus the Asiatic steppe and desert fauna, which in the region of the upper Rhine and

FIG. 186. Steppe mammals from the steppes and deserts of Asia, which invaded western Europe in Upper Palæolithic times; the first arrivals appearing during the cold, dry period of late Acheulean times, becoming more numerous in the dry period of Aurignacian and Solutrean times, and completely represented in Magdalenian times. The saiga antelope, the (*A*) steppe hamster, the (*B*) great jerboa, and the kiang, or Asiatic wild ass, are all shown one-twenty-fifth life size. The (*A*) steppe hamster is also shown one-fifth life size and the (*B*) great jerboa one-twelfth life size. Drawn by Erwin S. Christman.

Danube was restricted to two species of mammals in Aurignacian and Solutrean times, rises to nine or ten species in middle Magdalenian times, so that for the first time during the entire 'Reindeer Epoch' the steppe and tundra faunæ are equally balanced. There are also six or seven species of birds from the moors and uplands of central Asia. The bird life depicted in middle Magdalenian art includes the ptarmigan or grouse, the wild swan, geese, and ducks.

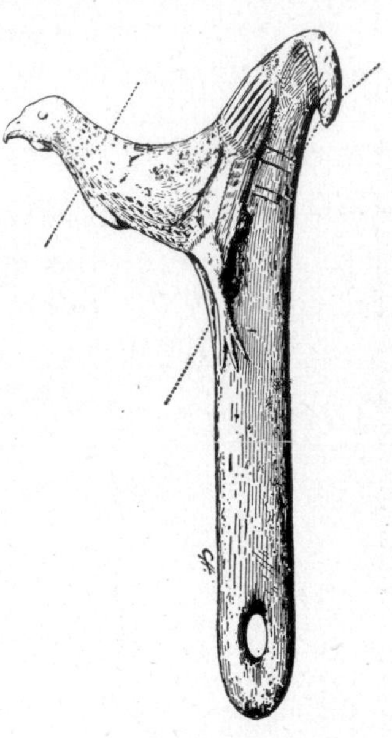

FIG. 187. Ptarmigan, or grouse, carved in reindeer horn, from Mas d'Azil. After Piette. The restored portions (head and feet) are indicated by dotted lines.

The present flora of the subarctic steppes in southeastern Russia and southwestern Siberia includes forests of pine, larch, birch, oak, alder, and willow, extending along the banks of the rivers and streams and interspersed with broad, low, grassy plains. There are many gradations between the low and high steppes;[7] the climate in summer is relatively warm, the temperature rising to 70°, while the average temperature in mid-winter hardly exceeds 30°; in general there is a strong contrast between the summer and winter seasons, the steppe lands in summer are practically rainless, so that the sand and dust rise with every wind. Thus, both in summer and winter sand and dust storms play an important rôle. The great snow-storms of the subarctic steppes are as destructive as those of the more northerly tundras and often result in great loss of life. Numerous discoveries tend to prove that similar conditions prevailed in western Europe during Magdalenian times. Thus at Châteauneuf-sur-Charente, a mingled tundra and steppe fauna is found containing the bones of many young animals which must have perished during a blizzard. It will be recalled that in this region is the station of Le Placard of late Solutrean and Magdalenian age. Near Würzburg, Bavaria, there is a fauna buried in the 'loess' containing twenty species of mammals of the tundras and steppes, together with the bison and the urus.[8]

Perhaps the strongest proof of the extension of cold, dry steppe conditions of climate is the migration of the saiga antelope (*Saiga tartarica*) into the Dordogne region, where it is represented both in carvings and engravings, and into other parts of southwestern France, where its fossil remains have been found in thirteen localities in association with a cold steppe fauna. In the same region have been found the remains of the musk-ox (*Ovibos*), one of the most distinctive members of the arctic fauna.

Human Races of Magdalenian Times

It appears that the Crô-Magnon race continued to prevail, yet anthropologists have long been divided in opinion as to the racial affinity of the men found in the Magdalenian industrial stage. The most famous burials are those of Laugerie Basse and Chancelade in Dordogne, each consisting of skeletons of inferior stature, not improbably belonging to women. They certainly represent a race somewhat different from the typical Crô-Magnons of Aurignacian times, as found at Crô-Magnon and in Grimaldi. The archæologist de Mortillet referred both these skeletons to a new race, the *race de Laugerie*. Schliz, who has most recently reviewed this subject, has, however, rightly treated all these people as Crô-Magnons of a modified type.

The Magdalenian skeleton of Laugerie Basse, found by Massénat in 1872, was resting on the back, with the limbs flexed, and with it was a necklace of pierced shells from the Mediterranean: the body apparently had been covered with a layer of Magdalenian implements. According to the length of the femur, the individual was 1.65 m., or 5 feet 1 inch in height; the bones were strong and compact; the skull was well arched, with a straight forehead and a cephalic index of 73.2 per cent.

The so-called Chancelade skeleton was found in the shelter of Raymonden in 1888, at a depth of 5 feet, and was also in a folded position, resting directly on the rock and covered with several layers of artifacts of the later Magdalenian culture; the limbs were so tightly flexed as to prove that they had been enveloped in bandages. This skeleton shows a well-arched skull, a high, wide forehead, and a dolichocephalic head form, but the limbs are comparatively small, the height not exceeding

Fig. 188. The *abri* of Laugerie Basse, Dordogne, a famous Magdalenian station and burial site of the skeleton of Laugerie Basse. This ancient rock shelter, like that of Crô-Magnon and many others, shows at the present day a cluster of peasants' dwellings around its base. Photograph by Belvès.

1.50 m., or about 4 feet 7 inches; the upper arm and thigh are short, compact, and clumsy, and the femur is crooked with comparatively thick ends; this skeleton is generally classed with the Crô-Magnon race, but Klaatsch considers that it may belong to a distinct type. We cannot disregard, says Breuil,[9] the anatomical characters attributed by Testut to the man of Chancelade and its resemblances to the actual Eskimo type; this indication is in favor of a new element, arriving perhaps from Asiatic Siberia, but acquiring in western Europe the artistic culture realized and conserved in certain districts by the Aurignacian tribes and their derivatives. All of the Aurignacian, Solutrean, and Magdalenian races, however, recall very forcibly the race of Crô-Magnon, which tends to prove that these transformations in culture were not made without a notable element of human continuity.

DISCOVERIES OF MAGDALENIAN AGE CHIEFLY ATTRIBUTED TO THE CRÔ-MAGNON RACE *

Date of Discovery	Locality	Nature of Remains
1863.	Bruniquel (Tarn-et-Garonne, France).	Skeletal fragments. Burial.
1864.	La Madeleine (Dordogne, France).	Skeletal fragments.
1869.	Laugerie Basse I (Dordogne, France).	Skeletal fragments.
1871.	Gourdan (Haute-Garonne, France).	Skeletal fragments.
1872.	Laugerie Basse II (Dordogne, France).	1 skeleton. Burial.
1872–1873.	Sorde (Duruthy) (Landes, France).	1 skeleton. Burial.
1874.	Freudenthal (near Schaffhausen, Switzerland).	Fragments of skulls and of pelvis.
1874.	Kesslerloch (near Thaingen, Switzerland).	Collar-bone.
1883.	Le Placard (Charente, France).	8 skulls, chiefly fragmentary.
1888.	Chancelade (Raymonden) (Dordogne, France).	1 skeleton, almost complete. Burial.
1894.	Les Hôteaux (Ain, France).	1 skeleton, almost complete. Burial.
1914.	Obercassel (near Bonn, Germany).	2 skeletons, male and female, almost complete. Burial. Early Magdalenian.
	Les Eyzies (Dordogne, France).	Skeletal fragments.
	La Mouthe (Dordogne, France).	1 tooth, 1 vertebra.
	Limeuil (Dordogne, France).	Skull fragments.
	Grotte des Hommes (Yonne, France).	3 skulls and other skeletal fragments.
	Brassempouy (Landes, France).	2 teeth.
	Grotte des Fées (Gironde, France).	Fragments of upper and lower jaw.
	Lussac (Vienne, France).	Fragment of lower jaw.
	Mas d'Azil (Ariège, France).	1 skull top. Early Magdalenian.
	Lourdes (Hautes-Pyrénées, France).	Skull fragments.
	Castillo (Santander, Spain).	Skull fragment. Early Magdalenian.
	Gudenushöhle (Austria).	1 infant's tooth.
	Andernach (north of Koblenz, Germany).	2 child's incisors and 7 rib fragments.

* After Obermaier,[10] R. Martin,[11] and others.

Another Magdalenian burial is that at Sorde, Landes, in the grotto of Duruthy; this skeleton was discovered in 1872, buried at a depth of 7 feet, the body being ornamented with a necklace and a girdle of the teeth of the lion and of the bear, pierced and engraved. Seven skulls found in 1883 in the grotto of Placard, Charente, also belong to the Magdalenian. The skeleton discovered in 1894 in the grotto of Les Hôteaux, Ain, was buried at a depth of 6 feet beneath Magdalenian implements; the body, resting on the back, was covered with red ochre; the thigh-bones were inverted, indicating that the limbs had been dismembered before burial—a custom observed among certain savages.

These are the best preserved Magdalenian remains which have been discovered in France up to the present time. The

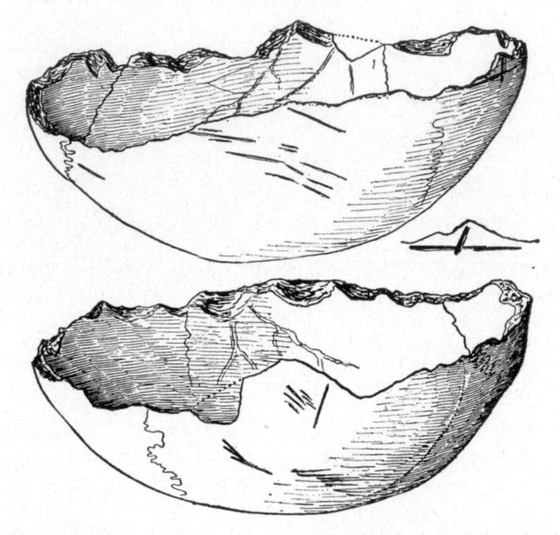

FIG. 189. Human skull-tops cut into ceremonial or drinking bowls, from the Magdalenian layer of Placard, Charente. After Breuil and Obermaier.

matter of chief significance is the survival of modes of burial characteristic of the Crô-Magnons in Aurignacian times, with the use of color and of ornaments and with the body in some instances folded and bandaged.

In the great grotto of Placard, near Rochebertier, Charente, a new feature in the mode of interment has been discovered—the separation of the head from the body.* The previous ceremonial burials, which began certainly among the Neanderthals in Mousterian times, always show the custom of burying the entire body; in the Upper Palæolithic there commences the new custom of imbedding the body in ochre or red coloring matter, and this

* This custom is observed again in Azilian times in the burials at Ofnet on the Danube (see page 475).

obtains from the Aurignacian burials of Grimaldi to the Azilian burial of Mas d'Azil. The flexing of the limbs occurs frequently in Upper Palæolithic times. It would appear as if the new ceremonial of Placard had been introduced in the earliest Magdalenian times, for in the lowest Magdalenian layers four skulls were found closely crowded together, with the top of the cranium turned downward; of other portions of the skeleton only a humerus and a femur were found. In an upper layer of the same industrial stage a woman's skull and jaw were found, surrounded by snail shells, many of them perforated. Still more singular is the occurrence in Magdalenian strata of this grotto of two separate skull-tops, fashioned by some sharp flint implement into bowls (Fig. 189).

Again, at Arcy-sur-Cure three skulls have been discovered placed closely together, and with them a flint knife in a layer superposed upon an Aurignacian industry. The Placard type of burial of the head only is shown again in the Azilian stage at Ofnet, Bavaria.

The uncertainty regarding the racial affinity of the men of Magdalenian culture has now been entirely removed by the discovery, in February, 1914, of two skeletons at Obercassel, near Bonn, the first instance of complete human skeletons of Quaternary age being found in Germany.[12] As reported by Verworn,[13] the skeletons lay little more than a yard apart; they were covered by great slabs of basalt, and lay in a deposit of loam deeply tinged with red. This red coloring matter, which extended completely over the skeletons and surrounding stones, indicates that it was a ceremonial burial similar to that practised by the Aurignacian Crô-Magnons. Along with the skeletons were found bones of animals and several specimens of finely carved bone, but no flint implements of any kind. The bone implements include a finely polished 'lissoir' of beautiful workmanship, placed beneath the head of one of the skeletons; the handle is carved into a small head of some animal resembling a marten; the sides show the notched decoration so typical of the French Magdalenian. The second specimen of carved bone is one of the small, flat, narrow horse-heads, engraved on both sides, such as are found at Laugerie Basse and in the Pyrenees. One of the skeletons is of a woman about twenty years of age, and, as is usual in young female skeletons, it exhibits the racial characters in a much less marked degree than the male skeleton, which belongs to a man of between forty and fifty years; the cephalic index is 70 per cent; the supraorbital ridges are well developed, and the orbits are distinctly rectangular; the limb bones indicate a body about 155 cm., or 5 feet 1 inch, in height.

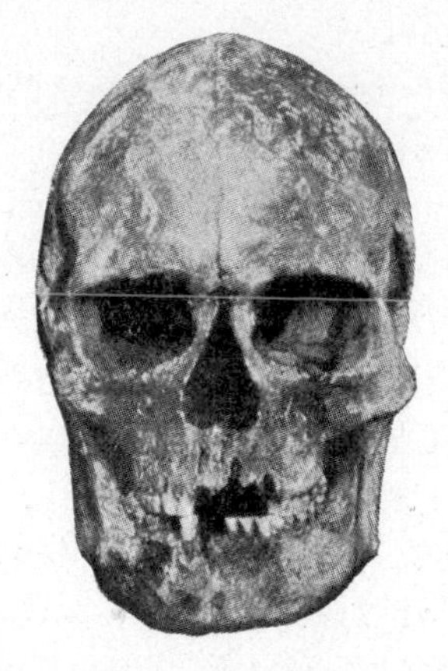

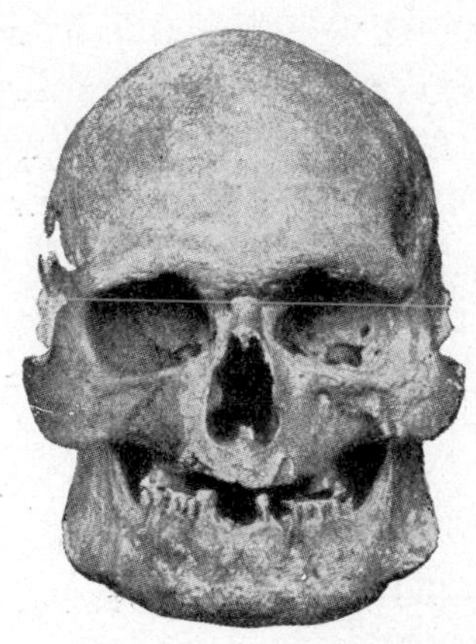

FIG. 190. The skulls of two skeletons of the Crô-Magnon race, one male (right) the other female (left), recently discovered at Obercassel near Bonn, associated with Magdalenian implements. After Bonnet.

In contrast to this more refined skull, the extremely broad and low face of the man is entirely disproportionate to the moderately broad forehead and well rounded skullcap; the breadth of the face is 153 mm. and exceeds the greatest width of the skull, which is only 144 mm. This is a markedly *disharmonic* type, the width of the face being due not only to the broad upper jaw but to the exceptional size and breadth of the cheek-bones. The skull is decidedly dolichocephalic, the cephalic index being 74 per cent; the brain capacity is about 1,500 c.cm.; the orbits are rectangular, and above them extends an unbroken supraorbital ridge, with a slight median frontal eminence; the nasal opening is relatively small; the lower jaw has a strongly marked chin; the crowns of the teeth have been worn down until the enamel has almost disappeared. While the muscular attachments indicate great bodily strength, the height does not exceed 5 feet 3 inches. As pronounced Crô-Magnon features, both of the Obercassel skulls show an unusually wide face; in both the profiles are straight and the root of the nose depressed, the nose is narrow, and the orbits are rectangular. But, observes Bonnet, the greatest width of these skulls is not found across the parietals, as in the typical Crô-Magnons, but just above the ear region, a much lower position; in this respect the Obercassel skulls resemble the skull of the Chancelade skeleton.

This very important discovery of two undoubted descendants of the Crô-Magnon race associated with bone implements of lower Magdalenian workmanship appears to prove conclusively that the Crô-Magnons were the art-loving race. The Obercassel skeletons confirm the evidence afforded by the burials in France that these people were of low stature; perhaps because of the severe climatic conditions of Magdalenian times they had lost the splendid physical proportions of the Crô-Magnons living along the Riviera in Aurignacian times. The skull also, while retaining all the pronounced Crô-Magnon characters, had undergone a modification in the point of greatest width.

In the reduction of the stature of the woman to 5 feet 1 inch and of the man to 5 feet 3 inches, and in the reduction of the brain capacity to 1,500 c.cm., we may be witnessing the result of exposure to very severe climatic conditions in a race which retained its fine physical and mental characteristics only under the more genial climatic conditions of the south.

The Four Industrial Phases of Magdalenian Culture

The industrial development belongs throughout to central and western Europe rather than to the Mediterranean. It is remarkable that it does not extend along the African coast, or even into Italy or southern Spain. It has been found to present four great steps or phases as follows:

The earliest types [14] of the incipient Magdalenian culture or

PROTO-MAGDALENIAN, are nowhere better represented than under the great shelter of Placard, in Charente, where the deep successive deposits compel a realization of the long period of time required for the evolution of the Magdalenian with its wonderful artistic culmination. Even prior to any discovery of the harpoon or of any example of the art of engraving comparable to the

FIG. 191. The great *abri*, or rock shelter, of La Madeleine, type station of the Magdalenian industry. Ruins of the abbey beyond. Photograph by Belvès.

classic series of higher levels we find three levels of incipient Magdalenian industry at Placard. Similar local horizons, recognizable from the type of their javelin points (*sagaies*) and from their decorative *motifs*, are also found at Kesslerloch, Switzerland, and as far east as Poland. From Dordogne they extend into the Pyrenees and into the Cantabrian Mountains of northern Spain, but not farther south. There is thus a very primitive Magdalenian industry wide-spread over central and western Europe, either autochthonous or influenced from the east, but certainly not from the Mediterranean. It is only above these primitive horizons that layers are discovered with the rudimentary harpoons, and then with the perfected harpoons with single and double rows of barbs. It would appear as if the basins drained by the Dordogne and the Garonne were at once the most densely populated and also the centres from which industry, culture, and art spread to the east and to the west.

In the heart of the Dordogne region is the great rock shelter of La Madeleine, the type station of Magdalenian culture, and around it are no less than fifteen stations. This station, in which the lowest industrial layer (*niveau inférieur*) is subsequent to the Proto-Magdalenian phase and belongs to the *early* Magdalenian, was extensively excavated by Lartet and Christy[15] during the decade following its discovery, in 1865, and more recently by Peyrony and others. The industrial deposit is situated at the base of an overhanging limestone escarpment on the right bank of the Vézère River; it extends for a distance of 50 feet with an average thickness of 9 feet, the lowest or early Magdalenian levels reaching down below the present level of the Vézère. It is a significant fact that the river floods which from time to time occur here also occasionally drove out the flint workers in Magdalenian times. It indicates an unchanged topography and similar conditions of rainfall. We must picture this cliff fringed with a northern flora, these river banks as the haunt of bison and reindeer, and the site of a long, narrow camp of skin-covered shelters.

Among the numerous specimens of typical Magdalenian industry and art which have been found here may be mentioned a geode of quartzite, apparently used to contain water, and stone crucibles, usually of rounded form, adapted to the grinding up of mineral colors for tattooing or artistic purposes; one of these crucibles, showing traces of color, still remains. The finest among the art objects is the spirited engraving, on a section of ivory tusk, of the woolly mammoth charging; this is one of the most realistic pieces of Palæolithic engraving which has ever been found; there are indications that the artist used this relatively small piece of ivory for the representation of three mammoths;

but in the reproduction (Fig. 199) all the lines are eliminated except those belonging to the single charging mammoth; we observe especially the elevation of the head and the tail, also the remarkably lifelike action of the limbs and body.

Very numerous industrial levels are discovered in eight or ten overlying hearths, which are, however, divided into three main levels, as follows:

Niveau supérieur (late Magdalenian culture).

Harpoons with a double row of barbs. Indications that the climate was colder and drier, resembling that of the steppes. Bison, horses, and reindeer abundant.

Niveau moyen (middle Magdalenian culture).

Harpoons with barbs on one side only; also bâtons de commandement. Indications that the climate was more moist, with frequent inundations from the river. Bison, reindeer, and horses less abundant.

Niveau inférieur (early Magdalenian culture).

Harpoons with a single row of barbs. Indications of animal sculpture. Remains of bison and of reindeer, but those of horses especially numerous.

In the Early Magdalenian we note the invention of the *harpoon;* its first crude form is that of a short, straight point of bone, deeply grooved on one face, the ridges and notches along one edge being the only indications of what later develop into the recurved barbed points of the typical harpoon. As noted above, this invention was destined to exert a very strong influence on the habits of these people. Large fish undoubtedly were very abundant in all the rivers at that time, and this new means of obtaining an abundant food supply probably diverted the Crô-Magnons in part from the more ardent and dangerous pursuit of the larger kinds of game. The discovery soon spread, and among a number of localities where prototypes of the harpoon are found may be mentioned Placard, in Charente; Laugerie Basse, in Dordogne; Mas d'Azil, on the Arize; and Altamira, in northern Spain. In the early Magdalenian also a great variety of flint drills or borers are developed in connection with the fashioning of bone, including the 'parrot-beak' type, or recurved flint. The microlithic flints, exclusively designed for fine and delicate artistic work, are more abundant than in any

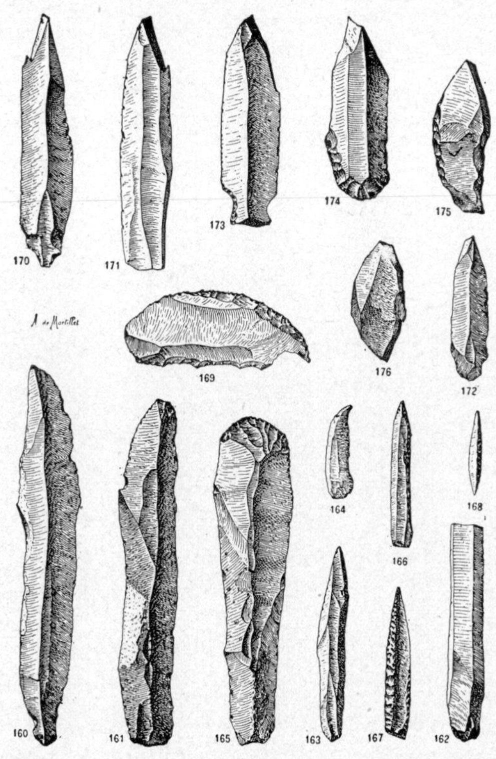

FIG. 192. Industrial and art implements of Magdalenian times, chiefly elongate flakes retouched at one or at both ends for various uses. After de Mortillet. 160. Long, narrow flint blade from the type station of La Madeleine. 161. A similar implement from the grotto of Mursens, Lot. 162. A 'knife' flake from Laugerie Basse, Dordogne. 163. A flint blade, very characteristic of the period, from La Madeleine. 164. A minute flake with cutting border and short, curved point. 165. An elongate flake shaped into a *grattoir*, or planing tool, at one end, from La Madeleine. 166. An elongate, pointed graving-tool, retouched at the end and at one side. 167. A pointed tool of chalcedony. 168. A minute pointed flake. 169. A 'parrot-beak' graving-tool of flint. 170. A straight flint graver, from Les Eyzies, Dordogne. 171. A similar graver, from Laugerie Basse. 172. A similar graver, from La Madeleine. 173. Flint graver with base retouched, from the Gorge d'Enfer. 174. A double-ended implement, *burin* and *grattoir*, from Laugerie Basse. 175. Flint *burin*, or graver, approaching the 'parrot-beak' type of 169, from Les Eyzies. 176. Double *burin*, or graver, of flint, from the Grotte du Chaffaud, Vienne. All figures are one-third actual size.

previous stage, and were used to shape and finish the bone implements which chiefly distinguish the Magdalenian culture. Other implements which enable us to recognize the early Magdalenian culture layers are javelin points of bone or reindeer-horn with oblique bases, small staves of reindeer-horn or ivory, oval plates of bone frequently decorated with engraved designs, and slender, finely finished needles.

The Middle Magdalenian implements were more widely distributed than the early types, the most characteristic weapon being the harpoon with a well-defined single row of barbs (Breuil,[16] Schmidt[17]). According to Breuil, this single-rowed harpoon is

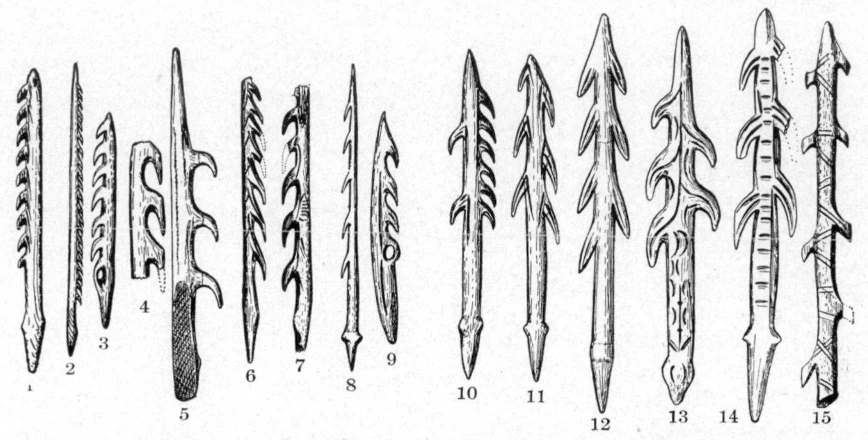

Fig. 193. Typical forms of Magdalenian bone harpoons. After Breuil. (*A*) 1 to 9, single-rowed harpoons, characteristic of the early and middle Magdalenian; 1, 4, 8, from Bruniquel; 2, 5, from Laugerie Basse; 6, from Mas d'Azil; 7, from La Mairie; 3 and 9, from Valle and Castillo. About one-quarter actual size. (*B*) 10 to 15, double-rowed harpoons, characteristic of the late Magdalenian; 10, 12, from Bruniquel; 11, from Massat; 13, from Mouthier; 14, from La Madeleine; 15, from Kesslerloch, Switzerland. About one-third actual size.

rare in the lower layers but abundant in the upper layers of middle Magdalenian times; with it occur examples of the single-rowed harpoon with swallow-tail base. Other implements of this stage are the bone javelin points with cleft base, small bone staves richly decorated, also numerous needles, finer and more slender than those of the early Magdalenian. It is very interesting to note that there are no distinctive inventions in the flint industry, which shows no important advances, although microlithic flints are still more abundant than before. For industrial purposes scrapers continue to be very abundant, as well as borers for the perforation of bone implements. The middle Magdalenian industry is best represented in the deposits of central and southern France, at Raymonden, Bruniquel, Laugerie Basse, Gourdan, Mas d'Azil, and Teyjat.

The chief weapon of LATE MAGDALENIAN times is the harpoon with the double row of barbs, which is found at all the principal discovery sites extending from stations in southwestern and southern France far to the east. Besides the double-rowed harpoon, the cylindrical chisel of reindeer-horn frequently occurs, often pointed at the end and with a small curve at the side; this, like other bone implements, was richly decorated with engraving. This late Magdalenian level is distinguished everywhere by the rich decoration of all the bone implements and weapons, as well as of the 'bâtons de commandement.' The quantity of bone needles, more numerous in this stage than ever before, attests the greater refinement of finish in the preparation of clothing.

This was the culminating point both in Magdalenian industry and art, and probably also in the morale and modes of living. Characteristic types of this late Magdalenian culture are found at La Madeleine, Les Eyzies, and Teyjat, and extend into the northern Pyrenees, at Lourdes, Gourdan, and Mas d'Azil. Their easterly geographical distribution will be described on a later page. The microlithic flints now reach their culminating point; to the small bladed flakes with blunted backs are added little feather-shaped flint blades, and still others with oblique ends, which begin to suggest the geometric forms of the succeeding Tardenoisian industry. Among the flint borers we notice a prevalent type with a stout central point, also the so-called 'parrot-beak' borer; for the preparation of skins, scrapers are made, as before, of thin flakes, slightly retouched at both ends to give a rounded or rectangular form.

Following the late or high Magdalenian stage is a period of decline in industry. In southern France[18] both flint and bone implements show unmistakable indications of the approach either of the succeeding Tardenoisian or Azilian stage. In the Pyrenees both the flints and the great polishers of deer-horn begin to resemble those which occur in the post-Magdalenian levels.

This industrial stage corresponds broadly with the period of decline in art, and with the change both in the industrial habits and in the artistic spirit of the Crô-Magnons.

The divisions of the Magdalenian are, therefore, as follows:

5. Decline of the Magdalenian art and industry.
4. Late Magdalenian.........typified at La Madeleine, Dordogne.
3. Middle Magdalenian........typified at La Madeleine, Dordogne.
2. Early Magdalenian.........typified at La Madeleine, Dordogne.
1. Proto-Magdalenian.........typified at Placard, Charente.

Flint and Bone Industry

Through the four successive stages of development which we have already traced (p. 382) there are perceived certain general tendencies and characteristics which clearly separate the Magdalenian from the preceding Solutrean culture.

Compared with Solutrean times, when the art of flint working reached its high-water mark, the Magdalenian palæoliths show a marked degeneracy in technique, having neither the symmetry of form nor the finely chipped surfaces which distinguish the Solutrean types; indeed, they do not even equal the grooved marginal retouch of the best Aurignacian work. The Magdalenian retouch shows no influence of the Solutrean; it is even more blunt and marginal than the late Aurignacian. In compensation for this decadence in the art of retouch, the Crô-Magnons now show extraordinary skill in producing long, narrow, thin flakes of flint, struck off the nucleus with a single blow; these 'blades,' which are very numerous, are often not retouched at all; occasionally a few hasty touches are used to attain a rounded or oblique end; in other cases a very limited marginal chipping along the sides or the development of an elongated pedicle (*soie*) produces very effective implements for graving and sculptural work.

For the art of engraving perfect *burins*, *burin-grattoirs*, and *burins doubles* were rapidly made from these thin flakes; also *burins* with oblique terminal edge and with the 'parrot-beak' end. For industrial purposes some of the flints were denticulated around the border, doubtless for the preparation of fibres and of thin strips of leather for the attachment of clothing to the body and for binding of the flint and bone lance-heads to wooden shafts. Extremely fine perçoirs have been found adapted to perforating the bone needles; the *grattoir*, single or double, was also fashioned out of these flakes, and the nucleus of the flint was used as a hammer. Hammers of simple rounded stones are also found.

But the notable feature of Magdalenian industry is the extensive and unprecedented use of bone, horn, and ivory. From the antlers of the reindeer are early developed the *sagaies* or

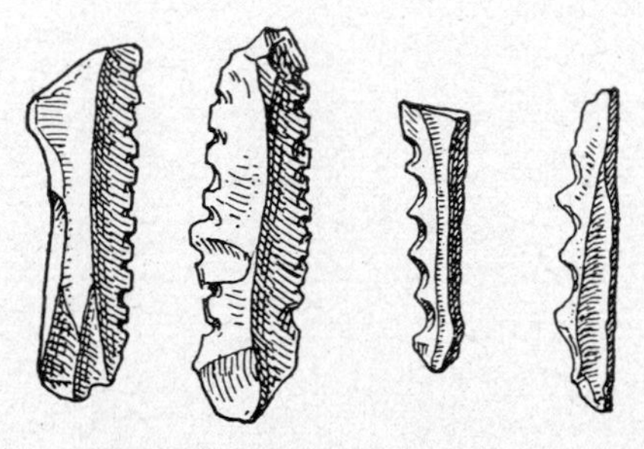

Fig. 194. Types of the flint blade with denticulated edge, a characteristic industrial tool of Magdalenian times, from Bruniquel, Les Eyzies, and Laugerie Basse. After Déchelette, by permission of M. A. Picard, Librairie Alphonse Picard et Fils.

javelin points of varying size, usually ornamented along the sides and with several forms of attachment to the wooden shaft, either forked, bevelled, or rounded. The ornamentation consists of engraved elongate lines or beaded lines, and of deep grooves perhaps intended for the insertion of poisonous fluids or the outlet of blood.

Of all the Magdalenian weapons the most characteristic is the harpoon, the chief fishing implement, which now appears for the first time marked by the invention of the *barb* or point retroverted in such a manner as to hold its place in the flesh. The barb does not suddenly appear like an inventive mutation, but it very slowly evolves as its usefulness is demonstrated in practice. The shaft is very rarely perforated at the base for the attachment of a line; it is cylindrical in form, adapted to the capture of the large fish of the streams. That a barbed weapon was also used in the chase seems to be indicated by drawings in the grotto of Niaux and lines engraved on the teeth of the bear, but these drawings indicate the form of an arrow rather than of a harpoon. The length varies from two to fifteen inches. The harpoons may have been projected by means of the so-called *propulseurs* or dart-throwers, which resemble implements so

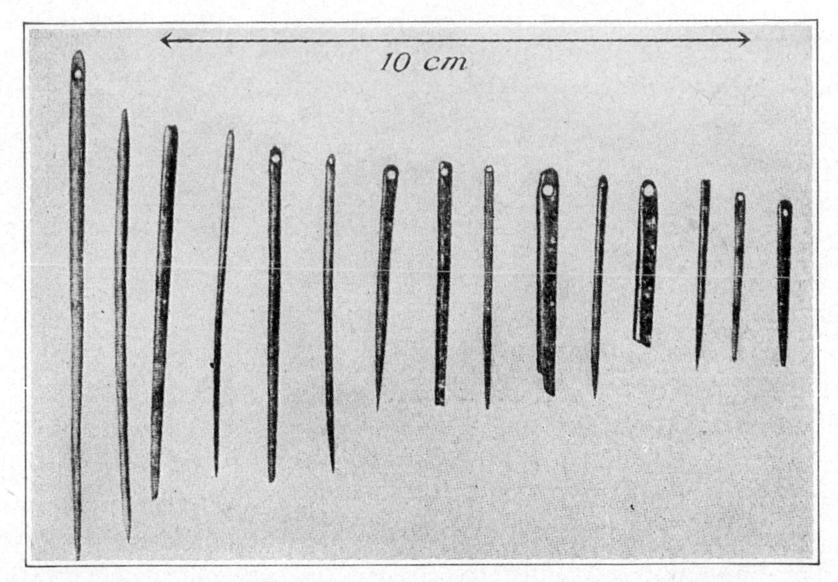

FIG. 195. Bone needles from the grotto of Lacave, Lot. After Viré.

employed by the Eskimo and Australians of to-day. These dart-throwers are often beautifully carved, as in the case of one found at Mas d'Azil, ornamented with a fine relief of the ibex.

Then there were *bâtons de commandement*, carved with scenes of the chase and with spirited heads of the horse and other animals, which quite probably were insignia of office. Reinach has suggested that bâtons were trophies of the chase, and according to Schoetensack they may have been used as ornaments to fasten the clothing. The discovery of mural painting and engraving suggests the possibility that these bâtons were believed to have some magical influence, and were connected with mysterious rites in the caverns, for a great variety of such ceremonial staffs is found among primitive peoples. Geographically, the bâtons spread from the Pyrenees into Belgium and eastward into Moravia and Russia.

Slender bone needles brought to a fine point on stone polishers indicate great care in the preparation of clothing. Associated with the borers are many other bone implements: awls, hammers, chisels, stilettos, pins with and without a head, spatulas, and polishers; the latter may have been employed in the preparation of leather. The borers, pins, and polishers appear from the very beginning of the period of sculpture. The name of poniard (*poignard*) is given to long points of reindeer-horn; one of these was found at Laugerie Basse.

History of Upper Palæolithic Art

Following the pioneer studies of Lartet, the history of the art of the Reindeer Period, as manifested in bone, ivory, and the engraved and sculptured horns of the deer, occupied the last thirty-five years of the life of Edouard Piette,[19] a magistrate of Craonne who pursued this delightful subject as an avocation. He was a pioneer in the interpretation of *l'art mobilier*, the mobile art. It must be remembered that in Piette's time the fourfold divisions of Upper Palæolithic culture so familiar to us were only partly perceived; his studies, in fact, related chiefly to the mobile art of Magdalenian times, and he undertook to follow its modifications in every successive grotto, beginning with his brochure *La Grotte de Gourdan*, in 1873, in which he first announced the idea which underlay all his later conclusions, that sculpture preceded line engraving and etching. He divided the art into a series of phases; that of the red deer (*Cervus elaphus*) he termed *Elaphienne*, that of the reindeer *Tarandienne*, that of the horse *Hippiquienne*, and that of the wild cattle *Bovidienne*. In concluding this early work of 1873, he remarked: "To write the history of Magdalenian art is to give the history of primitive art itself." He observed that in sculpturing the horn of the reindeer the artist was obliged to work in the hard exterior bone and to avoid the spongy interior; this defect in material suggested the invention of the bas-relief. The statuette he regarded as the assemblage of two bas-reliefs, one on either side of the bone. Thus he described the ivory head of the woman of Brassempouy, the only human face of Upper Palæolithic times which is even fairly well represented; also the two imperfect feminine torsos in ivory. In 1897, at the age of seventy, Piette undertook his last excavations, and the sum of his labors is preserved for us in the magnificent volume entitled *l'Art pendant l'âge du Renne*, published in 1907.

The pupil and biographer of Piette, l'Abbé Henri Breuil, observes that his scheme of art evolution is exact along its main lines.[20] It is true that human sculpture appears for the first time in the lower Aurignacian, that it survives the Solutrean, and even extends into middle Magdalenian times, but this enormous period cannot be placed in one archæological division as Piette supposed; in truth, he did not suspect the prolonged gestation of Quaternary art, but contracted into one small division the documents of numerous phases. At the same time, Piette was right in attributing the flower of the art of engraving accompanied by contours of animal forms in relief to the second and third levels of the Magdalenian industry, but he had no idea that this development had been preceded by a long period in which engraving had been practised in a timid and more or less sporadic manner as a parietal art on the walls of the caverns as well as on bone and stone. It is also true that a considerable facility in sculpture preceded the art of engraving, but it was arrested in its progress while engraving slowly developed; in the early choice of subjects the sculptors of middle and late Aurignacian times showed a preference for the human form, while later, in Solutrean and early Magdalenian times, they inclined principally toward animal figures, so that sculpture was not suddenly eclipsed. The first engravings made with fine points of flint on stone are hardly less ancient than the first sculptures, and modestly co-exist beside them up to the moment where engraving, greatly multiplied, largely supplants sculpture. Finally, observes Breuil, it is one of the glories of Edouard Piette to have understood that the painted pebbles of Mas d'Azil represented the last prolongation of the dying Quaternary art.

It is fortunate that the mantle of Piette fell upon a man of the artistic genius and appreciation of Breuil, to whom chiefly we owe our clear understanding of the chronological development of Upper Palæolithic art. In the accompanying table (p. 395) are assembled the results of the observations of Piette, Sautuola, Rivière, Cartailhac, Capitan, Breuil, and many others, largely in the order of sequence determined through the labors of Breuil.

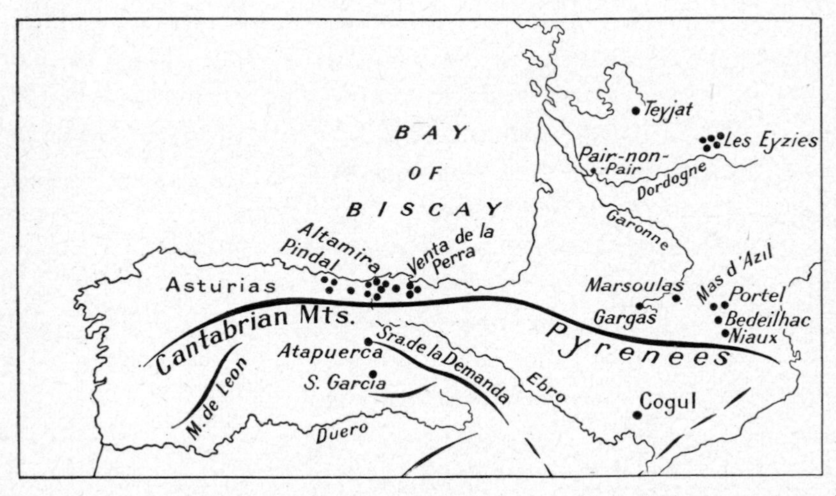

FIG. 196. Geographic distribution of the more important Palæolithic art stations of Dordógne, the Pyrenees, and the Cantabrian Mountains. After Breuil and Obermaier.

We are far from 1880, observes Cartailhac,[21] when the discovery by Sautuola of the paintings on the roof of the cavern of Altamira was met with such scepticism and indifference. Knowing the artistic instincts of the Upper Palæolithic people from their engraving and carving in bone and ivory, we should have been prepared for the discovery of a parietal art. The publication of the engravings in the grotto of La Mouthe by Rivière[22] in April, 1895, was the first warning of our oversight, and immediately Edouard Piette recalled Altamira to the memory of the workers on prehistoric art. The discovery of Sautuola ceased to be isolated. Led by the engravings found in La Mouthe,

	Sculpture	Incised Figures	Painted Figures
AZILIAN.		VI. No animal drawings.	VI. Conventional Azilian decoration. Flat pebbles (galets) colored in red and black. Mas d'Azil, Marsoulas, Pindal.
LATE MAGDALENIAN.		V. Entirely wanting.	V. No animal art. Various schematic and conventional figures and signs (bands, branches, lines, punctuated surfaces suggesting the Azilian galets).
MIDDLE MAGDALENIAN.	Slender human figurines in ivory and bone. Animal forms in reindeer and stag horn on implements of the chase and ceremonial insignia.	IV. Graffites feebly traced; fine lines indicating hair predominate in the drawings, as at Font-de-Gaume and Marsoulas. Perfected animal outlines and details. Fine animal outlines, Grotte de la Mairie, Marsoulas. Perfected engraving on bone and ivory.	IV. Polychrome animal figures with the contour in black and interior modelling obtained through a mingling of yellow, red, and black color. Constant association of *raclage* and of incisions with painting. *Mains stylisées*. Great, brilliant polychrome frescos of Marsoulas, Font-de-Gaume, Altamira. Animal outlines in black, Niaux.
EARLY MAGDALENIAN.	Animal sculpture. Bisons of Tuc d'Audoubert; high reliefs of horses, Cap-Blanc.	III. Deeply incised lines followed by light graffite contour lines. Incised outlines and hair, *e. g.*, mammoths of Combarelles. Striated drawings, Castillo, Altamira, Pasiega.	III. Figures of a flat tint and Chinese shading without modelling, also dotted animal figures as at Font-de-Gaume, Marsoulas, Altamira, Pasiega.
SOLUTREAN.	Bone sculpture in high relief; Isturitz, Pyrenees. Animal sculpture in the round, Předmost.	Engravings.	
LATE AURIGNACIAN.	Heavy human statuettes (idols) of Mentone, Brassempouy, Willendorf, Brünn. Human bas-reliefs of Laussel. Heavy human figurines of Sireuil, Pair-non-Pair.	II. Animal and human figures, at first very deeply incised, then less so; four limbs generally figured. Designs vigorous, somewhat awkward, as at La Mouthe, then more characteristic as at Combarelles.	II. Filling in lines at first feeble, then more and more strong, finally associated with contour modelling which ultimately covers the entire silhouette. Incised lines associated with painting as at Combarelles, Font-de-Gaume, La Mouthe, Marsoulas, Altamira.
EARLY AURIGNACIAN.	Animals in low relief.	I. Figures deeply incised, heavy, in absolute profile; stiff in form as at Pair-non-Pair, La Grèze, La Mouthe, Gargas, Bernifal, Hornos de la Peña, Marsoulas, Altamira. Archaic animal outlines of Castillo.	I. Linear tracings in monochrome, single black or red lines, indicating only a silhouette. Two limbs out of four are ordinarily figured. The most ancient paintings of Castillo, Altamira, Pindal, Font-de-Gaume, Marsoulas, La Mouthe, Combarelles, Bernifal.
	Statuary and bas-relief.	Mobile and parietal art in line.	Parietal and mobile art in color.

STAGES IN THE DEVELOPMENT OF UPPER PALÆOLITHIC ART

Daleau discovered the engravings in the grotto of Pair-non-Pair, Gironde. In 1902 there was the double discovery of the engravings in the grotto of Combarelles, and of the paintings in the grotto of Font-de-Gaume, communicated by Capitan and Breuil. Discoveries at Marsoulas, Mas d'Azil, La Grèze, Bernifal, and Teyjat soon followed.*

In 1908 Déchelette listed eight caverns in Dordogne, six in the Pyrenees, and seven along the Cantabrian Pyrenees of northern Spain, but there are now upward of thirty caverns in which traces of parietal art have been found, and doubtless the number will be greatly enlarged by future exploration, because the entrances of many of the grottos have been closed, and the remote recesses in which drawings are placed, as in the recent discovery of Tuc d'Audoubert, are very difficult to explore.

The chief divisions of Upper Palæolithic art are as follows:

1. Drawing, engraving, and etching with fine flint points on surfaces of stone, bone, ivory, and the limestone walls of the caverns.
2. Sculpture in low or high relief, chiefly in stone, bone, and clay.
3. Sculpture in the round in stone, ivory, reindeer and stag horn.
4. Painting in line, in monochrome tone, and in polychromes of three or four colors, usually accompanied or preceded by line engraving, with flint points or low contour reliefs.
5. Conventional ornaments drawn from the repetition of animal or plant forms or the repetition of geometric lines.

Drawings and Engravings of the Early Magdalenian

We have already traced the art of engraving, as it first appears in late Aurignacian times, into the Solutrean; in the latter it is but feebly represented. Its further development in early Magdalenian times is found in the engravings made with more delicate or more sharply pointed flint implements, capable of drawing an excessively fine line; these were doubtless the early Magdalenian *microliths*. The animal outlines, with an indication

* The whole history of these successive discoveries, beginning with the finding of an engraved bone, in 1834, in the grotto of Chaffaud, and concluding with the discoveries of Lalanne, and of Bégouen, in 1912, is summarized in the admirable little handbook by Salomon Reinach.[23] This convenient volume also includes outline tracings of the more important drawings and sculptures found in western Europe up to the present time.

of hair, are frequently sketched with such exceedingly fine lines as to resemble etchings; the figures are often of very small dimensions and marked by much closer attention to details, such as the eyes, the ears, the hair both of the head and the

FIG. 197. Primitive outline engravings of woolly mammoths of Aurignacian or early Magdalenian times, from the walls of the cavern of Combarelles. After Breuil.

FIG. 198. Engraved outlines and hair underlying the painting of one of the mammoths, from the wall of the *Galerie des Fresques*, Font-de-Gaume. After Breuil.

mane, and the hoofs; the proportions are also much more exact, so that these engravings become very realistic. Breuil ascribes to the early Magdalenian the engraved mammoth tracings of Combarelles. Engravings of this period are also found in the grottos of Altamira in Spain, and of Font-de-Gaume in Dordogne, and to this stage belongs the group of does at Altamira, distinguished by the peculiar lines of the hair covering the face. The subjects chosen are chiefly the red deer, reindeer, mammoth, horse, chamois, and bison. The striated drawings of Castillo and Altamira, which partly represent hair and are partly indications of shading, belong to this period.

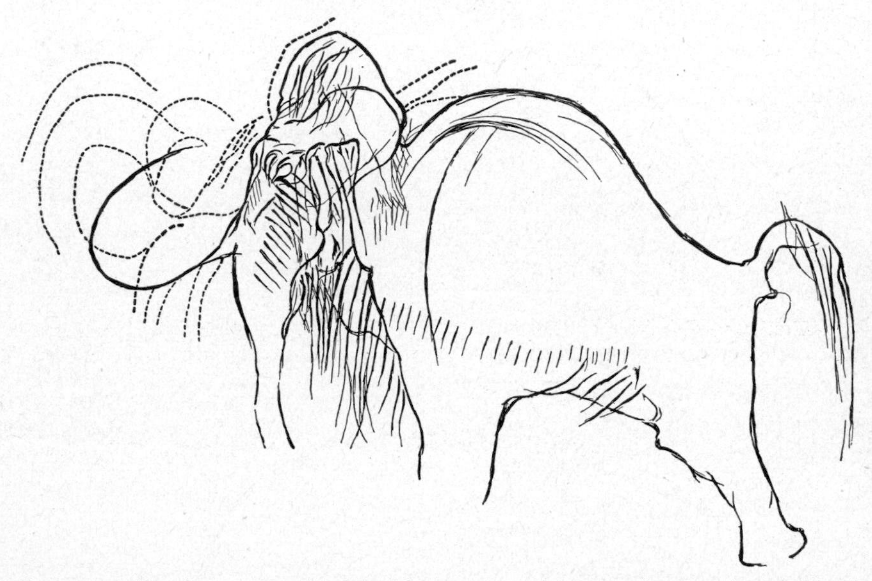

Fig. 199. Charging mammoth engraved on a piece of ivory tusk, from the station of La Madeleine. After E. Lartet. For the sake of showing this figure clearly, other outlines in this drawing, which were probably designed to indicate a herd of charging mammoths, are omitted or represented by dotted lines. This classic engraving, described on pages 384 and 385, is one of the most lifelike Palæolithic representations known of an animal in action.

The engravings in the grotto of La Mouthe were discovered by Rivière, in 1895, and were the means of directing attention afresh to the long-forgotten parietal art found in Altamira by Sautuola in 1880. The drawings at La Mouthe begin about 270 feet from the entrance and may be traced for a distance of 100 feet, scattered in various groups; they manifestly belong to a very primitive stage, probably early Magdalenian, the point of chief interest being that, while the greater part of the engravings are in simple incised lines, here and there the contour is enforced by a line of red or black paint; this is the beginning of a method pursued throughout the Magdalenian parietal art, in which the artist carefully sketches his contours with sharp-pointed flints before he applies any color. This treatment, at first limited to the simple outlines, led to tracing in many of the details with engraved lines, the eyes, the ears, the hair; thus Breuil has shown that in its final development a carefully worked-out engraving underlies the painting. In the La Mouthe drawings the proportions are very bad; they represent the reindeer, bison, mammoth, horse, ibex, and urus; spots of red are sometimes splashed on the sides of the animals; here and there is a bit of superior work, such as the reindeer in motion.

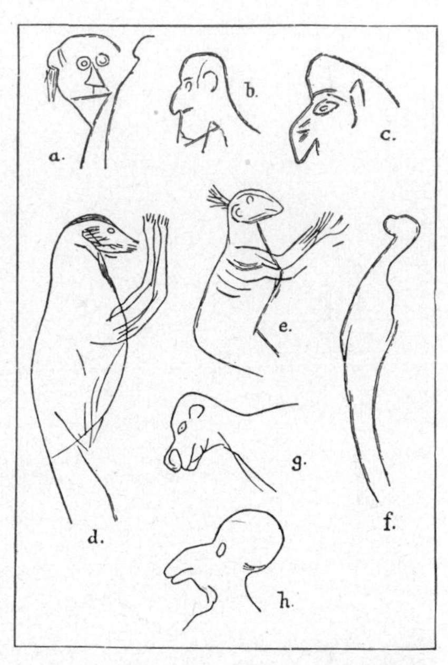

FIG. 200. Engraved outlines believed to represent human grotesques or masked figures found on the cavern walls of Marsoulas, Altamira, and Combarelles. After Obermaier.

The cavern of Combarelles, discovered in 1901, in Dordogne, near Les Eyzies, contains by far the most remarkable record of early Magdalenian art; there are upward of four hundred drawings and engravings representing almost every animal of early Magdalenian times, among them the horse, rhinoceros, mammoth, reindeer, bison, stag, ibex, lion, and wolf; there are also between five and six representations of the men of the time, both masked and unmasked; the style is more recent than that of the oldest drawings in Font-de-Gaume, but much more ancient than the period of polychrome art.* The gallery is 720 feet long, and barely 6 feet broad; the drawings begin about 350 feet from the entrance, and are scattered at irregular

* Only a few drawings from this cavern have as yet been published, such as the famous mammoth of Combarelles; the entire work is in the hands of Breuil.

intervals to the very end. In general the art is very fine and evidently largely the work of one artist; representations of the woolly rhinoceros and of the mammoth are very true to life; there is a pair of splendid lions, male and female; the drawings of the horse are abundant, and side by side we have a represen-

FIG. 201. Entrance to the cavern of Combarelles near Les Eyzies, Dordogne, where upward of four hundred wall engravings have been discovered. Photograph by Belvès.

tation of several types of horses, the pure forest type with the arched forehead, the small, fine-headed Celtic type, and a larger type reminding us of the kiang, or wild ass. Here the greater part of the work is engraving, as contrasted with the painted outlines in the cavern of Niaux and with the etched outlines of the Grotte de la Mairie.

Even a large cavern like Combarelles offers comparatively few surfaces favorable to these engraved lines; but, small or large, such surfaces were eagerly sought, sometimes near the floor, sometimes on the walls, and again on the ceilings; even with the brilliant light of an acetylene lamp it is now difficult to discover all these outlines, some of which are drawn in the most unlooked-for places. If the extremely fine incisions, such as those representing the hair of the mammoth, are so difficult to detect with a powerful illuminant, one may imagine the task of the Crô-Magnon artists with their small stone lamps and wick fed by the melting grease. One such lamp has been found in the grotto of La Mouthe, about 50 feet from the entrance; the workman's pick broke it into four pieces, only three of which were recovered. The shallow bowl contained some carbonized matter,

Fig. 202. Cave-bear engraved in outline, from the cavern of Combarelles. After Breuil.

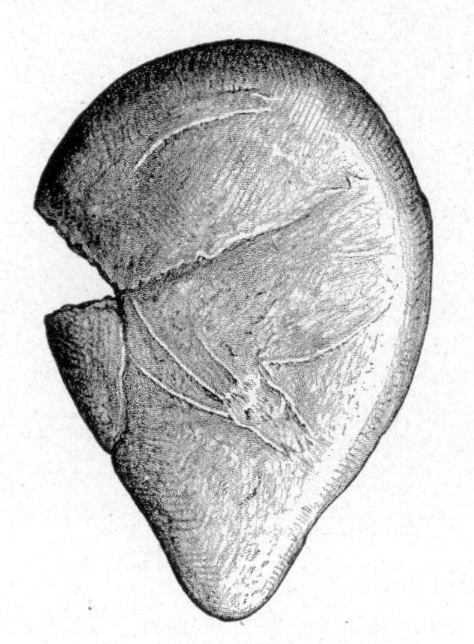

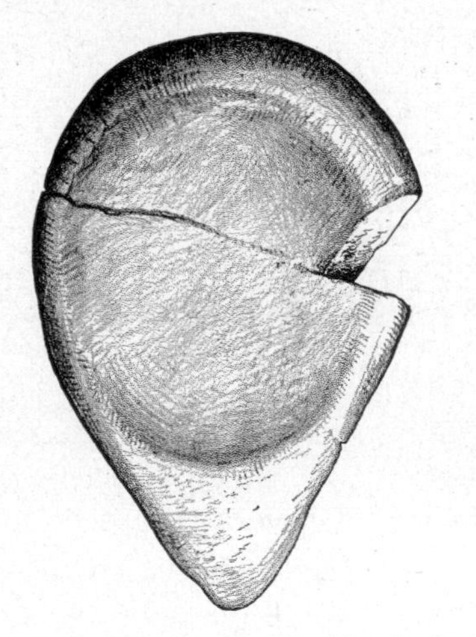

Fig. 203. Stone lamp of Magdalenian age discovered in the grotto of La Mouthe by E. Rivière. It is cut in sandstone and ornamented on the lower surface with the head and horns of the ibex. Such lamps were doubtless used by the artists to light the deep recesses of the caverns. After Rivière, redrawn by Erwin S. Christman. One-third actual size. (Compare Pl. VII.)

an analysis of which led Berthelot, the chemist, to conclude that an animal fat was used for lighting purposes. Like most other implements, this lamp is decorated—in this instance by an engraving of the head and horns of the ibex. Three of these lamps have been found in Charente and Lot, and it is noteworthy that lamps similar to those of the Magdalenian period are used in Dordogne at the present day.

FIG. 204. Entrance to the cavern of La Pasiega, not far from Castillo. The seated figure with the staff is M. l'Abbé Henri Breuil, the present leader in the study of Upper Palæolithic art. Photograph by N. C. Nelson.

In the great cavern of Castillo,* at Puente-Viesgo, discovered in 1903 by Alcalde del Rio, which is entered by the majestic grotto already described on p. 162, the animal drawings are mostly of an archaic character, belonging to the very beginnings

* The stations of Castillo, of Pasiega, and of Altamira were visited by the writer, under the guidance of Doctor Hugo Obermaier, in August, 1912.

of early Aurignacian parietal art. The most abundant subjects are horses and deer, which entirely replace the reindeer drawings so abundant in central France, outlines of the stag and of the doe being very numerous; on the other hand, the bison and the ox are rarely drawn. Belonging to the category of most primitive painting are the simple outlines in black of a horse and of a mammoth, the two limbs of one side being represented as inverted triangles, terminating in a sharp point, like the drawings of children. Of more recent style are the rather crude polychrome bisons, numerous hands outlined in red, and a vast number of tectiform signs and symbols which represent inferior work of the middle Magdalenian period.

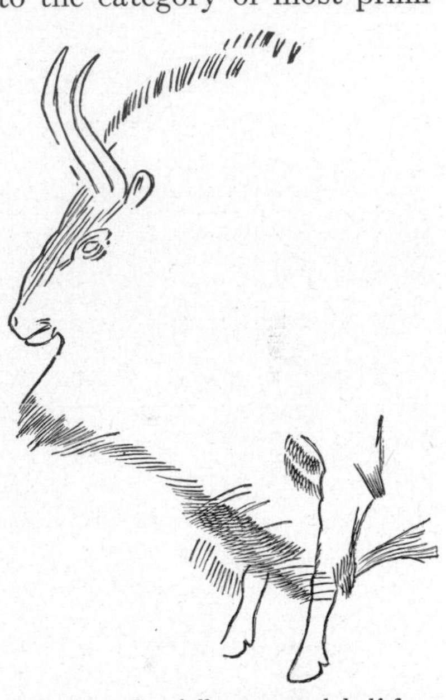

FIG. 205. Carefully engraved half-figure of a bison, from the cavern of Marsoulas; an example of the engraver's work preceding the application of color. After Breuil. One-eighth actual size.

On the other side of the same mountain is the grotto of Pasiega, discovered in 1912 by Doctor Hugo Obermaier. This small grotto, about 500 feet above the river, receives its name as a retreat of the shepherds. In the floor is a very narrow opening through which one rapidly descends by means of a tube of limestone barely large enough to admit the passage of the body. The interior is very labyrinthine. After passing through the *Galerie des Animaux* and the *Galerie des Inscriptions*, one reaches, after a most difficult détour, the terminal chamber, which Obermaier has called the *Salle du Trône*, the throne-room; here there is a natural seat of limestone, with supports at the sides for the arms, and one can still see the discoloration of the rock by the soiled hands of the magicians or of the artists. In this *salle* there are a few drawings and engravings on the walls, and a few pieces of flint have been discovered. In no other cavern, perhaps, is there a greater sense of mystery as to the influence, whether religious, magical, or artistic, which impelled men to seek out and enter these dangerous passages, the slippery rocks illumined at best by a very imperfect light, leading to the deep and dangerous recesses below, where a misstep would be fatal. The impulse, whatever it may have been, was doubtless very strong, and in this, as in other caverns,

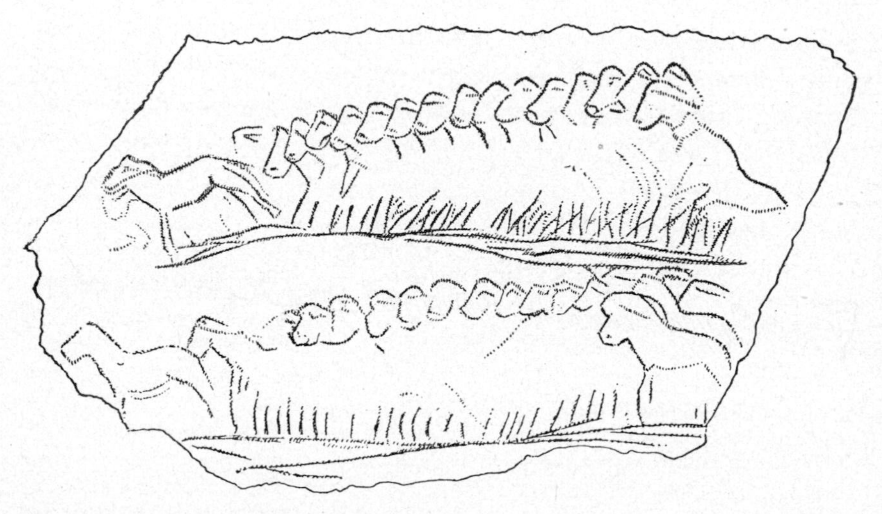

FIG. 206. Herd of horses engraved on a small slab of stone, found in the grotto of Chaffaud, Vienne, France. After Cartailhac. This impressionistic grouping and perspective is very exceptional in Palæolithic design. About nine-tenths actual size.

almost every surface favorably prepared by the processes of nature has received a drawing. No industrial flints have been found at the entrance to this cavern, but some have been traced into the interior. The art is considered partly of late Aurignacian, perhaps of Solutrean, and certainly in part of early Magdalenian times; in general it is much more recent than that of Castillo. It consists both of engravings and painted outlines, with proportions usually excellent and sometimes admirable. The paintings of deer are in yellow ochre, of the chamois in red. There are altogether 226 paintings and 36 engravings, in which are represented 50 roe-deer, 51 horses, 47 tectiforms, 16

Bos, 15 bison, 12 stags, 9 ibexes, 1 chamois, and 16 other forms, distributed in all parts of the cave. The outlines are in solid red color or in stripes of red or black, or there is a series of spots; the subjects are chiefly the stag, the doe, the wild cattle (which are rather common), the bison (which are less common), the ibex, and the chamois. Among the numerous representations of the horse there are two small engravings of a type with erect mane, both the feet and the hair being indicated with great care, the limbs well designed and of excellent proportions, clearly in early Magdalenian style. Of the utmost interest is the discovery here of two horses drawn with rounded forehead and drooping mane, the only instance in which the drooping mane

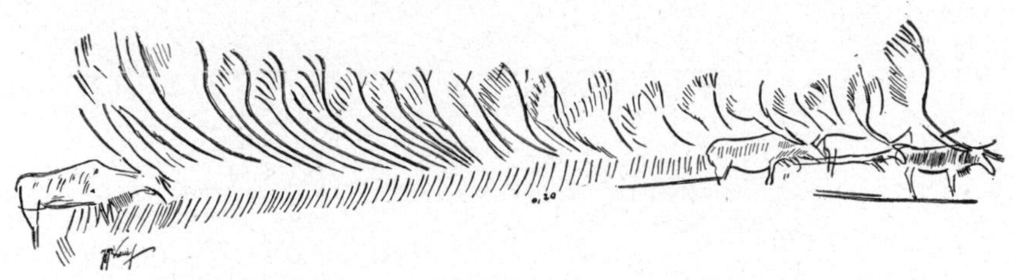

FIG. 207. Impressionistic design of a herd of reindeer engraved on the radius of an eagle nearly eight inches in length, found in the upper Magdalenian layers of the Grotte de la Mairie. After Capitan and Breuil.

of the modern type of horse (*Equus caballus*) has been observed in the cavern drawings.

In the advanced development of middle or high Magdalenian art, parietal engraving with finely pointed flint implements presents a nearer approach to the truth both of proportion and of detail than do the earlier stages. In this stage the engravings seem to consist chiefly of independent animal figures and to furnish a prelude to the application of color. A simple but striking example of approaching perfection of technique is seen in the bison (Fig. 205) engraved in the cavern of Marsoulas, where the profile is outlined and great shaggy masses of hair beneath the neck are admirably indicated. In these drawings the complicated details of the feet, with their characteristic tufts of hair, and of the head show far more careful observation. In the great series of bison at Font-de-Gaume the entire animal is sketched in with these finely engraved lines, as brought out through the wonderfully close observation and studies of Breuil. This is quite similar to the practice of the modern artist who sketches his figure in crayon or charcoal before applying the color.

There are two quite different styles in this engraving, one seen in the deep incised lines of the reindeer head in the cavern

FIG. 208. Stag and salmon engraved on an antler, from Lorthet, Hautes-Pyrénées. After Piette. This design is believed to represent a herd of stag crossing a stream, one of the very rare Palæolithic attempts at composition.

of Tuc d'Audoubert (Fig. 232), a complete design in itself, another seen in the deep incisions in the limestone outlining the horses and the bison as observed in the cavern of Niaux (Fig. 174). Here the engraved line is followed by the application of a black painted line, the effect being to bring out the body in the surrounding rock so as to give the silhouette a high relief.

In the drawings in the large on these curved wall surfaces, only part of which could be seen by the eye at one time, the difficulties of maintaining the proportions were extreme, and one is ever impressed by the boldness and confidence with which the long sweeping strokes of the flint were made, for one rarely if ever sees any evidences of corrected outline. Only a lifelong observer of the fine points which distinguish the different prehistoric breeds of the horse could appreciate the extraordinary skill with which the spirited, aristocratic lines of the Celtic are executed, on the one hand, and, on the other, the plebeian and heavy outlines of the steppe horse. In the best examples of Magdalenian engraving, both parietal and on bone or ivory, one can almost immediately detect the specific type of horse which the artist had before him or in mind, also the season of the year,

FIG. 209. Outlines of a lioness and a small group of horses of the Celtic or Arab type, a delicate wall engraving in the *Diverticule final* of the cavern of Font-de-Gaume. After Breuil.

as indicated by the representation of a summer or winter coat of hair.

The realism of most of the parietal art passes into the impressionism of the excessively fine engravings on bone or reindeer horn, executed with a few strokes, of a herd of horses or of reindeer (Fig. 207), or where a herd of deer is seen (Fig. 208) crossing a stream full of fishes, as in the well-known engravings on reindeer horn found in the grotto of Lorthet, in the Pyrenees. This is one of the very rare instances in Palæolithic art, either engraving or painting, which shows a sense of composition or the treatment of a subject or incident involving more than one figure. Others are the herd of passing reindeer found engraved on a bit of schist in the grotto of Laugerie Basse, the lion facing a group of horses engraved on a stalagmite at Font-de-Gaume, and the procession of mammoths engraved upon a procession of bison in the same cavern.

Beginnings of Painting

The beginnings of painting in Aurignacian times, consisting of simple contours and crude outlines in red or black, with little or no attempt at shading, pass in early Magdalenian time[24] into a long phase of monochromes, either in black or red, in which the technique pursues a number of variations, from simple linear treatment, continuous or dotted, to half tints or full tints, gradually encroaching on the sides of the body from the linear contour. Of this order are the figures in flat tints and shading, resembling those of the Chinese, without modelling; also the figures entirely covered with dots, such as are seen at Marsoulas,

Fig. 210. Early painting. A small horse of the Celtic or Arab type, with painted outline and body colored in black, from a wall of the cavern of Castillo, Spain. After Breuil.

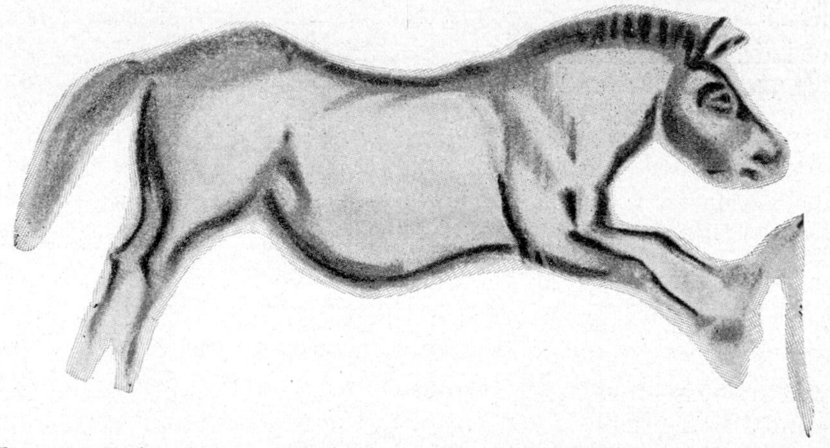

Fig. 211. Early painting Galloping horse of the Celtic or of the steppe type painted in black and white, from a wall of the cavern of Font-de-Gaume. After Breuil.

Font-de-Gaume, and Altamira. The tints, as in the drawing of the galloping steppe horse, pass inward from the black outline to enhance the effect of roundness or relief. In the splendid series of paintings in the cavern of Niaux there is little more than the black outline of the body, but the covering of the sides with lines, indicating the hair, lends itself to the rounded presentation of form. A somewhat similar effect is sought in the lines of the woolly rhinoceros painted in red in the cavern of Font-de-Gaume, which Breuil attributes to the Aurignacian stage, but which also suggests the early Magdalenian.

FIG. 212. Opening (cross) of the cavern of Niaux, in the Pyrenees, near Tarascon.

DRAWINGS IN VARIOUS CAVERNS OF THE EARLY AND MIDDLE MAGDALENIAN

The grandest cavern thus far discovered in France is that of Niaux (1906), which from a small opening on the side of a limestone mountain and 300 feet above the River Vic de Sos extends almost horizontally 4,200 feet into the heart of the mountain.[25] Not far from Tarascon on the Ariège it lay near one of the most accessible routes between France and Spain. Passing through the long gallery beyond the borders of the subterranean lake which bars the entrance, at a distance of half a mile we reach a great chamber where the overhanging walls of limestone have been finely polished by the sands and gravels transported by the subglacial streams; on these broad, slightly concave panels of a very light ochre color are drawings of a large number of bison and of horses, as fresh and brilliant as if they were the work of yesterday; the outlines drawn with black oxide of manganese and grease on the smooth stone resemble coarse lithography. The animals are drawn in splendid, bold contours, with no cross-hatching, but with solid masses of bright color here and there; the bison, as the most admired animal of the chase, is

FIG. 213. Engraved and painted horse, apparently of the Celtic type and with heavy winter coat, from the cavern of Niaux. There is a mark behind the right shoulder which has been interpreted as the sign of an arrow or spear head. After Cartailhac and Breuil. (Compare Fig. 174.)

drawn majestically with a superb crest, the muzzle most perfectly outlined, the horns indicated by single lines only, the eyes with the defiant expression highly distinctive of the animal when wounded or enraged. Here for the first time are revealed the early Magdalenian methods of hunting the bison, for upon their flanks are clearly traced one or more arrow or spear heads with the shafts still attached; the most positive proof of the use of the arrow is the apparent termination of the wooden shaft in the feathers which are rudely represented in three of the drawings. There are also many silhouettes of horses which strongly resemble the pure Asiatic steppe type now living in the desert of Gobi, the Przewalski horse, with erect mane and with no drooping forelock; in contrast to the bison, the eyes are rather dull and stupid in expression. There are also drawings of other types of horses, a very fine ibex, a chamois, a few outlines of wild cattle, and a very fine one of the royal stag; we find no reindeer or mammoth represented. In some of the narrower passages the rock has been beautifully sculptured by water, and

FIG. 214. Professor Emile Cartailhac at the entrance of the cavern of Le Portel, Ariège. Photograph by H. F. Osborn.

the artists have been quick to take advantage of any natural lines to add a bit of color here or there and thus bring out the outline of a bison.

Presenting the widest possible contrast to Niaux is the cavern of Le Portel, west of Tarascon, with its contracted entrance and a very rapidly descending passage hardly broad enough to admit the body. This narrow and tortuous cave terminates in an extremely small passage, so narrow as barely to admit the athletic and determined artist explorer, the Abbé Breuil. Here, as in Font-de-Gaume and other caverns, is one of the greatest mysteries of the cave art, namely, that these terminal and dangerous *diverticules finals* were wrought with some of the most careful and artistic designs. Le Portel, like Niaux, reveals a single style, but one altogether different. Very numerous bison are drawn in outline both in red and black; the sides of the body are often

FIG. 215. Finely engraved outlines of the Celtic horse and of the reindeer, in the Grotte de la Mairie, near Teyjat, Dordogne. After Capitan and Breuil.

dotted with red or hatched in close parallel lines. On a long horizontal panel are seen many bison in red, and one observes here a finely drawn pair of bison feet in the best Magdalenian style. The horse as represented here is of a quite different type with thin upper tail and a tail-tuft resembling that of the wild ass, so that one is almost tempted to believe that the kiang is intended, but the ears are too short; it has a high rump and a high, splendidly arched neck, like that of the stallion, and the eye is better drawn; the body is covered with long vertical or oblique lines which might be mistaken for stripes, but this hatching is a matter of technique only. Again, the mane is erect, and there is no forelock; in fact, none of these Magdalenian artists has represented the horse with the forelock, indicating that this character of the modern horse was unknown in western Europe and probably came in during Neolithic times.

Of an entirely different type are the beautifully engraved miniature figures of animals discovered in 1903 in the Grotte de

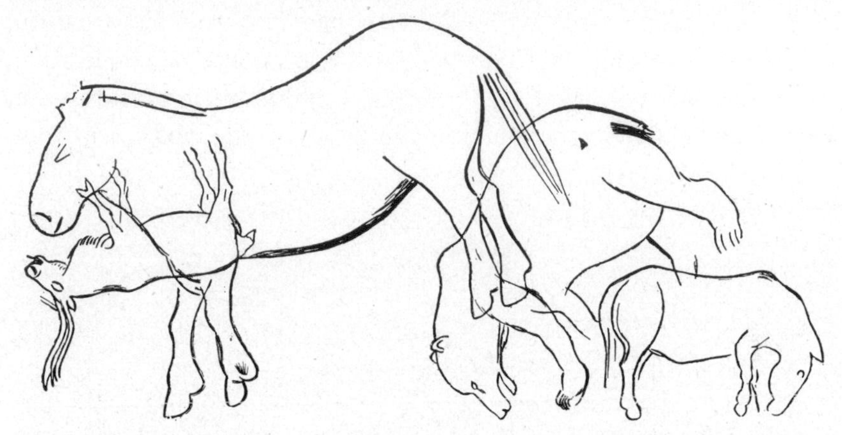

FIG. 216. Reindeer, cave-bear, and two horses of the large-headed forest type with arched forehead, engraved on a panel about twenty inches in length in the Grotte de la Mairie. After Capitan and Breuil.

la Mairie.[26] The outlines, from 18 to 20 inches in length, are sharply engraved on the limestone stalagmites; they are all in the middle Magdalenian style and include the stag, reindeer,

FIG. 217. Wild cattle, bull and cow (*Bos primigenius*), engraved in the Grotte de la Mairie, each figure being about twenty inches in length. After Capitan and Breuil.

bison, cave-bear, lion, wild cattle, and two very distinct types of horses: one of these types is large-headed with an arched forehead; this is probably the forest type and perhaps represents the horse most abundant at the Solutré encampment (see p. 288); the other horse is small-headed, with a perfectly flat, straight forehead, corresponding with the Arab or Celtic pony type.

Drawings and Paintings of the End of the Middle Magdalenian

The fourth and final developmental phase of painting flowers out toward the end of middle Magdalenian times in the grand period of polychromes. These are first etched with underlying

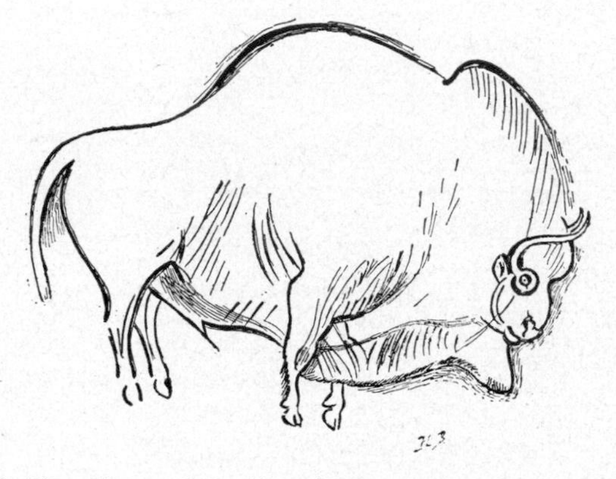

Fig. 218. Outline of one of the bison in the *Galerie des Fresques* at Font-de-Gaume, showing the preliminary etching or engraving preparatory to the polychrome fresco painting. After Breuil.

lines engraved with flint, the surface of the limestone having been previously prepared by the thinning or scraping of the borders (*raclage*) to heighten the relief of the drawing; then a very strong contour is laid down in black, and this may be followed by a further contour line in red (the use of black and red is very ancient); an ochreous brown color is mixed in, conforming well with what we know to be the tints of the hairy portions of the bison. Thus gradually a complete polychrome fresco art develops. The final stage of this art follows, in which the filling out of various tones of color requires the use of black, brown, red, and yellowish shades. The underlying or preliminary engraving now begins to recede, being retained only for the tracing in of the final details of the hair, the eyes, the horns, and the hoofs.

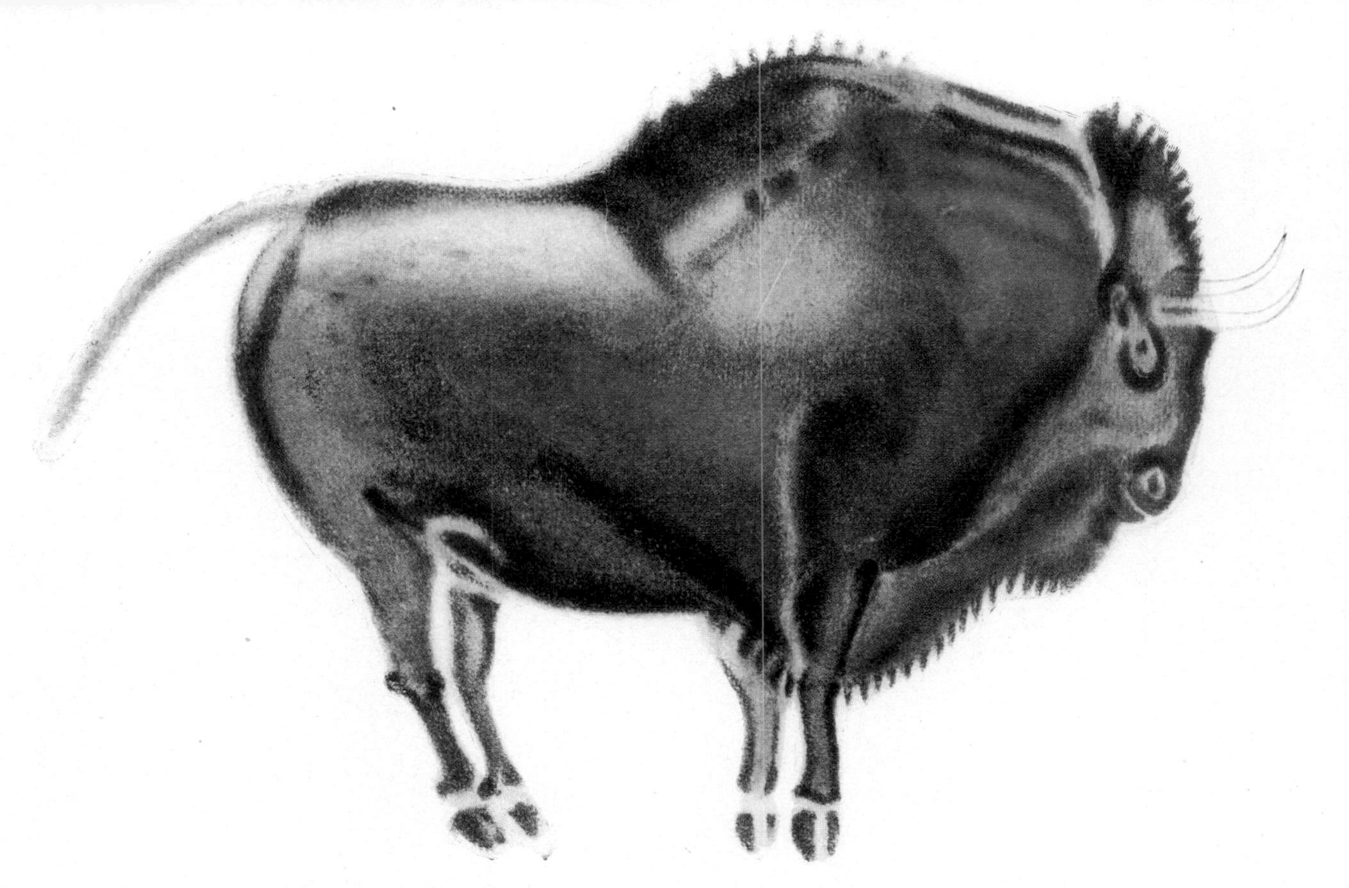

Pl. VIII. One of the bisons on the ceiling of Altamira, representing the final stage of polychrome art in which four shades of color are used. After Breuil.

The early stages of this art are seen in the cavern of Marsoulas, and its height is reached in the mural frescos of Font-de-Gaume and in the ceiling of Altamira, the latter still in a perfect and brilliant state of preservation.

To prepare the colors, ochre and oxide of manganese were ground down to a fine powder in stone mortars; raw pigment

FIG. 219. Entrance on the right to the grotto leading to the great cavern of Font-de-Gaume on the Beune. Photograph by N. C. Nelson.

was carried in ornamented cases made from the lower-limb bones of the reindeer, and such tubes still containing the ochre have been found in the Magdalenian hearths; the mingling of the finely ground powder with the animal oils or fats that were used was probably done on the flat side of the shoulder-blade of the reindeer or on some other palette. The pigment was quite permanent, and in the darkness of the Altamira grotto it has been so perfectly preserved that the colors are still as brilliant as if they had been applied yesterday.

The art of the grotto of Marsoulas, in the Pyrenees, is both of an earlier and of a later period; the engraved lines, as of the head and front of a bison, are beautifully done in advanced Magdalenian style, deep incisions representing the larger outlines and finer incisions representing the hair; here the outlines are also traced in color, and there are several masks or grotesques of the human face; these last are treated with a total disregard of the truth which characterizes the animal work. Among the few bison represented here, some are covered with dots or splashes of color, others show the painted outline which begins

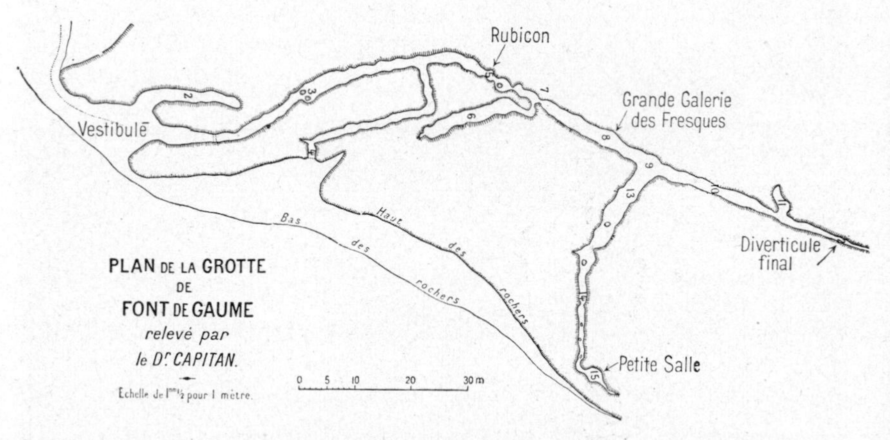

FIG. 220. Map of the cavern of Font-de-Gaume, showing the 'Rubicon,' the *Grande Galerie des Fresques*, in which the chief polychrome paintings are found, and the *Diverticule final*. After Capitan.

to extend over the surface with gradations of tint, anticipating the color effects attained in the finished paintings of Altamira and of Font-de-Gaume. All the details of the early technique are found here: the artist outlines the form with an engraved line; he traces in black color the contours of the head and of the body; he begins to apply masses of red over the figure. This beginning of polychrome art at Marsoulas is a step toward coloring the entire surface with red ochre and black, as in the finished paintings of a later period.

The grand cavern of Font-de-Gaume,[27] on the Beune, not far from Les Eyzies, contains the most complete record of Upper Palæolithic art, especially from the close of Aurignacian to the

Fig. 221. Narrow passage in the cavern of Font-de-Gaume, known as the 'Rubicon.' On the left wall at this point are two painted bison, and on both walls are marks left by the claws of the cave-bear. After Lassalle.

close of Magdalenian times. There are crude Aurignacian drawings, simple outlines painted in black, outlines supplemented by the indication of hair (examples of the early stages in the development of polychrome work as well as of the very highest stages), compositions like the lion and the group of horses, and the murals in the *Galerie des Fresques*, which show a general composition in the processions of animals, as well as some special compositions such as the reindeer and bison facing each other. The life depicted is largely that of the tundras, mammoths, rhinoceroses, and reindeer, but it also includes the steppe or Celtic type of horse, represented galloping (Fig. 211), and a

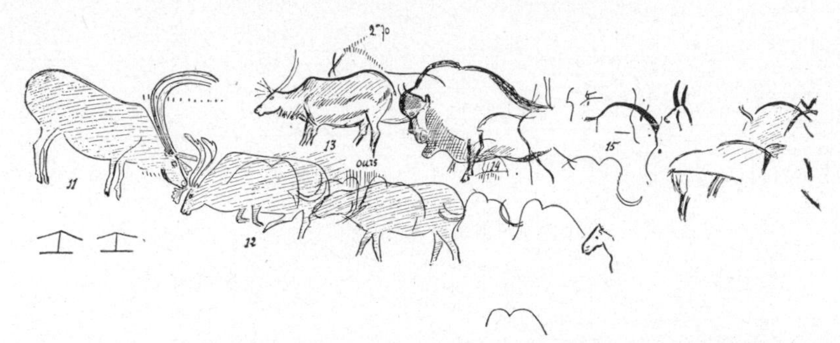

FIG. 222. Plan of a portion of the left wall decoration in the *Galerie des Fresques* at Font-de-Gaume, showing reindeer and the procession of bison. After Breuil.

small group of horses of the Arab or Celtic type. Of the meadow fauna the bison is generally represented in preference to the wild ox or urus.

Throughout the cavern the favorable surfaces of the walls are crowded with engravings, and in the *Galerie des Fresques*, beyond the narrow passage known as the 'Rubicon' (Fig. 221), we see altogether the finest examples of Upper Palæolithic art. On each side of this gallery is a peculiarly advantageous mural surface, broad, relatively smooth, and gently concave (Pl. VII), probably the best which any cavern afforded, and here we observe great processions of mammals superposed upon each other, like the records of a palimpsest, as if such a surface was so rare that it was visited again and again. The most imposing series is that of the bison, done in the finest polychrome style, mostly headed in one direction. The reindeer form another series and in some instances face each other, although mainly arranged in a long procession facing to the left. This superposition of drawing upon drawing ends with the latest superposition in finely incised lines of a great procession of mammoths upon that of the polychrome bisons. It is somewhat difficult to reconcile a religious or votive interpretation with the multiplication of these

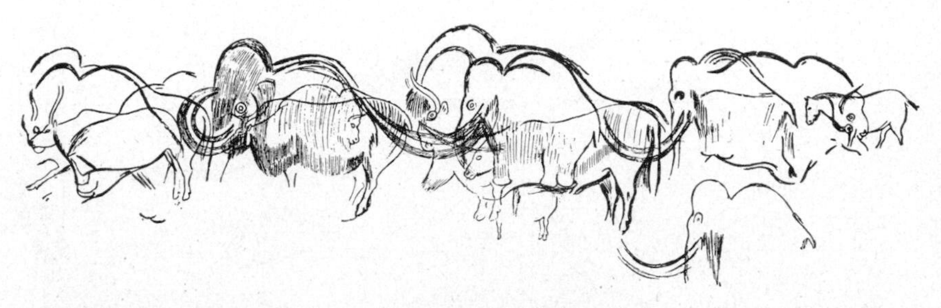

FIG. 223. Another portion of the left wall decoration of the *Galerie des Fresques*, showing the preliminary engraving (above), and the painting (below) of the great procession of mammoths, superposed upon drawings of the bison, reindeer, and horse. This section is about fourteen feet in length. After Breuil.

drawings upon each other. Moreover, it appears to be inconsistent with the reverent spirit which pervades the work in this and in all other caverns, for what impresses one most is the absence of trivial work or meaningless drawings.

It seems as if at every stage in their artistic development these people were intensely serious about their work, each drawing being executed with the utmost possible care, according to the degree of artistic development and appreciation.

In the great gallery of frescos we find not less than eighty figures, in some cases partly covered by a fine sheen of stalagmitic limestone; these include 49 bison, 4 reindeer, 4 horses, and 15 mammoths. The bison polychromes have suffered somewhat in color and are far less brilliant than those at Altamira. In the polychromes the color is applied either in long lines of red or black surrounding the contours of the animal or in flat tints placed side by side, or again the two colors are mingled and give

FIG. 224. Detail of the engraving of the central group of figures on the left wall decoration of the *Galerie des Fresques* (see Fig. 223), showing the etching of a mammoth superposed upon that of a bison, superposed in turn upon those of a reindeer and of a wild boar. These figures are on different scales, and in the present faded condition of the frescoes are difficult to detect. After Breuil.

intermediate tints with striking effect. On one of the finest of these bison is the underlying drawing of a reindeer, a wild boar, and the superposition of an excellent engraving of a mammoth, which is represented on an altogether different scale, so that it falls well within the body lines of the bison (Fig. 224). In each of these mammoths the grotesque but truthful contour is preserved in the drapery of hair which almost completely envelops the limbs; the emphasizing of the sudden depression of the dorsal line behind the head is everywhere the same and undoubtedly conforms very closely to nature.

After passing the *Galerie des Fresques* we penetrate to the final recess called the *Diverticule final*, through excessively nar-

FIG. 225. Entrance to the cavern of Altamira, showing the proximity of the roof of the cavern to the present surface of the earth. Photograph by N. C. Nelson.

row tubular openings barely admitting the body, and we are again overcome with the mystery as to what impulse carried this art into the dark, deep portions of the caverns. If it were due to a feeling partly religious which regarded the caverns with special awe, why do we find equally skilful and conscientious work on all the mobile utensils of daily life and of the chase, apart from the caverns? The superposition of one drawing upon another, which is especially characteristic of this cavern, does not seem to strengthen the religious interpretation.

It would appear that the love of art for art's sake, akin in a very rudimentary form to that which inspired the early Greeks, together with the fine spaces which these caverns alone afforded for larger representations, may be an alternative explanation.

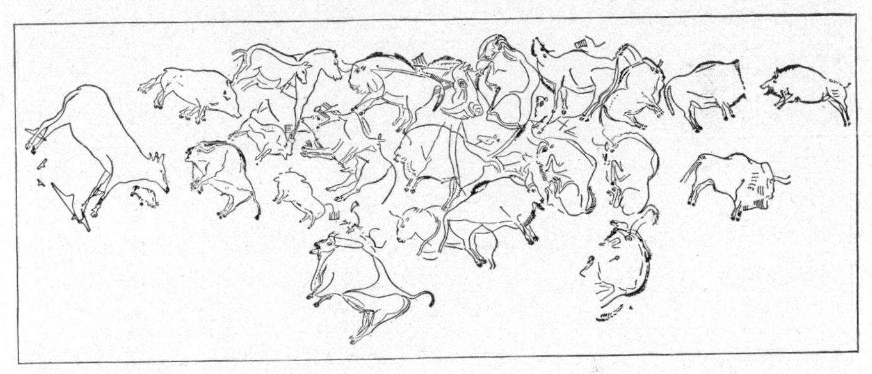

FIG. 226. Plan showing the grouping of bison, horses, red deer, and wild boar, in the polychrome paintings on the ceiling of Altamira. After Breuil.

There is no evidence that numbers of people entered these caverns. If this had been the case there would be many more examples of inartistic work upon the walls. It is possible that the Crô-Magnon artists constituted a recognized class especially gifted by nature, quite distinct from the magician class or the artisan class. The dark recesses of the caverns opening back of the grottos may have been held in awe as mysterious abodes. In line with this theory is the suggestion that the artists may have been invited into the caverns by the priests or medicine-men to decorate the walls with all the animals of the chase.

The polychromes of the ceiling of Altamira in northern Spain, which rank in the crude art of Palæolithic times much as the ceiling of the Sistine Chapel does in modern art, are somewhat more conventional in technique than those of Font-de-Gaume, but they are manifestly the work of the same school, and prove that the technique of art spread like that of engraving, of sculpture, and of the preparation of flint and bone implements all over southwestern Europe. One could not have more striking proof of the unity of race, of a community of life, and of an inter-

FIG. 227. The ceiling of Altamira, showing the round projecting bosses of limestone on which the recumbent figures of the bison are painted. After Lassalle.

change of ideas among these nomadic people than the close resemblance which is observed in the art of Altamira, Spain, and that of Font-de-Gaume, 290 miles distant, in Dordogne.

Very picturesque is the account of the discovery of this wonderful ceiling, made not by the Spanish archæologist Sautuola himself, but by his little daughter, who, while he was searching for flints on the floor of the cavern, was the first to perceive the paintings on the ceiling and to insist upon his raising his lamp aloft. This was in 1879, long before the discovery of parietal art in France. The ceiling is broad and low, within easy reach of the hand, and the oval bosses of limestone (Fig. 227), from

4 to 5 feet in length and from 3 to 4 in width, led to the development here of one of the most striking characteristics of all Palæolithic art, namely, the artist's adaptation of the subject to his medium and to the character of the surface upon which he was working. It seems to show a high order of creative genius that each of these projecting bosses was chosen for the representation of a bison lying down, with the limbs drawn up in different positions beneath the body (Fig. 228) and very carefully designed,

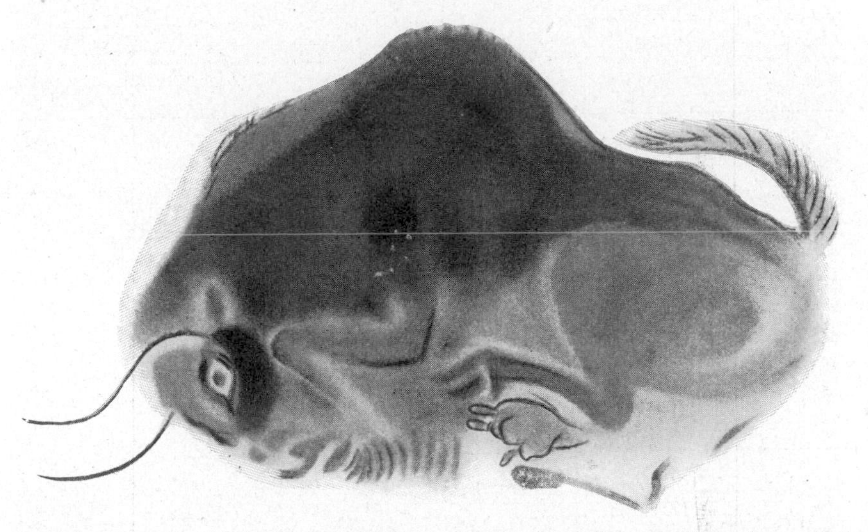

FIG. 228. Female bison lying down with the limbs drawn beneath the body, so that only the horns and tail project beyond the convex surface of the limestone boss on the ceiling of Altamira. After Breuil.

and with the tail or the horns alone projecting beyond the convex surface to the surrounding plane surface. This is the only instance known where the bison are represented as lying down, in most lifelike attitudes, showing the soles of the hoof, observed with the greatest care and represented by a few strong and significant lines. Thus while the Altamira coloring inclines to conventionality, the pose of these animals indicates the greatest freedom of style and mastery of perspective anywhere observed. In this wonderful group there is also a bison bellowing, with his back arched and his limbs drawn under him as if to expel the air. One striking feature in all these paintings is the vivid representation of the eye, which in every case is given a fierce and defiant character, so distinctive of the bison bull when enraged. We also observe a wild boar in a running attitude and several spirited representations of the horse and of the female deer. The cavern of Altamira, besides this *chef-d'œuvre*, contains work of a very advanced character, as indicated in the imposing en-

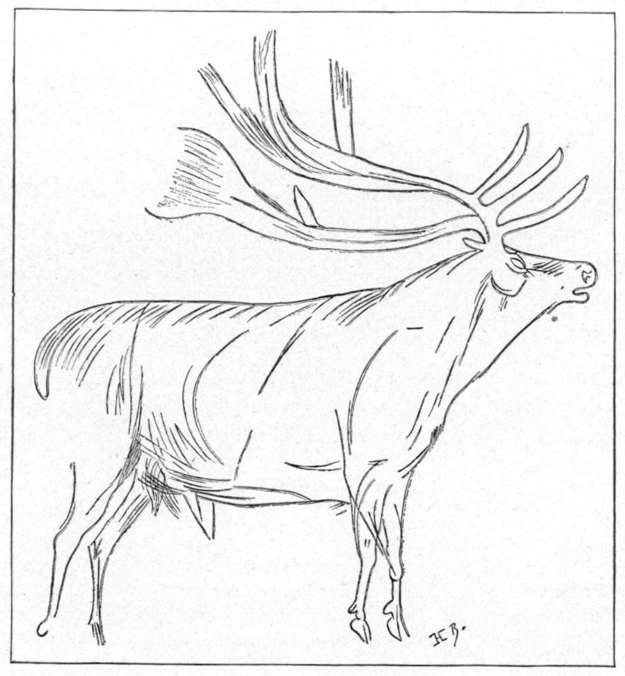

FIG. 229. The royal stag (*Cervus elaphus*) engraved on the ceiling of the cavern of Altamira. About twenty-six inches in length. After Breuil. One-eighth actual size.

graving of the royal stag (Fig. 229), which is altogether the finest representation of this animal which has thus far been discovered in any cavern.

Altamira, like Font-de-Gaume, presents many phases of the development of art in Magdalenian times. There is a Solutrean layer in the foyer of this great cavern, but Breuil is not inclined to attribute any of the art to this period. The first entrance of Altamira by the Crô-Magnon artists is dated by the discovery of engravings on bone of the female red deer, which are identical with those on the walls and which belong to very ancient Magdalenian times, the period at which the caverns of Castillo and La Pasiega were also entered.[28]

SCULPTURE

Animal sculpture in the round, which is indicated by the few statuettes found with the burial at Brünn, Moravia, and by

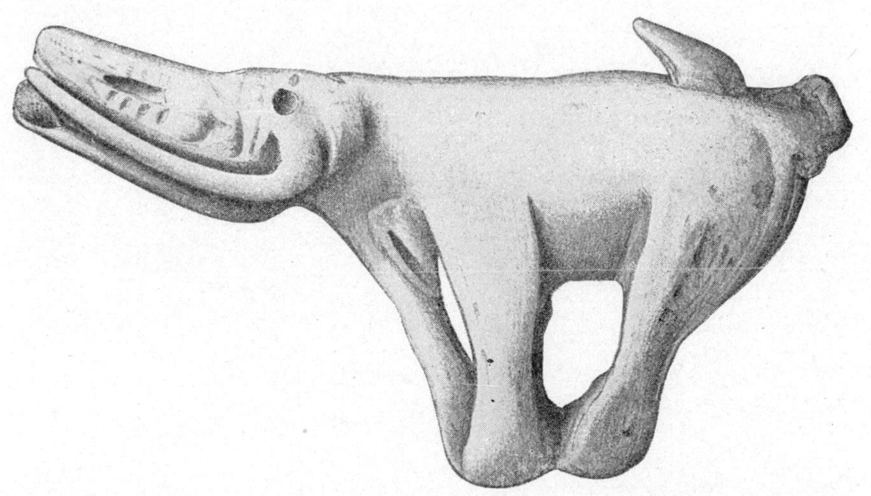

FIG. 230. Statuette of a mammoth in reindeer horn from the Abri de Plantade at Bruniquel. After Piette. "A statuette presenting the general form of the mammoth with some fantastic features. It formed part of a pendant of which the shank, terminating with a perforation, has been broken. The tusks were laid against this shank and strengthened it. The incisions bordered by notches suggest the nostrils of some imaginary monster. The trunk seems to grow out of the neck, not the head. The tail having been broken off in Palæolithic times, the owner made a hole in the back and inserted one there. The material was too thin to admit of representing the proper thickness of the animal. It was made to be viewed from the side."

the ivory mammoth statuette found at Předmost, continued into early Magdalenian times and certainly constitutes one of the most distinctive features of the art of that period, because in the later Magdalenian it took a different trend in the direction of decorative sculpture. Only two fine examples of early Magdalenian animal sculpture have been found, but these are of such a remarkable character as to indicate that modelling in the round was widely pursued at this time. These are the bisons discovered in 1912 in the cavern of Tuc d'Audoubert near Montesquieu, in the Pyrenees, and the fine bas-reliefs of horses at the shelter of Cap-Blanc, on the Beune, in Dordogne.

In company with Professor Cartailhac the writer had the good fortune to enter the cavern of Tuc d'Audoubert a few days after its discovery by the Comte de Bégouen and his sons; it is still in the making, for out from the entrance flows a stream of

FIG. 231. Entrance to the cavern of Tuc d'Audoubert, near Montesquieu-Avantès in the Pyrenees. This is one of the rare instances in which the stream that formed the cavern is still flowing from the entrance. Photograph by N. C. Nelson.

water large enough to float a small boat, by which the first of a series of superbly crystallized galleries is reached. After passing through a labyrinth of passageways and chambers a favorable surface was found where the Bégouen party showed us a whole wall covered with low-engraving reliefs, very simply done, fine in execution, with sure and firm outlines of the bison, the favorite subject as in all other caverns; horses fairly well executed and of the same steppe type as those in the near-by cavern of

Niaux; one superbly engraved contour of the reindeer, with its long, curved horns; the head of a stag with its horns still in the velvet; and a mammoth. All this work is engraved; there are no drawn outlines, but here and there are splashes of red

FIG. 232. Head of a reindeer deeply incised or engraved in the limestone wall of the cavern of Tuc d'Audoubert. After Bégouen.

and black color. Shortly afterward a great discovery was made in this cavern; it is described as follows by the Comte de Bégouen:* "To-day I am happy to give you excellent news from the cavern Tuc d'Audoubert. As you were the first to visit

* Letter of October 23, 1912.

this cavern, you will also be the first to learn that in an upper gallery, very difficult of access, at the summit of a very narrow ascending passage, and after having been obliged to break a number of stalactites which completely closed the entrance, my son and myself have found two superb statuettes in clay, about 60 cm. in length, absolutely unbroken, and representing bison.

FIG. 233. Two bison, male and female, modelled in clay, discovered in the cavern of Tuc d'Audoubert. The length of each of these models is about two feet. After Bégouen.

Cartailhac and Breuil, who have come to see them, were filled with enthusiasm. The ground of these chambers was covered with imprints of the claws of the bear, skeletons of which were buried here and there. The Magdalenians have passed through this ossuary and have drawn out all the canine teeth to make ornaments of them. Their steps left their fine impressions on the humid and soft clay, and we still see the outlines of several bare human feet. They had also lost several flakes of flint and the tooth of an ox pierced at the neck; we have collected them, and it seems as if they had only dropped yesterday; the Magdalenians also left an incomplete model of a bison and some lumps of kneaded clay which still carry the impression of their fingers. We produce the proof that in this period all branches of art were cultivated." This model of the male and female bison in clay has been described by Cartailhac as of perfect workmanship and of ideal art.

The procession of six horses cut in limestone under the sheltering cliff of Cap-Blanc is by far the most imposing work of

FIG. 234. One of a series of horses of the high-bred Celtic type, sculptured in high relief on the wall of the cliff shelter known as Cap-Blanc. The actual length of each of these sculptures is about seven feet. After Lalanne and Breuil.

Magdalenian art that has been discovered. The sculptures are in high relief and of large size and are in excellent proportion; they appear to represent the high-bred type of desert or Celtic horse, related to the Arabian, so far as we can judge from the long, straight face, the slender nose, the small nostrils, and the massive angle of the lower jaw; the ears are rather long and pointed, and the tail is represented as thin and without hair; they were found partly buried by layers containing implements of middle Magdalenian industry, and they are therefore assigned to an early Magdalenian date in which animal sculpture in the round reached its climax.

From the early to the middle Magdalenian period animal sculpture in bone, horn, and ivory was followed as decorative art in a bold and highly naturalistic manner. Adaptation of the animal

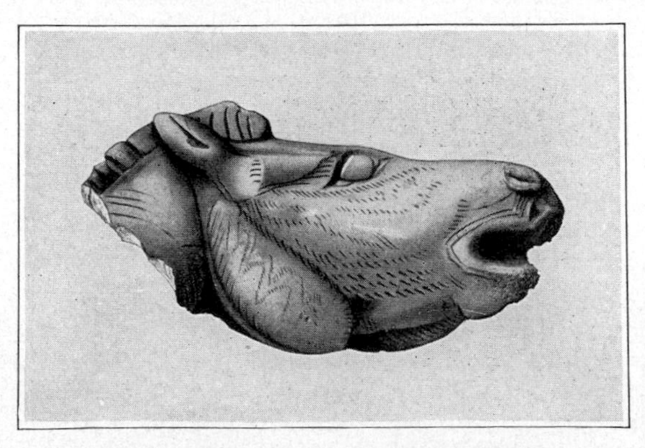

Fig. 235. Head of a horse sculptured on a reindeer antler, from the Magdalenian layer of Mas d'Azil on the right bank of the Arize. After Piette. Actual size.

figure to the surface and to the material employed is nowhere shown in a more remarkable way than in the bâtons, the dart-throwers, and the poniards. Of all the work of the Upper Palæolithic, these decorative heads and bodies are, perhaps, the

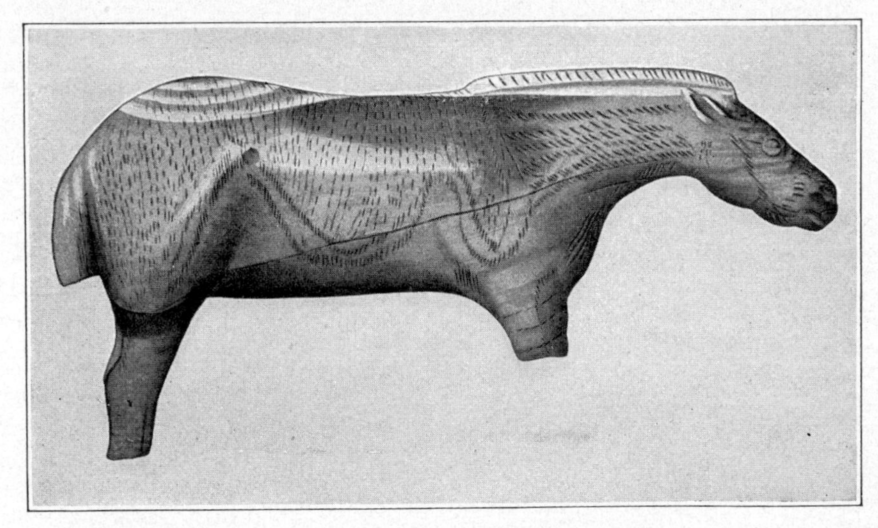

Fig. 236. Statuette carved on a fragment of mammoth tusk, representing a horse of Celtic type with mane erect, from the grotto of Les Espelugues, Lourdes. After Piette. About one and one-third actual size.

most highly artistic creations in the modern sense. The famous horse found in the late Magdalenian levels of Mas d'Azil (Fig. 235) and the small horses from the grotto of Espelugues, of the middle Magdalenian, are full of movement and life and show such certainty and breadth of treatment that they must be regarded as the masterpieces of Upper Palæolithic glyptic art. The ibex carved on the dart-thrower from the grotto of Mas d'Azil (Fig. 178) indicates observation and a striking power of

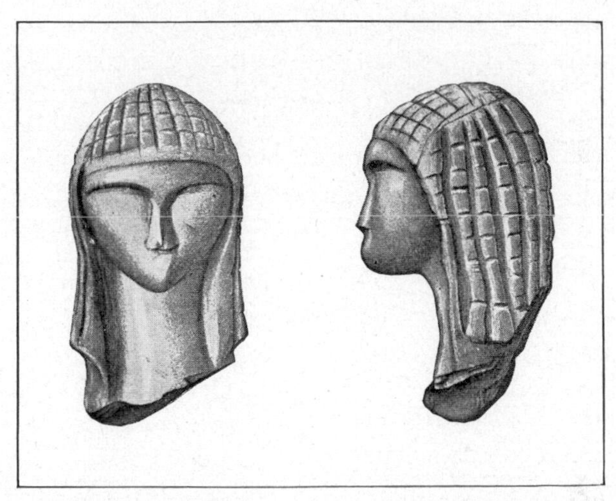

FIG. 237. Head of a woman with head-dress sculptured in ivory, from the Magdalenian levels of Brassempouy. After Piette. One and one-fifth actual size.

expression; while all the details are noted, the treatment is very broad.

The continuation of animal sculpture in the round is seen in the well-known horse statuette from the grotto of Lourdes; the partly decorative striping is a step in the direction of conventional treatment. The sculptured reindeer discovered by Bégouen in the grotto of Enlène is treated in a somewhat similar style.

Small human figurines again appear in the form of statuettes in bone or ivory, representing the renaissance of the spirit of human sculpture. Some of this work is apparently in search of beauty and with altogether different motives from the repellent feminine statuettes of middle and late Aurignacian times, for the subjects are slender and the limbs are modelled with relative skill. As in the earlier works, there is a partial failure to portray the features, which is in striking contrast to the lifelike treatment of animal heads. Very few examples of this work have been found, and most of them have been broken. To this period belong the Venus statuette of Laugerie Basse and the head of a girl carved in ivory found at Brassempouy (Fig. 237) with the features fairly suggested and an elaborate head-dress.

Geographic Distribution of the Magdalenian Culture

In Magdalenian times the Crô-Magnon race undoubtedly reached its highest development and its widest geographic distribution, but it would be a mistake to infer that the boundaries of the Magdalenian culture also mark the extreme migration points of this nomadic people, because the industries and inventions may well have spread far beyond the areas actually inhabited by the race itself.

Absence of Magdalenian influence around the northerly coasts of the Mediterranean is certainly one of the most surprising facts. Breuil has suggested that Italy remained in an Aurignacian stage of development throughout Magdalenian times and indicates that there is much evidence that Magdalenian culture never penetrated into this peninsula, for in Italy the Aurignacian industrial stage is succeeded by traces of the Azilian. This geographic gap, however, may be filled at any time by a fresh discovery. In Spain, also, the Magdalenian culture is known only in the Cantabrian Mountains, but never farther south, one of the earliest sites found in this region being the grotto of Peña la Miel, visited by Lartet in 1865, and one of the most famous the cavern of Altamira, discovered by Sautuola in 1875; to the northeast is the station of Banyolas. So far the eastern provinces of Spain have not yielded any implements of engraved or sculptured bone.

In contrast to this failure to reach southward, the Magdalenian culture is widely extended through France, Belgium, England,

Germany, Switzerland, Austria, and as far east as Russia. It would appear either that the men of Magdalenian times wandered far and wide or that there was an extensive system of barter, because the discovery of shells brought for personal adornment from the Mediterranean seashores to various Mag-

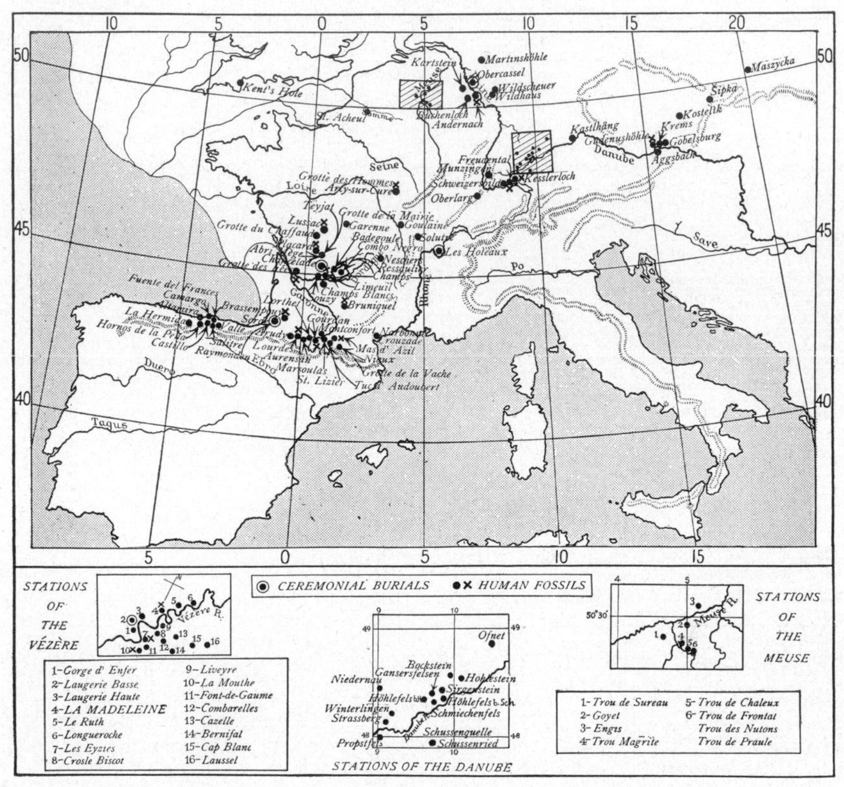

FIG. 238. Geographic distribution of the principal Magdalenian industrial stations in western Europe.

dalenian sites in France and in central Europe seems to indicate a wide-spread intercourse among these nomadic hunters and a system of trade reaching from the coasts of the Mediterranean and the Atlantic to the valley of the Neckar in Germany and along the Danube in Lower Austria. Another proof of this intercourse is the wide distribution not only of similar forms of implements but of very similar decorations; as an instance, Breuil notes the likeness of schematic engravings on reindeer horn in the two primitive Magdalenian layers of Placard, Charente, to those found in the Polish cavern of Mašzycka, near Ojcow, and to others in the corresponding layers of Castillo, near Santander, of Solutré on the Saône, and of various sites in Dordogne. A very distinctive geometric decoration on bone is that of broken zigzag lines with little intercalated transverse lines, which we notice at Altamira, in northern Spain, and which also occurs here and there in Dordogne and in Charente and extends to the grottos of d'Arlay in the Jura. Another style of ornament, with deep pectinate and punctuate lines, found in the very ancient Magdalenian of Placard, also occurs in the most ancient layers of Kesslerloch, Switzerland. Spiral ornaments like those on the bone weapons of Dordogne, of Arudy, and of Lourdes are found at Hornos de la Peña, in the Cantabrian Mountains. The spread of analogous decoration is still more striking when we find it occurring in the details of sculpture or in a certain type of dart-thrower (*propulseur*), which extended from the Pyrenees eastward to the Lake of Constance. Inventions like that of the harpoon and fashions like those of the decorative *motifs* were carried from point to point.

This influence does not lead to identity. Some of the phases of art and of decoration are confined to certain localities; for example, the engravings of deer on the bone shoulder-blades in the caverns near Santander, Spain, are not duplicated in France; also there are numerous local styles witnessed in the forms and decorations of the javelin, the lance, and the harpoon; these variations, however, do not conceal the element of community of culture and of similar fluctuations of industry and art between widely distant stations.

Many Magdalenian stations were crowded around the sheltered cliffs of Dordogne (Fig. 238). Besides these, we observe the Magdalenian sites of Champs, Ressaulier, and the grotto of Combo-Negro in Corrèze; south of Dordogne and Corrèze are other stations along the Garonne and the Adour. Some of the finest examples of Magdalenian art have come from Bruniquel, on the Aveyron, near the boundary between Tarn-et-Garonne and Tarn, where no less than four important sites have been excavated.

The culture map of France in Magdalenian times is covered from north to south with these ancient camp sites, either clustered along the river borders, where erosion has created shelters, or in the great outcrops of limestone along the northern slopes of

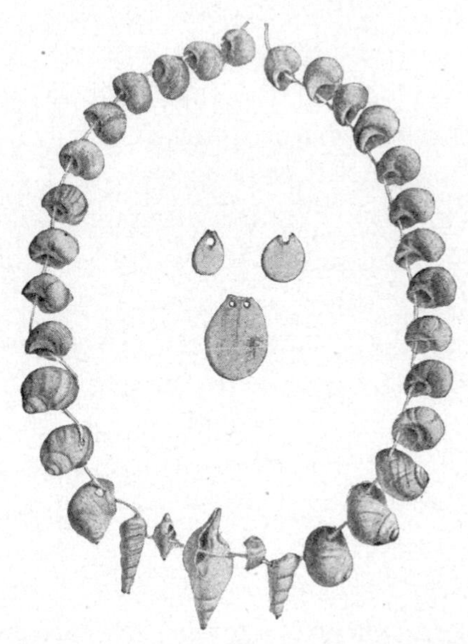

Fig. 239. Necklace of marine shells, from the cave of Crô-Magnon, mostly periwinkles, some related to species now living in the North Sea, *Purpura*, *Turitella*, and *Fusus*. After E. Lartet. The Crô-Magnon grotto dwellers used shells belonging to existing species, while in the deposits at La Madeleine and Laugerie Basse fossil shells are found. The use of seashore shells as ornaments in various parts of the interior of Europe indicates that they were brought long distances in trade. The remains of such ornaments were found with the skeleton of Aurignacian age from Paviland, Wales. Necklaces were also made of small plates of ivory and the perforated teeth of the cave-bear. One-third actual size.

the Pyrenees, where the exposure of the limestone has led to the formation of grottos and caverns; or on the plateaus where game abounded or flint could be found for the rapidly declining flint industry. Near the Gulf of Lyons are the stations of Bise, Tournal, Narbonne, and Crouzade; extending westward toward the headwaters of the Ariège are La Vache, Massat, and the great tunnel station of Mas d'Azil, formed by the River Arize; here the Magdalenian levels discovered by Piette have yielded some of the most notable Magdalenian works of art, including animal statuettes, bas-reliefs, and engravings with incised contours.

Farther west, on the headwaters of the Garonne, is Gourdan, where Piette began his remarkable excavations in 1871 and discovered two of the ancient Magdalenian phases of sculpture; then comes the more westerly group of Aurensan, Lorthet, and Lourdes, the latter a grotto which has yielded one of the finest examples of the horse sculptured in ivory, and which has since become famous as the site of a miracle and of modern pilgrimage. Between the Garonne and the Bay of Biscay lie the stations of Duruthy and the Grotte du Pape of Brassempouy, the latter occupied in Magdalenian times, but best known as a centre of late Aurignacian sculpture of statuettes.

To the northeast, in the very heart of the mountainous region of Auvergne, is the station of Neschers, where a flow of lava from Mount Tartaret descended over the slopes of Mont-Doré and covered a Mousterian industrial deposit with its mammoth fauna and then, after a lapse of time, became the site of a Magdalenian industrial camp, so that Boule has been able to determine the geologic age of the most recent volcanic eruptions in France, those of the Monts d'Auvergne, as having occurred between the periods of Mousterian and Magdalenian industry.

In view of the frequent occurrence of Aurignacian and Solutrean camps as well as of Neolithic stations in southeastern France, we are surprised at the extreme rarity there of Magdalenian flint implements. However, Capitan has recognized a Magdalenian station at Solutré, near the headwaters of the Saône, and not far from this site is the station of Goulaine, which has yielded an enormous flint scraper or anvil, the largest Upper Palæolithic implement ever found; it is carefully chipped around the entire curved edge and weighs over 4¼ pounds. To the north of the Dordogne is the celebrated grotto of Placard, in Charente, where the dawn of the Magdalenian industry has been discovered, and again directly north of this is the grotto of Chaffaud, at Savigné, where the first engraved bone of the 'Reindeer Age' was discovered in 1834; not far from this is the shelter

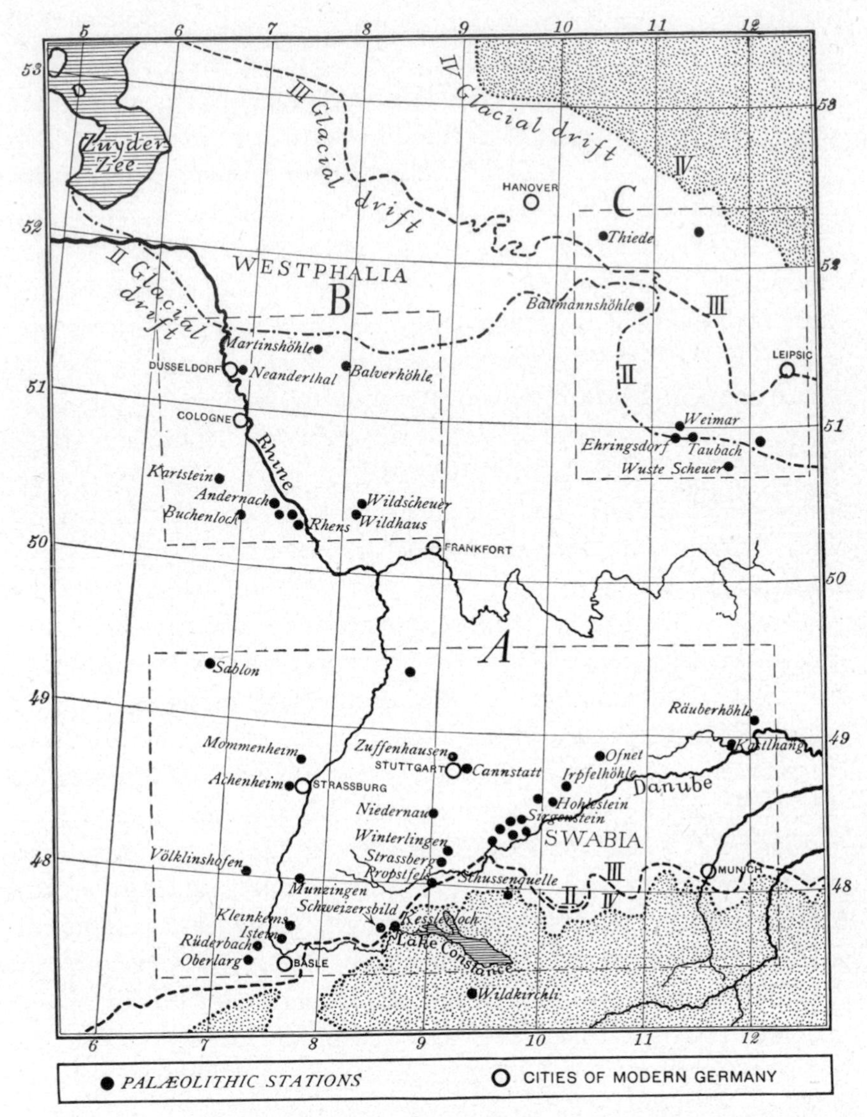

FIG. 240. Geographic distribution of the Magdalenian and other Palæolithic stations on the upper waters of the Rhine and of the Danube. The chief Magdalenian stations are: *Andernach, Bockstein, Buchenloch, Gansersfelsen, Höhlefels bei Hütten, Höhlefels bei Schelklingen, Hohlestein, Kartstein, Kastlhänghöhle, Kesslerloch, Martinshöhle, Munzingen, Niedernau, Oberlarg, Ofnet, Propstfels, Schmiechenfels, Schussenquelle, Schweizersbild, Sirgenstein, Strassberg, Wildhaus, Wildscheuer*, and *Winterlingen*. After R. R Schmidt, modified and redrawn.

of Garenne, near St. Marcel (Indre), which has afforded a fine figure of a galloping reindeer.

These geographic and artistic records are of intense interest as carrying the Périgord or Dordogne culture northward. Somewhat to the east, on the headwaters of the Cure, a tributary of the Yonne, there is an important group including over sixty open shelters formed in the Jurassic limestone, in which characteristic Magdalenian bone implements have been found. Of these the most famous are the Grotte des Fées, and the Grotte du Trilobite, both of which were first entered by the Neanderthals in Mousterian times and were again sought by the Crô-Magnons in Magdalenian times. Passing still farther north, the Crô-Magnons visited the borders of the Somme and sought the historic flint station of St. Acheul, which had been frequented by races of men for thousands of years previous, back to Pre-Chellean times.

To the northeast are the stations of Belgium, chiefly made known through the labors of Dupont, distributed along the valleys of the Lesse and of the Meuse and yielding characteristic Magdalenian flints as well as a number of engravings on bone. We may be sure that this region was under Crô-Magnon rule and that their control extended over into Britain, where, it will be recalled, a Crô-Magnon skeleton was found at Paviland, in western Wales. Here, again, in Magdalenian times the Crô-Magnon race was probably wide-spread over southern Britain. At Bacon's Hole, near Swansea, Wales, there is a wall decoration consisting of ten red bands, which, according to Breuil and Sollas, may possibly be of Palæolithic age. More definite is the Magdalenian industry observed at the Cresswell Crags, in Derbyshire; while near Torquay, Devonshire, is the famous station of Kent's Hole, discovered in 1824, in which a bone needle has been found and several harpoons with double rows of barbs belonging to the late Magdalenian industry.

In Germany, whereas only three Solutrean stations have been discovered,[29] there are no less than fourteen Magdalenian stations to attest the wide spread of that culture. Thus the favorite grotto of Sirgenstein, near the centre of the Magdalenian stations on the upper waters of the Danube, although abandoned in Solutrean times, was again entered by man during the early Magdalenian culture stage. Coincident with the return of man to this great grotto was the arrival of the banded lemming (*Myodes torquatus*), the herald of the cold tundra wave of life in the far north. At the very same time man with the banded lemming arrived at Schweizersbild, near the Lake of Constance;

FIG. 241. Reindeer engraved around a piece of reindeer antler, from Kesslerloch, Switzerland. This is a unique instance of the portrayal of landscape in Palæolithic art. After Heim. Slightly more than three-quarters actual size.

at a slightly earlier period, with the dawn of Magdalenian culture, man entered the sister station of Kesslerloch. It certainly appears that a cold moist climate accompanying the Bühl advance influenced all the Crô-Magnon peoples of this region just north of the Alpine glaciers and compelled them to seek the grottos and shelters. There are, however, some open stations in this general region, for example, at Schussenried, Württemberg; the Magdalenian culture layer is not found in a grotto, but lies under a deposit of peat mingled with the remains of the reindeer, horse, brown bear, and wolf. Again, among the best-known sites along the middle Rhine is the open-air station of Andernach. Demonstrating the eastward distribution of the art of engraving on ivory and bone is the presence in Andernach and in the grotto of Wildscheuer, near Steeten, on the Lahn, of engravings of this character. Thus far these are the only German stations in which such engravings have been found.

Of especial interest also is the open Magdalenian 'loess' station of Munzingen, on the upper Rhine, because it proves that the highest layers of the 'upper loess,' corresponding with the dry or steppe period of climate, were contemporaneous with the advanced or late Magdalenian industry, also because this final 'upper loess' stage about corresponds with the period when the last of the arctic tundra mammals began to abandon central Europe. It was at this critical geologic time that the late Magdalenian culture began to draw to a close. Kesslerloch, Switzerland, has yielded a considerable number of engravings on bone, including one of the finest examples of a browsing reindeer (Fig. 241), and Schweizersbild also has yielded a considerable number of rather crude engravings.

Frequented in Magdalenian times was that part of the Swabian Jura lying between the headwaters of the Neckar and of the Danube; along the course of the Danube, from Propstfels, near Beuron, in the southwest, to Ofnet, in the northeast, extend the other stations of Höhlefels bei Hütten, Schmiechenfels, and Bocksteinhöhle.

West of the Danube the industry was carried into the present region of Bavaria, as indicated by the recent discovery of Kastlhäng.[30] Here, beginning with the early Magdalenian (*Gourdanien inférieur* of the French school) and extending to the middle or high Magdalenian (*Gourdanien supérieur*), we find a complete series of Magdalenian stations; the middle Magdalenian layer is of exactly the same type as that found in the Abri Mège of Dordogne and in the lower levels of the Grotte de la Mairie; the same culture stage is again observed in southern Germany in the stations of Schussenquelle and of Höhlefels, and it extends eastward into Austria in the station of Gudenushöhle as well as into several Moravian stations, for example, that of Kostelík.

These facts are of extraordinary interest, for they show that the civilization, such as it was, of the Upper Palæolithic was very widely extended. This marks an important social characteristic, namely, the readiness and willingness to take advantage of every step in human progress, wherever it may have originated. At this point, therefore, it is interesting to compare the Magdalenian industry of Germany with that of France.[31] Germany shows the same technical and stylistic tendencies and the same evolutionary direction as France. The mammalian life was, of course, the same in both countries, for in each region the giant types of mammals still survived, and the banded lemming of the arctic appears in the sheltered valleys of the Dordogne as well as in Belgium and in Germany. The vicissitudes of climate were undoubtedly the same; we observe the alternation of cold moist climate in the early Magdalenian along the upper Danube as well as in the early Magdalenian of the type station of La Madeleine, Dordogne. Again, we observe the transition into the dry cold climate in the steppe character of the fauna both along the upper Rhine, at Munzingen, and also beneath the shelter station of La Madeleine, as recorded by Peyrony.

More vital still for this community of industrial culture was the community of race, for at Obercassel we find the same Crô-Magnon type as that discovered beneath the sheltering cliffs of Dordogne. It appears probable that the inventions of the central region of Dordogne travelled eastward when we note the fact that none of the prototypes of early forms of the harpoon which were common in southern France occur in any of the stations of central Europe, but the single-rowed harpoon is characteristic of the middle Magdalenian all over Germany. Other primitive Magdalenian bone implements, such as the bone spear point with the cleft base, the bâtons, and the needles, are also of rare occurrence in the German stations. In late Magdalenian times, however, a complete community of culture is established, for the industry of both countries in flint and bone appears to be very similar: flint microliths appear in increasing number and variety; beside the small flint flakes with blunted backs, numerous feather-shaped flakes of Pre-Tardenoisian type are found, as well as the types of graving flints. Some specialties of French Magdalenian culture did not find their way into Germany; for example, the graver of the 'parrot-beak' type has been found in France but has not been traced far eastward. In both countries, however,

Fig. 242. Entrance to the grotto of Kesslerloch, near Lake Constance. Photograph by N. C. Nelson.

are found upper Magdalenian chisels of reindeer horn and perfected bone needles, bâtons, and harpoons with double rows of barbs. On the other hand, works of art and decorative designs in horn and bone are almost entirely wanting in German localities, with the exception of the stations of Andernach and Wildscheuer previously mentioned. In late Magdalenian times, both in Germany and France, we find the Eurasiatic forest fauna becoming more abundant.

The two famous Swiss stations of Kesslerloch and Schweizersbild, near Lake Constance, appear throughout Magdalenian times to have been in very close touch with the cultural advances of Dordogne. Kesslerloch[32] has yielded 12,000 flints of small dimensions, resembling in their succession those of the type

FIG. 243. The famous shelter station of Schweizersbild, under a protecting cliff of limestone, near Lake Constance, Switzerland. On the right stands Dr. Jakob Nüesch, who has devoted three years to the excavation and study of this site. Photograph by N. C. Nelson.

station of La Madeleine; also needles, single and double harpoons, dart-throwers, bâtons, as well as the fine engravings mentioned above; bone sculpture is represented here in the unique head of a musk-ox (*Ovibos moschatus*), in carvings of the reindeer and of other animals on the bâtons and weapons of the chase. Kesslerloch lies on the edge of a moderately wide valley, traversed by a brook; in this sheltered, well-watered, hilly region, the trees flourished and harbored the forest animals, while the glaciers, retreating and leaving damp and stony areas, were closely followed by the tundra fauna; the woolly rhinoceros and mammoth persisted here longer than in other parts of Europe; the horse of Kesslerloch is said to show resemblances to the Przewalski horse of the desert of Gobi, in central Asia, and is consequently referred to the steppe type. The development of the flints takes place step by step with that of the sister cavern of Schweizersbild, and in early Magdalenian times these flints are found associated with the arrival of the great migration of the arctic tundra rodents, the banded lemmings (*Myodes torquatus*). A hearth with ashes and coals and many charred bones of old and young mammals, including the woolly rhinoceros, has been found here; the animal life altogether includes twenty-five species of mammals, among them the woolly mammoth, woolly rhinoceros, reindeer, and lion.

Less than four miles distant from Kesslerloch, in a small valley about two miles north of Schaffhausen, is the other famous Swiss station of Schweizersbild. The Crô-Magnons were attracted to this spot by the protecting cliff of isolated limestone rock rising sheer from the meadow-land, at the base of which is a shelter facing southwest, with an entrance of about 30 feet in height, commanding a wide view of the distant valley. In the accumulations at the base of this shelter we find a complete prehistory of the human, industrial, faunal, and climatic changes of this region of Switzerland from early Magdalenian into Neolithic times. It was not until the true early Magdalenian, after both the Aurignacian and Solutrean stages had closed, that man first found his way here during the *Bühl* advance, the period of the deposition of the *Upper Rodent Layer* with its cold arctic and steppe fauna;[33] but from this time the grotto was occupied at intervals until full Neolithic times. The beginning of these industrial deposits is estimated by Nüesch as having occurred between 24,000 and 29,000 years ago, but we have adopted a somewhat lower and more conservative estimate. In descending order the various layers of this shelter, as studied by Nüesch, are as follows:

Section of the Schweizersbild Deposits

Neolithic

6. Layer of humous earth, between 15 and 19 inches in thickness, containing Neolithic implements.

5. Gray culture layer, about 15 inches in thickness, including many fire-hearths, ornaments of shell, polished Neolithic flints, and unglazed pottery. The true forest fauna includes the brown bear, badger, marten, wolf, fox, beaver, hare, squirrel, short-horned wild ox (*Bos taurus brachyceros*), and reindeer, also the domesticated goat and sheep.

Upper Palæolithic

4. Thin layer of forest-living rodents, principally squirrels. Split bones and worked flints; no carvings in bone or horn; industry of late Magdalenian or close of *Magdalenian* Upper Palæolithic age; evidences that climate was changing, steppe conditions passing away, and forests becoming more dominant; only a few steppe species; the forest species include the reindeer, hare, pika, squirrel, ermine, and marten.

3. Yellow culture layer, steppe period, rich in fire-hearths and yielding 14,000 flints of *middle* [? and late] *Magdalenian* age; engravings on reindeer antlers, ornaments of shells and teeth. Mixed fauna with steppe and forest types predominant; of the few tundra forms, reindeer very abundant and also arctic fox, but banded lemming and other tundra types entirely lacking; steppe and desert fauna includes the kiang, Persian maral deer, Pallas's cat (*Felis manul*), steppe horse, and steppe suslik; of alpine type, the ibex; numerous forest species, pine marten, beaver, squirrel, red deer, roe-deer, and wild boar.

2. Arctic tundra rodent layer, 20 inches in thickness; period of the *Bühl* Postglacial advance; the banded lemming (*Myodes torquatus*) most abundant, mingled with *early Magdalenian* flint and bone implements; one fire-hearth; abundant tundra fauna, including all tundra types except the Obi lemming, and the musk-ox (*Ovibos moschatus*) which is found in Kesslerloch; indications of a very cold, moist climate; the banded lemming, arctic fox, arctic hare, reindeer, wolverene, ermine, also such forest forms as the wolf, fox, bear, weasel, and a number of northern birds.

1. Gravel bed and old river deposit, recognized by Boule as belonging to the moraines of the fourth glaciation.

This wonderful deposit of human artifacts and animal remains gives us a complete registration of the changes of climate in this region accompanying the changes of culture and the development of the Magdalenian race.

Turning our survey to the course of the Danube, we note that several Magdalenian stations extend into the provinces of Lower Austria, chief among them being both the open 'loess' station of Aggsbach, and that of Gobelsburg; there is also the Hundssteig near Krems, better known as the station of Krems, and the cavern known as the Gudenushöhle; in the latter sta-

FIG. 244. The open loess station of Aggsbach, on the Danube, near Krems. After Obermaier.

tion the characteristic bâtons, javelins, and bone needles have been found.*

The cavern district of Moravia attracted a relatively large population, and among the numerous stations are the grottos of Kříž, Žitný, Kostelík, Byciškala, Schoschuwka, Balcarovaskala, Kůlna, and Lautsch. Near the Russian border bone implements like those of Gudenushöhle on the Danube have been found at the station of Kůlna, and the industrial stratification of

* J. Bayer[34] has lately expressed the opinion that the industry of the open 'loess' stations of Munzingen, Aggsbach, and Gobelsburg is not really of Magdalenian age, but represents an atypical Aurignacian.

Šipka is very clear. Not far from Cracow, across the Russian border, the caverns in the region of Ojcow were entered by men carrying the Magdalenian culture. Another site in Russia is the grotto of Maszycka, and characteristic Magdalenian harpoons, needles, and bâtons de commandement with other implements have also been found to the eastward, in the neighborhood of Kiev, in the Ukraine.

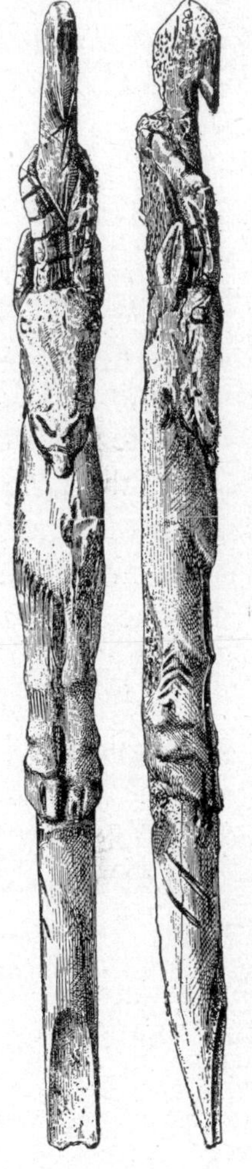

FIG. 245. Front and side views of a saiga antelope carved upon a bone dart-thrower from the Magdalenian deposits of Mas d'Azil. After Piette.

DECLINE OF THE MAGDALENIAN CULTURE

The highest point touched by the Crô-Magnon race in the middle or high Magdalenian appears to correspond broadly with the cold arid period of climate in the interval between the *Bühl* and *Gschnitz* advances in the Alpine region, during which the steppe mammals spread widely over southwestern Europe. The saiga antelope, for example, a highly characteristic steppe type, is represented in one of the most skilful bone carvings found in the late Magdalenian layers of Mas d'Azil; also the steppe type of horse is frequently represented in the most advanced engravings of late Magdalenian times. How far this cold, relatively dry climate influenced the artistic and creative energy of the Crô-Magnons is largely a matter of conjecture. The entirely independent records of La Madeleine, of Schweizersbild, and of Kesslerloch concur in associating the highest stage of Magdalenian history of art with the predominance of the steppe fauna and evidences of a cold dry climate. That the mammoth still abounded is seen in the mammoth engravings which are superposed on those of the bison in Font-de-Gaume.

The succeeding life period is that of the retreat of the tundra and steppe mammals and of the increasing rarity of the reindeer and of the mammoth in southwestern Europe; it corresponds broadly with the returning cold and moist climate of the second Postglacial advance known in the Alps as the *Gschnitz* stage. With the spread of the forests and the retreat to the north of the reindeer, the principal source both of the supply of food and clothing and of all the bone implements of industry and of the chase, a new set of life conditions may have gradually become established. If it is true, as most students of geographical conditions and of the climate maintain, that Europe at the same time became more densely forested, the chase may have become more difficult, and the Crô-Magnons may have begun to depend more and more upon the life of the streams and the art of fishing. It is generally agreed that the harpoons were chiefly used for fishing and that many of the microlithic flints, which now begin to appear more abundantly, may have been attached to a shaft for the same purpose. We know that similar microliths were used as arrow points in predynastic Egypt.

Breuil[35] observes very significant industrial changes in closing Magdalenian times: first, the beginning of small geometric forms of flints suggesting the Tardenoisian types; second, the occasional use of stag horn in place of reindeer horn; third, a modification in the form of bone implements toward the patterns of Azilian times; fourth, the rapid decline—one may almost say sudden disappearance—of the artistic spirit. Schematic and conventional designs begin to take the place of the free realistic art of the middle Magdalenian.

Thus the decline of the Crô-Magnons as a powerful race may have been due partly to environmental causes and the abandonment of their vigorous nomadic mode of life, or it may be that they had reached the end of a long cycle of psychic development, which we have traced from the beginning of Aurignacian times. We know as a parallel that in the history of many civilized races a period of great artistic and industrial development may be followed by a period of stagnation and decline without any apparent environmental causes.

Crô-Magnon Descendants in Modern Europe

We might attribute this great change, which affected all of western Europe, to the extinction of the Crô-Magnon race were it not for the existing evidence that the race survived throughout the Azilian-Tardenoisian or close of the Upper Palæolithic. On the close of the Palæolithic the race broke up throughout western Europe into many colonies, which can perhaps be traced into Neolithic and even into recent times. The anatomical evidence for this survival theory chiefly consists of the highly characteristic form of the head.

In Europe a very broad face and a long, narrow cranium is such an infrequent combination that anthropologists maintain that it affords a means of identifying the descendants of the prehistoric Crô-Magnon race wherever they persist to-day. Since Dordogne was the geographic centre of the race in Upper Palæolithic times, is it merely a coincidence that Dordogne is still the centre of a similar type? Ripley[36] has given us a valuable résumé of our present knowledge of this subject. The most significant trait of the long-headed people of Dordogne is that in many cases the face is almost as broad as in the normal Alpine round-headed type; in other words, it is strongly disharmonic; in profile the back part of the head rises and in front view the head is narrowed at the top; the skull is very low-vaulted; the brow ridges are prominent; the nose is well formed; the cheek-bones are prominent, and the powerful cheek muscles give a peculiarly rugged cast to the countenance. The appearance, however, is not repellent, but more often open and kindly. The men are of medium height, but very susceptible to environment as regards stature; they are tall in fertile places, and stunted in less prosperous districts. They are not degenerate at all, but keen and alert of mind. The present people of Dordogne agree with but one other type of men known to anthropologists, namely, the ancient Crô-Magnon race. The geographical evidence that here in Dordogne we have to do with the survivors of the real Crô-Magnon race seems to be sustained by a comparison of the characteristics of the prehistoric skulls found at Crô-Magnon, Laugerie Basse, and elsewhere in Dordogne, with the heads of the types of to-day. The cranial indices of the prehistoric skulls, varying from 70 per cent to 73 per cent, correspond with indices of the living head of 72 per cent to 75 per cent. None of the people of Dordogne are quite so long-headed as this, the average index of the living head in an extreme district being 76 per cent; but within the whole population there are much lower indices.

The probability of direct descent becomes stronger when we consider the disharmonic low-skulled shape of the Crô-Magnon head and the remarkable elongation of the skull at the back. In the prehistoric Crô-Magnons the brows were strongly developed, the eye orbits low, the chin prominent. The facial type has been characterized by de Quatrefages[37] as follows: "The eye depressed beneath the orbital vault; the nose straight rather than arched; the lips somewhat thick, the jaw and the cheekbones strongly developed, the complexion very brown, the hair very dark and growing low on the forehead—a whole which, without being attractive, was in no way repulsive."

In southern France we observe a continuity not only of the head form but of the prevalence of black hair and eyes. Why should this Crô-Magnon type have survived at this point and have disappeared elsewhere? In order to consider the particular cause of this persistence of a Palæolithic race, we must, with Ripley, broaden our horizon, and consider the whole southwest from the Mediterranean to Brittany as a unit.

The survival is partly attributed to favorable geographical environment and partly to geological and racial barriers. On the north the intrusion of the Teutonic race was shut off and competition was narrowed down to the Crô-Magnon and Alpine types.

If the people of Dordogne are veritable survivors of the Crô-Magnons of the Upper Palæolithic, they certainly represent the oldest living race in western Europe, and is it not extremely significant that the most primitive language in Europe, that of the Basques of the northern Pyrenees, is spoken near by, only 200 miles to the southwest? Is there possibly a connection between the original language of the Crô-Magnons, a race which once crowded the region of the Cantabrian Mountains and the Pyrenees, and the existing agglutinative language of the Basques, which is totally different from all the European tongues? This hypothesis, suggested by Ripley,[38] is very well worth considering, for it is not inconceivable that the ancestors of the Basques conquered the Crô-Magnons and subsequently acquired their language.

The prehistoric Crô-Magnon men would seem, therefore, to have remained in or near their early settlements through all the changes of time and the vicissitudes of history. "It is, perhaps," observes Ripley, "the most striking instance known of a persistency of population unchanged through thousands of years."

The geographic extension of this race was once very much wider than it is to-day. The classical skull of Engis, Belgium, belongs to this type. It has been traced from Alsace in the east to the Atlantic in the west. Ranke asserts that it is to be found to-day in the hills of Thuringia, and that it was a prevalent type there in the past. Verneau considers that it was the type prevailing among the extinct Guanches of the Canary Islands. Collignon[39] has identified it in northern Africa, and regards the Crô-Magnons as a subvariety of the Mediterranean race, an opinion consistent at least with the archæological evidence that this race came into Europe with the Aurignacian culture, which was circum-Mediterranean in distribution. Traces of Crô-Magnon head formation are found among the living Berbers.

At present, however, this race is believed to survive only in a few isolated localities, namely, in Dordogne, at a small spot in Landes, near the Garonne in southern France, and at Lannion in Brittany, where nearly one-third of the population is of the Crô-Magnon type. It is said to survive on the island of Oléron off the west coast of France, and there is evidence of similar descent to be found among the people of the islands of northern Holland. The people of Trysil, on the Scandinavian peninsula, are characterized as having disharmonic features, possibly representing an outcrop of the Crô-Magnon type.

Our interest in the fate of the Crô-Magnons is so great that the Guanche theory may also be considered; it is known to be favored by many anthropologists: von Behr, von Luschan, Mehlis, and especially by Verneau. The Guanches were a race of people who formerly spread all over the Canary Islands and who preserved their primitive characteristics even after their conquest by Spain in the fifteenth century. The differences from the supposed modern Crô-Magnon type may be mentioned first. The skin of the Guanches is described by the poet Viana as light-colored, and Verneau considers that the hair was blond or light chestnut and the eyes blue; the coloring, however, is somewhat conjectural. The features of resemblance to the ancient Crô-Magnons are numerous. The minimum stature of the men was 5 feet 7 inches, and the maximum 6 feet 7 inches; in one locality the average male stature was over 6 feet. The women were comparatively small. The most striking characters of the head were the fine forehead, the extremely long skull, and the pentagonal form of the cranium, when seen from above, caused by the prominence of the parietals—a Crô-Magnon characteristic. Among the insignia of the chiefs was the arm-bone of an ancestor; the skull also was carefully preserved. The offensive weapons in warfare consisted of three stones, a club, and several knives of obsidian; the defensive weapon was a simple lance. The Guanches used wooden swords with great skill. The habitation of all the people was in large, well-sheltered caverns, which honeycombed the sides of the mountains; all the walls of these caverns were decorated; the ceilings were covered with a uniform coat of red ochre, while the walls were decorated with various geometric designs in red, black, gray, and white. Hollowed-out stones served as lamps. We may conclude with Verneau that there is evidence, although not of a very convincing kind, that the Guanches were related to the

Crô-Magnons.[40] His observations on these supposed Crô-Magnons of the Canary Islands are cited in the Appendix, Note V. We regret that Verneau in his memoir[41] does not present his more recent views in regard to the prehistoric distribution of this great race.

(1) Breuil, 1912.7, p. 203.
(2) *Op. cit.*, p. 205.
(3) James, 1902.1.
(4) Heim, 1894.1, p. 184.
(5) Schmidt, 1912.1, p. 262.
(6) Fraunholz, 1911.1.
(7) Geikie, 1914.1, pp. 25, 26.
(8) Boule, 1899.1.
(9) Breuil, 1912.7, pp. 203–205.
(10) Obermaier, 1912.1, pp. 341, 342.
(11) Martin, R., 1914.1, pp. 15, 16.
(12) Verworn, 1914.1.
(13) *Op. cit.*, p. 646.
(14) Breuil, 1912.7, p. 201.
(15) Lartet, 1875.1.
(16) Breuil, 1912.7, p. 213.
(17) Schmidt, 1912.1, p. 136.
(18) Breuil, *op. cit.*, pp. 216, 217.
(19) Breuil, 1909.3.
(20) *Op. cit.*, p. 410.
(21) Cartailhac, 1906.1, pp. 227, 228.
(22) Rivière, 1897.1; 1897.2.
(23) Reinach, 1913.1.
(24) Breuil, 1912.1, p. 202.
(25) Cartailhac, 1908.1.
(26) Capitan, 1908.1, pp. 501–514.
(27) *Ibid.*, 1910.1, pp. 59–132.
(28) Breuil, 1912.1, pp. 196, 197.
(29) Schmidt, 1912.1, p. 116.
(30) Fraunholz, 1911.1.
(31) Schmidt, 1912.1, p. 154.
(32) Déchelette, 1908.1, vol. I, pp. 191–194.
(33) Nehring, 1880.1; 1896.1.
(34) Bayer, 1912.1, pp. 13–21.
(35) Breuil, 1912.7, pp. 212, 216.
(36) Ripley, 1899.1, pp. 39, 165, 173, 174–179, 211, 406.
(37) *Op. cit.*, p. 176.
(38) *Op. cit.*, p. 181.
(39) Collignon, 1890.1.
(40) Verneau, 1891.1.
(41) *Ibid.*, 1906.1.

North Africa and Spain

Before continuing with Chapter VI the reader should carefully study the note on the Capsian flint industry (see Appendix, Note XI, p. 514) of Spain and northwest Africa, of which the type station is Gafsa, a place about 180 miles southwest of the city of Tunis in the region lying between Tripoli and Algiers now known as Tunis. It would appear that this part of Africa was probably the home of the Tardenoisian industry described on p. 465.

The connection between Spanish and North African life in Palæolithic times has recently been fully described by Hugo Obermaier in his very interesting work, *El Hombre fósil*, published in Madrid in 1916.

CHAPTER VI

CLOSE OF THE OLD STONE AGE — INVASION OF NEW RACES — HISTORY OF THE MAS D'AZIL, OF FÈRE-EN-TARDENOIS — FOREST ENVIRONMENT AND LIFE — ORIGIN OF THE AZILIAN-TARDENOISIAN CULTURE — CHARACTERS AND CUSTOMS OF THE NEW RACES — TRANSITION TO THE NEOLITHIC AND RELATIONS OF THE OLD AND NEW RACES — APPARENT CHIEF LINES OF HUMAN DESCENT AND OF HUMAN MIGRATION INTO WESTERN EUROPE.

We have now reached the very close of the Old Stone Age, a period which is believed to extend between 10,000 and 7,000 years before the present era. The entrance to the final cultures of the Upper Palæolithic, known as the Azilian-Tardenoisian, marks a transition even more abrupt than that witnessed in any preceding stage. It is not a development; it is a revolution. The artistic spirit entirely disappears; there is no trace of animal engraving or sculpture; painting is found only on flattened pebbles or in schematic or geometric designs on wall surfaces. Of bone implements only harpoons and polishers remain, and even these are of inferior workmanship and without any trace of art. The flint industry continues the degeneration begun in the Magdalenian and exhibits a new life and impulse only in the fashioning of the extremely small or microlithic tools and weapons known as 'Tardenoisian.' Both bone and flint weapons of the chase disappear, yet the stag is hunted and its horns are used in the manufacture of harpoons. This is the 'Age of the Stag,' the final stage of the '*Cave Period*' in western Europe, and is subsequent to the 'Age of the Reindeer' in the south.

It would appear as if the very same regions formerly occupied by the great hunting Crô-Magnon race from Aurignacian to Magdalenian times were now inhabited by a race or races largely employed in fishing. The country is thickly forested.

The climate is still cold and extremely moist, and human life everywhere is in the grottos or entrances to the caverns.

Invasion of Four New Races in Closing Upper Palæolithic Times

How far this revolution is due to the decline of the Crô-Magnon race and how far to the invasion of one or more new races is very difficult to determine in the absence of the anatomical evidence derived from skeletal remains. Two new races had certainly found their way along the Danube as shown in the burials of Ofnet, in eastern Bavaria; one is extremely broad-headed and perhaps of central Asiatic origin, while the other is extremely long-headed and perhaps of southerly or Mediterranean origin. It is possible that these two races correspond respectively with the easterly and southerly industrial influences which are observed in the Azilian-Tardenoisian stage. The former is the first brachycephalic race to enter western Europe, for it will be recalled that all the previous races, the Crô-Magnons, the Brünns, and the Neanderthals, are dolichocephalic. The long-headed race found at Ofnet is very clearly distinguished from the disharmonic long-headed Crô-Magnon race by the narrowness of the face; in other words, it is an *harmonic* type of head and face, which may have been Mediterranean in origin, like the so-called 'Mediterranean race' of Sergi.

This fresh invasion of western Europe by two races arriving by one or more of the great migration routes from the vast Eurasiatic mainland to the east, races with a relatively high brain development, is certainly one of the most surprising features of the close of the Palæolithic Period, for we have long been accustomed to think that these fresh easterly and southerly invasions began only in Neolithic times.

As the Upper Palæolithic draws to an end, there is, according to Breuil, still another industrial influence making itself felt: it comes from the northeast along the shores of the Baltic.

Putting together all the fragmentary evidence which we possess, we may regard western Europe at the close of the Old

Stone Age as peopled by four and possibly by five distinct races, as follows:

5. Arriving late in Palæolithic times, a race along the shores of the Baltic, known only by its Maglemose industry; possibly a Teutonic race.

4. A south Mediterranean race, known only by its Tardenoisian industry, migrating along the northern shores of Africa and spreading over Spain; with a conventional and schematic art; probably an advance wave of the true 'Mediterranean' race of Sergi; possibly identical with race 3 below. (The same as Race 4, p. 278.)

3. A long-headed race found at Ofnet, in eastern Bavaria; possibly a branch of the true 'Mediterranean' race 4 above, but not related to the Brünn. (Possibly the same as Race 4.)

2. The newly arriving Furfooz-Grenelle race, broad-headed; known along the Danube at Ofnet, in eastern Bavaria, and northward in Belgium; possibly a branch of the 'Alpine' race. (The same as Race 5, p. 278.)

1. The surviving Crô-Magnons, in a stage of industrial decline, pursuing the Azilian industry, probably inhabiting France and northern Spain.

The broad-headed Ofnet race mentioned above is apparently the same as the Furfooz-Grenelle race, and may also correspond with the existing Alpine-Celtic race of western Europe. The long-headed race of Ofnet may correspond with the existing 'Mediterranean' race of Sergi.

The presence of the Crô-Magnon race in western Europe during Azilian-Tardenoisian times is not sustained, so far as we know, by any anatomical evidence, but is suggested by the mode of burial of two skeletons found by Piette in the Azilian deposits of the station of Mas d'Azil. This burial, like that of Ofnet, is typical of Upper Palæolithic and not of Neolithic times. These skeletons lay in the 'Azilian' layer (VI) described below. As the smaller bones were missing, Piette concluded that the remains had been for some time exposed to the weather before burial, and that the larger bones had been scraped and cleaned with flint knives, and then colored red with oxide of iron before interment. According to other authorities, the traces of scraping and cleaning are doubtful; there can be no question, however, that the separation of the bones of the skeleton and the use of coloring matter constitute strong evidence that this Azilian burial was the work of members of the Crô-Magnon race.

In addition to what we have said as to the survival of the Crô-Magnon race in the preceding chapter, the opinion of Cartailhac[1] may be cited: "The race of Crô-Magnon is well determined. There is no doubt about their high stature, and Topinard is not the only one who believes that they were blonds. We have traced them through the 'Reindeer Period' into the Neolithic Epoch, where they were widely distributed and positively related either to the ancient or actual populations of modern France, being especially characteristic of our region [France] and of the western Mediterranean. While the race of Crô-Magnon predominated in the south and in the west, that of Furfooz predominated in the northeast of France and in Belgium. These brachycephals were probably brown-haired or of dark coloring."

But before observing further the characters of these four or five races, let us examine their industries.

Discovery of the Azilian Type Station

As remarked above, it is believed that these industries prevailed between 7,000 and 10,000 years before our era, that is, between the close of Magdalenian times and the beginning of the Neolithic or New Stone Age. This transition period corresponds with the interval in which the Azilian-Tardenoisian culture swept all over western Europe and completely replaced the Magdalenian. From Castillo in the Cantabrian Mountains of northern Spain to Ofnet on the upper Danube there is a complete replacement by this new culture. The Magdalenian culture does not linger anywhere; it is totally eliminated; the suddenness of the change both in the animal life and in the industry is nowhere more clearly indicated than at the type station of Mas d'Azil in southern France, which may now be described.

In 1887 Edouard Piette commenced his exploration of the deposits in the great cavern of Mas d'Azil. This station takes its name from the little hamlet of Mas d'Azil in the foot-hills of the Pyrenees about forty miles southwest from Toulouse. Here the River Arize winds for a quarter of a mile through a lofty natural tunnel traversed by the highway from St. Girons to

Carcassonne. A rich layer of Magdalenian deposits first attracted Piette's attention, and he found here some of the finest examples of late Magdalenian art, but above these deposits he discovered a hitherto unrecognized industrial stage, to which he gave the name Azilian. The Azilian layers yielded over one thousand specimens of flattened and double-barbed harpoons

FIG. 246. Western entrance to the great station of Mas d'Azil. "Here the River Arize winds for a quarter of a mile through a lofty natural tunnel traversed by the highway from St. Girons to Carcassonne." Photograph by N. C. Nelson.

made of the horns of the stag, thus widely differing from the late Magdalenian harpoons which are rounded and made of the horns of the reindeer. The entire succession of deposits, as explored by Piette, is an epitome of the prehistory of Europe from early Magdalenian times to the Age of Bronze, and should be compared with the successive deposits of Castillo (p. 164), Sirgenstein (p. 202), Ofnet (p. 476), and Schweizersbild (p. 447).

The Mas d'Azil section is as follows:

Prehistoric and Neolithic

IX. Iron implements, pottery of the Gauls. At the top Gallo-Roman remains, glass and glazed pottery.

VIII. Middle Neolithic and Age of Bronze; layer of pottery, polished stone implements, traces of copper and of bronze.

VII. Dawn of the Neolithic. Fauna includes the horse, urus, stag, and wild boar. Chipped and polished flints, awls and polishers in bone; harpoons rare. Beginnings of pottery.

Upper Palæolithic

VI. Azilian, red archæological layer, masses of peroxide of iron. Extremely moist climate. Broad flat harpoons of stag horn perforated at the base, numerous flattened and painted pebbles (*galets*), flints of degenerate Magdalenian form, especially small rounded planers and knife flakes, awls and polishers in bone. No trace of reindeer in the fire-hearths; stag abundant, also roe-deer and brown bear; wild boar, wild cattle, beaver, a variety of birds. No trace of polished stone implements. Interred in this layer, beneath the deposits of streaked cinders and quite undisturbed, two human skeletons were found, which Piette believed had been macerated with flints and then colored red with peroxide of iron.

V. Sterile finely stratified loam layer, a flood deposit of the River Arize.

IV. Late Magdalenian culture layer; twelve double-rowed harpoons made of reindeer horn, a few fashioned from stag horn; numerous engravings and sculptures in bone. Remains of the reindeer rare in the hearths; those of the royal stag (*Cervus elaphus*) abundant.

III. A sterile flood deposit of the River Arize.

II. Middle and Early Magdalenian culture layers, with barbed harpoons of reindeer horn; flint implements of early Magdalenian type, bone needles. Bones of the reindeer abundant.

I. Gravel deposits. Interspersed fire-hearths.

The total thickness of these culture deposits is 8.03 m., or 26 feet 4 inches. The Azilian type layer (VI) containing flat harpoons of stag horn and painted pebbles, intercalated between the deposits of the Reindeer Age and the Neolithic layers, is, on account of its stratigraphic position, the most interesting and instructive of all the sites representing this phase of transition; and Piette was fully justified in giving to the corresponding culture period the name of *Azilian*.[2]

The transformation of art and industry, indicated in the Azilian culture layer, is as decided as that in the animal life.

We observe in this layer no trace of the animal engravings or sculptures which occur so abundantly in the late Magdalenian layer below; the use of pigments is confined to the paintings of schematic or geometric figures on the flattened pebbles. There is no suggestion of art in any of the bone implements, and the harpoons of stag horn are rudely fashioned; this type of harpoon appears to be the chief survivor of the rich variety of imple-

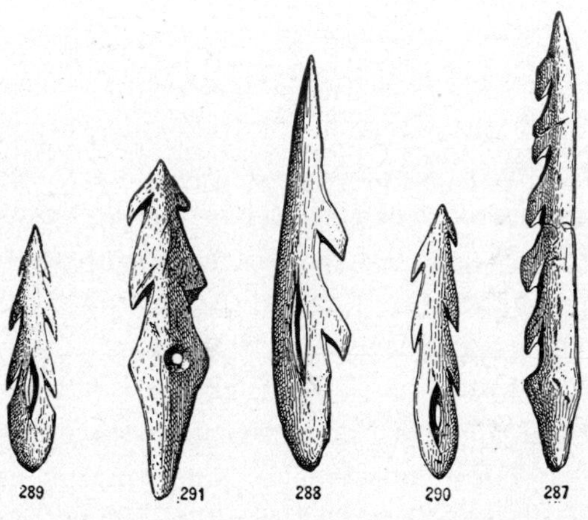

FIG. 247. Typical Azilian harpoons of stag horn. After de Mortillet. 287. A single-rowed harpoon from Mas d'Azil. 288. Harpoon with perforated base from the shelter of La Tourasse, Haute-Garonne. 289. Double-rowed harpoon from the same shelter. 290. A similar harpoon with the barbs alternate instead of opposite, from Mas d'Azil. 291. Harpoon with triangular base and round perforation from the Grotte de la Vache, near Tarascon. All one-third actual size, except 291, which is four-ninths actual size.

ments noted in the Magdalenian layer below. The stag horn harpoon, moreover, is fashioned with far less skill than the beautiful Magdalenian harpoons; like them it has two rows of barbs, but they are not cut with the same delicacy and exactness. As to the form of the new model, it is explained by the nature of the new material; the interior of the stag horn being composed of a spongy tissue, could not be utilized as could the harder and more compact interior of the reindeer horn; the craftsman, therefore, was obliged to fashion his harpoon out of the exterior of one side of the stag horn, and in consequence to make it flat.

There are no bone needles, no javelins or *sagaies;* nor are there any of the beautifully carved weapons of bone. There is also a reduction in the uses to which the split bones are put, such as the large *lissoirs* or polishers. The bone implements appear to be derived from an impoverished late Aurignacian stage; the same is true of the flint implements, for we observe a return of the keeled scraper (*grattoir carêné*). There is also a return of certain types of graving tools and of the knife-like form of the flake; even some of the small geometric types of flints resemble those of the Aurignacian levels.

The many shells of the moisture-loving snail *Helix nemoralis*, found in the fire-hearths of Mas d'Azil are proofs of the humidity of the climate, a fact confirmed by the contemporary flood deposits of the Arize. The frequent and heavy rains drove the last few representatives of the steppe fauna away to the north. These climatic conditions favored the formation of peat-bogs, so frequent to-day in the north of France, and also the growth of vast forests, inhabited by the stag, which extended over the whole country.

The pebbles of Mas d'Azil are painted on one side with peroxide of iron, a deposit of which is found in the neighborhood of the cave. The color, mixed in shells of *Pecten*, or in hollowed pebbles or on flat stones, was applied either with the finger or with a brush. The many enigmatic designs consist chiefly of parallel bands, rows of discs or points, bands with scalloped edges, cruciform designs, ladder-like patterns (scalariform) such as are found in the 'Azilian' engravings and paintings of the caverns, and undulating lines. These graphic combinations resemble certain syllabic and alphabetic characters of the Ægean, Cypriote, Phœnician, and Greco-Latin inscriptions. However curious these resemblances may be, they are not sufficient to warrant any theory connecting the signs on the painted pebbles of the Azilians with the alphabetic characters of the oldest known systems of writing.[3] Piette attempted to explain some of the exceedingly crude designs on these pebbles as a system of notation, others as pictographs and religious symbols, and some few as genuine alphabetical signs, and suggested that the cavern of Mas d'Azil was an Upper Palæolithic school where reading, reck-

FIG. 248. Azilian *galets coloriés*, flat, painted pebbles, from the type station of Mas d'Azil. After Piette.

oning, writing, and the symbols of the sun were learned and taught. The very wide distribution of these symbolic pebbles and the painting of similar designs on the walls of the caverns certainly prove that they had some religious or economic significance, which may be revealed by subsequent research.

The Tardenoisian Type Station

Turning from the region of the Pyrenees in Azilian times, we observe the region lying between the Seine and the Meuse in northern France as the scene of a contemporary industry. At the station of Fère-en-Tardenois, in the Department of the Aisne, is found an especially large number of the pygmy flints;[4] these present various geometric forms, including the primitive triangular, as well as the rhomboidal, trapezoidal, and semicircular; together, they were designated by de Mortillet as *Tardenoisian* flints, and in 1896, in monographing this microlithic flint industry, he traced them throughout France, Belgium, England, Portugal, Spain, Italy, Germany, and Russia, also along the southern Mediterranean through Algiers, Tunis, Egypt, and eastward into Syria and even India.

These geometric flints were at first attributed to a primitive invasion which was supposed to have occurred at the beginning of Neolithic times; thus the Tardenoisian industry was considered as contemporaneous with that of the Campignian, which is early Neolithic. It was further observed that the topographical location of the stations closely followed the borders of ocean inlets, or of river courses, and when the food materials found in the hearths were compared, it appeared that these flints were used principally by fishermen or tribes subsisting upon fish. From an examination of the flints, it would appear that a very large number of them were adapted for insertion in small harpoons, or that those of grooved form might even have been used as fish-hooks. Thus the picture was drawn of a population of fishermen. The Tardenoisian, therefore, was for a long time regarded as contemporaneous with the early Neolithic rather than with the close of Palæolithic times, but as exploration proceeded it was found that neither the remains of domestic animals nor any traces of pottery occur in any of these Tardenoisian deposits, which consequently have nothing in common with the true Neolithic culture.

The problem was finally solved in 1909, when the grotto of Valle near Gibaja, Santander, in northern Spain, was discovered by Breuil and Obermaier.[5] Here was a classic Azilian deposit containing all the well-known Azilian types of bone implements, such as fine harpoons, carvings in deer horn, bone javelins, polishers of deer bone, flint flakes resembling those of the late Magdalenian, also microlithic flints of typical geometric Tardenoisian form. This discovery established the fact that the lower levels of the Tardenoisian industry were not really to be distinguished from the Azilian, for here beneath layers with painted pebbles and harpoons of Azilian style were harpoons with single and double rows of barbs of Magdalenian pattern, but cut in stag horn instead of reindeer horn.

The mammalian life in this true Azilian-Tardenoisian layer includes the chamois, roe-deer, wild boar, and urus, or wild cattle. In a layer just below, which represents the close of the Magdalenian industrial period, there are found, although rarely, remains of the reindeer, an animal hitherto unknown in this part of Spain, also the wild boar, the bison, the ibex, and the lynx. After this discovery it could no longer be questioned that the Azilian and Tardenoisian were contemporary.

As to the relation of these two industries, Breuil remarks[6] that the prolongation of the Tardenoisian types of flints is observed in Italy and in Belgium, but neither the term 'Tardenoisian' nor the term 'Azilian' is sufficiently comprehensive to embrace the totality of these little industries, which will finally be distinguished clearly from each other. Of the two the Azilian represents the prolongation of an ancient period of industry, the progress of which was apparently from south to north, as we can trace the distribution of the characteristic flat harpoons of deer horn from the Cantabrian Mountains and the Pyrenees, through southern and central France, to Belgium, England, and the western coast of Scotland. The later industrial phase, the Tardenoisian, with its geometric trapeziform flints, originally appears along the southern Mediterranean in Tunis and to the

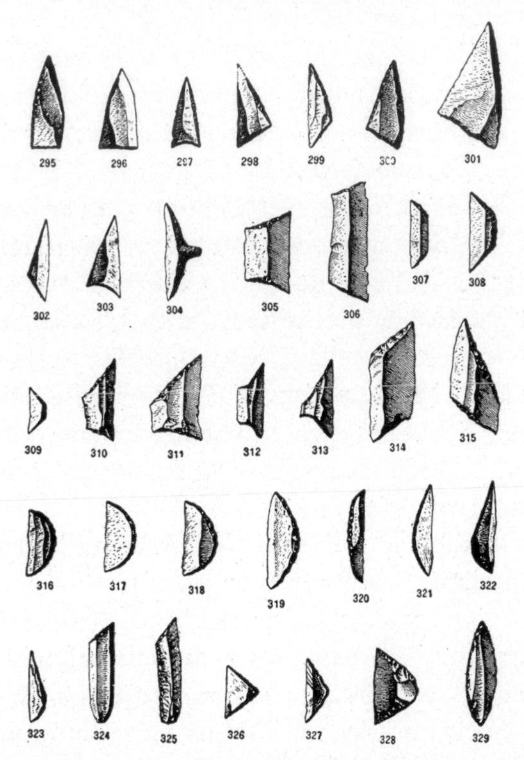

FIG. 249. Small geometric flints characteristic of the Tardenoisian industry. After de Mortillet. 295 to 303, 321, 322, 326. From various sites in northern France. 311. Uchaux, Vaucluse, France. 305, 315, 320. Valley of the Meuse, Belgium. 312, 313. Cabeço da Arruda, Portugal. 304, 314. Italy. 317, 318, 329. Tunis. 325. Egypt. 306, 310, 324, 328. Kizil-Koba, Crimea. 307 to 309, 316, 319, 323, 327. India. All one-half actual size.

eastward in the Crimea, while in France it represents a final phase of the Palæolithic, closely approaching the period of the earliest Neolithic or pre-Campignian hearths common along the Danube and observed in the vicinity of Liége. Thus the most comprehensive term by which to designate the *ensemble* of these implements, in Europe at least, would be Azilian-Tardenoisian.

Environment and Mammalian Life

It appears that the chief geographic change during this period was a subsidence of the northern coasts of Europe and an advance of the sea causing the circulation of warm oceanic currents and a more humid climate favorable to reforestation.

To the north, in Belgium, the tundra fauna lingered during the extension of the early Tardenoisian industry, for here we still find remains of the reindeer, the arctic fox, and the arctic hare mingled in the fire-hearths with flints of Tardenoisian type. This, observes Obermaier, constitutes proof that the Tardenoisian, with the Azilian, must be placed at the very close of Postglacial time and with the final stage of Upper Palæolithic industry.

To the south, in the region of Dordogne and the Pyrenees, the tundra fauna had entirely disappeared, as well as that of the steppes and of the alpine heights; the prevailing animal in the forests is the royal stag, adapted to forests of temperate type and associated with the Eurasiatic forest and meadow fauna which now dominated western Europe.

The only survivor of the great African-Asiatic fauna is the lion, which appears in the late Palæolithic stations in the region of the Pyrenees; the arctic wolverene also gives the fauna a Postglacial aspect, for, like the lion, it is never found in central or western Europe after the close of Upper Palæolithic times. Other enemies of the herbivorous fauna were the wolf and the brown bear.

Besides the red deer, or stag, the forests at this time were filled with roe-deer. To the south in the Pyrenees the moose still survived, and to the north there were still found herds of reindeer which survived in central Europe as late as the twelfth century. Wild boars were numerous, and in the streams were found the beaver and the otter. In the forest borders and in the meadows hares and rabbits were abundant. Through the forests and meadows of southern France and along the borders of the Danube ranged the wild cattle (*Bos primigenius*). It would appear from our limited knowledge of the life of Azilian-Tardenoisian times that bison were found chiefly in the northern parts of Europe. There is little direct evidence in regard to the wild horse, the remains of which do not occur in the hearths of Azilian times.

Our knowledge of the life of the Spanish peninsula at a period closely succeeding this is indirectly derived from the animal frescos in certain caverns of northern Spain, which have been attributed to the early Neolithic but are now referred rather to the late Palæolithic. Here are found representations of the ibex, the stag, the fallow deer, the wild cattle, and also of the wild horses. This would indicate that wild horses were still roaming all over western Europe at the close of Upper Palæolithic times. The presence of the moose in late Palæolithic times at Alpera, on the high plateaus of Spain, has been determined; this animal has also been found in the Pyrenees during the Azilian stage.[7]

The great contrast between the mammalian life of Magdalenian and that of Azilian-Tardenoisian times is witnessed in the stations along the upper Danube, as described by Koken.[8] In Höhlefels, Schmiechenfels, and Propstfels, associated with implements of the *late* Magdalenian industry, are found ten types of animals belonging to the forests and four characteristic of the forests and meadows, or fourteen species altogether. With these are mingled two alpine forms, the ibex and the alpine shrew; also two types of mammals belonging to the steppes, and no less than six mammals and birds from the tundras, namely, the reindeer, the arctic fox, the ermine, the arctic hare, the banded lemming, and the arctic ptarmigan.

In wide contrast to this assemblage of late Magdalenian life on the upper Danube, there appear in Azilian times along the shores of the middle Danube in the stations of Ofnet and of Istein the following characteristic forest forms: *Sus scrofa ferus* (wild boar), *Cervus elaphus* (stag), *Capreolus capreolus* (roe-deer), *Bos* (?) *primigenius* (urus), *Lepus* (rabbit or hare), *Ursus arctos* (brown bear), *Felis leo* (lion), *Gulo luscus* (common wolverene), *Lynchus lynx* (lynx), *Vulpes* (fox), *Mustela martes* (marten),

Castor fiber (European beaver), *Mus* (field-mouse), *Turdus* (thrush). It thus appears that the alpine, the steppe, and the tundra faunæ had entirely disappeared from this region.

Origin and Distribution of the Azilian-Tardenoisian Industry

This industry represents the last stage of the Old Stone Age. The decline in the art of fashioning flints, begun in Magdalenian times, appears to continue in the Azilian-Tardenoisian. As to the tiny symmetrical flints which are characteristic of this period, among the microliths of almost all the late Magdalenian stations pre-Tardenoisian forms are found which may be regarded as prototypes of the geometric Tardenoisian flints;[9] this represents a new fashion established in flint-making under influences coming from the south.

There was also a natural or local Azilian evolution from the Magdalenian types and technique. In general the flint implements which had so long prevailed in western Europe become smaller in diameter and more carelessly retouched, showing marked deterioration even from the late Magdalenian stages. For the preparation of hides and the fashioning of bone we discover unsymmetrical planing tools (*grattoirs*), also small, well-formed oval scrapers (*racloirs*), and microlithic scrapers. Borers (*perçoirs*) with oblique ends and gravers (*burins*) made of small flakes are the types of implements which most frequently occur, but the great variety of borers, so characteristic of the Aurignacian and the Magdalenian industries, had entirely disappeared in Azilian times.

The marks of industrial degeneration are also conspicuous in the bone implements, which show a very great deterioration in number and quality as compared with the Magdalenian, and which are principally confined to three types—the harpoons, the awls (*poinçons*), and the smoothers (*lissoirs*), together with very small bone borers (*perçoirs*). The distinctive feature of the Azilian bone industry is the flat harpoon of stag horn; it is known that the use of stags' antlers for fashioning harpoons began in the late Magdalenian, when most of them were still being fashioned from reindeer horn. These flat Azilian harpoons succeed the type of the double-rowed, cylindrical harpoons of the late Magdalenian, and are found mainly where the rivers, lakes, or pools offered favorable conditions for fishing. Thus the Azilian

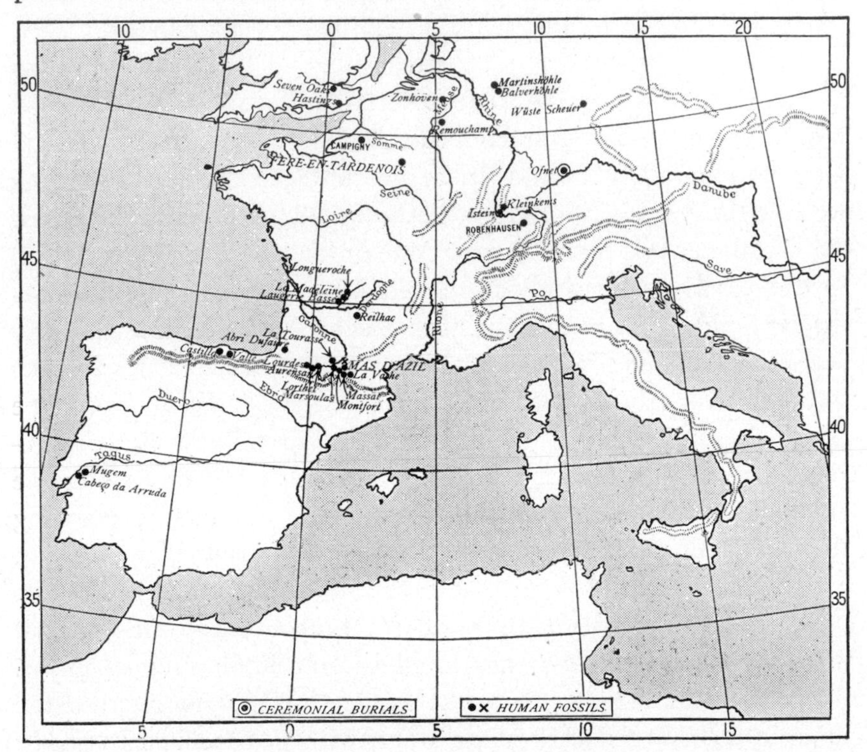

FIG. 250. Geographic distribution of the principal Azilian and Tardenoisian industrial stations in western Europe, also Campigny and Robenhausen.

bone-harpoon industry, like the Tardenoisian microlithic flint industry, was largely pursued by fisherfolk.

We may imagine that the gradual disappearance of the reindeer, an animal much more easily pursued and killed than the stag, was one of the causes of the substitution of the various arts of fishing for those of hunting.

It is to the excessively small or microlithic flints that the name Tardenoisian especially applies, and it is the vast multiplication of these microliths and their wide distribution over the whole area of the Mediterranean and of western Europe which constitutes the most distinctive feature of this industrial stage.[10] The triangular flint (Fig. 249) is certainly the most ancient Tardenoisian type. It occurs in the Azilian stations of the Cantabrian Mountains and of the Pyrenees, accompanied by the painted pebbles and with other flints of Azilian type, but without the graving-tools; to the east it is found in the stations of Savoy; and along the Danube it occurs at Ofnet, associated with remains of the lion and the moose, also with ornamental necklaces composed of the perforated teeth of the deer, identical with those found in the type station of Mas d'Azil in the Pyrenees. To the north this typical early Azilian culture extends to Istein, in Baden, where it includes the microlithic flint flakes, the gravers, and the little round scrapers associated here also with the stag and the prehistoric forest and meadow fauna of western Europe. Exactly the same stage of industrial development occurs in the grotto of Höhlefels, near Nuremberg, and in the shelter station of Sous Sac, Ain. We invariably find proofs of the variety of these pygmy flints as well as of their continuity from one station to another. All these facts compel us to assign a very long period of time to the spread of these industrial types.

The question which arises as to the sources of this special Tardenoisian industry again finds archæologists divided. Schmidt inclines to the autochthonous theory and regards the microlithic flint industry as an outgrowth of tendencies already well developed in the Magdalenian. Breuil, on the other hand,[11] dwells strongly on the evidence for circum-Mediterranean sources. In putting the questions, Who were the Azilians? Whence did they come? What were their ancestors? he is disposed to give the answer already quoted, that, whichever industry is examined, we are always obliged to look toward the south, toward some point along the Mediterranean, for the origin of these microlithic flints. In Italy, which he believes to have remained in an Aurignacian industrial stage throughout all the long period of Magdalenian time, he finds at Mentone a layer overlying the Aurignacian and containing small flints recalling the geometric forms of the Azilian, as well as a multitude of the small round scrapers (*racloirs*) characteristic of Azilian times. The upper layers at Mentone on the Riviera are paralleled by those observed near Otranto, in Sicily. It is certain, he continues, that

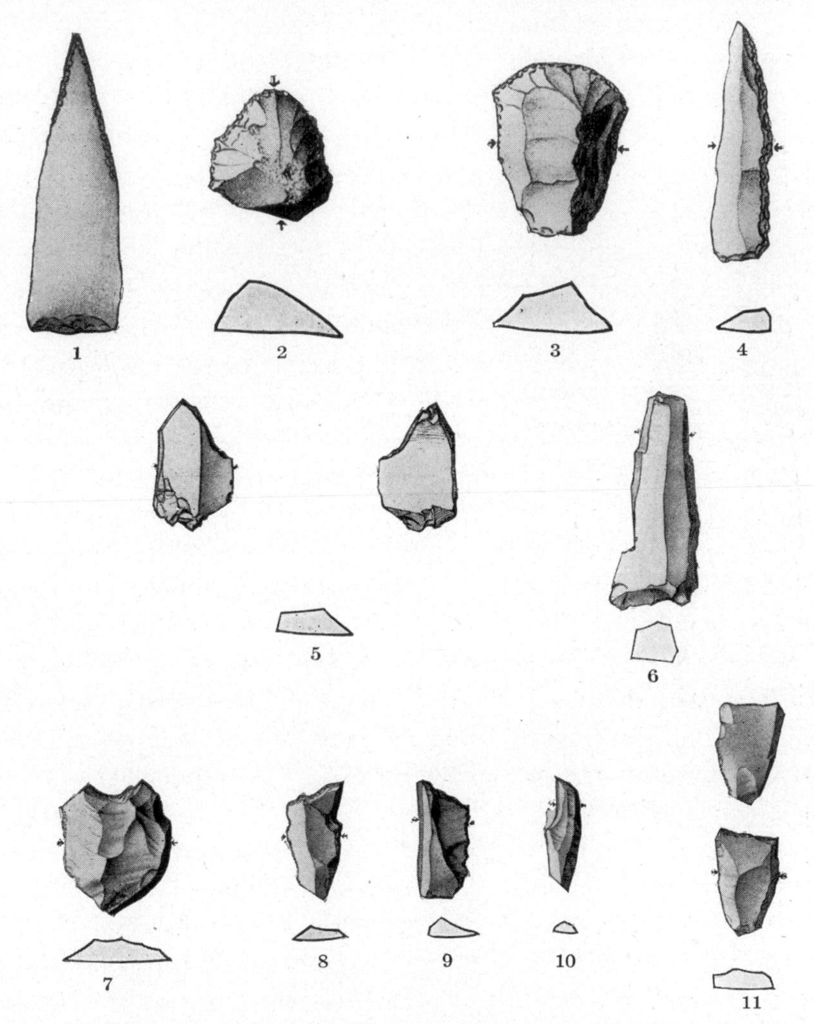

FIG. 251. Azilian stone implements of types surviving from the Magdalenian and earlier Palæolithic times. After R. R. Schmidt. 1. Finely flaked point from the large cave of Ofnet. 2, 3. Small Azilian *grattoirs*, or planing tools, from Istein, on the upper Danube. 4. Slender blade from Kleinkems. 5. Borer from Wüste Scheuer. 6. Polyhedral borer from Wüste Scheuer. 7. Incurved scraper from Istein. 8, 9, 10. Gravers or borers from Istein. 11. Double graver or borer with points at the right and left of the upper end. 1 to 4, actual size; 5 to 11, one-half actual size.

all around the Mediterranean there was a number of distinct centres where microlithic implements of geometric form appeared, and where the accompanying industries, in different stages of development, were related to an Upper Palæolithic culture consisting of a continuous Aurignacian type.

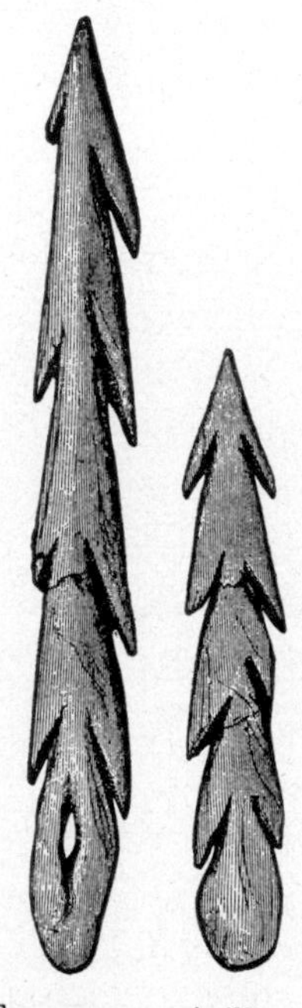

Fig. 252. Azilian double-rowed harpoons of stag horn, from Oban, on the west coast of Scotland. After Boule.

The labors of de Morgan, Capitan, and others have thrown great light on the Palæolithic of Tunis, where a flint culture was developed only slightly different from that of the Azilian of Valle, Santander, of the Mas d'Azil, Ariège, and of Bobache, Drôme. A resemblance is also found in Portugal; and southern Spain, despite its poverty of typical implements, shows a similar evolution. Near Salamanca, northwest of Madrid, Spain, the grottos contain schematic figures and colored pebbles resembling the Azilian. In Portugal the hearths of Mugem and Cabeço da Arruda are distinguished by their triangular microliths and are undoubtedly Pre-Neolithic, because there is neither pottery nor any trace of domesticated animals, excepting, possibly, the dog.

To the north of Europe the discoveries in Belgium have especial importance, for typical Azilian implements, including small round scrapers, lateral gravers, elongated triangular microliths, and knife flakes are found associated with the remains of the reindeer in the grotto of Remouchamp and at Zonhoven. It appears in Belgium, as in Italy, that the use of the Tardenoisian microlithic flint types is prolonged into a later time than that of the typical Azilian flint implements —the scrapers, gravers, borers, and knife flakes—which, as we have seen, appear at the end of the true Magdalenian.

On the other side of the English Channel we again find these flints always unmingled with pottery and usually distributed along the sea or river shores. The best-known stations are those of Hastings, directly across the Channel opposite Boulogne, and of Seven Oaks, near London; in Settle, Yorkshire, is the Victoria Cave station. To the north, in Scotland, four Azilian stations have been discovered around Oban, on the western coast near the head of the Firth of Lorne, while Azilian harpoons have also been found on the Isle of Oronsay, at its entrance.

Thus the spread of the very small Tardenoisian flint implements in the final stages of the Palæolithic precedes the southern advent of the Neolithic.

In Germany only six Azilian-Tardenoisian stations have thus far been discovered: two to the east of Düsseldorf, one in the neighborhood of Weimar, two on the headwaters of the Rhine, near Basle, and, by far the most important, the large and small grottos of Ofnet, on a small tributary of the Danube northwest of Munich. This last is exceptionally important because it is the only station where skeletons have been found buried with Azilian-Tardenoisian flints, thereby enabling us positively to determine the contemporary human races.

Burials in Azilian-Tardenoisian Times

The strange interment which gives Ofnet its distinction belongs to the period of Azilian-Tardenoisian industry.[12] This conclusion is not weakened by the absence of Azilian harpoons or painted pebbles, because at this time the cave of Ofnet served its frequenters only as a place of burial; there are no hearths or flint workshops to indicate continued residence, as during earlier Upper Palæolithic times.

This great ceremonial burial seems to afford the only positive evidence to be found in all western Europe of the kind of people who were pursuing the Azilian industry. The larger Ofnet grotto opens toward the southwest and has a length of 39 feet and a width of 36 feet. It was first entered in early Aurignacian times and shows successive layers of Aurignacian, early Solutrean, and late Magdalenian cultures, above which lies a thick deposit of the Azilian-Tardenoisian, in which is found the most remarkable interment of all Palæolithic times.

This is a ceremonial burial of thirty-three skulls of people belonging to two distinct races: respectively, brachycephalic and dolichocephalic, and certainly not related in any way to the Crô-Magnon race. In one group twenty-seven skulls were found embedded in ochre and arranged in a sort of nest, with the faces all looking westward. As the skulls in the centre were more

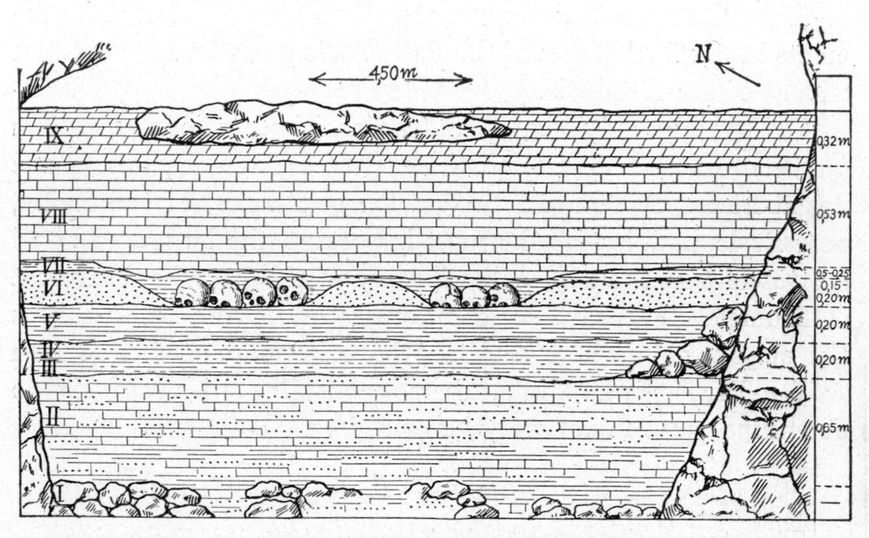

FIG. 253. Section across the entrance of the great grotto of Ofnet near the Danube, occupied at various times from the beginning of the Upper Palæolithic to the close of the Bronze Age. After R. R. Schmidt. *IX.* Deposits of the Middle Ages and cf the La Tène and Hallstatt cultures. *VIII.* Deposits of the Upper Neolithic. *VII.* Azilian layer containing the great burial of 33 skulls. *VI.* Late Magdalenian layer containing the banded lemmings of the tundras. *V.* Late Solutrean layer with typical laurel-leaf spear points. *IV, III.* Deposits of late and early Aurignacian age, *III* containing arctic rodents. *II.* Dolomite sand with a few teeth of the mammoth and bones of the woolly rhinoceros marked by the teeth of hyænas.

closely pressed together and crushed than those on the outside, it seems probable that these skulls were added one by one from time to time, those on the outside being the most recent additions. About a yard distant a similar nest was found, containing six more skulls embedded and arranged in exactly the same manner. The interment probably took place shortly after death and certainly before the separate bones had been disintegrated by decomposition, for not only the lower jaw but a number of the neck vertebræ were found with each skull. The heads had been severed from the necks by a sharp flint, the marks of which are plainly visible on some of the vertebræ.

It is noteworthy that most of these skulls are those of women and young children, there being only four adult male skulls. On this account some advance the theory of cannibalism; others that, being taken captive by a tribe of enemies, these unfortunate

FIG. 254. Burial nest of six skulls, all facing westward, from the large grotto of Ofnet. After R. R. Schmidt.

people were offered in sacrifice, in which case decapitation was the means of death. But, then, how explain the abundant ornaments of stag teeth and snail shells (*Helix nemoralis*) with which the skulls of the women and little children were decorated, and the treasured implements of flint with which all save one of the men and a few of the women and children were provided?

There are precedents for all these singular features of the Ofnet interment in other Upper Palæolithic burials, namely, the embedding in ochre, the offerings of ornaments of teeth and of

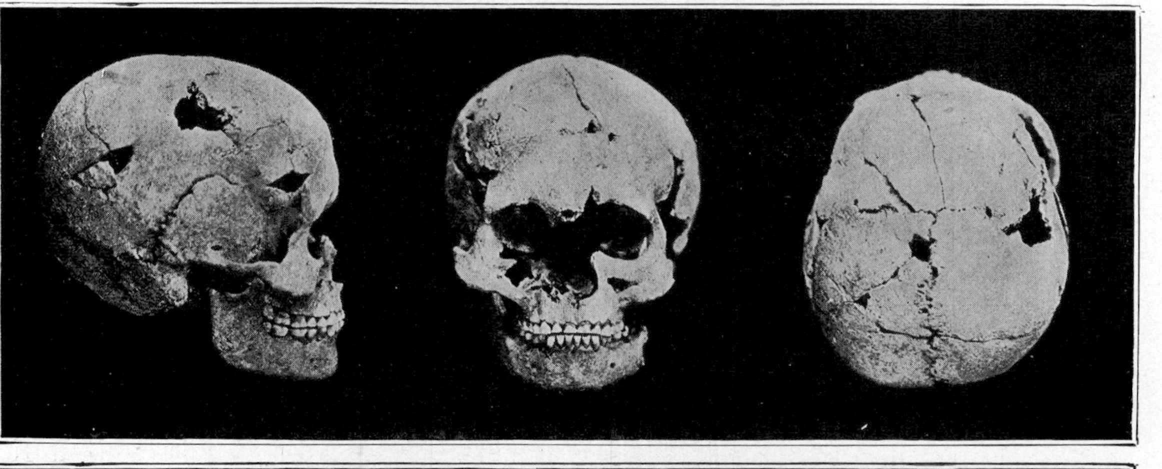

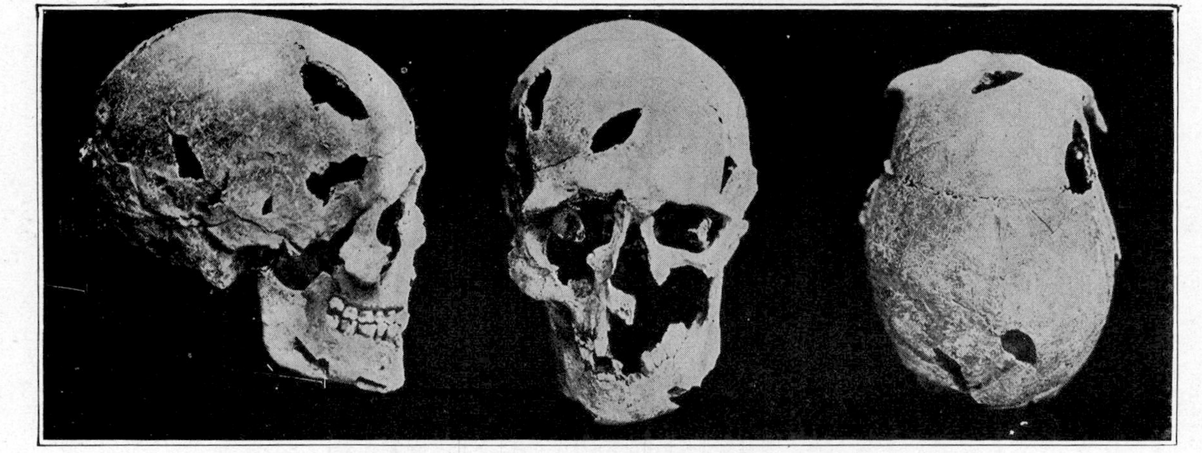

FIG. 255. Skulls of the two races of Ofnet. Three views of a broad-headed or *brachycephalic* skull (above) from the great burial at Ofnet. Three views of a narrow-headed or *dolichocephalic* skull (below) from

shells, the separate interment of the skull—all these were customs more or less characteristic of the Upper Palæolithic, but never observed in Neolithic times.

It will be recalled that the custom of burying the entire body, as well as that of embedding the body in ochre, is first observed among the late Neanderthals and obtained throughout the entire Upper Palæolithic from the Aurignacian burials of Grimaldi to the Azilian of Mas d'Azil. No other case, however, is known of the westward turning of the face: in most of the Upper Palæolithic burials the face of the departed looks toward the opening of the grotto; but, although the grotto of Ofnet opens toward the southwest, the skulls, without exception, were facing exactly to the west and looking toward the wall rather than toward the entrance of the cavern.

The New Broad-Headed and Narrow-Headed Races of Ofnet

The burials at Ofnet are the first observed in western Europe which present a mingling of races. This in itself is a fact of great interest; it is a prelude to what characterizes all the populations of western Europe at the present time, namely, the presence of races widely separated in origin and in anatomical structure, but closely united by similar customs, industries, and beliefs.

A second fact of even greater importance is the proof of the arrival in western Europe toward the close of Palæolithic times of two entirely new human stocks; one broad-headed, resembling the modern Alpine or Celtic type; the other narrow-headed, resembling the modern 'Mediterranean' type of Sergi. Beside these pure types there are several blended forms which are intermediate or mesaticephalic.

Of the eight brachycephalic heads, six are those of children; the two adult brachycephalic crania belong to young women and are, therefore, not quite so characteristic as male skulls would be, for in general racial type is more strongly marked in men than in women; the remaining skulls are either of a blended form or purely dolichocephalic.

The relationship of the broad-headed race to other prehistoric and existing broad-headed races of western Europe is also a matter of very great interest. The Ofnet brachycephals are regarded by Schliz[13] as closely similar to the type skull of the so-called Grenelle race, which, in turn, is closely similar to the Furfooz type. Thus the cephalic index of one (Fig. 255) of these broad, flattened skulls of Ofnet is 83.33 per cent; the face is relatively narrow, the zygomatic index being low—76.34 per cent; the brain capacity of the female skulls does not exceed 1,320 c.cm. The skull is further described as small, smooth, and delicately modelled, with a correspondingly feeble dentition, the teeth being small; the processes of muscular attachment are slightly developed, all of which characters indicate that the skull belonged to a woman about twenty-five years of age. The forehead is low, broad, and prominent. It is altogether typically parallel to the 'skull of Grenelle,' as well as to the female 'skull of Auvernier' described by Kollmann. The peculiarity of this broad-headed race, like that of Grenelle and of Furfooz, is that, while the forehead is of only moderate breadth, the posterior part of the skull is extremely broad. The broad-headed people of Ofnet are thus definitely considered by Schliz[14] as members of the Furfooz-Grenelle race.

The narrow-headed race of the Ofnet burials is distinct in every respect and presents resemblances to the branch of the 'Mediterranean' race found in the foreground of the Alpine regions to-day, in which the head is of a pear-shaped type. The best preserved of these dolichocephalic skulls (Fig. 255) presents an index of 70.50 per cent, with a brain capacity in the male of 1,500 c.cm., while the smallest brain capacity is that found in one of the female skulls with 1,100 c.cm. Among the five adult purely dolichocephalic skulls the face is not in the least of the broad or disharmonic Crô-Magnon type, but is in proportion with the cranium, and is thus truly *harmonic*. The resemblance of this narrow-headed Ofnet skull to that of the Brünn race, which we have described as occurring in Moravia in Solutrean times, is only partial, and Schliz concludes that among the narrow-headed people of Ofnet we have a form of dolichocephaly which is not identical with any of the known early dolichocephalic forms of western Europe, but which pursues an independent line of development similar to the narrow-headed races in the borders of the Alpine region of the present day. Thus this head type, of a uniform elliptic contour, seems to have become a stable racial element of the Alpine population, since we meet it again in later prehistoric times in the region of the southern and western foreground of the Alps. Among the children's skulls, two are of the narrow-headed, pear-shaped type similar to the Alpine dolichocephals of to-day, that is, with a narrow forehead and very broad posterior portions of the skull.

Central Origin of the Broad-Headed (Alpine?) Races

The affinity of the broad-headed Azilian-Tardenoisian tribes of the Danube to those found in the Upper Palæolithic of north-western Europe seems to be clearly established. The latter are sometimes known as the Grenelle race and sometimes as the Furfooz race. Boule[15] observes in regard to the skeletal remains of Grenelle which were found in the alluvium near Paris, in 1870, that it is quite impossible now, forty years after their discovery, to demonstrate their geologic antiquity. This is not the case with the Furfooz broad-heads, the age of which we regard as well established, but since the head type appears to be the same in both cases, we may speak of this race as the Furfooz-Grenelle.

In a cave near Furfooz, in the valley of the Lesse, Belgium, sixteen skeletons were discovered by Dupont in 1867. With the bones were found implements of reindeer horn and remains of the late Pleistocene fauna of northern Europe.[16] The reindeer and the tundra fauna of Belgium were contemporaneous with the early Tardenoisian culture and with the stag and forest fauna

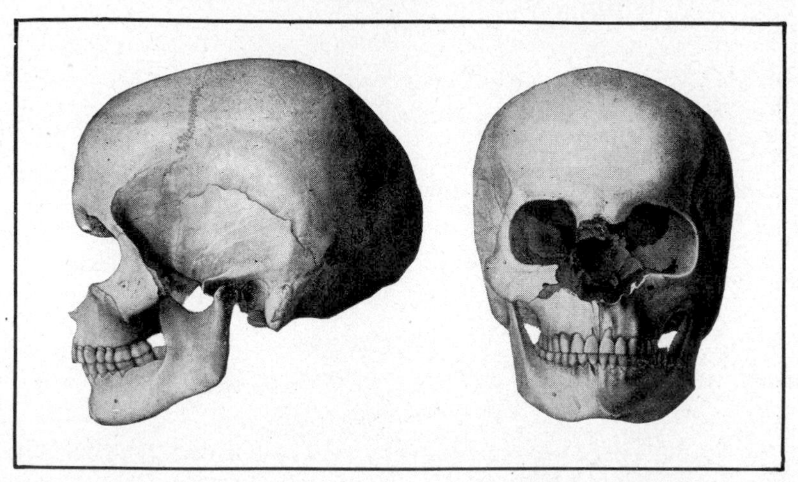

FIG. 256. Broad-headed skull of uncertain archæologic age, either Palæolithic or Neolithic, discovered at Grenelle, near Paris, in 1870. After de Quatrefages and Hamy. One-quarter life size.

of southern France, so that the skeletons of Furfooz may safely be referred to Azilian-Tardenoisian times.

Only two of the Furfooz skulls were preserved in good shape; they are of brachycephalic or sub-brachycephalic form, and, fol-

FIG. 257. Opening of the grotto of Furfooz on the Lesse, a tributary of the Meuse, near Namur, Belgium, where the skeletal remains of 16 individuals and the type skulls of the broad-headed Furfooz race were discovered in 1867. After Dupont.

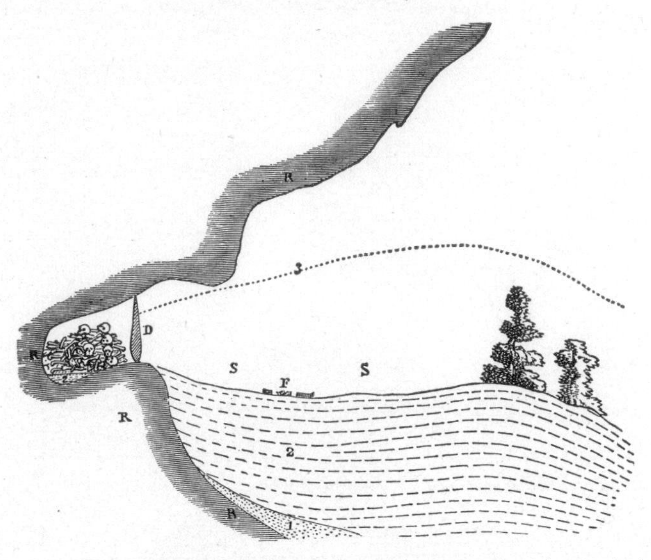

FIG. 258. Section of the grotto of Furfooz, showing the burial of 16 skeletons of the Furfooz race and the entrance of the grotto blocked by a mass of stone. After Dupont.

lowing the suggestion of de Quatrefages and Hamy, these skulls have been spoken of as belonging to the 'brachycephalic Furfooz race.' The men of this race may certainly be regarded as belonging to Upper Palæolithic times, whereas the brachycephalic

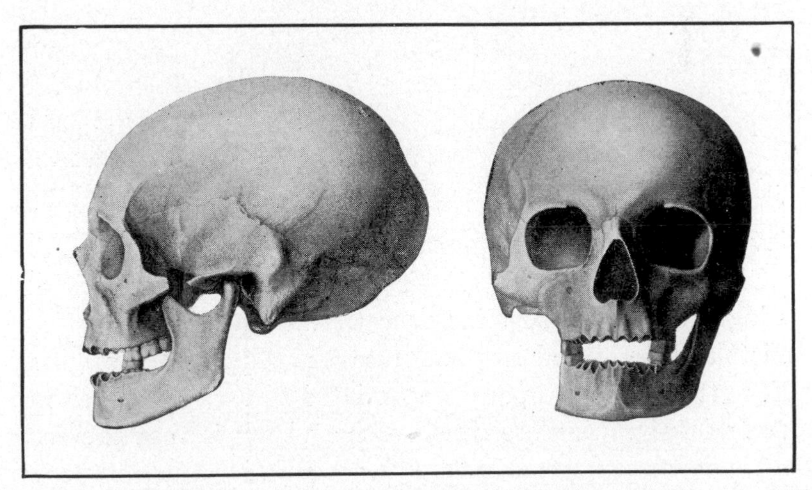

FIG. 259. One of the type skulls of the broad-headed Furfooz race, from the burial grotto of Furfooz, Belgium. After de Quatrefages and Hamy. One-quarter life size.

race found at Grenelle, near Paris, is probably Neolithic. This by no means prevents the Furfooz and the Grenelle types belonging to the same general brachycephalic race; it is altogether probable that they do, and that with them may be included the Ofnet broad-heads.

There are several opinions regarding the geographic centres from which these broad-heads entered Europe; it is generally

FIG. 260. Restoration of the broad-headed man of Grenelle, modelled by Mascré, under the direction of A. Rutot. This type of head is similar to that of Ofnet.

believed that they came from the high plateaus of central Asia. By Giuffrida-Ruggeri the Furfooz race is identified with the existing broad-headed Alpine race (*Homo sapiens alpinus*), and is mistakenly adduced as proof that the Alpine race originated in Europe and is not in any way related to the Mongolian races of central Asia. A more conservative view[17] is that the recent European broad-headed types commonly included under the Alpine race cannot yet be traced back to the Furfooz-Grenelle ancestors, because their connection is too problematical. Schliz, on the other hand, considers that the Furfooz-Grenelle race survived in northwestern Europe and corresponds with that which became the builders of the megalithic dolmens of Neolithic times, the latter being but slightly modified descendants of the original Furfooz race; he believes, moreover, that these broad-headed peoples first occupied central Europe and then extended to western Europe, where they correspond to the Alpine race, at least in part; that they also migrated to the north and were the basis of the broad-headed races now found in Holland and Denmark.

Southern Origin of the Narrow-Headed (Mediterranean?) Races

While it seems probable that the broad-heads represent a central migration from Eurasia, evidence of an industrial and cultural character indicates that the narrow-heads came from the south; this is seen both in the south Mediterranean origin of the Tardenoisian flint industry and in the new schematic influences on the decadent art of Upper Palæolithic times.

It seems, observes Breuil, as if the schematic influences in art during Upper Palæolithic times always extend from the south toward the north; they predominate entirely in the painted rocks of Andalusia, in the Pyrenees, and in Dordogne. In the grotto of Marsoulas, Haute-Garonne, the Azilian *motifs* are clearly superposed upon the Magdalenian polychromes. This purely schematic phase, which abruptly follows the figure art of middle Magdalenian times, first made itself felt in the late Magdalenian. There was a sudden loss of realism which does not indicate affiliation but rather the infiltration of strange elements from the south; the precursors of the destructive invasion of the Azilian-Tardenoisian tribes who were driven from their Mediterranean homes by the westward advance of the conquering Neolithic races. We imagine[18] that in southern Spain there dwelt in Upper Palæolithic times a population differing from the Magdalenians of France and of the Cantabrian Mountains in their lower artistic tastes. It would therefore appear that the schematic art had its home toward the south of the peninsula of Spain about the time of the invasion of the Azilian culture in France.

Northern Origin of the Baltic (Teutonic?) Races

For the first time the retreat of the Scandinavian ice-fields and the less severe climate permitted a northern migration route along the shores of the Baltic. This is the first known migration of any tribes along this route, which throughout all glacial times had been blocked by the vicinity of the Scandinavian and Baltic ice-fields, but which was now opened by the approach of the more genial climate which succeeded the long Postglacial Stage. Whether this Baltic invasion was the advance wave of a northern long-headed Teutonic race is wholly a matter of conjecture.

"Other peoples," observes Breuil,[19] "known at present only from their industries, were advancing toward the close of the Upper Palæolithic along the northern and southern shores of the Baltic and persisted for an appreciable time before the arrival of the tribes introducing the early Neolithic Campignian culture which accumulated in the kitchen-middens along the same shores. Like the southern races of Azilian-Tardenoisian times, these northerly tribes were truly Pre-Neolithic, ignorant both of agriculture and of pottery; they brought with them no domesticated animals excepting the dog, which is known at Mugem, at Tourasse, and at Oban, in northwestern Scotland. In the use of bone harpoons of elegant form and in the taste displayed in fine decorations engraved upon bone, these tribes suggest the culture of the Magdalenians, but a close examination shows that it could not have been derived from the Magdalenian type. The community of style with the painted and engraved figures found in western Siberia and in the central Ural region and north of the Altai Mountains denotes rather an Asiatic and Siberian origin.

"The decorative designs of these Baltic peoples were very different from those of the Crô-Magnons in Magdalenian times, and are not schematic; the conception of the animal figures, although naturalistic, is as crude as that of the early Aurignacian figures, and is far inferior to that of the Magdalenian stage." "It is probable," continues Breuil, "that in these northerly regions the closing cultures of the Upper Palæolithic developed along

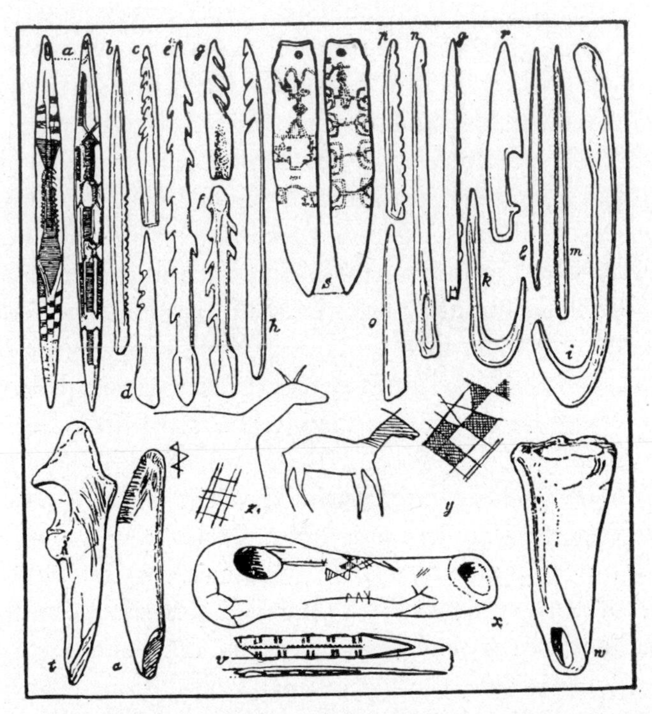

FIG. 261. Implements and decorations showing the conventional and crude animal designs of the art of the Baltic, from Maglemose, Denmark. After Reinecke and Obermaier. The implements include bone harpoons, fish-hooks, horn chisels, awls, spear points, and smoothers. About one-fifth actual size.

more or less parallel lines with those observed in the south in giving rise to ethnographic elements which travelled along the littoral regions of the northern seas."

This race and culture is described by Obermaier[20] as follows:

When primitive man took possession of Denmark the seacoast was so remote that he could also reach southern Scandinavia. The station of Maglemose in the 'Great Moor,' discovered and described by F. L. Sarauw, of Copenhagen, in 1900, is near the harbor of Mullerup on the western coast of Zealand and not far from the shore of an ancient freshwater lake formation. These people were lake-dwellers, living perhaps on rafts but not on dwellings supported by piles. From these rafts it is supposed the implements dropped into the lake. The 881 flint implements found here include scrapers, borers, cleavers, and knives, as well as microlithic flints. They show no trace of the Neolithic art of polishing, merely suggesting certain chipped styles observed in the 'kjöddenmöddings.' (See Figs. 263, 264, and 265.) The influence of the Palæolithic is much stronger, especially in the case of the microlithic Tardenoisian types. In the industrial culture of Maglemose, however, far more important than stone are implements of horn and bone. These the Maglemose folk obtained from the wild ox, moose, stag, and roedeer, fashioning them into tools of various types, some of which are shown in Fig. 261. Many of these tools are ornamented with conventional designs or very crude animal outlines on one or both surfaces.

The forests of this time consisted of the characteristic northern flora including numerous evergreens, the birch, aspen, hazel, and elm, but without any trace of the oak. There is absolutely no trace of pottery in the Maglemose deposits. Of great interest is the fact that skeletal remains of the domestic dog are found here.

The Maglemose culture of the Baltic region is regarded as contemporary with the Azilian and Tardenoisian in the south. It contains types, not of flint but of bone, which are prophetic of the Neolithic. Traces of this culture have been found throughout northern Germany, in Denmark, and in southern Sweden, as well as to the east and in the Baltic provinces. Although no human remains have as yet been discovered, it is highly probable that these people belonged to the northern Teutonic races

Conclusion as to the Relationships of the Palæolithic Races

Thus in southern, central, and northern Europe the close of Upper Palæolithic times is marked by the invasion of new Eurasiatic races, all in a Pre-Neolithic stage of industry and art. It is not improbable that these races were advance waves from the same geographic regions as the Neolithic tribes which followed them.

From the earliest Palæolithic to Neolithic times it does not appear that western Europe was ever a centre of human evolution in the sense that it gave rise to a single new species of man. The main racial evolution and the earlier and later branches of the human family were established in the east and successively found their way westward; nor is there at present any ground for believing that any very prolonged evolution or transformation of human types occurred in western Europe.

We should regard as wholly unproved the notion that either of these Palæolithic races of western Europe gave rise to others which succeeded them in geologic time; the only sequence of this sort to which some degree of probability may be attached is that the Heidelberg race was ancestral to the Neanderthal race.

In most instances, such races as the Piltdown, the Crô-Magnon, the Brünn, the Furfooz-Grenelle, and the Mediterranean arrived fully formed, with all their mental and physical attributes and tendencies very distinctly developed. There is some evidence, but not of a very conclusive kind, that the modification of certain of these races in western Europe was partly in the nature of a decline; this was apparently the case both with the Neanderthals and with the Crô-Magnons.

We may therefore imagine that the family tree or lines of descent of the races of the Old Stone Age consisted of a number of entirely separate branches, which had been completely formed in the great Eurasiatic continent, a land mass infinitely larger and more capable of producing a variety of races than the diminutive peninsular area of western Europe.

A review of these races in descending order, in respect to stature, the cephalic index, and brain capacity, is presented in the following table:

	Frontal Angle	Height of Skull	Cephalic Index	Brain Capacity	Height	Comparative Length of Arm and Leg
RECENT.				ccm.	ft. in.	
(*H. sapiens*).						
European (average).	90	59	....	1400–1500	5 7	69.73 %
UPPER PALÆOLITHIC.						
Ofnet Race (brachycephalic)............	....	....	86.21	1400	....	....
Ofnet Race (dolichocephalic)............	....	....	70.50	1500	....	....
Crô-Magnon Race (old man of Crô-Magnon type)............	....	....	73.76	1590	6	....
Grimaldi (Crô-Magnons)............	....	....	? 63– ? 76.27	1775–1880	5 10½– 6 4½	66.05 %– 69 %
Chancelade........	....	....	72.02	1700	4 11	....
Aurignac..........	....	....	65.7	....	5 3	....
Grimaldi Race.						
Grimaldi type (negroid)............	....	....	69.27	1580	5 1	63.12 %
Brünn Race.						
Brünn I...........	75	51.22	65.7 or 68.2	1350	....	....
LOWER PALÆOLITHIC.						
Neanderthal Race (*H. Neanderthalensis*).						
La Chapelle........	65	40.5	75	1626	5 3	....
Spy II............	67	44.3	75.7	? 1723	5 3	....
Spy I.............	57.5	40.9	70	? 1562	5 4	....
La Ferrassie I.......	....	...	....	....	5 5	? 68 %
La Ferrassie II......	....	....	....	....	4 10½	68 %
La Quina..........	....	....	....	1367 (approx.)	....	....
Krapina D.........	66	42.2	? 83.7	....	....	....
Neanderthal........	62	40.4	73.9	1408	5 4	....
Gibraltar..........	66 or 73–74	40	77.9	1250 or 1296	....	....
Pre-Neanderthaloids						
Piltdown Race.						
Piltdown..........	....	....	? 78 or ? 79	? 1300 ? 1500	....	....
Trinil Race (*Pithecanthropus*)...........	52.5	34.2	73.4 or 70	850–1000 900	5 7	....
ANTHROPOID APES.						
Apes (maximum)......	56	37.7	....	600	....	104 % (chimpanzee minimum.)

The chief authorities for these measurements are Schwalbe, Dubois, Keith, Smith Woodward, Boule, Sollas, Sera, Klaatsch, Fraipont, Makowsky, Verneau, Testut, and Broca.

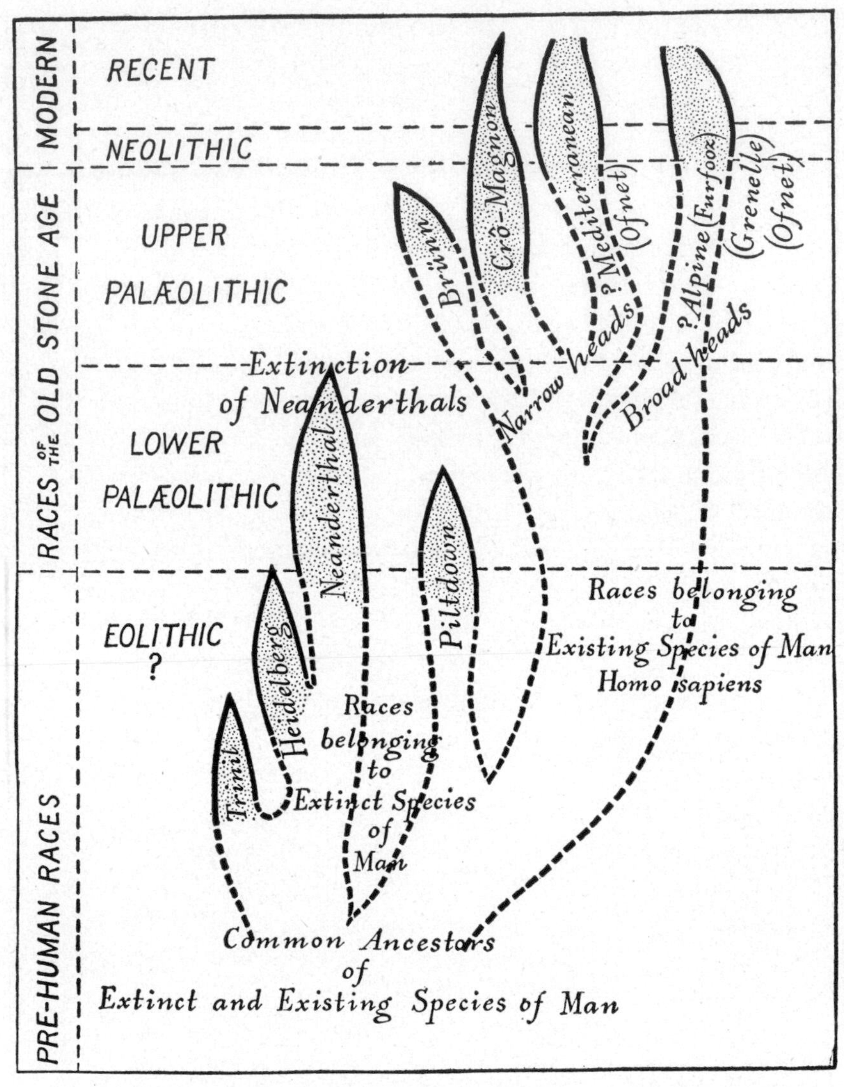

FIG. 262. Tree showing the main theoretic lines of descent of the chief Pre-Neolithic races discovered in western Europe. (The Grimaldi race is omitted on account of its aberrant character. The northern Teutonic long-heads are also omitted.) The Trinil, Heidelberg, and Neanderthal races are represented as offshoots of one great branch. The Piltdown race is represented as an independent branch of quite unknown relations to the other races. It is probable that the five or six branches of *Homo sapiens* discovered in the Upper Palæolithic separated from each other in Lower Palæolithic times in Asia. Of these the Brünn race is by far the most primitive.

The migration routes of invasion of the successive Lower Palæolithic races—the Piltdown, the Heidelberg, and the Neanderthal—are entirely unknown; we can only infer from the wide distribution of the Chellean and Acheulean cultures to the south, along the northern African coast, as well as to the east, that these races may have had a southerly or circum-Mediterranean origin. This does not mean that either of these Lower Palæolithic races were of negroid or Ethiopian affinity, because the Neanderthals show absolutely no negroid characters. In fact, throughout all Palæolithic time the solitary instance of the two Grimaldi skeletons furnishes the sole anatomical evidence we possess of the entrance of a negroid people into Europe, which contrasts widely with the overwhelming evidence of the dominance in western Europe first of the non-negroid Neanderthals, and then of the Crô-Magnons who probably belonged to the Caucasian stock.

The evidence as to the sources and migrations of the Upper Palæolithic races is also indirect. The theory of the Crô-Magnons entering Europe by the southerly or Mediterranean route we have seen to rest upon purely cultural or industrial grounds, namely, the spread of the Aurignacian industry around the Mediterranean shores. On the other hand, the succeeding culture, the Solutrean, and the succeeding race to enter Europe, the Brünn, both appear to be of central or of direct easterly origin. It is only toward the close of the Upper Palæolithic that another southerly or Mediterranean invasion occurs, bringing in the microlithic Tardenoisian culture, which, although anatomical evidence is wanting, would appear to be an advance wave of the great invasion of the true 'Mediterranean' race. During the Upper Palæolithic Epoch another invasion apparently occurs from the east along the central migration route, namely, that of the broad-headed Furfooz-Grenelle races.

Thus in surveying the whole period of the Old Stone Age we find that there is some evidence for the theory of an alternation of southerly, of easterly, and finally of northeasterly invasions of races bringing in new industries and ideas.

Transition to the Neolithic. The Campignian. The Robenhausian

Apart from the special and somewhat debated question of the place of the Campignian culture in the prehistory of Europe we may close our survey of the Upper Palæolithic by pointing out some of its contrasts with the Neolithic.

The arrival of the Neolithic cultures and industries in western Europe marks one of the most profound changes in all

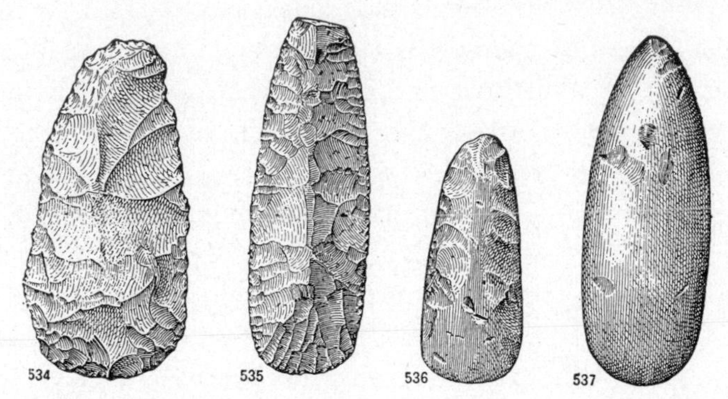

Fig. 263. Stages in the manufacture of the Neolithic stone ax, or *hache*. After de Mortillet. 534. *Hache* of flint, roughly flaked into shape, from Olendon, Calvados. 535. *Hache* of flint from Oise, ready for polishing. It has been finely chipped to a shape of perfect symmetry, with especial care to smooth out and reduce the large facets made by the preliminary flaking. 536. *Hache* of flint after the first polishing, from Abbeville, on the Somme. The cutting edge has been completely polished, but along the sides the facets made by flaking are plainly visible. 537. *Hache* of flint completely polished, from Le Vesinet, Seine-et-Oise. In this last stage one scarcely notices the faint traces of facets which show that this *hache* has passed through all the preceding stages. Two-ninths actual size.

prehistory and introduces us to a new period which must be treated in an entirely different historic spirit. This new era began between 7,000 to 10,000 years ago, or with the close of the Daun stage, the last geologic feature of Postglacial times.

There are two theories regarding the close of Upper Palæolithic and the beginning of Neolithic times. The older theory, which still has some adherents, is that the Upper Palæolithic races and industries suddenly gave way before the arrival of new and superior races bringing in the Neolithic culture. The newer theory is that there are evidences of gradual transfusions from the Upper Palæolithic into the Neolithic cultures and that these are found in some of the oldest Neolithic sites.

Fig. 264. Stone hatchet, or *tranchet*, from the type station of Campigny, after Salmon, d'Ault du Mesnil, and Capitan. One-half actual size.

In 1898 there appeared an article[21] by Philippe Salmon, d'Ault du Mesnil, and Capitan, entitled, "Le Campignien," defending the theory of an early and transitional Neolithic stage, the *Campignian.*[22] The type station of this early culture was pointed out by Salmon in 1886; it lies a little more than a mile northwest of the village of Blangy, on the River Bresle, on a site well placed for natural defense. The remains of the hut-dwellings of this camp and of various industrial objects appear to indicate that this station belongs to the earliest phase of the Neolithic Period. These Campignians owe little to the culture or industry of the races which previously occupied this region of western Europe; they are entire strangers, purely Neolithic in type.

Fig. 265. Stone pick, or *pic*, from the type station of Campigny, after Salmon, d'Ault du Mesnil, and Capitan. About one-half actual size.

While this is the age of polished, as distinguished from chipped, stone, the axe (*hache*) of polished stone is still very rare in the Campignian. There prevail flaked flint types common to all the previous stages of the Stone Age, such as the knives (*couteaux*), planers (*grattoirs*), and spear or dart heads (*pointes de sagaie*), but we notice the appearance of two entirely new flint implements: first, the triangular knife or stone hatchet (*tranchet*), of the type (Fig. 264) common in the Danish kitchen-middens; this knife has a broad, sharp cutting edge flaked on one side; second (Fig. 265), there is a sort of elongated axe or pick (*pic*) with chipped sides and an end more or less conical in shape.[23] These people also made use of large flakes of flint. If we regard the Campignian as a prolonged industrial stage in northern Europe, it certainly precedes the appearance of abundant axe heads of polished flint. In France it seems to appear occasionally as a local phase of the Neolithic.

FIG. 266. Restoration of the Neolithic man of Spiennes, Belgium, modelled by Mascré under the direction of A. Rutot.

The prevailing opinion at present is that the Campignian distinctly precedes the typical Neolithic of the Swiss lake-dwellings, a stage known as the *Robenhausian*. Thus the Neolithic culture becomes fully established in the period of the Swiss Lake Dwellings, remains of which are found at Moosseedorf, Wauwyl, Concise on Lake Neufchâtel, and Robenhausen on Lake Pfaeffikon. The latter is the *Robenhausian* type station.

Distinctive Features of the Neolithic Epoch

The first of these is the presence of implements of polished stone which find their way gradually into western Europe. The neoliths at first are greatly outnumbered by chipped and flaked implements, and some of the latter show a survival of the familiar types of the Old Stone Age, while others belong to entirely distinct types which had an independent development in the far East.

The chief economic change is seen in the rudimentary knowledge of agriculture and in the use of a variety of plants and seeds, accompanied by the gradual appearance of implements for the preparation of the soil and for harvesting the crops. This new source of food supply leads to the establishment of permanent stations and camps and more or less to the abandonment of nomadic modes of life. Near the ancient camp sites and villages, therefore, are found implements for the preparation of skins and hides, because the chase was still maintained for purposes of clothing as well as for food.

Still more distinctive of the Neolithic is the introduction of pottery, which is at first used in the preparation of food. In the hearths or kitchen-middens and in the refuse heaps of the camps we no longer find evidence of the splitting of the jaws of mammals and of the long and short bones of the limbs, or even of the larger foot bones, in search of marrow, which is such a universal feature of the Upper Palæolithic deposits.

The artistic impulse of the north is very crude and naturalistic. In the Spanish peninsula, accompanying and following the schematic period described in the early part of this chapter, there was a long stage of development in which men were painting on rocks, mostly in the form of silhouettes, naturalistic figures of animals and of people.[24]

The presence of the moose in these drawings concurs with that of the two bison represented in the cavern of Cogul and would tend to indicate that these paintings belong to Upper Palæolithic times, and it is now considered that they are of late Palæolithic age. The character of these animal designs is totally different from that of the Magdalenian period in the north and is analogous rather to that of the Bushmen of South Africa. The authors of these frescos represent not only the ibex, stag, and wild cattle but also the horse, moose, fallow deer, wolf, and occasionally the birds. There are many features in this art which show its absolute independence of origin from

Fig. 267. Fresco from the rock shelter of Alpera, Albacete, Spain, painted in dark red and representing a stag hunt, the hunters being armed with bows and arrows. Attributed to southern races arriving in late Palæolithic times. After Breuil and Obermaier.

that of the Magdalenian of the north, among them the frequent presence of composition and the almost invariable presence of human figures.

The frescos in the Spanish caverns of Alpera and of Cogul recall those of southern France but are almost always grouped in series of the chase, of encampment, and perhaps of war. This frequency of human figures, the representations of the bow and arrow, and the presence of a small animal which may be recognized as the domesticated dog are indications of an entirely distinct race coming from the south and bringing in a new spirit in art which has no relation whatever to that of the Magdalenian.

Neolithic Mammalian Life

Even in the oldest Neolithic deposits no trace of the horse as an object of food appears. The domestication of this animal was introduced from the east, and thus it ceased to be an object of the chase. The newly arriving tribes were undoubtedly attracted by the abundance of horses, both of the forest and Celtic types, which had survived from Upper Palæolithic times. A very distinctive feature of the modern horses, however, should be mentioned, that is, the presence of a forelock covering the face, no trace of which is indicated in any of the Upper Palæolithic carvings or engravings.

The wild animal life of western Europe at this time is a direct survival of the great Eurasiatic forest and meadow fauna which we have traced from the earliest Palæolithic times. It includes the bison, the long-horned urus, the stag, the roe-deer, the moose, the wild boar, the forest horse, the Celtic horse, the beaver, the hare, and the squirrel. The fallow deer (*Cervus dama*) also appears more abundantly. Among the carnivora are the brown bear, the badger, the marten, the otter, the wolf, the fox, the wildcat, and the wolverene. The lion has disappeared entirely from western Europe. The reindeer survives only in the north.

As observed above, two of these wild animals were early chosen by the invaders for domestication, namely, the plateau or Celtic horse and the forest horse. The former type is found in the Neolithic deposits of Essex, England. The wild urus (*Bos primigenius*) was hunted but was not domesticated.

Two new varieties of domestic cattle appear, neither of which has been previously observed in western Europe. The first of these is the 'Celtic shorthorn' (*Bos longifrons*), the probable ancestor of the small breeds of British short-horned and hornless cattle. The second is the 'longhorn' (*Bos taurus*), which shows some points of resemblance to the 'urus' (*Bos primigenius*) but is not directly related to it. Direct wild ancestors of this latter animal are said to occur in the Pleistocene of Italy. A new type of pig also appears, the so-called turf pig (*Sus scrofa palustris*).

The Neolithic invaders, or men of the New Stone Age, thus brought with them, or domesticated from among the animals which they found in the forests of western Europe, a great variety of the same types of animals as those domesticated to-day, namely, cattle, sheep, goats, pigs, horses, and dogs.

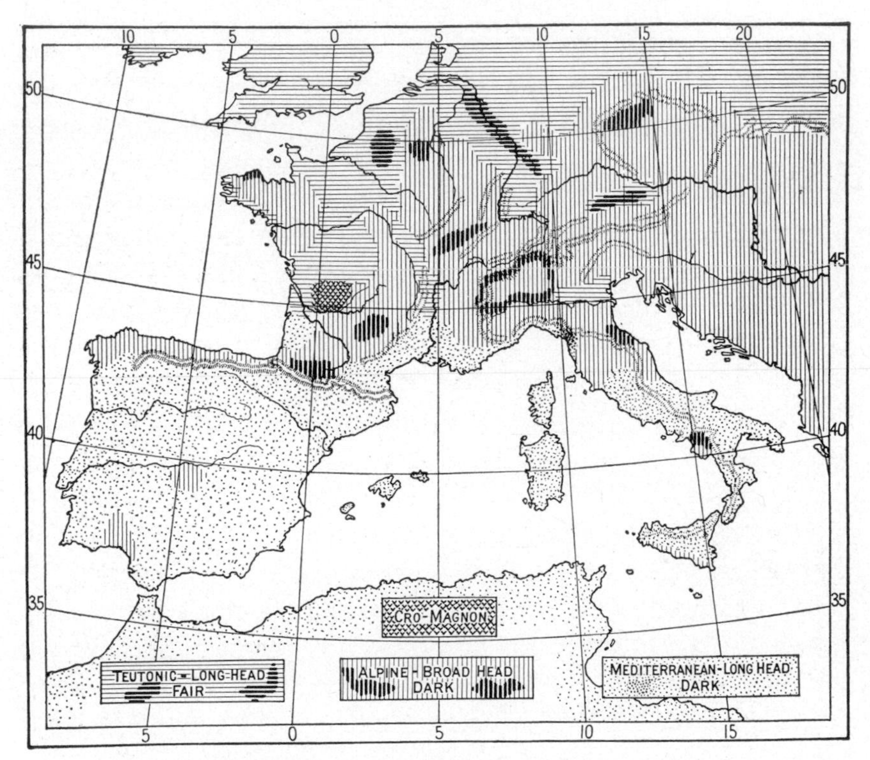

FIG. 268. Map showing the geographic distribution of the three principal cranial types of man inhabiting western Europe at the present time. Prepared after Ripley's maps in his *Races of Europe*. Also the restricted area neighboring the Vézère valley, where the supposed descendants of the disharmonic type of the Crô-Magnons are still to be found. Other small Crô-Magnon colonies are not represented. The heavy-faced lines show those districts where the race indicated is most numerous and found in the greatest perfection of type.

THE PREHISTORIC AND HISTORIC RACES OF EUROPE

Before the close of Neolithic times all the direct ancestors of the modern races of Europe had not only established themselves, but had begun to separate into those larger and smaller colonies which now mark out the great anthropological divisions of western Europe. It is therefore interesting to glance at the cranial distinctions of the men who successively entered western Europe in Upper Palæolithic and Neolithic times. The upper part of the table corresponds with that of Ripley.[25]

	Type	Head	Face	Hair	Eyes	Stature	Nose	Cephalic Index Average per cent
VI.	TEUTONIC (? Baltic).	Long, narrow.	High, narrow.	Very light.	Blue.	Tall.	Narrow, aquiline.	75
V.	MEDITERRANEAN (? Ofnet).	Long, narrow.	High, narrow.	Dark brown or black.	Dark.	Medium, slender.	Rather broad.	75
IV.	ALPINE, CELTIC (? Ofnet).	Round.	Broad.	Light chestnut.	Hazel-gray.	Medium, stocky.	Variable; rather broad; heavy.	87
III.	FURFOOZ-GRENELLE (? Ofnet).	Broad.	Medium.	?	?	?	?	79–85
II.	BRÜNN-PŘEDMOST (Moravia).	Long.	Low, medium.	?	?	?	?	68.2 or 65.7
I.	CRÔ-MAGNON.	Long.	Low and broad.	?	?	Tall to medium.	Narrow, aquiline.	? 63–? 76.27

MODERN, NEOLITHIC, AND UPPER PALÆOLITHIC EUROPEAN RACES OF THE EXISTING SPECIES OF MAN (*HOMO SAPIENS*)

It would appear that five out of these six great racial types had entered Europe before the close of Upper Palæolithic times, namely, I to V in the above table.

How about the sixth type; the narrow-headed, light-haired people of the north, the modern Teutonic type? This question cannot be answered at present. We have, however, high authority for the invasion of a new northern race, which may have been of the Teutonic type, as occurring before the close of Palæolithic times. These were the people described above, migrating along the shores of the Baltic with a new northern Maglemose culture and crude naturalistic art.

Conclusions as to the Old Stone Age

The above outline of the beginnings of the Neolithic Age shows that the Palæolithic represents a complete cycle of human development; we have traced its rise, its perfection, its decline. During this dawning period of the long prehistory of Europe the dominant features are the very great antiquity of the spirit of man and the fundamental similarity between the great steps of prehistory and of history.

The rise of the spirit of man through the Old Stone Age cannot be traced continuously in a single race because the races were changing; as at the present time, one race replaced another, or two races dwelt side by side. The sudden appearance in Europe at least 25,000 years ago of a human race with a high order of brain power and ability was not a leap forward but the effect of a long process of evolution elsewhere. When the prehistoric archæology of eastern Europe and of Asia has been investigated we may obtain some light on this antecedent development.

During this age the rudiments of all the modern economic powers of man were developed: the guidance of the hand by the mind, manifested in his creative industry; his inventive faculty; the currency or spread of his inventions; the adaptation of means to ends in utensils, in weapons, and in clothing. The same is true of the æsthetic powers, of close observation, of the sense of form, of proportion, of symmetry, the appreciation of beauty of animal form and the beauty of line, color, and form in modelling and sculpture. Finally, the schematic representation and notation of ideas so far as we can perceive was alphabetic rather than pictographic. Of the musical sense we have at present no evidence. The religious sense, the appreciation of some power or powers behind the great phenomena of nature, is evidenced in the reverence for the dead, in burials apparently related to notions of a future existence of the dead, and especially in the mysteries of the art of the caverns.

All these steps indicate the possession of certain *generic* faculties of mind similar to our own. That this mind of the Upper Palæolithic races was of a kind capable of a high degree of education we entertain no doubt whatever because of the very advanced order of brain which is developed in the higher members of these ancient races; in fact, it may be fairly assumed from experiences in the education of existing races of much lower brain capacity, such as the Eskimo or Fuegian. The emergence of such a mind from the mode of life of the Old Stone Age is one of the greatest mysteries of psychology and of history.

The rise and fall of cultures and of industries, which is at this very day the outstanding feature of the history of western Europe, was fully typified in the very ancient contests with stone weapons which were waged along the borders of the Somme, the Marne, the Seine, and the Danube. No doubt, each invasion, each conquest, each substitution of an industry or a culture had within it the impelling contest of the spirit and will of man, the intelligence directing various industrial and warlike implements, the superiority either of force or of mind.

(1) Cartailhac, 1903.1, pp. 330, 331.
(2) Déchelette, 1908.1, vol. I, pp. 314–320.
(3) *Op. cit.*, p. 320.
(4) *Op. cit.*, pp. 505–510.
(5) Breuil, 1912.6, pp. 2–6.
(6) *Ibid.*, 1912.7, pp. 232, 233.
(7) *Ibid.*, 1912.6, p. 20.
(8) Koken, 1912.1, pp. 172, 173, 176–178, 180, 181, 201.
(9) Schmidt, 1912.1, p. 40.
(10) Breuil, 1912.7, p. 225.
(11) *Op. cit.*, p. 233.
(12) Schmidt, 1912.1, p. 41.
(13) Schliz, 1912.1, pp. 242–244.
(14) *Op. cit.*, p. 252.
(15) Boule, 1913.1, p. 210.
(16) Dupont, 1871.1.
(17) Fischer, 1913.1, p. 356.
(18) Breuil, 1912.5.
(19) *Ibid.*, 1912.7, pp. 235, 236.
(20) Obermaier, 1912.1, pp. 467–469.
(21) Salmon, 1898.1.
(22) Munro, 1912.1, pp. 275–277.
(23) Déchelette, 1908.1, vol. I, p. 326.
(24) Breuil, 1912.5, p. 560.
(25) Ripley, 1899.1, p. 121.

APPENDIX

NOTE I

LUCRETIUS AND BOSSUET ON THE EARLY EVOLUTION OF MAN

Lucretius's conception* of the gradual development of human culture undoubtedly came from Greek sources beginning with Empedocles. His indebtedness is beautifully expressed in the opening lines of Book III of his *De Rerum Natura :*

> "O Glory of the Greeks! who first didst chase
> The mind's dread darkness with celestial day,
> The worth illustrating of human life—
> Thee, glad, I follow—with firm foot resolved
> To tread the path imprinted by thy steps;
> Not urged by competition, but, alone,
> Studious thy toils to copy; for, in powers,
> How can the swallow with the swan contend?
> Or the young kid, all tremulous of limb,
> Strive with the strength, the fleetness of the horse;
> Thou, sire of science! with paternal truths
> Thy sons enrichest: from thy peerless page,
> Illustrious chief! as from the flowery field
> Th' industrious bee culls honey, we alike
> Cull many a golden precept—golden each—
> And each most worthy everlasting life.
> For as the doctrines of thy godlike mind
> Prove into birth how nature first uprose,
> All terrors vanish; the blue walls of heaven
> Fly instant—and the boundless void throughout
> Teems with created things."

The same conception† of the early periods in the development of humanity is found in the *Histoire universelle* of Bossuet, in a curious passage undoubtedly suggested by Lucretius:

"Tout commence: il n'y a point d'histoire ancienne où il ne paraisse, non seulement dans ces premiers temps, mais encore longtemps après, des vestiges manifestes de la nouveauté du monde. On voit les lois s'établir,

* Lucretius, *On the Nature of Things*, metrical version by J. M. Good. Bohn's Classical Library, London, 1890.

† Bossuet, Jacques Bénigne, *Discours sur l'Histoire universelle* (first published in 1681), pp. 9, 10. Edition conforme à celle de 1700, troisième et dernière édition revue par l'auteur. Paris, Librairie de Firmin Didot Frères, 1845.

les mœurs se polir, et les empires se former: le genre humain sort peu à peu de l'ignorance; l'expérience l'instruit, et les arts sont inventés ou perfectionnés. A mesure que les hommes se multiplient, la terre se peuple de proche en proche: on passe les montagnes et les précipices; on traverse les fleuves et enfin les mers, et on établit de nouvelles habitations. La terre, qui n'était au commencement qu'une forêt immense, prend une autre forme; les bois abattus font place aux champs, aux pâturages, aux hameaux, aux bourgades, et enfin aux villes. On s'instruit à prendre certains animaux, à apprivoiser les autres, et à les accoutumer au service. On eut d'abord à combattre les bêtes farouches: les premiers héros se signalèrent dans ces guerres; elles firent inventer les armes, que les hommes tournèrent après contre leurs semblables. Nemrod, le premier guerrier et le premier conquérant, est appelé dans l'écriture un fort chasseur. Avec les animaux, l'homme sut encore adoucir les fruits et les plantes; il plia jusqu'aux métaux à son usage, et peu à peu il y fit servir toute la nature."

NOTE II

HORACE ON THE EARLY EVOLUTION OF MAN

Horace* also adopted the Greek conception of the natural evolution of human culture:

"Your men of words, who rate all crimes alike,
Collapse and founder, when on fact they strike:
Sense, custom, all, cry out against the thing,
And high expedience, right's perennial spring.
When men first crept from out earth's womb, like worms,
Dumb speechless creatures, with scarce human forms,
With nails or doubled fists they used to fight
For acorns or for sleeping-holes at night;
Clubs followed next; at last to arms they came,
Which growing practice taught them how to frame,
Till words and names were found, wherewith to mould
The sounds they uttered, and their thoughts unfold;
Thenceforth they left off fighting, and began
To build them cities, guarding man from man,
And set up laws as barriers against strife
That threatened person, property, or wife.
'Twas fear of wrong gave birth to right, you'll find,
If you but search the records of mankind.
Nature knows good and evil, joy and grief,
But just and unjust are beyond her brief:
Nor can philosophy, though finely spun,
By stress of logic prove the two things one,
To strip your neighbor's garden of a flower
And rob a shrine at midnight's solemn hour."

The Satires, Epistles and Ars Poetica of Horace, the Latin Text with Conington's Translation, pp. 29, 31. George Bell & Sons, London, 1904.

NOTE III

ÆSCHYLUS ON THE EARLY EVOLUTION OF MAN

Æschylus, in *Prometheus Bound,** presents one of the earliest known as well as one of the noblest conceptions of the natural development of the human faculties:

"And let me tell you—not as taunting men,
But teaching you the intention of my gifts,
How, first beholding, they beheld in vain,
And hearing, heard not, but, like shapes in dreams,
Mixed all things wildly down the tedious time,
Nor knew to build a house against the sun
With wicketed sides, nor any woodwork knew,
But lived, like silly ants, beneath the ground
In hollow caves unsunned. There came to them
No steadfast sign of winter, nor of spring
Flower-perfumed, nor of summer full of fruit,
But blindly and lawlessly they did all things,
Until I taught them how the stars do rise
And set in mystery, and devised for them
Number, the inducer of philosophies,
The synthesis of Letters, and, beside,
The artificer of all things, Memory
That sweet Muse-mother."

NOTE IV

'UROCHS,' OR 'AUEROCHS,' AND 'WISENT'

Kobelt† discusses the habits of the wild cattle and of the bison as follows:

"One is inclined to consider the ancient wild cattle of Europe, the Urochs, or Auerochs, as the inhabitants of boggy forests. The Auerochs survived to the seventeenth century in the forests of Poland and then became extinct. It is described as of a black color with a light stripe along the back.

"The bison, or Wisent, is generally regarded as the inhabitant of the open steppe, or at least of dryer, opener woods; it differs so little from the American bison that both can be considered only as races of one species, the *Bison priscus* of Pleistocene times, which spread over the temperate zone of both hemispheres. The American bison has always avoided the woods and roamed the prairies in countless herds. But all reliable historic records describe the Wisent as a forest animal, and its few remaining survivors are

* Æschylus, *Prometheus Bound.* Elizabeth Barrett Browning. *Poetical Works of Elizabeth Barrett Browning,* pp. 148, 149. Oxford edition, 1906. Henry Frowde, London, Edinburgh, Glasgow, New York, and Toronto.

† Kobelt, W., *Die Verbreitung der Tierwelt,* pp. 403–7. C. H. Tauchnitz, Leipsic, 1902.

entirely limited to the forests. Apparently it was never so widely and generally distributed as the Auerochs and reached western Europe later, for it is not found in the north, and never in conjunction with the mammoth and rhinoceros. Remains of the bison have also been found in Asia Minor. In Lithuania the bison lives together in herds, resenting the approach of all strangers. In the Caucasus it lives wild in certain high valleys and here it is a true mountain animal, its favorite haunts being the forests of beech, hornbeam, and evergreens from 4,000 to 8,000 feet above sea-level. Only in winter does it descend to lower levels. It is uncertain whether the Wisent does not also occur in Siberia. Kohn and Andree assert positively that it is found in large numbers in the wooded mountains of Sajan, in Siberia (1895)."

According to Kobelt, much confusion in the nomenclature of these animals has resulted from the fact that, after the extinction of the 'Urochs,' or 'Auerochs,' in the seventeenth century, the term 'Auerochs' was frequently used by writers as synonymous with 'Wisent,' or bison, an entirely different animal.

NOTE V

THE CRÔ-MAGNONS OF THE CANARY ISLANDS*

"In the museums of the Grand Canary, Teneriffe, and Palma a considerable number of prehistoric vessels are preserved. Anthropologists are agreed that the natives of the archipelago at the time of its conquest, in the fifteenth century, were a composite people made up of at least three stocks: a Crô-Magnon type, a Hamitic or Berber type, and a brachycephalic type. These natives were in a Neolithic stage of civilization. Their arms were slings, clubs, and spears. Most of the people went naked, except for a girdle round the loins, and there was no intercommunication between the islands. Their stone implements were of obsidian or of basalt. Only four polished axes are known from the Grand Canary and one from Gomera. The axes are of chloromelanite, and of a type contemporary with megalithic structures in France. The first colonists probably brought the knowledge of making pottery with them, but each island developed an individuality of its own. Even the painted ware of the Grand Canary appears to be of local origin and not due to external influence. Although undoubted Lybian inscriptions in the Grand Canary and lava querns of Iron Age type prove that the archipelago was visited before its conquest by the Spaniards without affecting the general civilization of its inhabitants."

* Abercromby, Hon. John, *The Prehistoric Pottery of the Canary Islands and Its Makers.* Royal Anthropological Institute, November 17, 1914. *Nature,* December 3, 1914, p. 383.

GUANCHE CHARACTERISTICS RESEMBLING CRÔ-MAGNON*

The following excerpts are quoted from the account given by the distinguished anthropologist, Dr. René Verneau, of his observations during a five years' residence in the Canary Islands.

Page 22.

"Without doubt the race that has played the most important rôle in the Canaries is the Guanche. They were settled in all the islands, and in Teneriffe they preserved their distinctive characteristics and customs until the conquest by Spain in the fifteenth century.

"The Guanches, who at that time were described as giants, were of great stature. The minimum measure of the men was 1.70 m. (5 ft. 7 in.).

"I myself met a number of men in the various islands who measured over 1.80 m. (5 ft. 11 in.). Some attained a height of 2 m. (6 ft. 6½ in.). At Fortaventure the *average* height of the men was 1.84 m. (6 ft. $\frac{3}{10}$ in.), perhaps the greatest known in any people.

"It is a curious fact that the women who gave birth to such men were comparatively small—I observed a difference of about 20 cm. (8 in.) in the heights of the two sexes.

"Their skin was light colored—if we may believe the poet Viana—and sometimes even absolutely white. Dacil, the daughter of the last Guanche chief of Teneriffe, the valiant Bencomo, who struggled so heroically for the independence of his country, had a very white complexion and her face was quite freckled. The hair of the true Guanche should be blond or light chestnut, and the eyes blue.

"The most striking characteristic of the Guanche race was the shape of the head and the features of the face. The long skull gave shape to a beautiful forehead, well developed in every way. Behind, above the occipital, one notices a large plane contrasting strongly with the marked prominence of the occipital itself. In addition, the parietal eminences, placed very high and very distinct from each other, combined to give the head a *pentagonal form*."

Page 29.

"The Guanche chiefs were much respected. At Teneriffe the coronation of the chief took place in an enclosure surrounded with stones (the Togaror), in the presence of nobles and people. One of his nearest kinsmen brought him the insignia of power. According to Viera y Clavijo, this was the humerus of one of his ancestors, carefully preserved in a case of leather; according to Viana, it was the skull of one of his predecessors.

"The chief (Menceg) placed the relic on his head, pronouncing the sacramental formula: 'I swear upon the bone of him who has borne this royal crown, that I will imitate his acts and work for the happiness of my

* Verneau, Dr. R., *Cinq années de séjour aux îles Canaries.* (Ouvrage couronné par l'Académie des sciences, 1891.)

subjects.' Each noble, in turn, then received the bone from the hands of the chief, placed it upon his shoulder and swore fidelity to his sovereign. . . . These chiefs led a very simple life: their food was like that of the people, their apparel but little more elaborate, and their dwellings—like those of their subjects—consisted of *caves*, only theirs were a little larger than those of the common people. They did not disdain to inspect their flocks or their harvests in person, and were, indeed, no richer than the average mortal."

Page 31.

"Above all, the ancient Canarians sought to develop strength and agility in their children. From an early age the boys devoted themselves to games of skill in order to fit them to become redoubtable warriors. The men delighted in all bodily exercises and, above all, in wrestling. At Gran Canaria (Grande Canarie) they often held veritable tourneys, which were attended by an immense number of people. These could not take place without the consent of the nobles and of the high priest.

"Permission obtained, the combatants presented themselves at the place of meeting. This was a circular or rectangular enclosure, surrounded by a very low wall, allowing free view of the details of the combat. Each warrior took his place upon a stone of about 40 cm. diameter ($15\frac{1}{2}$ in.). His offensive weapons consisted of three stones, a club, and several knives of obsidian: his defensive weapon was a simple lance. The skill of defense consisted in evading the stones by movements of the body, or parrying the blows with the lance, without moving from the stone on which stand had been taken. These combats often resulted fatally for one of the combatants."

Page 34.

"The Guanche understood the use of the sword, and although it was of wood (pine), it could cut, they say, as if it were of steel.

"To parry blows, they used a lance, as mentioned above, but they also had shields made of a round of the dragon-tree (*Dracæna draco*).

"The Guanches were essentially shepherds. While their flocks pastured they played the flute, singing songs of love or of the prowess of their ancestors. Those songs which have come down to us show them to have been by no means devoid of poetic inspiration.

"When the care of their stock permitted, they employed their leisure in fishing. For this they employed various means—sometimes nets, sometimes fish-hooks, sometimes a simple stick."

Page 47.

"The Guanches were above all troglodytes—that is to say, they lived in caves. There is no lack of large, well-sheltered caves in the Canary Islands. The slopes of the mountains and the walls of their ravines are honeycombed with them. The islanders may have their choice.

"The caves are almost never further excavated. They are used just as they are.

"Here is a description of one of these caves, the *Grotto of Goldar:*

"The interior is almost square—5 m. (16 ft. 4 in.) along the left side, 5.50 m. (18 ft.) along the right. The width at the back is 4.80 m. (15 ft. 6 in.). A second cave, much smaller, opens from the right wall. All these walls are *decorated with paintings*. The ceiling is covered with a uniform coat of red ochre, while the walls are decorated with various geometric designs in red, black, gray, or white. High up runs a sort of cornice painted red, and on this background, in white, are groups of two concentric circles, whose centre is also indicated by a white spot. On the rear wall the cornice is interrupted by triangles and stripes of red."

Page 61.

"The Guanches never polished their stone weapons."

Page 168.

"Inhabited caves are very numerous at Fortaventure. The population in certain parts—Mascona, for example—must be quite numerous to judge by the number of these caves. At a little distance, in the place known as Hoya de Corralejo, one may still see the *Togaror*, or tribal meeting place. It is an almost circular enclosure about 40 m. (131 ft. 2 in.) in diameter, surrounded by a low wall of stones. Six huts, from 2.50 to 4 m. (8 ft. 2½ in.—13 ft. 1½ in.) in diameter, designed no doubt for the sacred animals, stood near the Togaror."

Page 245.

"A great number of Canarians still live in caves. Near Caldera de Bandama (Gran Canaria) there is a whole village of cave dwellers."

Page 264.

At Teneriffe Dr. Verneau received hospitality in a cabin worthy of the Palæolithic Age.

"I had no need to make any great effort to imagine myself with a descendant of those brave shepherds of earlier times. My host was an example of the type—even though the costume was lacking—and his dwelling completed the illusion. The walls, which gave free access to the wind, supported a roof composed of unstripped tree trunks covered with branches. Stones piled on top prevented the wind from tearing it off.

"Hung up on poles to dry were goatskins, destined to serve as sacks for the gofio (a kind of millet), bottles for water, and shoes for the family. A reed partition shut off a small corner where the children lay stretched out pell mell on skins of animals. For furniture, a chest, a *hollowed-out stone* which *served as a lamp*, shells which served the same purpose, a water jar, three stones forming a hearth in one corner, and that was all."

(And this host was the most important personage in the place.)

Page 289.

Another time, also at Teneriffe, Dr. Verneau had a similar experience. "An old shepherd invited me to his house and offered me some milk. What was my surprise on seeing the furnishing of his hut! In one corner was a bed of fern, near by a Guanche mill and a large jar, in all points similar to those used by the ancient islanders. A reed flute, a wooden bowl and a goatskin sack full of gofio completed the appointments of his home. I could scarcely believe my eyes on examining the jar and the mill. Seeing my astonishment, the old man explained that he had found them in a cave where 'the Guanches' lived, and that he had used them for many years. I could not persuade him to part with these curiosities. To my offers of money he answered that he needed none for the short time he had still to live."

NOTE VI

THE LENGTH OF POSTGLACIAL TIME AND THE ANTIQUITY OF THE AURIGNACIAN CULTURE

The most recent discussion on the length of Postglacial time was that held at the Twelfth International Congress of Geology, in Ottawa, in 1913 (*Congrès Géologique International, Compte-rendu de la XII Session*, Canada, 1913, pp. 426–537). The notes abstracted by Dr. Chester A. Reeds from the various papers are as follows:

"American estimates of Postglacial time have been made chiefly from the recession of waterfalls since the final retreat of the great ice-fields in North America. The retreat of the Falls of St. Anthony, Minnesota, has been estimated by Winchell at 8,000 years and by Sardeson at 30,000 years. The retreat of the Falls of Niagara has been estimated as requiring from 7,000 to 40,000 years; it has proved a very uncertain chronometer, because of the great variation in the volume of water at different stages in its history. The recession of Scarboro Heights and other changes due to wave action on Lake Ontario have been estimated by Coleman as requiring from 24,000 to 27,000 years. Fairchild has estimated that 30,000 years have elapsed since the ice left the Lake Ontario region of New York.

"In Europe the most accurate chronology is that of Baron de Geer on the terminal moraines and related marine clays of northern Sweden. For the retreat of the ice northward over a distance of 370 miles in Sweden 5,000 years were allowed; for the time since the disappearance of the ice in Sweden, 7,000 years; for the retreat of the ice from Germany across the Baltic, 12,000 years; giving a total of 24,000 years as compared with a total of between 30,000 and 50,000 years allowed by Penck for the retreat of the ice-fields of the Alps."

NOTE VII

THE MOST RECENT DISCOVERIES OF ANTHROPOID APES AND SUPPOSED ANCESTORS OF MAN IN INDIA

It is possible that within the next decade one or more of the Tertiary ancestors of man may be discovered in northern India among the foot-hills known as the Siwaliks. Such discoveries have been heralded, but none have thus far been actually made. Yet Asia will probably prove to be the centre of the human race. We have now discovered in southern Asia primitive representatives or relatives of the four existing types of anthropoid apes, namely, the gibbon, the orang, the chimpanzee, and the gorilla, and since the extinct Indian apes are related to those of Africa and of Europe, it appears probable that southern Asia is near the centre of the evolution of the higher primates and that we may look there for the ancestors not only of prehuman stages like the Trinil race but of the higher and truly human types.

As early as 1886 several kinds of extinct Old World primates, including two anthropoid apes related to the orang and to the chimpanzee, were reported from the Siwalik hills in northern India, and recently Dr. Pilgrim, of the Geological Survey, has described three new species of Siwalik apes resembling *Dryopithecus* of the Upper Miocene of Europe, also an anthropoid which he has named *Sivapithecus* and regards as actually related to the direct ancestors of man, a conclusion which may or may not prove to be correct. Another extinct Indian ape, *Palæopithecus*, is of very generalized type and is related to all the anthropoid apes.

NOTE VIII

ANTHROPOID APES DISCOVERED BY CARTHAGINIAN NAVIGATORS*

The *Periplus of Hanno* purports to be a Greek translation of a Carthaginian inscription on a tablet in the "temple of Chronos" (Moloch) at Carthage, dedicated by Hanno, a Carthaginian navigator, in commemoration of a voyage which he made southward from the Strait of Gibraltar along the western coast of Africa as far as the inlet now known as Sherboro Sound, the next opening beyond Sierra Leone.

Hanno is a very common Carthaginian name, but recent writers think it not improbable that this Hanno was either the father or the son of that Hamilcar who led the great Carthaginian expedition to Sicily in 480 B. C. In the former case the *Periplus* might be assigned to a date about 520 B. C.; in the latter, some fifty years later.

The narrative was certainly extant at an early period, for it is cited in the work on *Marvellous Narratives* ascribed to Aristotle, which belongs to

*Bunbury, E. H. *History of Ancient Geography*, vol. I, pp. 318–333. John Murray, London, 1879.

the third century B. C., and Pliny also expressly refers to it. The authenticity of the work is now generally conceded.

According to the narrative the farthest limit of Hanno's voyage, which was undertaken for purposes of colonization, brought him and his companions to an island containing a lake with another island in it which was full of wild men and women with hairy bodies, called by the interpreters gorillas. The Carthaginians were unable to catch any of the men, but they caught three of the women, whom they killed, and brought their skins back with them to Carthage. "Pliny, indeed, adds that the skins in question were dedicated by Hanno in the temple of Juno at Carthage, and continued to be visible there till the destruction of the city. There can be no difficulty in supposing these 'wild men and women' to have been really large apes of the family of the chimpanzee, or pongo, several species of which are in fact found wild in western Africa, and some of them, as is now well known, attain a stature fully equal to that of man."

NOTE IX

THE JAW AND SKULL OF THE PILTDOWN MAN

The skull and jaw fragments, as described on pages 130–144, on which were founded the new genus and species of the human race, *Eoanthropus dawsoni*, have aroused a wide difference of opinion among anatomists which is still (February, 1918) unsettled.

Many anatomists questioned the association of the Piltdown jaw with the Piltdown skull. Some anatomists held that the jaw is not prehuman and does not belong with the skull at all. After reconsidering the original discovery and subsequent geological and anatomical evidence, Dr. A. Smith Woodward still (letter of January 27, 1917) feels convinced that the jaw and skull fragments are prehuman and belong to a single individual of the Piltdown race. His opinion is supported by W. P. Pycraft, D. M. S. Watson, and other British anatomists who have made a very careful investigation and comparison of the original Piltdown specimens with similar bones of anthropoid apes.

On the other hand, Gerrit S. Miller, Jr.,* from a careful comparative study of a cast of the Piltdown jaw with the jaws of various types of chimpanzee, still maintains that the portions of the Piltdown jaw preserved, including the upper eye-tooth, or canine, are generically identical with those of an adult chimpanzee. This new species of chimpanzee, which Miller believes to be characteristic of the European Pleistocene, he names *Pan vetus*. If Miller's theory be correct it would deprive the Piltdown specimen of its jaw and incline us to refer the Piltdown skull to the genus *Homo* rather than to the supposed more ancient genus *Eoanthropus*.

* Miller, Gerrit S., Jr., *The Jaw of the Piltdown Man*. Smithsonian Institution, Washington, November 24, 1915.

Miller's theory, however, has not been strengthened by the recent researches of the British Museum above alluded to, nor by the additional excavations of Smith Woodward near the locality where the jaw was found, both of which are said to confirm the original opinion of Dawson and Smith Woodward that the jaw belongs with the skull.

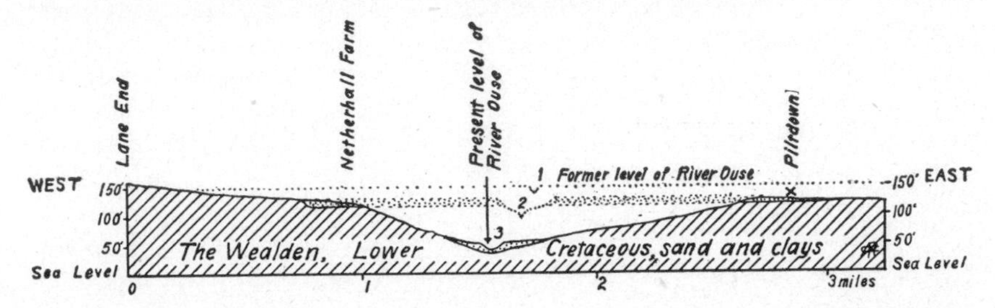

Fig. 269. Geologic section of the valley of the Ouse River at Piltdown, England, showing earlier (1, 2) and present (3) river levels. The cross indicates the location of the Piltdown quarry and theoretic former level of the River Ouse which has since cut a deep valley nearly 100 ft. below its level when the Piltdown skull was deposited. Drawn by C. A. Reeds.

As to the geological age of the Piltdown race, if confirmed by future discovery, the presence in Germany near Taubach, Weimar, of teeth similar to those in the Piltdown jaw, found in Sussex, England, would tend to confirm the opinion expressed in the first edition of this work that the Piltdown race belongs to Third Interglacial times.

NOTE X

FAMILY SEPULTURE OF LA FERRASSIE, FRANCE

The only instance of the knee-flexed burial position known in the Lower Palæolithic is the unique family sepulture at the Mousterian station of La Ferrassie, in Dordogne, discovered by D. Peyrony in the years 1909–1911. It includes the remains of two adults and two children. One of the adult skeletons lay upon its back with the legs strongly flexed. The body lay upon the floor of the cave without any sign of a cavity to contain it. The head and shoulders had been protected and surrounded by slabs of stone, while the rest of the body may have been covered by pelts or woven branches. The second skeleton was that of a woman with the arms folded upon the breast, while the legs were pressed against the body, indicating that they were bound with cords or thongs. Two children were interred in shallow graves.

This sepulture, like that of Spy, Belgium, of late Mousterian times, was apparently a case of genuine burial, testifying to the ancient reverence for the dead, joined, perhaps, with the belief in a life after death. In the Ferrassie burial, close to the children's remains, there was a grave filled with ashes and bones of the wild ox. Similarly, in the interment at La Chapelle-aux-Saints there was a cavity containing a bison horn and a second cavity where large bones of the same animal were found, indicating possibly the remains of sacrificial offerings or funeral feasts.

NOTE XI

PALÆOLITHIC HISTORY OF NORTHWESTERN AFRICA AND SOUTHERN SPAIN

The flint workers of Lower and Upper Palæolithic times who inhabited the existing geographic regions of Morocco, Algeria, and Tunis sought the flint-bearing limestones for the manufacture of their implements and fashioned them into forms which are closely similar to those found in Spain and France. As a result of the explorations of J. de Morgan, L. Capitan, and P. Boudy between 1907 and 1909* it appears that Palæolithic man in Africa became acquainted with fewer types of implements than his contemporaries in Europe. It is true that we find the Lower Palæolithic represented by typical Chellean coups de poing, and there were also true Acheulean implements and true Mousterian implements marking the close of Lower Palæolithic time.

As to the great antiquity of man in these regions, it appears likely that there was a kind of pre-Chellean industry at Gafsa, as at St. Acheul in France, with flakes roughly adapted to the functions of racloirs, points, knives, etc. It is, in fact, very possible so to interpret the very coarse flakes found by Boudy in such abundance in the lower deposits of hill 328 at Gafsa. The Chellean and then the Acheulean culture would have succeeded to this earliest stage, being characterized by an industry strikingly similar for these two epochs. The Mousterian, with its predominance of racloirs, points, and discs, appears in Tunis to have been only a modality, a stage of the great Chelleo-Mousterian period, just as it was in Europe.

Then follows the Aurignacian, the first stage of the Upper Palæolithic cultures, in which the forms of the flints are, in the opinion of Capitan, extremely similar to those of the Lower Aurignacian of northern Spain and of France. It was at this time, it is believed, that the great wave of industrial migration and perhaps the men of the Crô-Magnon race passed from these northwestern African stations into Spain and France; for it has been noted that the Lower Aurignacian of western Europe comes from the south and not from the east of Europe. The flint-making stations during the long Lower Palæolithic are widely distributed, as indicated by the black dots of the accompanying map (Fig. 270).

* J. de Morgan, L. Capitan, and P. Boudy, "Stations préhistoriques du sud Tunisien," *Rev. l'Ecole d'Anthr.*, 1910, pp. 105–136, 206–221, 267–286, 335–347; 1911, pp. 217–228.

But now a very important change occurs, as indicated in the stations marked by a crossed circle, in the genesis of new modes of fashioning the flints which are for a long time peculiar to this region and which—centring

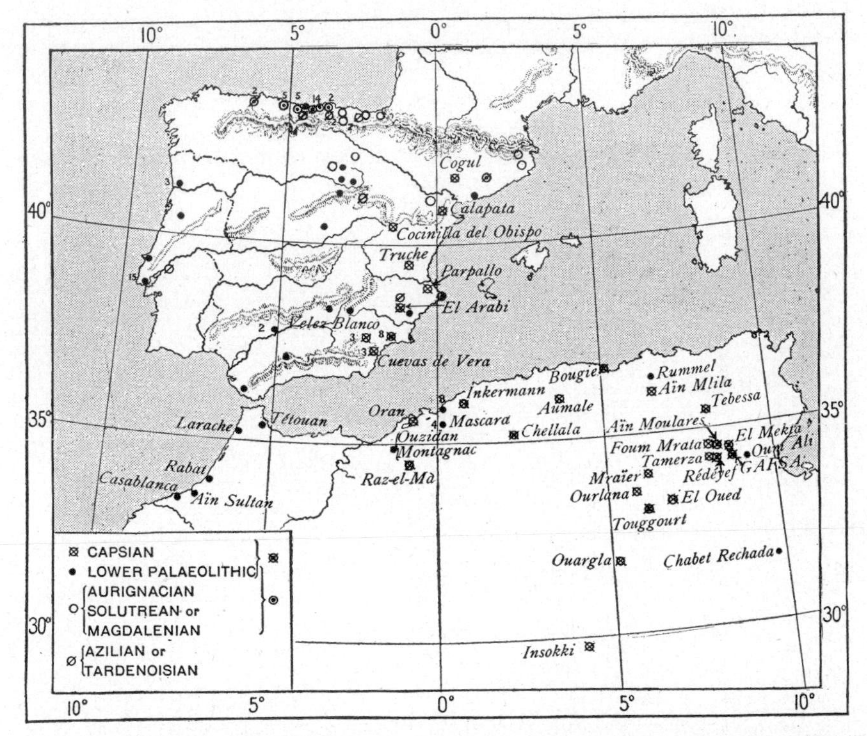

FIG. 270. Extension of the Early Palæolithic and Capsian industries throughout Spain and northwest Africa. It is supposed that at this time there was a land connection across the Straits of Gibraltar. Stations too closely grouped to be shown separately are as follows:

Africa.—At Mostaganem (8) are the eight stations of Aboukir, Aïn-bou-Brahim, Karouba, Ouled Zérifa, Aïn-el-Bahr, Oued Melah, Oued Ria, and Mazouna. Near Mascara are the sites of Aïn-Hadjar, Aïn-Ksibia, Palikao, and Aïn-Harça.

Spain.—At Vélez Blanco are the three stations of Ambrosio, Cueva Chiquita de los Treinta, and Fuente de los Molinos; at the Cuevas de Vera are the three caves known as Serrón, Zájara, and Humosa; while the figure 8 marks the eight caves of Palomarico, Las Perneras, Bermeja, Las Palomas, Tazona, Ahumada, Cueva de los Tollos, and Cueva del Tesoro. Only the Capsian stations of Spain are named here. For the names of others see Fig. 272, p. 519.

in the stations crowded around Gafsa in the heart of Tunis—receive the name of CAPSIAN.

The explanation of the life and art of the Capsian is probably that of a climatic change in this region of Africa from a moist and semiforested condition favorable to the larger kinds of game to an arid condition in which the larger kinds of game became less numerous and the chase was abandoned. This is Capitan's opinion, that the Capsian corresponds to new climatic conditions in northern Africa; for in the depths of the limestone caves it appears that men's food partly consisted of the animals of the chase, but more commonly of edible land snails belonging to species still existing in this region and occurring in great abundance during the winter and spring rains. This change of climate came after the close of Mousterian time, namely, the period which we estimated (p. 281) at about 25,000 years B. C. on the theory that the Fourth Glaciation closed not less than 25,000 years ago (p. 41).

LOWER PALÆOLITHIC OF AFRICA

When we consider that the genuine Chellean industry is completely lacking in central Europe* we are driven to the conclusion that this industry came to France and England not from the east but from Africa in the south. Therefore it becomes clear why, in passing to the aforesaid countries from northern Africa, this industry was more widely distributed in Spain than in Italy. Without doubt the same conditions of migration prevailed throughout the entire Lower Palæolithic. The Acheulean and Mousterian industries followed the same route, for both are typically represented in northern Africa and there is no convincing evidence of these industries having followed any different course.

THE CAPSIAN—UPPER AND LOWER

The succeeding Aurignacian industry of the Mediterranean also had its centre of dispersion in the northwestern part of Africa—a centre known through the labors of de Morgan, Capitan, and Boudy, and, more recently, through those of Pallary, Gobert, and Breuil. Obermaier regards the Lower Capsian as presenting an industry containing only the Lower Aurignacian (types of Châtelperron) and Upper Aurignacian (types of La Gravette) and considers that the Middle Aurignacian is wanting in northern Africa. This Middle Aurignacian culture is regarded as of French origin, having apparently extended southward only in the Cantabrian region, where it is typically represented at Castillo, Hornos de la Peña, and the Cueva del Conde.

The Upper Capsian, then, is regarded as extending from Post-Aurignacian time through the entire epoch of the Solutrean and the Magdalenian of western Europe. Thus for a very long period of time there was no contact whatever between the industry of northwestern Africa and of southwestern Europe. During this period the Capsian itself developed

* Obermaier, Hugo, *El Hombre fósil*, 1916, p. 203.

its peculiar forms, and toward the close of the Upper Palæolithic this industry spread into Spain as indicated by the dotted area and arrows in the accompanying map (Fig. 271, *B*).

In the development of the Capsian itself* it is found that the industry varies according to the sites, each with its own evolution of types. For example, at the rock shelter of El Mekta flint knives with blunted backs were of large size, probably because they were used to cut the flesh of game. At Sidi-Mansour, on the contrary, the dwellers, being snail-eaters, used only blades as fine as needles and of a type found also at El Mekta, but fewer in number. This, then, is the origin of the *microlithic* flints which were first discovered at the station of Fère-en-Tardenois, in

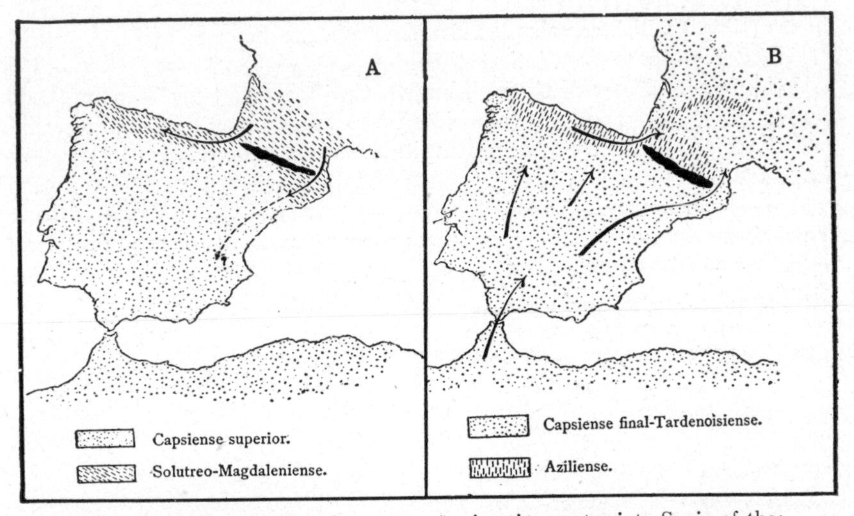

FIG. 271. Maps showing the supposed migration routes into Spain of the:
A. Solutrean and Magdalenian industries from France.
B. Late Capsian (Tardenoisian) industry from Africa. After Obermaier.

France, and hence received the name of Tardenoisian. If the conclusions of de Morgan, Capitan, and Boudy are well founded, the Upper Capsian industry of Africa is the true parent of the Tardenoisian of France.

On the other hand, the identity of the *Lower Capsian* with the Aurignacian in Europe is strongly insisted upon by the same authors. The Lower Capsian is a Tunisian phase of the Aurignacian of Europe and absolutely identical with it. The forms from the rock shelters of Rédéyef, Foum-el-Maza, and, above all, El Mekta are absolutely typical. In the latter station occur, moreover, forms closely paralleling those distinctive of the Aurignacian of Europe, Lower, Middle, and Upper—the great picks; the large flakes finely retouched; the long, fine blades retouched on one or both sides, often curved, with blunted backs; the notched blades; the

* Obermaier, Hugo, *El Hombre fósil*, 1916, pp. 346, 347.

nuclei with edges worked into grattoirs; and, above all, the blades with square-edged grattoirs across the ends, often presenting a lateral burin, so characteristic of the Aurignacian. Thus these authors conclude that human evolution and probably the human stock in Tunis was uniform with that of Europe throughout all Aurignacian time until its very close, and that, following this, an independent evolution in North Africa took place.

Little is known of the anatomy of these Lower Capsian workmen. In an abri about two kilometres from Rédéyef, and associated with a flint industry characteristic of the Lower Capsian, there were found numerous fragments of human bones much altered, friable, and with very irregular surfaces. Recognizable among this skeletal débris were a decidedly thick cranial vault, and portions of two large thigh-bones (femora) and of shin-bones (tibias) which are also thick and very much flattened (platycnæmic). It is interesting to recall that the abundant skeletal remains found at Grimaldi were chiefly of the well-known Crô-Magnon type with markedly platycnæmic tibias, and were associated with flint implements characteristic of the Aurignacian culture, which Capitan considers identical with the Lower Capsian.

INDUSTRIES OF NORTH AFRICA	GEOGRAPHIC CONDITIONS	INDUSTRIES OF EUROPE
Upper Capsian (Late Upper Palæolithic) (final phase of Capsian = Tardenoisian)	Reunion with Spain and France	Close of the Upper Palæolithic Tardenoisian and Azilian Stages
(Middle Upper Palæolithic)	Separation from Spain and France	Solutrean and Magdalenian Stages
Lower Capsian (Beginning of the Upper Palæolithic)	Union with Spain and France	Aurignacian Stage
Lower Palæolithic Mousterian, Acheulean, and Chellean Stages	Union with Spain and France	Lower Palæolithic Mousterian, Acheulean, and Chellean Stages

PALÆOLITHIC HISTORY OF SPAIN

Having now considered northern Africa, it is interesting to look at Spain as influenced by Africa on the south, by the industrial and artistic life of France on the north, and as having an important independent evolution of its own. These conditions are fully described in Hugo Obermaier's recent work, *El Hombre fósil*,* to which the reader is referred. Over eighty Palæolithic stations have been discovered in Spain. Spain shares with the greater part of Africa (including Egypt), with Syria, Mesopotamia, and parts of India, the extraordinarily wide distribution of in-

* Obermaier, Hugo, *El Hombre fósil*, 1916.

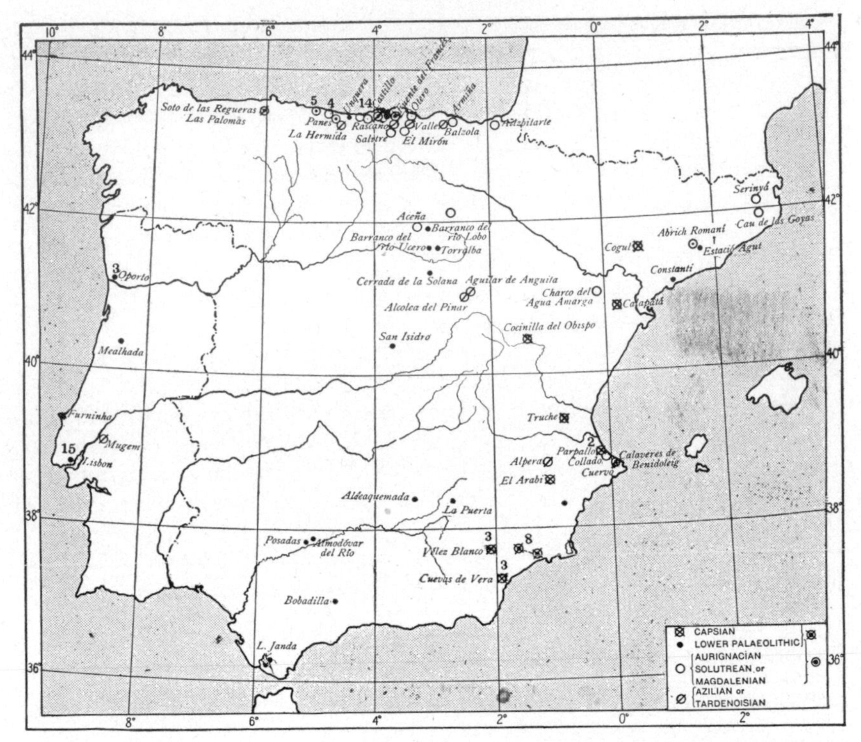

FIG. 272. Upper and Lower Palæolithic stations of Spain and Portugal. Stations too closely grouped to be shown separately on this map are as follows:

North.—5, Cueva del Conde, Cueva del Río, Collubil, Viesca, La Cuevona; 4, Cueto de la Mina, Balmori, Arnero, Fonfría; 14 (also marked 'Castillo'), four symbols represent the fourteen closely grouped stations of Castillo, Altamira, Hornos de la Peña, Camargo, Cueva del Mar, Truchiro, Astillero, Nuestra Señora de Loreto, Villanueva, Pendo, Cobalejos, San Felices de Buelna, Peña de Carranceja, and El Cuco. A little west of Fuente del Francés is San Vitores.

West.—At Oporto are the three stations of Paços, Ervilha, and Castello do Queijo. In or near Lisbon are the fifteen stations of Agonia, Alto do Duque, Amoreira, Bica, Boticaria, Casal da Serra, Casal das Osgas, Casal do Monte, Estrada de Aguda-Queluz, Leiria, Moinho das Cruzes, Pedreiras, Peñas Alvas, Rabicha, and Serra de Monsanto.

Southeast.—At Vélez Blanco are the three stations of Ambrosio, Cueva Chiquita de los Treinta, and Fuente de los Molinos; at the Cuevas de Vera are the three caves known as Serrón, Zájara, and Humosa; while between the two sites marked 8 are the eight caves of Palomarico, Las Perneras, Bermeja, Las Palomas, Tazona, Ahumada, Cueva de los Tollos, and Cueva del Tesoro.

dustries resembling those of the three Lower Palæolithic stages—the Chellean, the Acheulean, and the Mousterian.

By what types of man these industries were pursued in these different countries it would be premature to say. At the beginning of the Upper Palæolithic a profound change occurs, for in the Aurignacian industry we have to do with a Mediterraneo-European culture exhibiting advances in technique which are not developed elsewhere.

IMPORTANT PALÆOLITHIC SITES IN SPAIN AND PORTUGAL

Provinces and Stations	Palæolithic Cultures						
	Lower			Upper			
	Chellean	Acheulean	Mousterian	Aurignacian	Solutrean	Magdalenian	Azilio-Tardenoisian
SPAIN							
GUIPÚZCOA							
Aïtzbitarte (Landarbaso)	..	..	..	..	..	+	..
VIZCAYA							
Armiña	..	..	..	..	..	+	..
Balzola	..	..	..	..	..	+	+
SANTANDER							
Mirón, El	..	..	..	+?	..	..	..
Valle	..	..	..	..	..	+	+
Otero	..	..	..	..	..	+	..
Salitre	..	..	..	+	+	+	..
Rascaño	..	..	..	..	..	+	+
Fuente del Francés	..	..	+	..	+	+	..
Astillero	..	+	..	..	..	..	..
Nuestra Señora de Loreto	..	..	..	..	..	+	..
Castillo	..	+	+	+	+	+	+
Pendo, Cueva del (San Pantaleón)	..	..	..	..	+	+	+
Cobalejos (Puente Arce)	..	..	+	..	+	+	..
Camargo	..	..	..	+	+	+	..
Hornos de la Peña	..	..	+	+	+	+	..
Altamira	..	..	..	..	+	+	..
OVIEDO							
Panes	..	+	..	..	..	+ or	+?
Cueto de la Mina	..	..	..	+	+	+	..
Conde, Cueva del	..	..	+	+	..	..	..
Paloma, Cueva de la	..	..	..	..	..	+	+
SORIA							
Torralba	+	..	..	..	..	..	..
MADRID							
San Isidro	+	+	..	..	..	..	..
CÓRDOBA							
Posadas-Almodóvar del Río	+	..	..	..	..	..	..
JAÉN							
Campos de Olivar de Puente Mocho	+	+	..	..	..	..	..
CÁDIZ							
Laguna de la Janda	+	+	+	..	..	..	..
BARCELONA							
Abrich Romaní	..	..	+	..	..	+?	..
GERONA							
Serinyá	..	..	..	+?	..	+?	..
					Capsian		
LÉRIDA							
Cogul	..	..	..		+		..
ALMERÍA							
Vélez Blanco (three stations)	..	..	..		+		..
MURCIA							
Bermeja, Cueva de la	..	..	+		+		..
ALBACETE							
Alpera	..	..	..		..		+
VALENCIA							
Parpallo, Cueva del	..	..	..		+		..
Maravillas, Cueva de las	..	..	..		+		..
Truche (Turche), Abrigo de la	..	..	..		+		..
PORTUGAL							
Mugem, in the valley of the Tagus (four stations)	..	..	..		..		+
Furninha	+	..	..		..		..
Lisbon and environs (fifteen stations)	+	+	+		..		..

At the close of Upper Aurignacian time the community of culture ceases in Spain itself, and this country divides sharply into two regions, namely, *northern* and *southern.*

In the *northern* region we observe a close similarity with the industrial evolution of France during the entire period of Solutreo-Magdalenian time. The true Solutrean extended from France throughout the northern part of the Iberian Peninsula. In Cantabria, Early Solutrean is represented by laurel-leaf points found at Castillo, Hornos de la Peña, and elsewhere; while Late Solutrean types—shouldered points, and laurel-leaf and willow-leaf points with concave base—appear at Altamira, Camargo, and the Cueva del Conde. True Solutrean strata have not yet been discovered in the east of Spain, although the discovery—made by H. Breuil—of a willow-leaf point at El Arabi would seem to indicate that there may have been some slight infiltration of the Solutrean along the seacoast. Implements suggesting the Solutrean found in Almería (Cueva Chiquita de los Treinta) and Murcia (Cueva de las Perneras) are doubtful, as it is very possible that they represent Neolithic types. The true Magdalenian appears also to be an intrusion restricted to the northern part of the peninsula. It is found in the east in the provinces of Gerona and Barcelona, but occurs chiefly in the Whole Cantabrian region. The homogeneity of the Magdalenian in these parts with that of France is very marked, not only in the stratification and types of Palæolithic implements but also in the objects of mobiliary art.

SOUTHERN AND EASTERN SPAIN—THE CAPSIAN

At the same time the *southern* and *eastern* regions of Spain were completely under the influence of the Upper Capsian industry of northern Africa and in these regions the typical forms of the Lower Capsian (= Lower and Upper Aurignacian) tend to become reduced in size and to evolve toward the geometric forms until they finally acquire the aspect of the Tardenoisian microliths. Thus we find that in the Upper Capsian of eastern and southern Spain, as in northern Africa, true Solutrean and Magdalenian implements are unknown. These implements are replaced by the *microlithic industry,* chiefly characterized by trapezoidal forms which can be traced eastward along the coast of Africa to Egypt, Phœnicia, and even to the Crimea. A notable part of this industry found its way also into Sicily.

The final phase of the Upper Capsian of Spain is essentially identical with the Tardenoisian of France. Certain discoveries have been made in Guadalajara, in Murcia, and in Albacete (Alpera). To these must be added other Azilio-Tardenoisian stations no less important found in Portugal in the valley of the Tagus. At Mugem and at other stations heaps of sea-shells of a great variety of species prove that when the Upper Capsian men were living they sought the same kinds of food in Spain as in northern

Africa. In these heaps the trapezoidal forms of implements predominate, closely similar to those of the Tardenoisian. The animal life of these deposits does not include any sort of domestic animal except the dog.

Of great interest are the numerous burials—chiefly of women and children, more rarely of men—in which the skeletons occur most often in the folded position. The human type has not been determined, but long-headed (dolichocephalic) skulls greatly predominate, while short-headed (brachycephalic) skulls occur but rarely. It is probable, therefore, that these people belonged to the small, long-headed, dark-skinned Mediterrean race.

Inasmuch as the origins of the Tardenoisian of France are found in the final Capsian stage of Spain, reinforced by African elements, Obermaier regards the Spanish Tardenoisian as somewhat older than the French.

CAPSIAN AND AZILIO-TARDENOISIAN ART

Obermaier observes that it is as yet impossible to determine the period of the commencement of this peculiar art of central and southern Spain, but considers that a transition from the naturalistic art of the Quaternary to the conventionalized schematic art was effected by almost imperceptible degrees. This would imply that no sudden changes took place at this time in the population of Spain, but that the tribes of Upper Capsian culture evolved *in situ* into the Azilio-Tardenoisian stage, and eventually, owing to the influence of exterior civilizations, into the Neolithic. Final phases of this schematic art contain idols and representations of faces which coincide absolutely with Neolithic idols in the collections of L. Siret, F. de Motos, and others. Moreover, they present similarities to certain designs from the dolmens of the final Neolithic.

This art is characterized by its numerous reproductions of the human figure. In almost all the important rock shelters of the eastern region (Alpera) it has been possible to distinguish layers of more recent designs painted over the classic Quaternary paintings, and classified—on account of their superposition—as "Post-Palæolithic." Of these a small portion are figures still retaining the naturalistic style—representations of animals and men—but poor in conception, stiff and lifeless, in most cases bearing no comparison with the vigor and *abandon* of the figures of Alpera. The greater part of these designs consist of geometric or conventionalized signs or figures.

Still purer in style and more abundant are the instances of this conventionalized mural art in southern Spain, where M. de Góngora, Vilanova, Jiménez de la Espada, González de Linares, M. Gómez Moreno, F. de Motos, H. Breuil, J. Cabré, and E. Hernández-Pacheco have devoted themselves sedulously to its study. Numerous painted rock shelters are known, but almost all without the slightest trace of Palæolithic art and with numerous conventionalized (schematic) petroglyphs, in Andalusia

(Vélez Blanco, Ronda, and Tarifa) and throughout the Sierra Morena (Fuencaliente). In many cases it would be difficult to guess the derivation of these designs of human or animal figures, were it not for the existence of gradations in conventionalization from the naturalistic design to the final geometric scheme. With these, arranged in a regular manner, there occur further a great number of ramiform, pectiniform, stelliform, serpentine, and alphabet-like signs, with designs in zigzags, circles, and dots.

Another important centre is found in western Spain (Estremadura) the notable designs of which are mentioned by Lope de Vega in 1597—

FIG. 273. Detail from the Late Palæolithic designs painted on the sides of two natural recesses in the rock shelter of Alpera. After Obermaier.

doubtless referring to the paintings of Canchal de las Cabras in Las Batuecas.

Slight infiltrations of the same art have been recognized in northern Spain at Castillo, Santander, and at the open station of Peña Tú, near Vidiago, Oviedo. As a notable exception to the naturalistic art prevailing north of the Pyrenees we may mention the paintings in this same geometric style found in the cave of La Vache, near Tarascon, Ariège, in southern France.

Of equally great interest is the explanation which this art affords of the remarkable painted pebbles of Mas d'Azil which are now seen to be partly pictographic in origin, chiefly schematized representations of the human figure which gradually begin to assume shapes closely resembling those of the Phœnician alphabet. As early as 1912 Henri Breuil was considering this pictographic theory and beginning to refer to the 'Azilian signs' at Las Batuecas as reminiscent both of the painted pebbles of Mas d'Azil and of the mural paintings of Andalusia. But chiefly he made clear the importance of the "dotted lines, ramiform, pectiniform, and stelliform signs, zigzags, circles, and figures vaguely resembling alphabetic forms." A very ingenious study of these schematic Azilian signs has been made by Obermaier in *El Hombre fósil*, where he endeavors to trace the conventionalized descendants of the *human figure* of the ancient naturalistic style as shown in Fig. 274. The demonstration of this theory may in

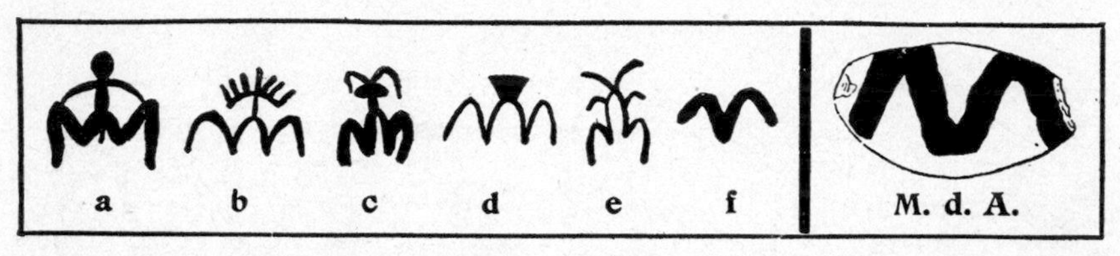

FIG. 274. Figures from Piedra Escrita (*a–e*) and from Cimbarillo de María Antonia (*f*), compared with a design occurring on the painted pebbles of Mas d'Azil, showing a progressive conventionalization of the human figure. After Obermaier.

good time make possible a logical interpretation of a great part of these same painted pebbles of the Azilian. Obermaier feels confident that they should be considered as religious symbols, and that these petroglyphs of Spain will supply a proof that many of the designs on these pebbles plainly show conventionalized human figures.

Some years ago A. B. Cook drew attention to the fact that a native tribe in central Australia, the Arunta, is distinguished by each clan having a deposit of 'churingas' in a cave. There the churinga of each individual of the clan, be it man or woman, is the object of vigilant protection. They are made of wood or stone, and in the latter case show a striking resemblance in form and decoration to the Azilian pebbles. The Australian sees in each churinga the incarnation of one of his ancestors, whose spirit has passed to him and whose qualities he has inherited. It is noteworthy that, according to Australian beliefs, they can acquire the gift of speech by means of the 'bull-roarer,' an amulet of stone or bone.

By analogy with the preceding, it is possible that some of the Azilian pebbles represent such 'stones of the ancestors,' an incarnation of masculine or feminine forefathers whose symbols were the objects of an especial cult. F. Sarasin found in the cave of Birseck, near Arlesheim, Switzerland, a typical Azilian deposit with painted pebbles which had all been intentionally broken, without exception. He advanced the not improbable theory that this evidenced an act of the extremest hostility against the sanctuary of a tribe, performed in order to despoil its members forever of the protection of their ancestors, seeking in this way to subjugate or annihilate them.

In the Capsian silhouettes there is little likeness to the naturalistic art of the Crô-Magnons in the north of Spain and in France. We are reminded rather of the rock paintings of the Bushmen and of the hunting-scenes depicted by North American Indians, but on the whole there is greater tendency to grouping and composition of standing figures, masculine and feminine, in ceremonies and in the chase. The male figures are mostly nude, and occasionally have head ornaments of feathers; while the

FIG. 275. Various types of bows and arrows shown in the paintings of the 'Cueva de la Vieja' at Alpera. After J. Cabré.

female figures are represented with kirtles, head-dresses, and ornaments on the body, arms, and ankles. Masculine figures in the chase are accompanied by hunting-dogs and exhibit the bow and arrow. If these drawings are correctly assigned to the close of the Upper Palæolithic, this is the most ancient representation of this primitive weapon of the chase of which we have record. The arrow seems to be single-barbed, as shown in the accompanying cut from Alpera. It may have been pointed with flint fastened on one side to the shaft. We recall that double-barbed arrow-heads were in use in Magdalenian times, as shown in the cavern of Niaux.

BIBLIOGRAPHY

A

Agassiz, L.

1837.1 Discours prononcé à l'ouverture des séances de la Société Helvétique des Sciences Naturelles à Neuchâtel le 24 Juillet, 1837, par L. Agassiz, Président. *Actes, Soc. Helvétique, Sci. nat., 22e Sess.*, 1837, pp. v-xxxii.

1840.1 Etudes sur les glaciers. Ouvrage accompagné d'un atlas de 32 planches. 8vo. Neuchâtel, 1840.

1840.2 On Glaciers and Boulders in Switzerland. *Rept. 10th Meeting, Brit. Assoc. Adv. Sci.*, Glasgow, 1840, pp. 113, 114 (Trans. Sections).

Alcalde del Rio, H.

1912.1 Les cavernes de la région cantabrique (Espagne). (With Breuil and Sierra.) See Breuil, H., 1912.2.

1913.1 La Pasiega. (With Breuil and Obermaier.) See Breuil, H., 1913.1.

Anthony, R.

1910.1 L'encéphale de l'homme fossile de La Chapelle-aux-Saints. (With M. Boule.) *C. R. Acad. Sci.*, Paris, tome 150, 1910, pp. 1458–1461.

1911.1 L'encéphale de l'homme fossile de La Chapelle-aux-Saints. (With M. Boule.) See Boule, M., 1911.1.

1912.1 L'encéphale de l'homme fossile de La Quina. *C. R. Acad. Sci.*, Paris, tome 155, 1912, pp. 91–93.

Arcelin, A.

1869.1 L'Age du Renne en Mâconnais, etc. (With Ferry, H.) See Ferry, H., 1869.1.

d'Ault du Mesnil, G.

1896.1 Note sur le terrain quaternaire des environs d'Abbeville. *Rev. de l'Ecole d'Anthropol.*, Paris, 1896, année VI, pp. 284–296.

1898.1 L'Age de la Pierre. (With Salmon, P., et Capitan.) See Salmon, P., 1898.1.

Avebury, Lord (Sir John Lubbock).

1913.1 Prehistoric Times as Illustrated by Ancient Remains and the Manners and Customs of Modern Savages. Seventh edition, thoroughly revised and entirely reset. (Henry Holt & Co.) 8vo, 1913.

B

Bächler, E.

1912.1 Das Wildkirchli, die älteste prähistorische Kulturstation der Schweiz und ihre Beziehungen zu den altsteinzeitlichen Niederlassungen des Menschen in Europa. *Schr. Ver. für Geschichte des Bodensees*, Heft XLI.

Bardon, L.

1909.1 Découverte d'un squelette humain moustérien à la Bouffia de La Chapelle-aux-Saints (Corrèze). (With Bouyssonie.) See Bouyssonie, A., 1909.1.

Bayer, J.

1912.1 Das geologisch-archäologische Verhältnis im Eiszeitalter. *Zeitschr. für Ethnol.*, 44 Jahrgang, Heft 1, 1912, pp. 1–22.

Bégouen, Le Comte.

1912.1 Les statues d'argile préhistoriques de la caverne du Tuc d'Audoubert (Ariège). *C. R. Acad. Inscrip. et Belles-Lettres*, 1912, pp. 532–538.

1912.2 Une nouvelle grotte à gravures dans l'Ariège, la caverne du Tuc d'Audoubert. *Congr. Internat. d'Anthropol. et d'Archéol. préhist.*, XIVe *Sess.*, Genève, 1912, pp. 489–497.

Berry, R. J. A.

1914.1 The Place in Nature of the Tasmanian Aboriginal as Deduced from a Study of his Calvaria.—Part II, His Relation to the Australian Aboriginal. (With A. W. D. Robertson.) *Proc. R. Soc. Edinburgh*, vol. XXXIV, part II, 1914, pp. 144–189.

Blanckenhorn, M.

1911.1 Die Pithecanthropus-Schichten aus Java. (With Selenka, L.) See Selenka, L., 1911.1.

Bonarelli, G.

1909.1 *Palæanthropus* (n. g.) *heidelbergensis* (Schoet.). *Perugia Riv. ital. Palaeont.*, vol. 15, 1909, pp. 26–31.

Bonnet, R.

1914.1 Diluviale Menschenfunde in Obercassel bei Bonn. (With Verworn and Steinmann.) III, Die Skelete. See Verworn, M., 1914.1.

Boucher [de Crèvecœur] de Perthes, J.

1846.1 Antiquités celtiques et antédiluviennes: Mémoire sur l'industrie primitive ou des arts à leur origine. Tome I, 1846. Tome II, 1857. Tome III, 1864. Paris, 8vo.

Boule, M.

1888.1 Essai de paléontologie stratigraphique de l'homme. *Rev. d'Anthropol.*, 1888, sér. 3, tome III, pp. 129–144, 272–297, 385–411, 647–680.

1899.1 Sur l'existence d'une faune d'animaux arctiques dans la Charente à l'époque quaternaire. (With Chauvet, G.) *C. R. Acad. Sci.*, Paris, tome 128, pp. 1188–1190.

1905.1 L'origine des éolithes. *L'Anthropol.*, tome XVI, 1905, pp. 1–11.

1906.1 Les Grottes de Grimaldi (Baoussé-Roussé). Tome I, fasc. II—Géologie et Paléontologie. Publiées sous les auspices de S. A. S. Albert Ier, Prince de Monaco. Monaco, 4to.

1908.1 L'homme fossile de La Chapelle-aux-Saints (Corrèze). *C. R. Acad. Sci.*, Paris, 1908, tome 147, pp. 1349–1352.

1908.2 L'homme fossile de La Chapelle-aux-Saints. *L'Anthropol.*, tome XIX, 1908, pp. 519–525.

1909.1 L'homme fossile de La Chapelle-aux-Saints (Corrèze). *L'Anthropol.*, tome XX, 1909, pp. 257–271.

1910.1 L'encéphale de l'homme fossile de La Chapelle-aux-Saints. (With R. Anthony.) *C. R. Acad. Sci.*, Paris, tome 150, 1910, pp. 1458–1461.

1910.2 Les Grottes de Grimaldi (Baoussé-Roussé). Tome I, fasc. III—Géologie et Paléontologie (suite). Monaco, 1910.

1911.1 L'encéphale de l'homme fossile de La Chapelle-aux-Saints. (With R. Anthony.) *L'Anthropol.*, tome XXII, 1911, pp. 129–196.

1912.1 La taille et les proportions du corps de l'*Homo neanderthalensis*. *C. R. Inst. franç. Anthrop.*, 1912, pp. 57–60.

1913.1 L'homme fossile de La Chapelle-aux-Saints. *Ext. Ann. Pal.*, tome VI, 1911, pp. 111–172 [1–64], Pl. XVII–XX [Pl. I–IV]; tome VII, 1912, pp. 21–192 [65–208], Pl. IV–XIX [Pl. V–XVI]; tome VIII, 1913, pp. 1–70 [209–278], Paris, 4to.

Bourgeois, l'Abbé.

1867.1 Découverte d'instruments en silex dans le dépôt à *Elephas meridionalis* de Saint-Prest, aux environs de Chartres. *C. R. Acad. Sci.*, Paris, tome 64, pp. 47, 48.

Bourrinet.

1906.1 L'Abri Mège, une station magdalénienne à Teyjat (Dordogne). (With Capitan, Breuil, and Peyrony.) See Capitan, 1906.1.

1908.1 La grotte de la Mairie à Teyjat (Dordogne). Fouilles d'un gisement magdalénien. (With Capitan, Breuil, and Peyrony.) See Capitan, 1908.1.

1912.1 Les gravures sur cascade stalagmitique de la grotte de la Mairie à Teyjat (Dordogne). (With Capitan, L., Breuil, and Peyrony.) See Capitan, L., 1912.1.

Bouyssonie, les Abbés A. et J.

1909.1 Découverte d'un squelette humain moustérien à la Bouffia de La Chapelle-aux-Saints (Corrèze). (With Bardon.) *L'Anthropol.*, tome XIX, 1909, pp. 513–518.

Breuil, l'Abbé H.

1906.1 L'Abri Mège, une station magdalénienne à Teyjat (Dordogne). (With Capitan, Bourrinet, and Peyrony.) See Capitan, L., 1906.1.

1906.2 La caverne d'Altamira à Santillane près Santander (Espagne). (With Cartailhac.) See Cartailhac, E., 1906.1.

1908.1 La grotte de la Mairie à Teyjat (Dordogne). Fouilles d'un gisement magdalénien. (With Capitan, Bourrinet, and Peyrony.) See Capitan, 1908.1.

1908.2 Les peintures et gravures murales des cavernes pyrénéennes. (With Cartailhac.) See Cartailhac, E., 1908.1.

1909.1 L'Aurignacien présolutréen. Épilogue d'une controverse. *Rev. préhist.*, année 4, 1909, pp. 5–46.

1909.2 Crânes paléolithiques façonnés en coupes. (With Obermaier, H.) *L'Anthropol.*, tome XX, 1909, pp. 523–530.

1909.3 L'évolution de l'art quaternaire et les travaux d'Édouard Piette. *Rev. Archéol.*, sér. 4, tome XIII, pp. 378–411.

1910.1 La caverne de Font-de-Gaume aux Eyzies (Dordogne). (With Capitan and Peyrony.) See Capitan, L., 1910.1.

1910.2 Les peintures et gravures murales des cavernes pyrénéennes. IV—Gargas, Cne. d'Aventignan (Hautes-Pyrénées). (With Cartailhac.) See Cartailhac, E., 1910.1.

1911.1 L'abri sculpté de Cap-Blanc à Laussel (Dordogne). (With Lalanne.) *L'Anthropol.*, tome XXII, 1911, pp. 385–408.

1912.1 L'âge des cavernes et roches ornées de France et d'Espagne. *Rev. Archéol.*, tome XIX, 1912, pp. 193–234.

1912.2 Les cavernes de la région cantabrique (Espagne). (With Alcalde del Rio, and R. P. K. Sierra.) See Alcalde del Rio, 1912.1.

1912.3 Les gravures sur cascade stalagmitique de la grotte de la Mairie à Teyjat (Dordogne). (With Capitan, L., Peyrony, and Bourrinet.) See Capitan, L., 1912.1.

1912.4 La statuette de mammouth de Předmost. (With Maška and Obermaier.) See Maška, 1912.1.

1912.5 Les peintures rupestres d'Espagne. (With Serrano Gomez and Cabre Aguilo.) IV—Les Abris del Bosque à Alpéra (Albacete). *L'Anthropol.*, tome XXIII, 1912, pp. 529–562.

1912.6 Les premiers travaux de l'Institut de Paléontologie humaine. (With Obermaier.) *L'Anthropol.*, tome XXIII, 1912, pp. 1–27.

1912.7 Les subdivisions du paléolithique supérieur et leur signification. *Congr. Intern. d'Anthrop. d'Archéol. préhist., C. R.*, XIVe *Sess.*, Genève, 1912, pp. 165–238.

1913.1 Travaux executés en 1912. (With Obermaier.) Travaux de l'Institut de Paléontologie humaine. *L'Anthropol.*, tome XXIV, 1913, pp. 1–16.

1913.2 La Pasiega à Puente-Viesgo (Santander, Espagne). (With Obermaier and Alcalde del Rio.) Peintures et gravures murales des cavernes paléolithiques. Institut de Paléontologie humaine. Monaco, 4to, 1913.

Broca, P.

1868.1 Sur les crânes et ossements des Eyzies. *Bull. Soc. d'Anthropol.*, Paris, sér. 2, tome III, pp. 350–392.

1875.1 Instructions craniologiques et craniométriques de la Société d'Anthropologie de Paris. *Ext. Mém. Soc. d'Anthropol.*, tome II, sér. 2, 203 pp., 6 Pls., Paris, Masson et Cie., 8vo., 1875.

Brückner, E.

1909.1 Die Alpen im Eiszeitalter. See Penck, A., 1909.1.

Büchner, L. W. G.

1914.1 A Study of the Curvatures of the Tasmanian Aboriginal Cranium. Communicated by Professor R. J. A. Berry. *Proc. R. Soc. Edinburgh*, vol. XXXIV, part II, 1914, pp. 128–143.

Buckland, W.

1823.1 Reliquiæ Diluvianæ; or, Observations on the Organic Remains contained in Caves, Fissures, and Diluvial Gravel, and on Other Geological Phenomena, attesting the action of an Universal Deluge. London, 4to, 1823.

Butler, S.

1911.1 Evolution, Old and New; or, the Theories of Buffon, Dr. Erasmus Darwin, and Lamarck, as compared with that of Charles Darwin. With a Preface by R. A. Streatfield (dated October, 1911), New York (Dutton), 8vo.

C

Cabre Aguilo, J.

1912.1 Les peintures rupestres d'Espagne. (With Breuil and Serrano Gomez.) See Breuil, H., 1912.5.

Capitan, L.

1898.1 L'Age de la Pierre. (With Salmon, P., and d'Ault du Mesnil.) See Salmon, P., 1898.1.

1906.1 L'Abri Mège, une station magdalénienne à Teyjat (Dordogne). (With Breuil and Peyrony.) *Rev. de l'Ecole d'Anthropol.*, année VI, 1906, pp. 196–212.

1908.1 La grotte de la Mairie à Teyjat (Dordogne). (With Breuil, Bourrinet and Peyrony.) Fouilles d'un gisement magdalénien. *Rev. de l'Ecole d'Anthropol.*, année XVIII, 1908, pp. 153–173.

1910.1 La caverne de Font-de-Gaume aux Eyzies (Dordogne). (With Breuil and Peyrony.) Peintures et gravures murales des cavernes paléolithiques publiées sous les auspices de S. A. S. le Prince Albert Ier de Monaco. Monaco, 4to, 1910.

1912.1 Les gravures sur cascade stalagmitique de la grotte de la Mairie à Teyjat (Dordogne). (With Breuil, Peyrony, and Bourrinet.) *Congr. Intern. d'Anthropol. et d'Archéol. préhist., C. R.*, XIVe *Sess.*, Genève, pp. 498–514.

1912.2 Station préhistorique de la Ferrassie, Commune de Savignac-du-Bugue (Dordogne). (With Peyrony.) *Rev. Anthropol.*, année XXI, no. 1, 1912, pp. 29–50.

Cartailhac, E.

1903.1 La France préhistorique d'après les sépultures et les monuments. Deuxième édition, avec 162 gravures dans le text. Paris, 8vo, 1903.

1906.1 La caverne d'Altamira à Santillane près Santander (Espagne). (With Breuil.) Peintures et gravures murales des cavernes paléolithiques publiées sous les auspices de S. A. S. Prince Albert Ier de Monaco. Monaco, 4to, 1906.

1908.1 Les peintures et gravures murales des cavernes pyrénéennes. (With Breuil.) III—Niaux (Ariège). *L'Anthropol.*, tome XIX, 1908, pp. 15–46.

1910.1 Les peintures et gravures murales des cavernes pyrénéennes. (With Breuil.) IV—Gargas, Cne. d'Aventignan (Hautes-Pyrénées). *L'Anthropol.*, tome XXI, 1910, pp. 129–150.

1912.1 Les Grottes de Grimaldi (Baoussé-Roussé). Tome II, fasc. II—Archéologie. Peintures et gravures murales des cavernes paléolithiques publiées sous les auspices de S. A. S. Prince Albert Ier de Monaco. Monaco, 4to, 1912.

Chamberlin, T.

1895.1 Glacial Studies in Greenland. III—Coast Glaciers between Disco Island and Inglefield Gulf. *Journ. Geol.*, vol. III, 1895, pp. 61–69.

1905.1 Geology. (With Salisbury, R. D.) American Science Series, Advanced Course, vols. I and II. Second edition, revised, New York, 8vo, 1905.

de Charpentier, J.

1841.1 Essai sur les glaciers et sur le terrain erratique du bassin du Rhône. Lausanne, 8vo, 1841.

Chauvent, G.

1899.1 Sur l'existence d'une faune d'animaux arctiques dans la Charente à l'époque quaternaire. (With Boule, M.) See Boule, M., 1899.1.

de Christol.

1829.1 Notice sur les ossemens humains fossiles des cavernes du département du Gard. *Ext.* [Acad. Montpellier], 25 pp. et planche. Montpellier, 8vo, 1829.

Christy, H.

1875.1 Reliquiæ Acquitanicæ. (With Lartet, E.) See Lartet, E., 1875.1.

Collignon, R.

1890.1 L'anthropologie au conseil de revision; méthode à suivre. Son application à l'étude des populations des Côtes-du-Nord. *Bull. Soc. d'Anthropol.*, Paris, sér. 4, tome I, 1890, pp. 736–805.

Commont, V.

1906.1 Les découvertes récentes à Saint-Acheul, l'Acheuléen. *Rev. de l'Ecole d'Anthropol.*, Paris, année XVI, 1906, pp. 228–241.

1908.1 Les industries de l'ancien Saint-Acheul. *L'Anthropol.*, tome XIX, 1908, pp. 527–572.

1909.1 L'industrie moustérienne dans la region du nord de la France. *Congr. Préhist. de France, Ve Sess.*, 1909, pp. 115–157.

1909.2 Saint-Acheul et Montières. Notes de géologie, de paléontologie et de préhistoire. *Mém. Soc. Géol. du Nord*, tome VI, iii.

1912.1 Moustérien à faune chaude dans la vallée de la Somme à Montières-les-Amiens. *Congr. Intern. d'Anthropol. et d'Archéol. préhist., C. R.*, XIVe *Sess.*, Genève, 1912, pp. 291–300.

Cope, E. D.

1893.1 The Genealogy of Man. *Amer. Nat.*, vol. XXVII, 1893, pp. 321–335.

D

Dana, J.

1875.1 Manual of Geology: Treating of the Principles of the Science with Special Reference to American Geological History. Second edition, New York, 8vo, 1875.

Darwin, C.

1871.1 The Descent of Man and Selection in Relation to Sex. Vols. I and II. London (Murray), 8vo, 1871.

1909.1 The Descent of Man and Selection in Relation to Sex. Second edition, revised and enlarged, New York (Appleton), 8vo, 1909.

1909.2 The Origin of Species by Means of Natural Selection, or the Preservation of Favored Races in the Struggle for Life. With additions and corrections. From sixth and last English edition, New York (Appleton), 8vo, 1909.

Dawkins, W. Boyd.

1880.1 Early Man in Britain and His Place in the Tertiary Period. London, 1880.

1883.1 On the Alleged Existence of *Ovibos moschatus* in the Forest-Bed, and on its Range in Space and Time. *Quart. Journ. Geol. Soc.*, London, 1883, vol. XXXIX, pp. 575–581.

Dawson, C.

1913.1 On the Discovery of a Palæolithic Human Skull and Mandible in a Flint-Bearing Gravel overlying the Wealden (Hastings Beds) at Piltdown, Fletching (Sussex). With an Appendix by Prof. G. Elliot Smith. (With A. S. Woodward.) *Quart. Journ. Geol. Soc.*, London, vol. LXIX, part I, 1913, pp. 117–151, Pls. 15–21.

1913.2 Prehistoric Man in Sussex. *Zoologist*, ser. 4, vol. 17, pp. 33–36.

1914.1 Supplementary Note; On the Discovery of a Palæolithic Human Skull and Mandible in a Flint-Bearing Gravel, etc. (With A. S. Woodward.) With an Appendix by Prof. Grafton Elliot Smith. *Quart. Journ. Geol. Soc.*, vol. LXX, 1914, pp. 82–99, Pls. 14, 15.

Déchelette, J.

1908.1 Manuel d'archéologie préhistorique celtique et gallo-romaine. Tome I—Archéologie préhistorique (1908). Tome II—Archéologie celtique ou protohistorique. Première partie—Age du Bronze (1910). Deuxième partie—Premier Age du Fer ou Epoque de Hallstatt (1913). Appendices (1910). Appendices (Supplément) (1912). Paris, 8vo, 1910–1913.

Desnoyers, J.

1863.1 Note sur des indices matériels de la coexistence de l'homme avec *l'Elephas meridionalis* dans un terrain des environs de Chartres, plus ancien que les terrains transport quaternaires des vallées de la Somme et de la Seine. *C. R. Acad. Sci.*, Paris, tome 56, 1863, pp. 1073–1083.

Dietrich, W. O.

1910.1 Neue fossile Cervidenreste aus Schwaben. *Jahreshefte, Ver. vaterl. Naturk.*, Württemberg, 66 Jahrg., 1910, pp. 318–336.

Dubois, E.

1894.1 *Pithecanthropus erectus*, eine Menschenaehnliche Uebergangsform aus Java. Batavia, 4to, 1894.

Dupont, É.

1866.1 Etudes sur les fouilles scientifiques exécutées pendant l'hiver de 1865–1866 dans les cavernes des bords de la Lesse. *Bull. Acad. R. de Belgique*, sér. 2, tome XXII, 1866, pp. 31–54.

1871.1 Les temps antéhistoriques en Belgique. L'homme pendant les âges de la pierre dans les environs de Dinant-sur-Meuse. Deuxième édition. Bruxelles (Muquardt), 8vo, 1871.

E

Eccardus, J. G.

1750.1 De Origine et Moribus Germanorum eorumque vetustissimis colonis, migrationibus ac rebus gestis. (Ioh. Guil. Schmidii), 4to, Goettingæ, ciɔ iɔ ccl (1750).

Elbert, J.

1908.1 Über das Alter der Kendeng-Schichten mit *Pithecanthropus erectus* Dubois. *N. Jahrb. Mineral. Géol. u. Pal.*, XXV Beil.-Bd., 1908, pp. 648–662.

Ewart, J. C.

1904.1 The Multiple Origin of Horses and Ponies. *Trans. Highl. Agri. Soc. Scotland*, 1904, pp. 1–39.

1907.1 On the Skulls of Horses from the Roman Fort at Newstead, near Melrose, with Observations on the Origin of the Domestic Horses. *Trans. R. Soc. Edinburgh*, vol. XLV, part III, no. 20, 1907, pp. 555–587.

1909.1 The Possible Ancestors of the Horses Living under Domestication. *Science*, n. s., vol. XXX, no. 763, August 13, 1909, pp. 219–223.

F

de Ferry, H.

1869.1 L'Age du Renne en Mâconnais. Mémoire sur le gisement archéologique du clos du Charnier à Solutré, Département de Saône-et-Loire. (Compte rendu des fouilles opérées en 1867 et 1868 par MM. H. de Ferry et A. Arcelin.) *Trans. Intern. Congr. Prêhist. Archéol.*, IIIe *Sess.*, London, 1868 (published 1869), pp. 319–350, Pls. I, II.

Fischer, E.

1913.1 Fossile Hominiden. *Sonderabd. Handwörterbuch Naturwiss.*, Bd. IV, pp. 332–360, Jena, 8vo, 1913.

Fraipont, J.

1887.1 La race de Neanderthal ou de Canstadt en Belgique. (With Lohest, M.) *Arch. Biol.*, tome VII, 1887, pp. 587–757.

Fraunholz, J.

1911.1 Die Kastlhäng-Höhle, eine Renntierjägerstation im bayerischen Altmühltale. Mit einem Beitrag von Max Schlosser. (With Obermaier.) *Beiträge, Anthropol. u. Urgesch. Bayerns*, Bd. XVIII, 1911. (Unpaged separate.)

G

Gaudry, A.

1876.1 Matériaux pour l'histoire des temps quaternaires. Fasc. I. Paris, 4to, 1876.

1890.1 Le Dryopithèque. *Mém. Soc. Géol. de France, Pal. Mém.* no. 1. Paris, 4to, 1890.

Geikie, J.

1894.1 The Great Ice Age and Its Relation to the Antiquity of Man. Third edition, largely rewritten. London, 8vo, 1894.

1914.1 The Antiquity of Man in Europe, being the Munro Lectures, 1913. Edinburgh, 8vo, 1914.

Godwin-Austen.

1840.1 On the Geology of the Southeast of Devonshire. *Trans. Geol. Soc.*, ser. 2, vol. VI, pp. 433–489, Pl. XLII.

Gorjanovič-Kramberger, K.

1901.1 Der paläolithische Mensch und seine Zeitgenossen aus dem Diluvium von Krapina in Kroatien. *Mitt. Anthrop. Gesell. Wien*, Bd. 31, pp. 163–197, 4 Pls., 13 Figs.

1903.1 Nachtrag (to the above). *Mitt. Anthrop. Gesell. Wien*, Bd. 32, pp. 189–216, 4 Pls., 17 Figs.

1906.1 Der diluviale Mensch von Krapina in Kroatien. Ein Beitrag zur Paläoanthropologie. Studien über Entwicklungsmechanik des Primatskelettes mit besonderer Berücksichtigung der Anthropologie und Descendenzlehre. . . . Herausgegeben von Dr. Otto Walkhoff, Wiesbaden, 4to, 1906.

1909.1 Der vordere Unterkieferabschnitt des altdiluvialen Menschen in seinem genetischen Verhältnis zum Unterkiefer des rezenten Menschen und den der Anthropoiden. *Zeitschr. Abstammungs- u. Vererbungsl.*, Bd. I, pp. 411–439.

Gregory, W. K.

The Dawn Man of Piltdown, England. *Am. Mus. Jour.*, vol. XIV, May, 1914.

H

Harlé, E.

1899.1 Notes sur la Garonne. *Bull. Soc. d'Hist. Nat. Toulouse*, année XXXII (Oct., 1899), pp. 149–198.

1908.1 Faune quaternaire de la province de Santandér (Espagne). *Bull. Soc. Géol. de France*, sér. 4, tome VIII, 1908, pp. 82–83.

1910.1 Les mammifères et oiseaux quaternaires connus jusqu'ici en Portugal. Mémoire suivi d'une liste générale de ceux de la Péninsule Ibérique. Ext. tome VIII, "*Communicações,*" *Service Géol. du Portugal.*

Haug, E.

1907.1 Traité de Géologie. Tome I—Les Phénomènes géologiques (1907). Tome II—Les Périodes géologiques (1911). Paris, 8vo.

Hauser, O.

1909.1 *Homo aurignacensis* Hauseri, etc. See Klaatsch, H., 1909.1.

Heim, A.

1894.1 Ueber das absolut Alter der Eiszeit. *Vierteljahrschrif. naturf. Gesell. Zurich,* Bd. 39, 1894, pp. 180–186.

Hilzheimer.

1913.1 Studienreise zu den paläolithischen Fundstellen der Dordogne. See Wiegers, 1913.1.

Hrdlička, Dr. A.

1914.1 The Most Ancient Skeletal Remains of Man. *Report, Smithsonian Institution,* etc., 1913, pp. 491–552, Pls. 1–41. Publication 2300. Government Printing Office, Washington, 8vo, 1914.

Huntington, E.

1907.1 The Pulse of Asia. New York, 8vo, 1907.

J

James, W.

1902.1 The Varieties of Religious Experience. A Study in Human Nature. Being the Gifford Lectures on Natural Religion delivered at Edinburgh in 1901–1902. New York, 8vo, 1902.

Johnson, J. P.

1913.1 The Stone Implements of the Tasmanians. *Nature,* vol. 92, no. 2298, November 13, 1913, p. 320.

K

Keane, A. H.

1901.1 Ethnology. Cambridge Geographical Series. Stereotyped edition. Cambridge, 8vo. 1901.

Keith, A.

1911.1 Ancient Types of Man. Harper's Library of Living Thought. New York, 12mo. 1911.

1911.2 Discovery of the Teeth of Palæolithic Man in Jersey. *Nature,* vol. 86, no. 2169, May 25, 1911, p. 414.

1911.3 The Early History of the Gibraltar Cranium. *Nature,* vol. 87, no. 2184, September 7, 1911, pp. 313, 314.

1912.1 Cranium of the Crô-Magnon Type found by Mr. W. M. Newton in a Gravel Terrace near Dartford. *Rpt.* 82d *Meeting, Brit. Assoc. Adv. Sci.*, Dundee, 1912, pp. 516, 517.
1912.2 Hunterian Lecture on Certain Phases in the Evolution of Man. (Abstract.) *Brit. Med. Journ.*, 1912, vol. I, pp. 734–737, 788–790.
1913.1 The Piltdown Skull and Brain Cast. *Nature*, vol. 92, no. 2294, October 16, 1913, pp. 197–199.
1913.2 The Piltdown Skull and Brain Cast. *Nature*, vol. 92, no. 2297, November 6, 1913, p. 292.
1913.3 The Piltdown Skull and Brain Cast. *Nature*, vol. 92, no. 2299, November 20, 1913, pp. 345, 346.

Kennard, A. S.
1913.1 [Discussion of] On the Discovery of a Palæolithic Human Skull and Mandible . . . at Piltdown, Fletching (Sussex). See Dawson, C., 1913.1, p. 150.

King, W.
1864.1 The Reputed Fossil Man of the Neanderthal. *Quart. Journ. Sci.*, vol. I, pp. 88–97, Pls. I, II.

Klaatsch, H.
1909.1 *Homo aurignacensis Hauseri*, ein paläolithischer Skeletfund aus dem unteren Aurignacien der Station Combe-Capelle bei Montferrand (Périgord). (With Hauser.) *Prähist. Zeitschr.*, Bd. I, 1909 (Heft 3–4, 1910), pp. 273–338.

Koken, E.
1912.1 Die diluviale Vorzeit Deutschlands, von R. R. Schmidt. II—Geologischer Teil von Ernst Koken. Die Geologie und Tierwelt der paläolithischen Kulturstätten Deutschlands. See Schmidt, R. R., 1912.1.

Kraemer, H.
Weltall und Menschheit. Geschichte der Erforschung der Natur und der Verwertung der Naturkräfte im Dienst der Völker. Band II. Berlin, n. d.

L

Lalanne, G.
1911.1 L'abri sculpté de Cap-Blanc à Laussel (Dordogne). (With Breuil H.) See Breuil, H., 1911.1.

Lamarck, J.
1809.1 Philosophie Zoologique. Paris (Duminil-Leseur), 8vo, 1909.
1815.1 Histoire naturelle des animaux sans vertèbres. . . . Tomes 1–7 (1815–1822). Paris (Verdière), 8vo, 1815–1822.

Lartet, E.
1861.1 Nouvelles recherches sur la coexistence de l'homme et des grands mammifères fossiles réputés caractéristiques de la dernière période

géologique. *Ann. Sci. Nat.*, sér. 4, Zoologie, tome XV, 1861, pp. 177–253, Pl. X.

1875.1 Reliquiæ Acquitanicæ. (With Christy.) Being Contributions to the Archæology and Palæontology of Périgord and the Adjoining Provinces. Edited by Rupert Jones. London, 4to, 1875.

Leverett, F.

1910.1 Comparison of North American and European Glacial Deposits. *Zeitschr. für Gletscherk.*, Bd. IV, 1910, pp. 241–316.

Lubbock, Sir J. (See Avebury, Lord).

1862.1 On the Evidences of the Antiquity of Man afforded by the Physical Structure of the Somme Valley. *Nat. Hist. Rev.*, 1862, pp. 244–269.

Lyell, Sir C.

1863.1 The Geological Evidences of the Antiquity of Man with Remarks on the Theories of the Origin of Species by Variation. Second revised edition. London (Murray), 8vo, 1863.

1867.1 Principles of Geology or the Modern Changes of the Earth and Its Inhabitants Considered as Illustrative of Geology. Tenth and entirely revised edition. Vol. I, 1867. Vol. II, 1868. London (Murray), 8vo, 1867–1868.

1877.1 Principles of Geology or the Modern Changes of the Earth and its Inhabitants Considered as Illustrative of Geology. Eleventh and entirely revised edition. Vol. I, 1877. Vol. II, 1872. New York (Appleton), 8vo, 1872–1877.

M

MacCurdy, G. G.

1905.1 The Eolithic Problem. Evidences of a Rude Industry Antedating the Paleolithic. *Amer. Anthropol.*, n. s., vol. VII, no. 3, 1905, pp. 425–479.

Mahudel.

1740.1 Sur les prétendues pierres de foudre. *Hist. Acad. R. Inscript. et Belles-Lettres*, Paris, tome XII, 1740, pp. 163–168.

Makowsky, A.

1892.1 Der diluviale Mensch im Löss von Brünn. *Mitt. Anthropol. Gesell. Wien*, Bd. XXII (N. F. Bd. XIII), pp. 73–84.

Marett, R. R.

Anthropology. Home University Library of Modern Knowledge. New York (Henry Holt & Co.), 12mo, n. d.

Martin, H.

1910.1 Astragale humain du Moustérien moyen de La Quina. (*Ext., Bull. Soc. prêhist. de France*, 1910, p. 391.) [Reviewed by M. Boule.] *L'Anthropol.*, tome XXII, 1911, pp. 312, 313.

Martin, R.

1914.1 Lehrbuch der Anthropologie in systematischer Darstellung. Mit besonderer Berücksichtigung der anthropologischen Methoden. Für studierende Ärzte und Forschungsreisende. Jena, 8vo, 1914.

Martins, C.

1847.1 Recherches sur la période glaciaire et l'ancienne extension des glaciers du Mont-Blanc depuis les Alpes jusqu'au Jura. *Rev. deux mondes* 1847, tome 17, pp. 919–942.

Maška, K.

1886.1 Fund des Unterkiefers in der Schipka-Höhle. *Verh. Berliner Gesell. f. Anthropol., Ethnol. u. Urgesch.*, 1886, pp. 341–350.

1912.1 La statuette de mammouth de Předmost. (With Obermaier and Breuil.) *L'Anthropol.*, tome XXIII, 1912, pp. 273–285.

Massénat, É.

1869.1 Objets gravés et sculptés de l'Augerie Basse (Dordogne). *Matér. pour l'hist. de l'homme*, année V, sér. 2, pp. 348–356.

Morlot, A.

1854.1 Notice sur le Quaternaire en Suisse. *Bull. Soc. Vaudoise, Sci. nat.*, 1854, pp. 41–45.

de Mortillet, A.

1869.1 Essai d'une classification des cavernes et des stations sous abri, fondée sur les produits de l'industrie humaine. *C. R. Acad. Sci.*, Paris, tome 68, 1869, pp. 553–555.

de Mortillet, G.

1872. Classification des âges de la pierre. Classification des diverses périodes de l'âge de la pierre. *C. R. Congr. Intern. d'Anthropol., d'Archéol. Préhist., VIe Sess.* Bruxelles, 1872, pp. 432–444.

Munro, R.

1893.1 [On the Relation between the Erect Posture and the Physical and Intellectual Development of Man.] *Rpt. 63d Meeting, Brit. Assoc. Adv. Sci.*, Nottingham, 1893, Presidential Address, Section of Anthropology, pp. 885–889.

1912.1 Palæolithic Man and the Terramara Settlements in Europe. Being the Munro Lectures in Anthropology and Prehistoric Archæology in connection with the University of Edinburgh. Edinburgh, 8vo, 1912.

N

Nehring, A.

1880.1 Übersicht über vierundzwanzig mitteleuropäische Quatär-Faunen. *Zeitschr. deutsch. geolog. Gesell.*, 1880, pp. 468–509.

1896.1 Die kleineren Wirbeltiere vom Schweizersbild bei Schaffhausen. *N. Denkschr. allg. schweiz. Gesell. gesam. Naturwiss.*, Bd. XXXV, 1896, pp. 40–77.

Neumeyer, M.

1890.1 Erdgeschichte. Band I, 1895. Band II, 1890. Leipzig, R. 8vo, 1890–1895.

Nicolle, E. T.

1910.1 Report on the Exploration of the Palæolithic Cave-Dwelling known as La Cotte, St Brelade, Jersey. (With Sinel, J.) *Man*, 1910, nos. 101–102, pp. 185–188.

Niezabitowski, E.

1911.1 Die Überreste des in Starunia in einer Erdwachsgrube mit Haut und Weichteilen gefundenen *Rhinoceros antiquitatis* Blum. (*tichorhinus* Fisch.). *Bull. Acad. Sci. Cracovie*, Classe des Sci. Mathémat., etc., 1911, sér. B; Sci. nat., pp. 240–266.

Nüesch, J.

1902.1 Das Schweizersbild, eine Niederlassung aus palæolithischer und neolithischer Zeit. Die praehistorische Niederlassung am Schweizersbild bei Schaffhausen. Die Schichten und ihre Einschlüsse. *N. Denkschr. allg. schweiz. Gesell. gesam. Naturwiss.*, Bd. XXXV, zweite Verbesserung, pp. 1–120.

O

Obermaier, H.

1909.1 Crânes paléolithiques façonnés en Coupes. (With Breuil.) See Breuil, H., 1909.2.

1909.2 Les formations glaciaires des Alpes et l'homme paléolithique. *L'Anthropol.*, tome XX, 1909, pp. 497–522.

1909.3 Die Aurignacienstation von Krems (N.-O.). (With Strobel.) See Strobel, 1909.1.

1911.1 Die Kastlhäng-Höhle, eine Renntierjägerstation im bayerischen Altmühltale. (With Fraunholz und Schlosser.) See Fraunholz, J., 1911.1.

1912.1 Der Mensch der Vorzeit. München, R. 8vo, 1912.

1912.2 Les premières travaux de l'Institut de Paléontologie humaine. (With Breuil.) See Breuil, H., 1912.6.

1912.3 La statuette de mammouth de Předmost. (With Maška et Breuil.) See Maška, 1912.1.

1913.1 La Pasiega à Puente-Viesgo (Santander, Espagne). (With Breuil and Alcalde del Rio.) See Breuil, H., 1913.2.

Osborn, H. F.

1894.1 From the Greeks to Darwin. An Outline of the Development of the Evolution Idea. New York, 8vo, 1894.

1910.1 The Age of Mammals in Europe, Asia and North America. New York, 8vo, 1910.

P

Penck, A.

1908.1 Das Alter des Menschengeschlechts. *Zeitschr. für Ethnol.*, Jahrg. 40, Heft 3, 1908, pp. 390–407.

1909.1 Die Alpen im Eiszeitalter. (With Brückner, E.) Band I, II, III. Leipzig, R. 8vo, 1909.

Peyrony, M.

1908.1 La grotte de la Mairie à Teyjat (Dordogne). (With Capitan and Breuil.) See Capitan, L., 1908.1.

1910.1 La caverne de Font-de-Gaume aux Eyzies (Dordogne). (With Breuil and Capitan.) See Capitan, 1910.1.

1912.1 Les gravures sur cascade stalagmitique de la grotte de la Mairie à Teyjat (Dordogne). (With Breuil, Bourrinet, and Capitan.) See Capitan, 1912.2.

Piette, E.

1907.1 L'art pendant l'Age du Renne. Album de cent planches dessinées par J. Pilloy. Paris, small folio, 1907.

Pilgrim, G.

1913.1 The Correlation of the Siwaliks with Mammal Horizons of Europe. *Records, Geol. Survey India*, vol. XLIII, part 4, pp. 264–326, Pls. 26–28.

Q

Quatrefages, A.

1884.1 Hommes fossiles et hommes sauvages. Etudes d'Anthropologie. Paris, 8vo, 1884.

R

Reeds, C. A.

1915.1 The Graphic Projection of Pleistocene Climatic Oscillations. *Bull. Geol. Soc. Amer.*, vol. 26, no. 1, 1915, pp. 106–109.

Reid, C.

1908.1 The Pre-Glacial Flora of Britain. (With E. M. Reid.) *Journ. Linn. Soc.* Botany, vol. XXXVIII, 1908, pp. 206–227.

1913.1 [Discussion of] On the Discovery of a Palæolithic Human Skull and Mandible . . . at Piltdown . . . Sussex. See Dawson, C., 1913.1.

Reinach, S.

1889.1 Antiquités nationales. Déscription raisonnée du Musée de Saint-Germain-en-Laye. I—Epoque des alluvions et des cavernes. Paris, 8vo [1889], 322 pp.

1913.1 Répertoire de l'Art quaternaire. Paris, 12mo, 1913.

1906.1 Das Schädelfragment von Brüx und verwandte Schädelformen. *Zeitschr. für Morphol. und Anthropol.*, Sonderheft, 1906, pp. 81–182, Pls. I–II.

1914.1 Kritische Besprechung von Boule's Werk: "L'homme fossile de La Chapelle-aux-Saints" mit eigenen Untersuchungen. *Zeitschr. Morph. u. Anthropol.*, Bd. XVI, Heft 3, pp. 527–610.

1914.2 Über einen bei Ehringsdorf in der Nähe von Weimar gefundenen Unterkiefer des *Homo primigenius*. *Anat. Anzeiger*, Band 47, nos. 13–17. Oktober, 1914, pp. 337–345.

Selenka, L.

1911.1 Die Pithecanthropus-Schichten auf Java. (With Blanckenhorn.) Geologische und paläontologische Ergebnisse der Trinil-Expedition (1907–1908). Herausgegeben von M. Lenore Selenka und Prof Max Blanckenhorn, Leipzig, 4to, 1911.

Serrano Gomez, P.

1912.1 Les peintures rupestres d'Espagne. (With Breuil and Cabre Aguilo.) See Breuil, 1912.5.

Sierra, R. P. L.

1912.1 Les cavernes de la région cantabrique (Espagne). (With Alcalde del Rio and Breuil.) See Alcalde del Rio, 1912.1.

Smith, G. E.

1912.1 Presidential Address to the Anthropological Section (B. A. A. S.). *Rpt. 82d Meeting, Brit. Assoc. Adv. Sci.*, Dundee, 1912, pp. 575–598.

1913.1 The Controversies concerning the Interpretation and Meaning of the Remains of the Dawn-Man Found near Piltdown. [Abstract.] *Meet. Manchester Lit. and Philosoph. Soc.*, November 18, 1913.

1913.2 On the Discovery of a Palæolithic Human Skull and Mandible in a Flint-Bearing Gravel overlying the Wealden (Hastings Beds) at Piltdown, Fletching (Sussex). With an Appendix by Prof. Grafton Elliot Smith. See Dawson, C., 1913.1.

1913.3 The Piltdown Skull. *Nature*, vol. 92, no. 2292, October 2, 1913, p. 131.

1913.4 The Piltdown Skull and Brain Cast. *Nature*, vol. 92, no. 2296, October 30, 1913, pp. 267, 268.

1914.1 Supplementary Note on the Discovery of a Palæolithic Human Skull and Mandible at Piltdown (Sussex). (With Dawson and Woodward.) With an Appendix by Prof. Grafton Elliot Smith. See Dawson, C., 1914.1.

Smith, W.

1894.1 Man the Primeval Savage. His Haunts and Relics from the Hill-Tops of Bedfordshire to Blackwall. London, 8vo, 1894.

Sollas, W. J.

1900.1 Evolutional Geology. Presidential Address to the Geological Section (B. A. A. S.). *Rpt. 70th Meeting, Brit. Assoc. Adv. Sci.*, Bradford, 1900, pp. 711–730.

1911.? Ancient Hunters and Their Modern Representatives. London, 8vo. 1911.

1913.1 Paviland Cave: An Aurignacian Station in Wales. (The Huxley Memorial Lecture for 1913.) *Journ. R. Anthropol. Inst. of Gr. Brit. & Ireland*, vol. XLIII, 1913, pp. 325–373.

Steinmann, C.

1914.1 Diluviale Menschenfunde in Obercassel bei Bonn. (With Verworn and Bonnet.) IV—Über das geologische Alter der Fundstelle. See Verworn, M., 1914.1.

Strobel, J.

1909.1 Die Aurignacienstation von Krems (N.-Ö.). (With Obermaier, H.) Mit einem Anhang von Oskar von Troll. *Jahrb. Altertumskunde*, Bd. III, 1909, pp. 129–148, Pls. XI–XXI.

T

Tomes, C. S.

1914.1 A Manual of Dental Anatomy, Human and Comparative. Edited by H. W. Marett Tims and A. Hopewell-Smith. Seventh edition. (J. and A. Churchill.) London, 8vo, 1914, 616 pp.

von Troll, O.

1909.1 Die Aurignacienstation von Krems (N.-Ö.). (With Strobel and Obermaier.) Mit einem Anhang von Oskar von Troll. See Strobel, J., 1909.1.

U

Upham, W.

1893.1 Estimates of Geologic Time. *Amer. Journ. Sci.*, vol. XLV, 1893, pp. 209–220.

V

Verneau, R.

1886.1 La race de Crô-Magnon. *Rev. Anthropol.*, sér. 3, tome I, 1886, pp. 10–24.

1891.1 Cinq années de séjour aux îles Canaries. Paris, 1891.

1906.1 Les Grottes de Grimaldi (Baoussé-Roussé). Tome II, fasc. I—Anthropologie. Monaco, 4to, 1906

Verworn, M.

1914.1 Diluviale Menschenfunde in Obercassel bei Bonn. (With Bonnet and Steinmann.) I—Fundbericht, Verworn. II—Die Kulturstufe des Fundes, Verworn. III—Die Skelete, Bonnet. IV—Über das geologische Alter der Fundstelle, Steinmann. *Die Naturwissenschaften*, Heft 27, Jahrg. 2, 3 Juli 1914, pp. 645–650.

de Vibraye.

1864.1 Note sur des nouvelles preuves de l'existence de l'homme dans le centre de la France à une époque où s'y trouvaient aussi divers animaux qui de nos jours n'habitent pas cette contrée. *C. R. Acad. Sci.*, Paris, tome 58, 1864, pp. 409–416.

Villeneuve, L.

1906.1 Les Grottes de Grimaldi (Baoussé-Roussé). Tome I, fasc. I—Historique et Déscription. Monaco, 4to, 1906.

Volz, W.

1907.1 Das geologische Alter der Pithecanthropus-Schichten bei Trinil, Ost-Java. *N. Jahrb. Miner., Geol. u. Paläontol., Festband*, 1907, pp. 256–271.

W

Walcott, C. D.

1893.1 Geologic Time as Indicated by the Sedimentary Rocks of North America. *Amer. Geol.*, vol. XII, no. 6, 1893, pp. 343–368, Pl. XV.

Wiegers, F.

1913.1 Eine Studienreise zu den paläolithischen Fundstellen der Dordogne. (With Schuchhardt and Hilzheimer.) *Zeitschr. f. Ethnol.*, Jahrg. 45, Heft I, 1913, pp. 126–160.

Wilser, L.

1898.1 Menschenrassen und Weltgeschichte. *Naturwiss. Wochenschr.*, Band XIII, Heft 1, 1898.

Woodward, A. S.

1913.1 On the Discovery of a Palæolithic Human Skull and Mandible in a Flint-Bearing Gravel overlying the Wealden (Hastings Beds) at Piltdown, Fletching, Sussex. (With Dawson, C.) With an Appendix by Prof. Grafton Elliot Smith. See Dawson, C., 1913.1.

1914.1 Supplementary Note on the Discovery of a Palæolithic Human Skull and Mandible at Piltdown (Sussex). (With Charles Dawson.) With an Appendix by Prof. Grafton Elliot Smith. See Dawson, C., 1914.1.

1914.2 On the Lower Jaw of an Anthropoid Ape (*Dryopithecus*) from the Upper Miocene of Lérida (Spain). *Quart. Journ. Geol. Soc.*, London, vol. LXX, pp. 316–320, Pl. XLIV.

1915.1 A Guide to the Fossil Remains of Man in the Department of Geology and Palæontology in the British Museum (Natural History), Cromwell Road, London, S. W. With 4 plates and 12 text-figures. Printed by order of the trustees of the British Museum. 8vo, 1915, 33 pp.

INDEX

INDEX*

***Authors' names are given in the bibliography and in the reference lists at the end of each chapter.**

D

I

J

K

L

M

N

O

P

Q

R